Children's Writer's and Illustrator's Market UK 2008/09

WHERE AND HOW TO SELL WHAT YOU WRITE AND DRAW

David and Charles

A DAVID & CHARLES BOOK
Copyright © David & Charles Limited 2007

David & Charles is an F+W Publications Inc. company
4700 East Galbraith Road
Cincinnati, OH 45236

First published in the UK in 2007

A catalogue record for this book is available from the British Library.

ISBN-13: 978-0-7153-2849-1
ISBN-10: 0-7153-2849-2

Printed in Great Britain by CPD, Wales
for David & Charles Ltd.
Brunel House, Newton Abbot, Devon

Head of Publishing: Ali Myer
Editor: Emily Pitcher
Features Editor: Mic Cady
Lead Compiler: James Brooks
Compiler: Emma Cox
Assistant Editor: Sarah Wedlake
Desk Editor: Demelza Hookway
Proofreader: Ellie Irwin
Art Editor: Martin Smith
Designer: Joanna Ley

Production Director: Roger Lane

Visit our website at www.davidandcharles.co.uk

David & Charles books are available from all good bookshops; alternatively you can
contact our Orderline on 0870 9908222 or write to us at FREEPOST EX2 110, D&C
Direct, Newton Abbot, TQ12 4ZZ (no stamp required UK only);
US customers call 800-289-0963 and
Canadian customers call 800-840-5220.

www.writersmarket.co.uk

CONTENTS

INTRODUCTION

The books we read in childhood help to shape what we become. Stories encourage us to make sense of the world, and to create inner worlds of the imagination. They break down new experiences, emotions and learning, helping the reader to understand things better. They captivate the imagination, and can take the reader to the far-flung destinations of their dreams, igniting the mind and giving the first taste of escapism.

Writing and illustrating for children makes a real difference, and is not something that is ever undertaken lightly. Books can be lessons in life, and many tackle tough issues – from the basic learning of colours, numbers and experiences, to therapeutic books about coping with adversity and making tough moral choices, all having the same result of promoting thought and confidence in the reader and so encouraging the transition to adulthood. Peter Dickinson writes novel after novel of astonishing breadth and imagination, more often than not presenting his protagonists with difficult moral choices. Margaret Mahy, Phillip Pullman, David Almond and many, many others all make you think: what would you do in the shoes of their heroes and heroines?

Even for the very youngest audience, books teach and encourage learning – not just learning about counting, colours, animals and names, but learning about independence, freedom of thought and the differences between right and wrong, good decisions and bad decisions. Nursery rhymes offer a plethora of experiences, nearly always sending the protagonist out on their own to make decisions for themselves, often with the help of some very colourful characters, and nearly always with a positive and happy ending.

MOVING WITH THE TIMES

Times, taste and children may change, but the importance of reading and learning never diminishes. The way it manifests itself may change, adapt and reach new heights, but children still have the hunger and need to discover the world around them. Indeed, many books that were first published several years ago remain staunch favourites in the children's bestseller lists, and there are many books that we read as children that we go back to again and again, even into adulthood. *The Very Hungry Caterpillar,* by Eric Carle, is a feast for any child (or parent), and was first published in 1969, while the Beatrix Potter stories never seem to lose their appeal or charm. And not a year seems to go by without *The Chronicles of Narnia* books being re-released with a sparkling new livery, or a dazzling film with a budget to match being announced. The likes of Enid Blyton, Roald Dahl, Lewis Carroll and Kenneth Grahame have all stood the test of time, their books still being enjoyed by children and adults around the world.

TODAY

Today's household names of Jacqueline Wilson, Meg Cabot, Garth Nix and of course, JK Rowling all signify the diversifying of the modern offerings. Lavishly illustrated books, with captivating covers and awesome stories are accompanied by fancy websites, television programmes and films, but the base of it is still the story and the characters. Fly-away success series such as *Harry Potter* and Nix's *Abhorsen, The Seventh Tower* and *The Keys to the Kingdom* show that there is still a massive market out there, hungry for what your imagination can sculpt and, above all, keen on reading and learning.

The prevalence of televisions, the internet and games in today's modern culture is vilified and pilloried by many, but surely additional outlets for stories, characters, illustrations, learning and, above all, your imagination and creativity, isn't necessarily a bad thing, is it?

CHILDREN'S WRITER'S AND ILLUSTRATOR'S MARKET

Over the following pages of this book, we have tried to provide you with advice and information from bastions of your imagination. From Duncan Cameron's insight as a recently-published illustrator, to Margaret Mahy's advice and wisdom from a lifetime of writing; Peter Dickinson's reflections on his awe-inspiring work and advice on finding inspiration through to Caroline Buckingham's wonderful insight on what to expect when you do get accepted by the publishing house. All of them invaluable, and all of them written to encourage you to make the most of your talent.

The directory listings in the rest of the book have been researched, written and designed to give you as much information as possible and, above all, to provide details on as many markets for your work and ways in which to reach them as we can.

THE FUTURE

What defines a book, programme, film, game, play or website for children is the subject of much debate. Is it something that the child selects for itself? Or is it selected for a child by an authority figure? Some of these products are clearly targeted at a certain age group, while others cross the line and are picked up by adults as well – many books written for adults have become firm favourites with children. Whatever the definition and product, they all have one thing in common – they are meticulously crafted. They are thought about and delivered to captivate the imagination and to provide the cornerstones of a child's development: learning. And whatever happens in the future, and no matter what awesome technological advances are made, there will always be children and they will always be hungry to read, imagine and learn. That's something that will never change.

The Editor

Please join us at www.writersmarket.co.uk/childrens. As well as all the information and inspiration that can be found in this book, you'll find much more: daily news about the world of writing and publishing, regular updates and additions to the directory listings, and a growing community of writers.

WRITING FOR CHILDREN

WHERE DO YOU START? HOW DO YOU START? WHEN WILL IT FINISH?

Margaret Mahy shares some of her wisdom from a lifetime of writing

MARGARET MAHY

Margaret is one of the world's best loved authors for children. Her work has been translated into 15 languages. She has won numerous awards, including many from New Zealand (her home), as well as leading awards in the UK, the US and in Europe. In 2006, when she won the Hans Christian Andersen Author Award, the jurors' statement said: 'Mahy's language is rich in poetic imagery, magic, and supernatural elements. Her oeuvre provides a vast, numinous, but intensely personal metaphorical arena for the expression and experience of childhood and adolescence. Equally important, however, are her rhymes and poems for children. Mahy's works are known to children and young adults all over the world.'

▶ *'I've got nothing to do on Sunday afternoon. Maybe I'll dash off a children's book'.*
What? Write a whole book on Sunday afternoon?
'Just a children's book. And picture book stories are very short'.
But you've got to think about them. Thinking takes time.
'I don't want to think! It's too much like work…OK! Just tell me what to do'.

Well then (just to begin with!) READ! Read! Reading can be a way of thinking. Read and re-read those stories you loved as a child. Think about the way simple language can take on power and significance. Was it the sound of the words you loved back then? Was it what was happening in the story? Was it a mixture of both? Did certain words in the story take on power and mystery? I remember the power and mystery of the word 'soporific' in *The Tale of the Flopsy Bunnies* – a basically simple story by Beatrix Potter. You probably have similar memories. Read…remind yourself, and work it out.

All this sounds dangerously close to thinking. Or are you telling me to copy some story I loved?

Certainly not! Anyhow you probably won't want to. Once you've got your own ideas, you'll love them best of all.

IDEAS? WHERE DO YOU GET IDEAS FROM?

The whole world around you is flickering with ideas for stories. Learn to notice them. You turn on the bath tap and suddenly see a spider scuttling away from the advancing water. There's a story there.

You love the girl next-door, but she is entranced by the boy across the road…the one who leads a dangerous life on a motorbike

What is going on around you at home…at school? What do you remember from back then? What do you think you'll remember tomorrow? Do you remember things that went wrong? Or the funny things? Or the things that seemed frightening but turned out happily? And how do those past things flow into present ones? Because they often do. And of course a writer must make things up too. Real life is allowed to melt into fantasy in a story. And fantasy is always better if it has a bit of real life mixed into it. Real life and imagination dance together.

Then there is the question of shape. All stories have a certain shape and your story should have a beginning, a middle and an end. The world may flicker with stories, but writers have to recognise the story that suits them.

Sometimes you may have to tease such stories out of the world and (as you put them on paper) you must impose that ancient shape on them…give the idea a beginning, a middle and an end.

INVENTING STORIES AND WORLDS

Of course sometimes a story seems to come in on you from nowhere. A writer seems to get ideas about characters and events that have nothing to do with the real world. Sometimes the whole story can be an invention, but so what? Writers are allowed to make things up, though invented stories still need shapes.

Many years ago now I wrote a story called *A Lion in the Meadow*. Some time after I had written it… some time after it had been published…I realised that the story came from the memory of words in a story my father used to tell me when I was about three years old, but when I came to write the story down I had invented an end for it. (An ending that I hoped would be as rewarding for any adult reading the story as for the child listening to it.)

WRITING THE STORY

So! You have that idea. You have worked it out… roughly worked it out. As you write it the story will go on growing and branching out. It is like an explosion in your thoughts. Turn that explosion into lines on a page, leave wide gaps between the lines when you write your story down for the first time.

Now you are beginning to take charge of it. Read it aloud to yourself. Are there any sentences that are too long? Have you used the same word twice in a line? Is the beginning of the story too long for the middle and the end? Would you have enjoyed listening to or reading that story yourself when you were a child? Can you imagine children and parents sharing what you have set down on that first page?

> ## THE WORLD MAY FLICKER WITH STORIES, BUT WRITERS HAVE TO RECOGNISE THE STORY THAT SUITS THEM

THINK ABOUT THE WORDS

Is your language too sophisticated for children? A long word here and there can be fun, but on the whole language has got to be accessible. Read your story again. And again. Remember you are an adult writing for children. Would you have understood the words of this story – would you have caught on to the events – when you were three…or five…or ten?

WALKING AND TALKING YOUR STORY

Writers need to work their way into their stories. Sometimes it is a good idea to find a lonely path or stretch of beach and walk along it, telling yourself the story aloud as you go. Of course if you come around a corner and run into a neighbour you may get an odd look, but a writer has to live a brave life. Talking aloud you not only get a good, clear idea of how the story should sound, but often new ideas push in on you as you march and mutter. These new ideas just seem to slide in sideways and sometimes they make your story richer and funnier or more frightening than it was to begin with. Who cares if people think you are slightly mad?

BEAR IN MIND THAT MOST PUBLISHERS WANT A PICTURE BOOK STORY THAT WILL FIT INTO 32 PAGES

If you have remembered to leave spaces between the lines there will be room for you to put in your corrections. Often it is useful to put your changes down in a different coloured ink – it makes them easy to read later on. And of course you should think all over again about the idea you have had. Is it the sort of story a little child would enjoy? Is it suitable for kids aged about nine or ten…middle school kids? Is it a story for a teenager? You have probably had an idea from the very beginning, but sometimes writing it down changes the way you feel about it.

PICTURE BOOKS

Let's say you think you have written a picture book story. Bear in mind that most publishers want a picture book story that will fit into 32 pages. Remember the story will need to be set down in reasonably big print and pictures will take up most of those 32 pages. On the whole a picture book story needs to be a really short story.

And of course a picture book story needs pictures on every page. You may want to be your own illustrator, or you may need a publisher to find an illustrator for you. It can be handy to do a few rough drawings to show what action you think should go with what words. And if your story is accepted and the publisher finds a good illustrator for you, it is helpful if you can talk things over with the illustrator, either face to face or by email.

THE BALANCE OF PICTURES AND WORDS

The illustrator may sometimes want pictures to take over part of the story. I once wrote a story called *The Boy Who Was Followed Home*. The illustrator, Steven Kellogg, wrote from the USA asking me if pictures could carry the climax of the story, which is a lot to ask of a writer. However, I thought that by agreeing to this I would turn our book from a story with pictures into a true picture book, so I agreed.

However I did insist that there should be a few words on the final page so that both the ear and the eye would be satisfied.

Even when you are the writer, you may sometimes have a clear idea of how the characters should look. When the illustrator has done a few rough pictures of his or her own, he or she often sends them to the author, asking 'Is this how you thought of things?' You and the illustrator should be able to work things out together, even when you are on different sides of the world. Remember the illustrator is a partner when it comes to picture books. Good illustrations can sell a book. They are what people notice when they drift through a bookshop. 'Hey! Look at this! Isn't it great? What's the story like?' Treat the illustrator with respect.

BOOKS FOR OLDER CHILDREN

Of course as children get older they can cope with more sophisticated stories…more words and fewer pictures…longer books too – stories that will take up anything between 150 and 200 pages. There can be a few books for older readers that are 300 or 400 pages long. And every now and then there will be a very long story – say 800 pages. But this is rare. If you are submitting a first book don't challenge an editor too much. Somewhere between 100 and 200 pages is a handy length.

Girls will read stories about girls but they also enjoy stories directed at boys. Boys are much less likely to read stories that deal with girls even when the stories are exciting. Middle School children (particularly boys) enjoy straightforward adventure stories or funny stories. It is probably a good idea to have boys and girls sharing an adventure and to begin with something funny or exciting, just to catch the reader's attention. Of course readers' ideas about just what is funny or exciting can vary a great deal, but a lot of readers enjoy getting into the story quite quickly. Young adults like adventure stories too, but they may want something rather more complicated – stories about the mixed-up world we live in; stories in which questions of relationship dominate, because these can be adventures too.

READING, READING

Get your story onto the page then read and re-read it to yourself, remembering what you once liked and why you liked it. Sometimes it is a good idea to leave several days between one reading and another. That way the story has a chance to renew itself in your head and you may notice things you missed out on the first time around.

When, at last, your story sounds right – when it seems as good as you can possibly get it (and remember you must be stern with your story, stern with yourself too) – make for the computer or the typewriter if you haven't done so already. Print the story on one side of good, clean pages. Then send it to a publisher with a polite letter. Remember the editor who works for the publisher sees hundreds of stories every year. It is hard to take an editor by surprise. Cross your fingers when you send it off.

GETTING THE STORY PUBLISHED

The publishing company is a company of magicians. If they like your story they may turn it into a finished book. The editor is probably your first outside reader – the expert reader who is going to decide whether the publishers should make a book out of your story or send it back to you.

Remember it is no use sending a story for children to a publisher who only publishes non-fiction for adults or a picture book text to a publisher who specialises in young adult novels.

Most writers have to try several times to get a book published, and one editor may like a story that another editor rejects. After all, there are an enormous number of stories arriving on any editor's desk. If you have faith in your story, be prepared to send it to several publishing houses, one after the other. If you try several publishers at the same time, you should always mention this in your accompanying letter. Of course if you are very lucky and if you have worked hard on your story it may be accepted first time round, but that doesn't happen very often.

Let us suppose a book is finally accepted. The author will now be confronted with a possible book launching, with reviews, both good and bad, along with various interviews. Some people will reject the story, others may love it. It is now the publisher's job to see that the book is displayed in all bookshops and that it gets publicity and attention. The author does not have to become involved in these processes, but most authors will be willing to be interviewed about their books. Of course some authors will choose to be reclusive, but the book is out in the world and from now on, it belongs to the reader.

MARGARET MAHY

THE ROLE OF THE EDITOR

The editor should be an accomplished reader, not only able to recognise a good story, but able to pick out any faults the author, tangled up in the story as authors often are, may have missed. Are some of the descriptions too long and detailed? Do some of the characters behave in ways you wouldn't expect such a character to behave?

The editor is going to want to produce a good story, but one that will sell. And of course editors can be wrong. Several editors apparently turned down the first *Harry Potter* book, but when it was finally published it became one of the great book successes of all time. So the writer can argue with the editor's suggestions, but he or she should always think about them very carefully.

A WORLD OF STORIES

FANTASY, SCIENCE FICTION, ADVENTURE: PETER DICKINSON HAS WRITTEN THEM ALL

Here he reflects on a lifetime of writing, revealing his inspirations and how he has kept his imagination at full tilt.

PETER DICKINSON

Peter is a distinguished author, writing for both children and adults. He has written more than 50 books, many of which have won awards, including the coveted Carnegie Medal and the Whitbread Award. He has won the Phoenix Award twice, for *The Seventh Raven* in 2001. The Phoenix Award gives Peter particular pleasure because it recognises work published 20 years ago that did not receive its due recognition at the time. His books for adults have a devoted following, and like his work for children, are characterised by a breathtaking imagination, insights into the worlds of others, and wonderful writing. You can find out much more about Peter and his books by going to www.peterdickinson.com, from which this article is derived with permission.

▶ THE CHANGES TRILOGY

The Weathermonger (1968), *Heartsease* (1969), and *The Devil's Children* (1970)

STORY: Science fiction, set in a near-future England in which use of machines is equated with witchcraft.

I have mixed feelings about these first three books. In the UK, four out of five adults who know anything about the field mention them to me first, implying – no doubt unintentionally – that everything since then has been downhill all the way. But I recognise that if I were writing them now, with the rest of my work already done, there would be no possibility of my recapturing that well-spring of freshness, the writerly innocence that must have been part of that first appeal, giving readers the impression that here was a new voice.

The Weathermonger sprang from a nightmare (the first chapter is a tidied-up version). I had lain awake re-telling the dream, putting myself in charge of it, outwitting or defeating its monsters, in order to get back to sleep, but instead had spent the rest of the night finishing the story in my head. I then wrote a draft, largely hoping to unblock my first adult book, with which I was then stuck.

I'd no expectation of continuing the series, or even writing another children's book, but I'd greatly enjoyed the straightforward story-telling, and the change of voice from that of my adult book, and I felt that there was more to be done with my invented England. My original notion concerned a gang of kids getting an old trawler going, in somewhere like Hull, in order to escape. The technicalities would have been way beyond me, however, and anyway I wanted to write about the landscape round Painswick, in the West Cotswolds, which had long been my own personal *Great Good Place*. So I set *Heartsease* there, simplified the trawler down to a tug and gave myself an adult American, immune (very questionably) from the *Changes* effect, to understand the technicalities. The adventures work OK, I hope, but I imagine that the real energies of the book derive from my love of that area.

Having dealt with the end and middle of the *Changes*, it seemed logical to complete the job by writing about the start in *The Devil's Children*.

This is a more willed book than its predecessors, which had come flooding out of my unconscious like a mountain spring.

THE DANCING BEAR (1972)

STORY: Byzantine slave boy journeys into Hun territory to rescue captured daughter of the house, taking the trained household bear with him to act as a kind of passport (everyone would welcome the entertainment provided by a dancing bear) as he moves from the complexities of the city into the equally dangerous simplicities of the nomad Huns.

This was the first of my books to evolve from a story I'd told my sons to stop them squabbling in the back seat during our weekly commute to and from Hampshire. They'd asked for 'a new story, with a big battle in it', and the basic plot evolved itself in about twenty minutes from the start of the journey.

THE BLUE HAWK (1975)

STORY: An imaginary priest-ruled kingdom. A boy priest saves the hawk that is about to be sacrificed to renew the soul of the king, and by that one act brings the whole theocratic structure down.

Another told-in-the-car story – yes, there's a battle at the end. I'd already been thinking in a very vague way about those great stacks of special-offer cans you sometimes see in supermarkets, and the impulse to nudge one out and bring the whole pyramid down. Could you do that with a whole society? It would need to be a very rule-dominated one, in which not even the smallest detail could be allowed to change. The obvious thing was an all-powerful priesthood, and something breaking one of its rituals. A boy-priest, therefore, a dramatic ritual, a sacrifice…I don't remember why I chose the hawk.

> ## "THE BASIC PLOT EVOLVED ITSELF IN ABOUT TWENTY MINUTES FROM THE START OF THE JOURNEY"

TULKU (1979)

STORY: Set at the time of the Chinese Boxer Rebellion of 1900. Theodore, the son of American missionaries, escapes when the rebels destroy his father's settlement and falls in with a foul-mouthed female ex-music-hall star, now a plant-hunter. They flee together into Tibet, and reach a major Tibetan temple. With his strict Calvinistic upbringing, Theodore is at first repelled and horrified by lamaistic Buddhism, but eventually comes to terms with it.

This was yet another car story, again arising from a demand for a new one, with a battle in it. I wondered what new kind of battle I could come up with, and then I remembered that in Rudyard Kipling's *Kim* the old lama carries a scar on his forehead that he'd got as a young man when he and his comrades had gone out to fight the monks of a neighbouring monastery over a bit of land, using their long iron pen-cases as swords. OK, a battle with pen-cases.

So how do we get our hero into the forbidden territory of Tibet? I remembered that, around 1900, there had been a major uprising in China against foreign influence, called the Boxer Rebellion, in which a lot of Christians had been killed. So our hero escapes from them and falls in with a plant-hunter – I'd just got seriously interested in gardening and knew that there were some of them in south west China at the time – and the Boxers chase them into Tibet. I don't remember what happened after that, because the book changed course almost as soon as I'd started. The plant-hunter was just about to appear on the scene. Theodore was standing on the edge of the ravine looking back at the smoking ruins of the settlement. He heard the plod of hooves on the road behind him. At that point I said 'This guy's going to be a snore – I think I'll make him a woman.' So Theodore turned, and there was Mrs Jones, ready to gallop away with the book and win the Carnegie Medal for me.

THE SEVENTH RAVEN (1981)

STORY: Posh children's opera group is held hostage by South American guerrillas in west London.

Major hijackings were just beginning, and it struck me what a worthwhile target a churchload of kids – a lot of them with influential parents – might make. Despite that I wanted my story light-hearted, and full of excitement.

I was totally thrilled when, twenty years later, my story won the Phoenix Award, which is given each year to a book which didn't win any major prizes when it first came out, but the committee thinks is still worth something.

EVA (1988)

STORY: Future world, grossly overpopulated. A girl, horrendously injured in a road accident, is given the body of a chimpanzee to replace her human body and let her continue living. But her new body brings with it elements of the chimpanzee nature to which she then has to adjust, and at the same time cope with the attempts of powerful commercial interests to exploit her unique status.

I had no intention of writing *Eva* when I fed the first blank sheet into my typewriter. I thought I was trying to write a story about mythical first-women – Eve of course, and the shadowy figures of classical myth, and as many of the other cultural traditions I could find and work in, as well as 'African Eve' – the single unknown ancestress whom mitochondrial research suggests must have existed in Africa a few hundred thousand years ago.

To start with I needed a kid in a coma.

I had very little by way of plot, so to start myself thinking about it I settled down to get the set-up written, this kid waking up from her coma…I'd done about half a dozen pages, messing around, waiting for something to suggest itself, when my body gave a violent physical twitch, and my hair seemed to stand on end. My God, I thought, I know what they've done to her!

And from then on I was writing *Eva*.

AK (1990)

STORY: Peace is declared after a long civil war in a central African country. Paul, a boy soldier attached to one of the guerrilla bands, is told to bury his beloved AK rifle so that he can go to school and start to live a normal life. His group commander joins the new government, but soon there is a military coup and he is thrown into prison. Paul digs up his gun and travels to the capital to try to get him out.

No such choice makes sense, but if I were forced to choose I would say this is probably my best book. I was listening to a programme on the BBC World Service about the children who were being recruited or kidnapped to join guerrilla groups in central Africa. I heard someone say 'Even a hardened government soldier may hesitate a fatal half second before he guns down a child.' As with *Eva*, the hair on my nape stood on end. I knew I had to write about that.

I wasn't trying to tell readers what ought to be done about child guerrillas, or the tragic mess that parts of Africa were, and still are, in. That isn't fiction's job. Fiction is a gateway for the imagination.

I was trying to help people understand what it might feel like to be a child like that in the middle of a mess like that. Without that kind of imaginative understanding, nothing that anyone can do to help will be any use, however wonderful their intentions and however great their generosity.

THE ROPEMAKER (2001)

STORY: High fantasy novel about people from a simple and unmagical valley journeying through an all-controlling and magic-riddled empire to find the magician who can renew the spells that keep their valley safe.

This was, effectively, another car story, though I told it on foot, to my wife, Robin.

There are two main problems with car stories. First, you already know most of what is going to happen and you no longer have the excitement of discovery to spur you on. Few surprises wait for you round the next bend. Secondly, you find that in telling the story aloud you've got away with all sorts of stuff that won't stand up in print. You are dealing with a construction kit some of whose parts are missing while many of the rest don't fit, and when you attempt to adapt one to do so, it distorts its fit with something else, while the whole thing seems to lack any internal girderwork to support the structure.

But I'd been there before with car stories, and I kept at it.

ANGEL ISLE (2006)

STORY: Sequel to *The Ropemaker*, which finishes with an epilogue set twenty generations after the main story, describing runaway Saranja returning to Woodbourne only to find it gutted by fire after a raid by the northern horsemen, because the magic that protected the Valley has now collapsed. The prologue to Angel Isle is identical, and the story is again a quest, but one which turns out very differently.

I'm a much slower writer than I used to be, and I cursed myself many times for tackling something of this size at my age, but I'm glad I did. *The Ropemaker* doesn't seem to me to have much by way of a central moral spine, but this story seemed to grow one as it went along. It is about the corruption of power, both in the symbolic form of the magical power that once again has total control of the Empire, and also as political domination, the Empire itself being under attack by an aggressive, scientifically advanced mercantile confederation from overseas. The war in Iraq was just getting underway when I started, and there are some deliberate parallels with that in the mutual incomprehension of the two sides, but that's not all the book is about. Despite the effort it was in the end fun to write, and I hope it's a fun read.

WHAT NEXT?

A few years back I started writing on a PC. It makes writing seem a very different kind of process – easier in some ways, harder in others. I've slowed down quite a bit in the last few years, though. Funny to think there's only three or four books left for me, so they'd better be good, hadn't they?

The story I'm working on now is seen through the eyes of a new-born baby who…but no, I had better find out who the stranger is before I start talking about her.

> # "FUNNY TO THINK THERE'S ONLY THREE OR FOUR BOOKS LEFT FOR ME, SO THEY'D BETTER BE GOOD, HADN'T THEY?"

BOOKS THAT MATTER

ALL WRITERS SHOULD READ: HERE IS A SELECTED READING LIST

Mic Cady chooses a mixture of classics and lesser-known books

If you are a writer then, almost by definition, you will be a reader. Sometimes you'll read for pleasure, sometimes to seek inspiration. Some classic books for children need little introduction, while others seem to come and go on the cultural radar. The selection below includes some of the best writing for children ever published, but it is a personal choice. Add your own choices and comments at www.writersmarket.co.uk.

PICTURE BOOKS

First up, *Whistle up the Chimney*, written by Nan Hunt and illustrated by Craig Smith. It is the story of how Australian granny Mrs Millie Mack buys some firewood that includes bits from a bogie louvre (a kind of railway goods wagon). This has magical properties, so when Mrs Millie Mack lights her fire in the evenings miniature trains appear and whoosh round her house, to the delight of Mrs Millie Mack and her cat. Every picture is a delight, packed with amazing detail that it will take you and your children weeks and months to spot and wonder about. It is a marvel from start to finish, but you'll have some trouble tracking it down – try abebooks.com, a website that all writers should know anyway.

Over in the Meadow, by Paul Galdone, is a classic picture book. Both entertaining and educational, it can be used to help children to read and to count. It works because the rhymes are simple but funny and effective, and because the pictures are deceptively simple and delightful. Paul also wrote and illustrated

The Little Red Hen and *Henny Penny*. Again, these are charming stories with wonderful pictures and an underlying wicked humour that adult readers will enjoy. The villian in *Henny Penny* is the notorious Foxy Loxy, a wily fox who has plans to eat Henny Penny and her chums for dinner.

Margaret Mahy's *The Man Whose Mother was a Pirate*, with illustrations by Margaret Chamberlain, is a true picture story. Wonderful, rich pictures take Mahy's gloriously dotty story to even dottier places.

Much more contemporary is *I Am Not Sleepy and I Will Not Go to Bed* by Lauren Child. Bright, clever pages, using a mixture of painting, drawing, collage, montage and photographs, tell the story of Charlie's efforts to get his sister Lola off to bed, and her excuses not to go, involving tigers, lions, hippos, etc. Other books by Lauren Child include the prizewinning *I Will Not Ever Never Eat a Tomato*, and *Clarice Bean, That's Me*.

IMAGINATION AND FANTASY

I read *Lord of the Rings* so many times that I knew every scene, and looked forward with pleasure to getting there again. The book is a classic, a giant achievement by any standards. Tolkien creates a complete world, with its own dynamic that works on its own terms. The book is a journey – Frodo travels, and grows up as he does so, and so does the reader as Tolkien takes us from the innocence of the Shire to the evil heart of Mordor. Tolkien's masterpiece is sometimes criticised because its 'villain' – Sauron – is never seen, but one of the key points about *Lord of the Rings* is that there is a bit of Sauron in all of us, and that we can all be tempted and have to battle to resist temptation. One of the many failings of Peter Jackson's films is that he leaves out Frodo's return to a corrupted Shire, where innocence has been swept away. Frodo lets his travelling companions restore order, while he begins his preparations for another sort of journey altogether.

Ursula le Guin's *Earthsea* novels are essential reading, and also involve journeys of discovery. Another of her books, *The Dispossessed,* is a brilliantly imagined and thoughtful novel about anarchism. (As an aside, her website at www.ursulakleguin.com is full of great writing and great advice for writers.)

Anything by Terry Pratchett is a must. His *Discworld* novels get better and better, and wiser and wiser, but don't forget *Truckers, Diggers and Wings*, and the *Tiffany Aching* series.

Peter Dickinson can write about anything. Whether it's terrorists, African child fighters, magic, or prehistoric people, he writes utterly convincingly and beautifully. I'd go so far as to say that for any aspiring writer, reading Peter is obligatory.

Susan Cooper's *The Dark is Rising* sequence is – to use that phrase – unputdownable. And she's still writing great stuff now – read *King of Shadows*. It took me a little while to get into the story (about repressed grief, love, Shakespeare and much else), but once it worked its magic, I was gripped.

Alan Garner's first two books – *The Weirdstone of Brisingamen* and *The Moon of Gomrath* – still hold their own thirty years on. Clever stories, great villains, and a wizard in the shape of Cadellin, set against the background of real Cheshire landscapes, are all stirred together to make two classic fantasy novels.

Robert Westall wrote a stream of books across many genres, often ignoring the conventions of genre altogether, and a good thing, too! *The Devil on the Road* is about time travel, love, loyalty, fate, and magic, among other things; *The Kingdom by the Sea* is about growing up, friendship, betrayal and hope; *Urn Burial* about a sinister crashed spaceship; *The Machine-Gunners* about childhood and war; oh, read everything he wrote!

C S Lewis's *The Chronicles of Narnia* surely count as classics, and I loved them, but if I had to rescue anything of his from a fire it would be the remarkable *Space Trilogy*. Far too little known, these books were written for adults, but older children (I first read them at school) will be taken into three very different worlds, by turns unnerving, sublime and, in the last book, *That Hideous Strength,* a terrifying view of society collapsing into a ghastly swamp of human stupidity, greed, wickedness and the 'banality of evil'.

And to raise a few eyebrows, I'll put Philip Pullman's wonderful *His Dark Materials* books right next to C S Lewis. Pullman is criticised in some areas for being anti religious, and even anti God, but for me Pullman's vast canvas of characters, settings, themes and moral questioning is as rich and deep as anything written, inviting the reader to go on his or her own moral journey.

To end this category: *Skellig*, by David Almond. This book is entrancing in every sense of the word from page one to the end. What's it about? Shan't tell – just go out and get it, and read it. This book made me cry, but with pleasure, surprise, and joy.

QUIRKY

Love that Dog by Sharon Creech really does defy all categories and genres. As Benjamin Zephaniah says about it: 'Is it a diary? Is it a novel? Who cares?' Who cares, indeed. You'll be able to read this funny, beguiling and moving story in one short sitting, but you'll be much the richer for it.

Framed, by Frank Cottrell Boyce, is about how life in Manod (north Wales) is transformed by art. Well, that's one take on this sublime, subtle, eccentric and hugely funny book. Frank writes wonderfully and, in

BOOKS THAT MATTER

MIC CADY

FEATURE

Framed, uses clever narrative tricks to take the story forward and to add to the fun. He also wrote *Millions*, which also uses his remarkable writing skills to tell a warm, funny and moving story.

Finally, *Green Smoke*, by Rosemary Manning. This most innocent and charming of stories was published in 1957, and it speaks volumes of a time that feels impossibly remote. A little girl called Susan is walking alone on a beach and meets a dragon. They become friends, sharing buns and stories and adventures. It is a delight from page one, beautifully and elegantly written, and very funny. It has wonderful illustrations by Constance Marshall that capture the feel of the story exactly.

Like all the best stories, *Green Smoke* is magic in and of itself, and lets you enter your own magical, internal world. It is also a story about stories and story-telling.

Here Susan and the dragon are discussing parties:

'Is that what you did at parties?' asked Sue. 'Told stories?'

'Of course,' answered the dragon. 'What do you do at yours?'

'Well, we play games, and sing, and eat buns, and jellies.'

'Oh, we did all those things as well,' said the dragon. 'But the story-telling was the most important. Don't you ever tell stories at your parties?'

'No,' said Sue. 'I don't think we ever do.'

'And your dear father and mother,' went on the dragon, 'don't they sit and tell each other stories in the long winter evenings?'

'I don't think so,' said Sue, 'I've never heard them.'

'Extraordinary,' said the dragon. 'I suppose none of you know any. How sad. I'd better start teaching you some good stories at once.'

Pure magic; pure story-telling.

REMEMBER THE PARENTS

Many stories are read to children, of course.

Picture books are shared by the reader and the read-to, both enjoying the experience of discovering the story and the pictures. For many parents, it is the highlight of the day to sit quietly with their children sharing a book. It is the best possible bonding experience. And of course a loved book will be read many times; often more times than the parent would quite like! And this is where writers and illustrators can come to the rescue.

A book with witty, funny or subtle pictures and a good accompanying story, well told, will rescue the reader from boredom even when the book has been read many, many times. This is why someone such as Allan Ahlberg, whose books are loved by child and parent alike, is blessed by one and all.

Children are harsh critics, and a book will often only get one chance. If after the first reading the child says 'Don't like it', the book is probably doomed to gather dust, unopened, unloved.

Reading books are somewhat different. The parent reader can take more risks here, perhaps reading books that are stretching the child's understanding and imagination, but in a good and positive way. I know a couple who are already reading *Winnie the Pooh* to their two-month old – good for mum and dad and baby too!

THE CONSUMER MARKET FOR CHILDREN'S BOOKS

FACTS, FIGURES AND TRENDS

By Steve Bohme, Research Director, Book Marketing Ltd

BML

BML is the premier source of information and research on the book industry, undertaking a range of private and syndicated research projects, and publishing a variety of market reports. BML's continuous survey, 'Books and the Consumer', provides detailed information on British book buying behaviour including comprehensive profiles of the different types of consumers; a detailed understanding of the performance of publishers and retailers; comparisons between competitors; market segmentation by brand, price, retailer, genre and format and an accurate reflection of changes in the marketplace.

▶ MARKET SIZE AND GROWTH

In 2006, more children's books were bought by consumers than in any previous year on record. The 79m children's titles purchased in 2006 was 36% higher than in 1997 (58m), while spending on children's books has grown at nearly twice that rate over the last decade, up from £232m to £391m. Growth in purchases of children's books has exceeded that of adult books, so that children's titles have increased their share of consumer book purchases over this period, from 24% to 26% of volume, and from 14% to 17% of value.

While J K Rowling's *Harry Potter* series has been the children's book phenomenon of the last decade,

TABLE 1: CHILDREN'S BESTSELLERS, 2006

		Vol. (000s)	Val. (£000s)
1. *Doctor Who Annual 2007*	-	304	1,381
2. *The Beano Annual*	-	235	1,068
3. *The End*	Lemony Snicket	204	1,017
4. *Wintersmith*	Terry Pratchett	197	2,000
5. *Candyfloss*	Jacqueline Wilson	183	1,729
6. *Harry Potter/Half-Blood Prince*	J K Rowling	176	810
7. *Horrid Henry & the Football Fiend*	Francesca Simon	166	663
8. *Starring Tracy Beaker*	Jacqueline Wilson	140	1,151
9. *Bratz Annual 2007*	-	140	617
10. *Horrid Henry's Christmas Cracker*	Francesca Simon	127	521

NB. excludes £1 books specially created for World Book Day. Source: Nielsen BookScan © Nielsen 2007

growth in the children's market has not been entirely down to these books. Indeed, 2006's record-breaking volume figures came despite the fact that no new *Harry Potter* title was released in that year.

LEADING TITLES, AUTHORS AND GENRES

In fact, 2006 was the first year for nearly a decade in which a *Harry Potter* title did not head the children's bestseller list. Instead, the number one title in terms of volume sales was the *Dr Who Annual 2007*, ahead of *The Beano Annual* and *Lemony Snicket's Series of Unfortunate Events: The End*. The fourth placed title, Terry Pratchett's *Wintersmith*, recorded the highest value sales of any children's book in 2006, ahead of Jacqueline Wilson's *Candyfloss*.

An analysis of sales since 2002, however, reveals the dominance of *Harry Potter* titles in the children's fiction market in recent years. Eight of the ten bestselling children's titles between 2002 and mid-2007 are *Potter* titles, while the remaining top 10 slots are taken by two of the titles in Philip Pullman's *His Dark Materials* trilogy (Table 2).

BML

BML began monitoring the volume and value of books bought by consumers in 1997.

If J K Rowling has dominated the children's and teenage reading book market since 2002, Julia Donaldson has been ascendant in the pre-school

> **2006 WAS THE FIRST YEAR FOR NEARLY A DECADE IN WHICH A *HARRY POTTER* TITLE DID NOT HEAD THE CHILDREN'S BESTSELLERS**

and picture book market. Five of her titles fill six of the top ten places in the bestseller list for this sector over the period 2002–07. The remaining top ten slots include classic titles, such as *The Very Hungry Caterpillar*, and perennially popular characters, such as *Thomas the Tank Engine* and the *Mr Men* (Table 3). The 2006 bestseller list (Table 1) points to the enduring popularity of annuals, with three titles in the top ten. However, as Fig. 1 illustrates, annuals account for a relatively small share of children's book purchases as a whole. General reading books (including adventure, horror, fantasy, fairy tales, etc), accounted for 42% of children's book purchases in 2006, while general non-fiction (including educational and general interest books in subjects such as science, history, English and maths) accounted for 18% of the market. One in six books purchased by consumers were picture/character fiction, while activity books and early learning each commanded a 9% share.

TABLE 2: CHILDREN'S FICTION BESTSELLERS, 2002–07

		Vol. (000s)	Val. (£000s)
1. *Harry Potter/Order of the Phoenix* (hbk)	J K Rowling	3,039	33,866
2. *Harry Potter/Half-Blood Prince* (hbk)	J K Rowling	2,939	27,925
3. *Harry Potter/Deathly Hallows* (hbk)	J K Rowling	2,672	23,030
4. *Harry Potter/Goblet of Fire* (pbk)	J K Rowling	1,031	5,543
5. *Harry Potter/Prisoner of Azkaban* (pbk)	J K Rowling	945	4,664
6. *Harry Potter/Chamber of Secrets* (pbk)	J K Rowling	756	3,727
7. *Northern Lights* (pbk)	Philip Pullman	680	3,884
8. *Harry Potter/Philosopher's Stone* (pbk)	J K Rowling	591	3,119
9. *Harry Potter/Order of the Phoenix* (pbk)	J K Rowling	571	3,112
10. *The Amber Spyglass* (pbk)	Philip Pullman	563	3,250

hbk = hardback edition pbk = paperback edition. Source: Nielsen BookScan © Nielsen 2007

TABLE 3: PRE-SCHOOL AND PICTURE BOOK BESTSELLERS, 2002–07

		Vol. (000s)	Val. (£000s)
1. *The Gruffalo* (pbk)	Julia Donaldson	499	2,524
2. *The Very Hungry Caterpillar* (hbk)	Eric Carle	388	1,852
3. *Room on the Broom* (pbk)	Julia Donaldson	342	1,849
4. *The Gruffalo's Child* (pbk)	Julia Donaldson	272	1,261
5. *The Snail and the Whale* (pbk)	Julia Donaldson	243	1,235
6. *My Thomas Story Library* (pbk)	W Awdry	242	529
7. *Mr. Christmas* (pbk)	Roger Hargreaves	225	491
8. *The Smartest Giant in Town* (pbk)	Julia Donaldson	223	1,173
9. *Dear Zoo: Lift the Flaps* (hbk)	Rod Campbell	220	1,040
10. *The Gruffalo's Child* (hbk)	Julia Donaldson	219	1,855

hbk = hardback edition pbk = paperback edition. Source: Nielsen BookScan © Nielsen 2007

SOURCE OF PURCHASE

The profile of children's book purchases by source is rather different from that of adult titles, with a relatively smaller proportion bought from specialist bookshops, supermarkets and the internet, and a relatively higher proportion bought from non-specialist retailers and via direct mail.

However, as with adult books, the direct mail and non-specialist retail channels have lost share in the children's market over the last decade. As Fig. 2 illustrates, each of these channels accounted for nearly one in four children's books bought in 1997, but only one in six purchases in 2007. Instead, relatively more children's books have been bought from supermarkets and the internet, although these channels have not yet had quite as much of an impact in the children's as the adult market. Indeed, whereas in the adult market the shares of both chain and other specialist bookshops (e.g. independents, bargain and specialist bookshops) were lower in 2006 than in 1997, in the children's market, chain bookshops have gained share over the last 10 years.

END USERS

Another prominent trend in the children's market over the last decade has been the increasing

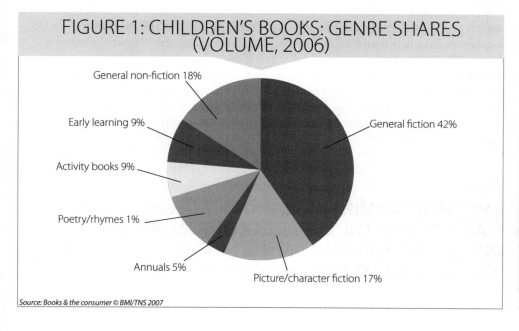

FIGURE 1: CHILDREN'S BOOKS: GENRE SHARES (VOLUME, 2006)

General non-fiction 18%
Early learning 9%
Activity books 9%
Poetry/rhymes 1%
Annuals 5%
Picture/character fiction 17%
General fiction 42%

Source: Books & the consumer © BMI/TNS 2007

FIGURE 2: CHILDREN'S BOOKS: SOURCE SHARES (VOLUME, 1997–06)

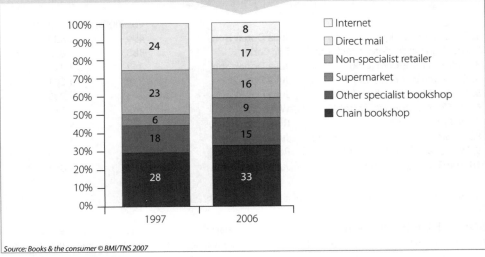

Source: Books & the consumer © BMI/TNS 2007

likelihood that a children's book will be bought for an adult reader. The proportion of children's titles purchased for an end user aged 17 or over rose from one in eight in 1997, to one in five in 2006 (peaking at one in four titles in 2005, when the 6th *Harry Potter* title was released).

This trend reflects the cross-over appeal of children's authors such as J K Rowling, Philip Pullman and C S Lewis, and also the fact that adults will read authors such as Terry Pratchett whether the book is an adult or children's title (Table 4).

While some authors are popular among both boys and girls (Roger Hargreaves and Enid Blyton among the 0–7s; J K Rowling and Lemony Snicket among 7–16s, and Rowling, Pratchett and Pullman among 17+s), others are more or less popular depending on the gender of the book recipient.

As Table 4 indicates, Daisy Meadows has been one of the top five authors bought for girls in the 0–7 and 8–16 age brackets during the period 2002 to mid 2007, and Jacqueline Wilson features in the top five bought for females aged 8–16 and 17+. In contrast, leading authors bought for males during this period, which don't appear in the equivalent top fives bought for females, include W Awdry, Dr Seuss, Francesca Simon, Terry Deary, Anthony Horowitz, Darren Shan, Christopher Paolini and Conn Iggulden

Source: Books & the Consumer © BML/TNS 2007. NB that not all of these will necessarily be books read by adults for themselves. In some cases, adults state that they are the end user where they are reading a book to a very young child.

CHILDREN'S BOOK BUYERS

If those aged 17+ are sometimes the end users of children's books, they are also responsible for most of the purchasing in this market. Indeed, 12–16s, who represent 9% of the 12–74 population, accounted for only 2% of children's book purchases in 2006. The heaviest buyers of children's books are those aged 35–44 (19% of the population, but purchasing 29% of books in 2006). Those aged

> ANOTHER PROMINENT TREND IN THE CHILDREN'S MARKET OVER THE LAST DECADE HAS BEEN THE INCREASING LIKELIHOOD THAT A CHILDREN'S BOOK WILL BE BOUGHT FOR AN ADULT READER

TABLE 4: CHILDREN'S BOOK PURCHASES: TOP 5 AUTHORS BOUGHT FOR EACH GROUP (VOLUME, 2002–07)

All 0–7
1. *Roger Hargreaves*
2. *Enid Blyton*
3. *W Awdry*
4. *Julia Donaldson*
5. *Daisy Meadows*

Girls 0–7
1. *Roger Hargreaves*
2. *Daisy Meadows*
3. *Julia Donaldson*
4. *Enid Blyton*
5. *Beatrix Potter*

Boys 0–7
1. *W Awdry*
2. *Roger Hargreaves*
3. *Enid Blyton*
4. *Dr Seuss*
5. *Francesca Simon*

All 8–16
1. *Jacqueline Wilson*
2. *J K Rowling*
3. *Lemony Snicket*
4. *Terry Deary*
5. *Anthony Horowitz*

Girls 8–16
1. *Jacqueline Wilson*
2. *J K Rowling*
3. *Lemony Snicket*
4. *Daisy Meadows*
5. *Enid Blyton*

Boys 8–16
1. *J K Rowling*
2. *Terry Deary*
3. *Anthony Horowitz*
4. *Lemony Snicket*
5. *Darren Shan*

All 17+
1. *J K Rowling*
2. *Terry Pratchett*
3. *Philip Pullman*
4. *C S Lewis*
5. *Jacqueline Wilson*

Women 17+
1. *J K Rowling*
2. *Philip Pullman*
3. *Terry Pratchett*
4. *Jacqueline Wilson*
5. *C S Lewis*

Men 17+
1. *J K Rowling*
2. *Terry Pratchett*
3. *Philip Pullman*
4. *Christopher Paolini*
5. *Conn Iggulden*

Source: Books & the Consumer © BML/TNS 2007

FIGURE 3: CHILDREN'S BOOKS: AGE OF BUYER (VOLUME, 2006)

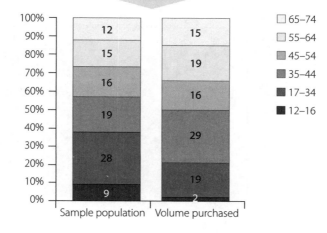

Source: Books & the Consumer © BML/TNS 2007

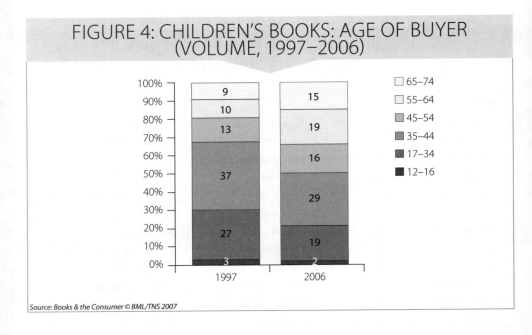

FIGURE 4: CHILDREN'S BOOKS: AGE OF BUYER (VOLUME, 1997–2006)

Source: Books & the Consumer © BML/TNS 2007

> **THE PATTERN IS AT LEAST IN PART A REFLECTION OF CHANGES IN THE DEMOGRAPHIC MAKE-UP OF THE BRITISH POPULATION**

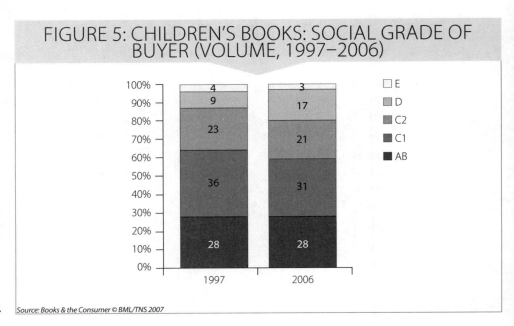

FIGURE 5: CHILDREN'S BOOKS: SOCIAL GRADE OF BUYER (VOLUME, 1997–2006)

Source: Books & the Consumer © BML/TNS 2007

55–74 are also relatively heavy buyers in this market, representing a quarter of the population, but accounting for a third of purchases (Fig. 3).

While 17–44s buy more children's books than any other age band shown in Fig. 3, their importance to the market has declined over time. Indeed, the proportion of children's books bought by 17–44s has fallen from 64% to 48% over the last decade (Fig. 4). In contrast, echoing patterns in the adult market, and reflecting changes in the demographic and socio-economic conditions of the British population, the 55–74 age group has increased its share from 19% to 34% over this period.

Another significant trend in the demographics of buyers of children's books is the increase in importance to the market of lower social grades, specifically those in social grade 'D' (i.e. semi and unskilled manual workers). Their share of the market has doubled from 9% to 17% over the last 10 years, while C1s (junior managerial, administrative and professional workers) and C2s (skilled manual workers) have lost share (Fig. 5). Once again, the pattern is at least in part a reflection of changes in the demographic make-up of the British population, but also may relate to the widening of the range of

17–44s BUY MORE CHILDREN'S BOOKS THAN ANY OTHER AGE BAND

sources of children's books over the last decade (see Fig. 2), and perhaps also the impact of high profile titles such as *Harry Potter*.

While C1s are becoming increasingly less important to the children's market, they still account for more purchases than any other social grade (31% in 2006). Equally, while Ds have grown in importance, they remain relatively light buyers of children's books, accounting for 17% of purchases in 2006, while representing 25% of the population (Fig. 6). ABs (higher and intermediate managerial, administrative and professional workers) have maintained their position as the heaviest buyers in this sector, representing 18% of the population, while buying 28% of children's books in 1997 and 2006.

FIGURE 6: CHILDREN'S BOOKS: SOCIAL GRADE OF BUYER (VOLUME, 2006)

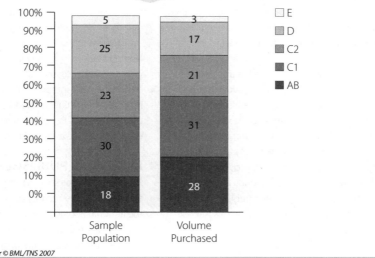

CALL YOURSELF AN ILLUSTRATOR?

YOUR RELATIONSHIP WITH YOUR PUBLISHER IS VERY IMPORTANT

Duncan Cameron shares his experience of having his first book published.

DUNCAN CAMERON

Duncan was born in London in1971 and grew up in Norfolk. He studied fine art at the University of the West of England, Bristol and at UWIC, Cardiff. He is a practising artist and sculptor and art & design lecturer at Strode College. He lives with his family in Somerset, has a Studio at Spike Island in Bristol and is an enthusiastic scuba diver. His book *Shipwreck Detective* was published by Dorling Kindersley in 2006 and he is currently working on new illustration and sculpture projects.

▶ I didn't consider myself an illustrator. I had never had any illustration published before I worked on *Shipwreck Detective* and I am still likely to respond with 'who, me ?' when the term is used.

I previously described myself as a sculptor and I did drawings to support my work, but had become frustrated about the lack of space in my life for creative activity, sandwiched as it always was between teaching and family commitments. I wanted to make more time for my drawing, and to justify this I needed to find a way to make it pay.

I had wanted to illustrate a book for a number of years, so I decided to approach publishers directly with my ideas and, as I remember it, this is what happened.

DON'T BELIEVE THAT THEY PUT YOUR LETTERS IN THE BIN

I put together a small pack of colour photocopies of relevant artwork, a summary of my book ideas and a covering letter of introduction. I didn't have a useful reference book with details of publishers in so I simply looked through my bookcases and pulled out illustrated books that I liked the look of and sent my eight letters to the relevant publishers.

Although I'm an optimistic character I half expected not to get any responses, as common advice from people (who have no qualifications to give such advice), is that cold-call applications end up in the bin. But this was not my experience. I got seven replies and all were positive, although frequently brief, and in summary suggested that my ideas 'were too specialist.' The email reply from Dorling Kindersley, however, said that my ideas were too limited in their appeal but they liked my drawings and wanted to know if I could send some more examples. Encouraged, I emailed back saying that I 'happened' to be in London in a couple of weeks and so we arranged to meet at their offices.

MEETING A PUBLISHER

Arriving at DK it all seemed very real and exciting, and clutching my security pass I stepped out onto the Penguin floor in their imposing offices on the Strand in central London, half expecting to be given a cursory five minute once over before being politely asked to leave. We ended up having a two-hour talk about my work, sculpture, diving and ideas and a lot of the focus surprisingly fell upon my handwritten journals. My wider art practice and sculpture was about shipwrecks, and therefore much of the artwork and collaged material in my journals centred around this theme. The three people I met were encouraging and friendly, and as we talked the idea was born to develop a book about shipwrecks, ecology and diving that contained real factual information but which looked like an artist's journal.

I stepped back onto the Strand full of excitement at the reception I had received and the imminent publishing sensation that seemed assured.

DEVELOPING AN IDEA

This enthusiastic 'talk' went on for a year and a half over a series of meetings where I learnt many new publishing terms.

The ideas passed between different editors as people came and went at DK and I had to develop and pitch drawings about science experiments, museums and lobsters, until finally the shipwreck

idea came back into favour and we started talking about developing some example spreads.

I was pleased that we were back on shipwrecks as privately I was still ecstatic that I hadn't somehow found myself being shoehorned into my first commission illustrating a history of paint drying. For almost the first two years I had no contract and hadn't been paid, and I was beginning to wonder if the encouraging talking would ever actually lead to a book and possibly even a fee.

I did appreciate, however, that although my 'supporters' on the inside, most notably art editor Caroline Buckingham (see article on page 35), were very enthusiastic there were others within DK who were nervous about such an unusual project and said as much at meetings: 'What did you say? It's handwritten by a sculptor and it's got a compass and a cockroach stuck in it!?'.

WORKING WITH A WRITER

It was suggested by DK that a writer be brought onto the project to work with me and to provide a fictitious narrative to sew all of the ideas together.

ONCE WORKING ON A PROJECT

- Don't do any final artwork until you've agreed the layout with the publisher.

- Don't place text onto the original artwork, as this will cause problems when it comes to translations for co-editions. Remember to leave space for the gutter.

- Keep a record of time spent working to give you some idea of what is achievable in a certain period of time, and also therefore what would be a fair fee for future work.

- Leave extra space for any text you want inserting, as translated text for co-editions might take up more room.

- Prepare addressed postage envelopes for your work in advance, so that you don't have to think about it when the pressure is on and you're racing to meet a deadline.

- Organise your emails and meeting notes so you can find information quickly.

- Draw where and when you can, but make some space in your life to allow for sleep.

- Maintain a clear sense of what are you trying to achieve; it's easy to drift, or be pushed off-course over months of work and lose the focus and original intention.

- Scan or at least photocopy all artwork before you post it in case it gets lost. Also make sure you insure the package and send it by a traceable means, rather than just dropping it in the postbox.

- You might have an opinion about the cover but be prepared to be overruled. The publisher has the final decision.

DUNCAN CAMERON

FEATURE

"SCAN OR AT LEAST PHOTOCOPY ALL ARTWORK BEFORE YOU POST IT IN CASE IT GETS LOST"

I admit to feeling challenged by this at the time, but could see that it would make sense of the journal structure, and I had to admit that I had no track record as a writer. It became very clear when we met that we would get on, and that writer Richard Platt (see article on page 31) not only knew a lot about shipwrecks, and had written many books, but like me had a keen sense of humour and a fund of distracting anecdotes.

Although development discussions with DK were consistently supportive, I also soon learnt to appreciate having another independent voice to talk to and bat ideas about with. We agreed on a list of potential shipwrecks and the importance of covering different parts of the globe and, after agreeing on the things I wanted to draw, Richard put together a plot which saw the fictional me travelling from wreck to wreck clutching a journal.

My concerns about having someone else voicing the fictional me were assuaged by the friendly correspondence that we maintained throughout the weeks of development, as the plot had me variously pursued by oil companies, harassed by sharks and my sister injured by cat litter. We didn't always agree and Richard was very happy, or so he told me, to allow me to comment on his writing or question the tone of a particular phrase. I posted him developmental sketches and we moved steadily towards the book as we see it now, although many colourful details were lost as editing decisions were made later on to reduce text length.

STARTING OUT AS A BOOK ILLUSTRATOR

- Believe in yourself and your work, and be positive and enthusiastic.

- Think carefully about the type of work that you want to do and shape your portfolio accordingly – you don't want to work on a project that you won't enjoy.

- Get as much advice as you can and get hold of a publishing reference book.

- Don't take setbacks personally; it's a numbers game, and a publisher has to be persuaded that the idea you have will lead to book sales.

- Try and arrange to meet up as it's always better to discuss ideas over a table, and never underestimate the importance of being able to get on well with people.

- You don't have to have an agent, but if like me you're rubbish at negotiating business details and contracts then it's a good idea, and they find you work.

- Keep a list of new terminology and everyone's job titles and contact details.

- Be honest and ask for explanations when you don't understand something.

- Get someone to look over your contract with you, try and maintain ownership of your original artwork and aim to secure a fair royalty and an advance fee.

- Keep smiling – remember you are the one who wanted to do this and no-one likes a complainer.

HOW BOOKS GET COMMISSIONED

There are many internal preparatory meetings and several book fairs each year, including Bologna (specialising in books for children) and Frankfurt (the world's biggest book fair), at which new titles are pitched and sold to European and global publishers. Once titles are selected a presentation pack is assembled and these are taken to the book fairs to sell the book.

It was at this stage that I finally got paid for a bit of work, creating the first three spreads and working up the plot details, key sales points and trying to make it clear why this book would sell and how it differed from the competition.

If the proposed title is well received at a book fair then predicted sales are set against costs, and if the sums add up the book is commissioned. I remember reading through pages of information in my contract about how I would only get miniature royalty percentages for co-editions in distant countries, but I was so excited that I would even appear in these places that I signed on the dotted line. I got my brother in-law who is a lawyer to look through it all, and talked to Richard Platt about the terminology. The only revision I insisted on was that I should have the original artwork returned to me after printing.

HANDLING THE WORKLOAD

Once under contract it becomes very clear what is expected of you: in my case, 96 pages of illustrations to be delivered in three sections and all by a date in March, seven months hence. I hadn't really appreciated quite how much drawing 96 pages represented until I had to draw a page plan. Even this sheet of miniatures took several days, and then there were the 'scamps' – also small versions but slightly larger with more detail. The format of the scamps changed a number of times and with each I had to provide lists of research, composition details, collaged elements and links to the story. I sat through the autumn half term on the floor of my empty college laying scamps out in lines and trying to track the story. These plans were fed into schedules that specified which double-page spreads I would deliver, and by when, and so I set to work.

As it was I sat up drawing at my kitchen table, often until 3 or 4 in the morning, listening to the World Service and then packing up the work every few days to post to London in my teaching lunch hour. This is not to be taken as advice as it was no way to carry on, and if I've learnt anything it's that I won't say yes to a project of this scale again without making time to do some drawing in daylight. I didn't work in page order but had many spreads in different states of completion at any one time, grouped in related areas of research. I have spreads that I think worked well and others that I still wince at even now as I recall a compromise or late night struggle with the rendering of a diver's fingers.

IT'S A COMPLEX BUSINESS

The first spreads I submitted were covered in my handwriting and arrows, and I had these returned so that I could remove it all with a scalpel. I admit to not understanding how the book could look handwritten and be published in Norway (say) when I can't write Norwegian. The answer of course was for DK to develop a font with my handwriting that enables them to print the journal in any language

> ## KEEP A LIST OF NEW TERMINOLOGY AND EVERYONE'S JOB TITLES AND CONTACT DETAILS

and so there is now a font called 'Duncan Cameron' owned by DK and available in bold or regular.

This also meant that not only did I have to draw the spreads but with each spread I had to submit tracing paper overlays to show both text and annotation positioning. The feedback from DK was encouraging and it was agreed that the book would sell for slightly more money, which meant we could include more 'add-on' elements and that almost every other spread had something that could be folded out or opened up.

I developed a very close working relationship with Jo Little, then a DK designer, whose thankless task it was to pass on opinions at DK, scan my artwork and digitally fit the text while continuously reminding me not to drop writing into the gutter in the fold of the spread, where it would have been lost in the printed, bound book.

KNOW YOUR SUBJECT

I sat drawing the WWII wreck of the passenger steamer *Vironia* for many hours working from a small photo of her sister ship. I was very pleased with my atmospheric dark pen rendering of the imagined gloomy deep-sea wreck, black and imposing in the Baltic depths. Having submitted the spread and continued my research I then found an article that described the *Vironia* as a 'sleek white beauty, the swan of the north'. The black ship I had studied in shape but essentially 'made-up' certainly wasn't a swan but I persuaded everyone that any ship mired in decades of rust looks pretty black.

I would sit under the dull flattening light of a standard lamp trying to make sure that the type of fish I was drawing actually did live in that part of the world and at one point I remember scissoring off the head of a hammerhead to change it into a bull shark, pleased that the collaged quality of my work allowed for such frequent interventions.

It occurred to me, as I drew famous wreck divers, that they might of course actually see the book one day and I remember asking DK who else checked what I was doing and the answer was essentially that although editors would go through it all, I was the diver and I should get it right.

Getting it right meant a lot of internet research and this was to keep me awake at night which was fine as I needed to be drawing anyway.

END IN SIGHT

As autumn became winter and I became the father to a fourth small child I know that there were concerns that I wouldn't be able to do the work in time. Editors came and visited me in Bristol, weekly schedules were juggled as I waited for research material and some ideas were abandoned.

There was to be no real treasure hunt (as had been discussed), or flashing lights on the cover and the 'Americans' (the US arm of DK) decided that the whole book should be about a third bigger. My work was returned for re-sizing amid a cloud of expletives.

Communication was relentlessly by email, a form of dialogue that I accept as vital but am not natural at. To make sense of the endless back and forth I would print off key chains of agreed actions and bulldog clip them together by month. I'm sure that there is a digital way of ordering all this more environmentally but I printed them out and used a giant felt marker.

I remember Caroline, by now a good friend and supporter, hiding the cover from me in a meeting until finally showing me the metallic finish that saw it through to the shelves. This seemed at the time to be so far removed from the concept of a worn travel journal that I felt we'd all got a bit lost, but I do now concede that it can be seen in shops and gives the work a certain nautical bling. The final days arrived with their frantic negotiations and deadlines and I opted to deliver the last bits of artwork by hand to give me another day and I sat in the DK offices as people ran about finding me pictures of airplanes and starfish to work from until it was all done and the cleaners had gone home.

Once the work was finished I had to wait for the five months or so that it takes for the many final adjustments to be made and for the printers to actually produce the masterpiece on the other side of the world. Then one day, almost three years after I had first sent off my letters, a parcel arrived and I found myself holding a book, a real book, a sparkly blue book with my name on the front.

With enthusiasm and a sense of occasion I sat down on my daughter's bed that evening and announced that 'tonight I would be reading *Shipwreck Detective* as the bedtime story' only to be shot down by two pairs of dark little eyes and the comment 'Do we have to, it's just ships and stuff.'

> ## "ONCE UNDER CONTRACT IT BECOMES VERY CLEAR WHAT IS EXPECTED"

WRITING CHILDREN'S NON-FICTION

WRITING NON-FICTION FOR CHILDREN CAN BE JUST AS REWARDING AS WRITING FICTION

And you might actually earn a living. Richard Platt explains how.

RICHARD PLATT

Richard Platt has written 70 books. More than 30 were published by Dorling Kindersley, including four *Eyewitness Guides*: *Cinema, Pirate, Spy* and *Shipwreck*. He collaborated with Stephen Biesty on the highly successful *Cross-Section* series. His *Eureka!* was chosen as a 2004 Outstanding Science Trade Book by the CBC and NSTA. Richard's *Pirate Diary* won the Blue Peter Best Book with Facts Award and a Smarties Silver.

▶ Do you want to earn a living by writing children's books? Of course you do! That's why you are reading this. Then put down your dog-eared manuscript of *Cuggly-Wuggly Bunnie Goes to Market* and start a new book. Try *Keeping and Caring for Pet Rabbits*. You've a seriously better chance of getting it published. Fiction can come later.

Of course, this title may not hold the slightest interest for you, and there are already many non-fiction books about rabbit husbandry, but my point is that everybody, really EVERYBODY, wants to write children's stories. What's more, they believe they can do it. Remember *Budgie the Helicopter*? You can't compete with a brand like the Royal Family. My local education authority even runs a course called 'Write and Illustrate Your Own Children's Story Books.' Three

evenings. Anyone can do it, you see, it's easy. With illustrated fiction promoted like this, it's hardly surprising that children's publishers are deluged with manuscripts and naff watercolours. The competition is fierce, and unless you are a *very* talented illustrator who has a way with words, you are unlikely to succeed. Non-fiction, by contrast, is the road less travelled. Which is surprising, considering that nearly four out of every ten children's book sold is non-fiction, and in libraries, roughly half of all loans to children are non-fiction. The attraction for a would-be author is that if you have a good idea for a children's non-fiction book, there is a reasonable chance that you might actually be able to sell it to a publisher. In the world of fiction, the chances are very much slimmer. But where do you start?

WRITE WHAT YOU KNOW

This is as true in non-fiction as it is in fiction. Getting that first book published is the highest hurdle you're likely to face in your career as a writer, and it's much easier if you really do have some inside knowledge about the subject. My first book wasn't for children, but it was about something I knew and loved: photography. I had been writing *how-to* articles for budding amateur snappers, (and was the proud editor of *The Kodak Pocket Guide to Photographing your Cat*) when a packager approached me to write

"DON'T EVER IMAGINE THAT BECAUSE A BOOK IS FOR CHILDREN, IT WILL BE EASIER TO WRITE OR RESEARCH THAN A BOOK FOR ADULTS.

a book on photography. This makes it sound easy, I know, but it was my specialist knowledge that got me that first commission.

If you have a passion or enthusiasm about a subject, this will show up in what you write, and increase your chances of finding a publisher. It probably doesn't matter how esoteric your knowledge is, as long as you can present it in an interesting way that appeals to children. In fact, in some ways, the more odd and quirky the subject you choose, the more it will stand out from the crowd.

DON'T WRITE IT BEFORE YOU'RE COMMISSIONED

Have you heard of the slush pile? It's the heap of unread manuscripts that blocks a corridor at every agent and publisher. Don't enlarge it. Write a proposal, not a manuscript. If your idea is good enough and new enough, it *will be* commissioned. The idea that publishers want to read a completed manuscript is a fallacy. Yes, they want to be sure that you can string a sentence together, but a sample chapter can demonstrate that. A complete manuscript (unless it's a really short book) has got to be read, and that means paying someone to read it and write a report. Better to write a concise summary explaining what the book is about, then provide a list of chapters or topics. Close with a short list of points that make your book unique, and a note on competing titles. If it fits on a side of A4, a commissioning editor can read this in five minutes, and if necessary ask you for more information. And don't worry about somebody nicking your idea. It probably happens, but it's never happened to me.

TIMELY, RELEVANT, AND TO LENGTH

It's dull, I know, but craftsmanship counts for a lot. You would be amazed at the number of authors who deliver work too late, too long, or on some subject other than that commissioned – or all three! I should know. I have also worked as a non-fiction editor. I spent a lot of my time cutting and rewriting manuscripts I had commissioned, and a lot more on the phone, asking authors when I was going to see a MS. If you can produce a correctly-spelled, grammatical manuscript of the right length, to a deadline and a brief, you stand a far, far better chance of getting further proposals accepted.

YOUR REPUTATION PRECEDES YOU

Some editors are wonderful, and really improve what you write. Some, though are impossible. The worst are themselves failed writers who will mangle your manuscript until it's unrecognisable. But do try, try VERY hard to get on with all of them. If your editor tells you that 'The People In Marketing' think a larger type or more pictures would add sales, just say 'OK' and obediently cut your MS by a third. If you don't do it, somebody else will. We're not talking about a cure for childhood cancer here, it's only a children's book.

You have to remember that publishing is a surprisingly small world, and people have long memories. Editors regularly move from one company to the next, and climb the corporate tree as they do so. The woman who edited one of my first books is now in charge of the whole children's non-fiction list at a major publisher. If you get on well with an editor, and you don't act like a prima donna, you'll make friends and get further commissions. If, on the other hand, you chafe at every request, and argue over the position of a comma, you won't be invited back to the party.

BUY MORE BOOKS

Don't ever imagine that because a book is for children, it will be easier to write or research than a book for adults. Only by reading, reading, reading can you assemble enough detail to engage a young audience. I once worked out that I buy more non-fiction books each year than my local library.

I have got nearly 3,000 of them, and I also borrow from the London Library, and travel up to the British Library to look at material I can't find anywhere else. The devil *really is* in the detail. It's not enough just to tell children that 'the first space capsules didn't have lavatories.' They want to know EXACTLY how astronauts coped. Did they pee into a bottle? Where did they keep it it? What did they do when it was full? Did space suits have flies? (In case you are wondering, micro-meteorites of freeze-dried Mercury and Gemini wee form a significant impact hazard for current space shots.)

GSOH

Never underestimate the value of humour. I got to write my first children's book as a result of a juvenile gag. I was working as an editor on the Dorling Kindersley *Children's Encyclopedia*. The editor and designer had spent many days closeted together trying to figure out how to present the topic of Human Reproduction in a way that would not offend the Idaho potato farmer. To reduce the building tension, I produced a spoof page, entitled *Bonking*, full of myths, misconceptions and playground-standard jokes. It made the team laugh, as intended, but then did the rounds of the whole company. It also brought me to the attention of Peter Kindersley, who had recently looked at the portfolio of fresh-out-of-art-school Steve Biesty. Steve's drawings were intricate, beautiful, but rather dry, and PK was looking for a writer with a sense of humour to lighten them up. Thanks to my prank, I got the gig. The book that Steve and I produced together, *Incredible Cross Sections*, went on to sell two million copies (and no, alas, I wasn't on a royalty.)

> ## "YOU HAVE TO REMEMBER THAT PUBLISHING IS A SUPRISINGLY SMALL WORLD, AND PEOPLE HAVE LONG MEMORIES"

AGENTS

Like banks that won't lend you an umbrella if it's raining, agents are reluctant to take on unproven talent. And since many publishers won't accept proposals directly from authors, how do you find either an agent or a publisher? There's no real solution to this egg/chicken paradox. To understand the problem, step into the agent's shoes for a moment. Busy, published authors are a revenue stream. After you have negotiated the contract, you just count the money. For each £1,000 that Rich Writer earns, you get £100. Kerching! (Sorry Pat [my agent], of course there is more to it than that, but I've only got 2,000 words.) On the other hand, unpublished authors fall on the right-hand-side of the balance sheet. You have to hustle their proposals and MSs for them, put up with their whining phone calls and the rest of it.

If this sounds negative, it's not. I have relied on an agent for years, and I wouldn't be without one. To earn their 10%, they need only to squeeze a tiny amount more from a publisher, and in my experience, any agent worth their salt can do this. Publishers claim that they don't like dealing with agents, but what they really mean is that they hate having to pay out more to authors. Good agents actually act as a lubricant between the author and the publisher, because they take the friction out of the financial side, and because when things go wrong, the editor can phone the agent, and get them to apply pressure to the author, rather than performing this unpleasant task themselves. And yes, now (sometimes) I get a royalty. Thanks, Pat.

THE DOWNSIDE

Non-fiction publishing is no bed of roses. In the wider world of literature, writing for children is a ghetto, and non-fiction is a ghetto-within-the-ghetto. Only the most successful non-fiction writers, such as Terry 'Horrible' Deary, are really household names. I've had nearly 70 books published, and I'm still a nanocelebrity. A few librarians and a handful of 8-year-olds know my name. Instead of opening supermarkets, I get to judge the guy competition at my local village bonfire. My own mother asked me 'When are you going to write a *real* book, darling?'

Don't mention the 'R' word, either. Non-fiction publishers are very reluctant to pay royalties, though they are more willing to do so if the book is your idea, rather than one generated in-house. When they do pay royalties, the rates for illustrated books can be very low – typically 4–5%, and are often based on publishers' net receipts, which are roughly half the published price. Contracts are famously and fiendishly complicated, with big cuts to royalty percentages for high discount sales. I once received 1/20p (read it again, one twentieth of a penny) on copies of books sold in a US home-book-party scheme.

It's also hard work. When I tell people I'm a writer, those who don't quip 'Great, I'll have a banana Java-chip frappucino' imagine a life of dissipation: rise at 11, gin for breakfast, 500 words before lunch, then slope off to my club. The reality is that I start at 8.30, take only half an hour for lunch, and don't usually

> ## " I START AT 8.30, TAKE ONLY HALF AN HOUR FOR LUNCH, AND DON'T USUALLY FINISH UNTIL 6. IT'S A BUSINESS, AND TO MAKE A LIVING YOU HAVE TO TREAT IT AS SUCH. "

finish until 6. It's a business, and to make a living you have to treat it as such. I need to write four or five books a year to pay the mortgage, and sometimes I have lived on interest-free credit cards to bridge insolvent, bookless gaps.

Despite these drawbacks, I wouldn't do anything else. I get to spend hours – days – finding out about fascinating subjects in a bewildering, amazing diversity of disciplines. I get to indulge my juvenile sense of humour on impressionable youngsters who should probably be protected against such things. And I get paid for doing it. What could be better?

FICTION V NON-FICTION

(Figures for 2006)
Total sales = 78.6million books
Total value = £390.6million
of these:
50million (£254.4million) = fiction
28.6million (£136.1million) = non-fiction

Source: Books & the Consumer © BML/TNS 2007

PUBLISHING HOUSE PERSPECTIVES

IF YOU'RE ON 'THE OUTSIDE' WHAT IS IT LIKE ON 'THE INSIDE'?

Caroline Buckingham gives insider tips about the world of illustrated publishing

CAROLINE BUCKINGHAM

Caroline Buckingham has worked in publishing for 20 years, 18 of which were at Dorling Kindersley. She worked in both the Adult and Children's book divisions and also spent nine years on the digital media side of the business. She started at DK as a designer and eventually became Publishing Manager. She has worked as a freelance illustrator since 2006.

So, what is it like to be commissioned by a big publishing house? Let's assume you're an author, illustrator or contributor (based out-of-house) who's going to work on an illustrated non-fiction children's book with either an editor or a designer (based in-house). If the publishing house is like Dorling Kindersley – where I used to work – your editor or designer may be part of a larger team of people all working on the same project. How do things get to the point when you can actually start work?

THE IDEA: WHO COMES UP WITH IT?

All books start with an idea. Publishing houses are always looking for original ideas. They can come from the in-house team, the managers above them, or from an individual outside the company (you,

for example). If the idea is generally thought to be a good one by the sales and marketing teams who, in DK's case, are based in the UK, US and scores of other countries worldwide, then you might get to move on to a full sales presentation.

THE SALES PRESENTATION: THERE IS NEVER ENOUGH TIME OR MONEY TO DO EXACTLY WHAT YOU WANT

Once an idea for a book gets the go-ahead, you may be asked to help work up samples of what will go in it: a dummy jacket, some mocked-up pages, and a document which outlines the content in full and lists any titles already out in the shops which might be directly competitive. There are certain times in the year when a publisher's sales and marketing teams go out and attempt to pre-sell ideas for new books. The Frankfurt Book Fair, at the beginning of October, is the most important. And, for children's publishers, there is also a Children's Book Fair in Bologna in April.

Remember that, as the idea for a new book begins to take shape, it's unlikely to be the only title your in-house editor and designer are working on. They may be producing as many as 20 new presentations for each book fair. This work must be dovetailed with books already in production. If they seem twitchy, it's because they're probably overworked and under-resourced.

Inevitably, no matter how well received a presentation is, it will need adjustment and a lot of detailed planning before you get the OK to start the book. This may take weeks, or even months, which is frustrating. The final publication date is already fixed. Everyone's anxious to get going. What can they possibly be spending their time deciding?

Behind the scenes, there is probably a heated dialogue between sales, production and creative teams. They will be trying to iron out in detail what goes in the book, who it's aimed at, and how much it's going to cost to produce and manufacture (many books are now printed and bound in the Far East where it's cheaper). This process takes effort and perseverance by all concerned.

PUBLISHING HOUSES ARE ALWAYS LOOKING FOR ORIGINAL IDEAS

THE BUDGET: THERE IS EVEN LESS MONEY THAN YOU FIRST THOUGHT

OK, this is how it goes: The team comes up with a figure, a reasonable amount – a figure they think they can make the book for. They're told to halve it. Wait three weeks. They're told to halve it again. Wait another month. Then they're told to take off another 15%. Wait one more week. OK, they finally get the thumbs up from the accountants, so everyone can get going. Oh, hang on, two months later there's another finance meeting…

'We're just taking another look at the budget. Can you slice off another 20%? We're re-running the origination for the whole division.'

'Erm, haven't we done that already?'

'Yes.'

'But we've already started the book. And it won't be the same if we have to cut even more content.'

'Yes, but you still have to take 20% off all the books on your list.'

'But…'

'Just go and take the 20% off, will you?'

The team goes off muttering about how they're going to explain losing 75 already-researched pictures and 5,000 already-written words.

(Six months later in a sales and marketing meeting: 'Why aren't there as many pictures in this book as you promised?')

In a big, complex, systems-heavy, risk-averse publishing company the hurdles are numerous. It's sometimes a wonder that anything gets published at all.

THE SCHEDULE: I CAN START, GREAT. HOW LONG HAVE I GOT? NO, SERIOUSLY…

Schedules are always tight. This is due to a number of factors, but most often it's down to the endless fiddling around that goes on in finalising the presentation and the budget. People selling the title in the UK want the book to suit the UK market, people selling the title in the US want the book to suit the US and, needless to say, they differ. Some titles may even go back to a new sales presentation stage. This is time-consuming, expensive, and frustrating. But the sales team want to feel sure they can sell as many copies as possible and maximise profit on the project.

Meanwhile, the end date remains unchanged – even though neither you nor the team have been able to start work. When you're finally confronted with the harsh reality of delivery dates that now look near-impossible, the best thing you can do is be honest about what you can achieve and make sure you communicate effectively with the people you're working for. There is nothing worse than revealing that you're going to be weeks late on material that's expected in the next day or so.

THE IN-HOUSE TEAM: ONLY ON RARE OCCASIONS DO YOU GET TO WORK WITH THE PERFECT TEAM

By and large, the designers and editors you work with will be a good bunch. Most likely, they'll have been battling for months to get the go-ahead for a project they (hopefully) feel passionate about.

In illustrated publishing, the best designers think editorially and the best editors have a

GETTING THE WORKING RELATIONSHIP RIGHT

- If anything is not clear in the briefing make sure you ask. It's important that you know what is expected of you before you start work.

- Make sure you have a signed contract.

- Be flexible. The person you deal with in-house does not always have the level of control you might expect. Their decisions may be changed by people further up the ladder.

- Communicate with your contact clearly and often. Even if you don't hear from them make sure they know what you're doing, especially if you think deadlines look dodgy.

- If you have a problem, face up to it immediately and discuss it.

- Be as organised and efficient as you can.

design eye. Unfortunately you rarely find teams like this. An in-house working relationship is very intense. Designers and editors are thrown together. They may be working very long hours on a subject they're neither familiar with nor interested in, and they're probably on a schedule that makes them tetchy, irritable, and impatient.

In my time as a manager at DK I was lucky to have had hard-working, flexible, talented staff working for me. Sadly, I have also had to deal with rude, aggressive, and unreasonable people. I've had to manage both lazy people and over-enthusiastic

THE BEST DESIGNERS THINK EDITORIALLY AND THE BEST EDITORS HAVE A DESIGN EYE

workaholics. And I've had to break up teams who've been fighting like cats and dogs. Hopefully you won't get caught in this kind of crossfire, but you will come across all sorts of characters. Just try to deal with them all equally professionally and objectively.

THE END RESULT: THAT WAS GREAT, MOSTLY

So, if all goes according to plan, you will be proud to see your name in the finished book. You will have earned some cash and may have learned something about a subject that's new to you. Hopefully, you'll have enjoyed the experience and worked with some enthusiastic, interesting people. With luck, if you've done a good job, you'll be asked to work on another title. And if you're really lucky you'll have made some good friends along the way. I certainly have.

GETTING THE WORKING RELATIONSHIP WRONG

- If you're difficult to work with, it's unlikely you'll get another job with the same company. Or with any other one. Be warned: the publishing industry is small and incestuous.

- Don't go to the wall on minor issues – they're just not worth it.

- Avoid giving people in-house any surprises – it makes them twitchy.

GO FOR IT!
WRITING AND ILLUSTRATING CHILDREN'S BOOKS

Author/illustrator Cliff Wright gives you inspiration and urges you to follow your own vision.

CLIFF WRIGHT

Cliff's first book was the self-written and illustrated *When the World Sleeps*, the runner-up in the Mother Goose Award 1989–90. It was followed by *Crumbs!* in 1990 and *The Tangleweed Troll* in 1993. Since then he has illustrated many children's picture-books by other authors, as well as illustrating two *Harry Potter* book covers (*The Chamber of Secrets* and *The Prisoner of Azkaban*), and has continued to illustrate his own books as well as illustrate for others. He has developed a range of drawing-based workshops called 'Nature of Seeing', from the belief that everyone can draw. 'Nature of Seeing' takes him round the world and involves him more and more. He received a peace award for this in 2006. He also holds exhibitions of his work.

What are you willing to risk to see your dreams come to print? Your fears? Criticism? Rejection? Welcome to the journey of any successful writer or artist. Though plenty of folk may discourage and dissuade, have faith in your ideas. The usual line is that it's very competitive, there's not much chance of being published, etc, etc. I believe, however, that the opposite is true and that everyone has a book inside them.

This doesn't mean that your baby will plop out fully-formed and perfect. Believe in your dream and your soul but NOT at the expense of valid criticism. If everyone is telling you it's rubbish then there's probably some truth in it. You can always begin another idea or adapt the one you're on. It can be a fine line, because I believe it's equally important to be able to overcome those potentially debilitating rejections if you really feel that the editor has missed your point. Yes, go for it! Take all the feedback, but don't take it personally.

SO, HERE'S MY VERSION OF HOW TO GET STARTED

Having spent four years at Brighton University I headed out into the big wide world, armed with a prolific but directionless portfolio, with a couple of partially completed picture-book ideas. These projects were worked up to a rough dummy of the whole book with one or two completed paintings. I began to nervously visit, and send ideas to many publishers and design companies, etc, mostly in London. Sometimes this would involve three or four visits in a day, often two or three times a week.

> **YOUR PUBLISHER IS TAKING A HUGE RISK (ESPECIALLY FOR A FIRST-TIME AUTHOR) AND HAS USUALLY BEEN IN THE BUSINESS A LONG TIME, SO THEY'RE WORTH LISTENING TO**

It seemed at times a never-ending trudge of rejection letters or five-minute meetings. What I found though, was that I was getting the best response from children's book publishers – a couple took a genuine interest and gave me enough feedback to feel that I might get somewhere.

ONE OF THE BOOK IDEAS WAS THUS DEVELOPED

At times on the creative journey it can be so easy to fold underneath all the rejections. But the experience helped me to develop a harder head and an ability to take on board the comments and process them, rejecting some and finding others helpful.

My first book (based on an idea that suddenly arrived when driving past a local hill) involved a boy waking up at night, looking out of his window and seeing the moon fall out of the night sky, hit the hill and roll into the forest. Actually, in this case, the story did arrive fully-formed and not one element of it was changed at any time. The way it was told, on the other hand, required considerable effort and being open to all and any suggestions that were made. For example, it was soon apparent that words were unnecessary and that the story was better told just with pictures. The fact that some of the publishers I was seeing at that time told me they would never take the chance on a first-time author with a wordless picture-book became a real test of my own conviction!

on returning after lunch I was asked to consider changing the ending of the story. My experience has thrown up many such 'tests' – difficult and challenging at the time but ultimately greatly rewarding. On that day I was fortunate in that, following discussion, it was decided that the original ending would be retained; on another day who knows what might have happened? The book, entitled *When the World Sleeps*, was runner-up for the Mother Goose Award in 1989–90 and firmly started my particular career ball rolling.

Following that first book I worked on two more of my ideas and began to receive offers to illustrate other authors' words. More often than not, these came through other publishers rather than direct from the author. At this time I was also advertising my work in *Contact*, a directory of illustration, which brought interest from new clients, publishers, design companies and advertising agencies. I love the challenge of collaboration because it frees me from the restriction of my own thoughts. In the same way, I can hopefully bring something new to the vision that the author has for his/her work. Sometimes it seems to me that this cross-mingling of different ways of seeing is where the essence of being an artist/author really resides.

> ## BE PERSISTENT BUT ALWAYS KNOW THAT YOUR IDEAS HAVE A LIMIT...ALWAYS BE PREPARED TO ACCEPT CRITICISM – IT'S JUST ANOTHER IDEA

BEING PUBLISHED

Thus it happened, one golden-tinged day two and a half years after college, that I found myself sitting shell-shocked in the offices of Hutchinson Children's Books (having had the book rejected again only moments before in the same building by Andersen Press). The words that I heard were taking a moment to become reality: 'would you come back after lunch, because we'd like to publish your book for you?' (Thank you Anne McNeil.) The edges of the cloud that I then floated on were greyed, when

Having illustrated and written many titles I've come to understand how fine and fascinating the balancing act is between author/artist and publisher/editor. As the writer one can become attached to one's ideas, especially on a long project like a picture-book. (My first book took six months to complete, now it's down to one or two!) There needs to be an element of your truth – it is through deeply personal outpourings that wider realities are understood. But it is also wise to stay flexible within your integrity.

- Be inspired by everything around you that ignites your soul's passion.

- Spend hours in bookshops finding the kind of books that speak your language – devour them and target the publishers of them with your ideas. It will save time in the long run.

- The alternative is to do what I did initially, a kind of directionless blanket bombing, leading to all those rejections. You are saving their time too – if their list isn't suitable just try someone else.

- Try to see the person you submit your manuscript to in person. At the very least you can then ask why your baby was not suitable for them at that particular time. Be persistent but always know that your ideas have a limit; the world and its countless ways do not have such a restriction, so always be prepared to accept criticism – it's just another idea.

- Cherish your ideas as you would the touch of your lover but be ready to let them go if no-one understands your voice. Take solace from the fact that we are all in the same boat, or have been, or will be.

Your publisher is taking a huge risk (especially for a first-time author) and has usually been in the business a long time, so they're worth listening to. As with many things it can also be a world that is very market-led, but churning out similar ideas just because they sold yesterday is not a good place to start a creative collaboration. Originality is where the challenge and excitement begins. However, I believe that it is never helpful to carry the attitude that I am 'The Artist' and that's the end of it. After all, however original ideas may seem, they are often only borrowed.

YOUR WORLD, YOUR VISION

So who are you? Where is your passion? What can your message add to the world? What do you know that no-one else knows? Are you ready to realise the huge impact and importance of your unique voice, while at the same time recognising that it is just an idea and only a part of the big picture? If you can find a sense of that then your ideas can move and give space for new thoughts to flow in.

For myself, I find inspiration from many sources. Number one has to be the 'real' world that I surround myself with. From watching a spider construct a web or seeing the way a fox moves. Or from two friends thinking the same thoughts at the same

WHAT DO YOU KNOW THAT NO-ONE ELSE KNOWS?

time, or from the vast unlimited creative potential that I see in everyone that I've taught on drawing workshops. From the fineness of touch that I feel from a Michelangelo or Rackham drawing – a quality which exists at the end of YOUR fingertips. From discovering that we all draw what we think we see rather than what is really there. So it follows that we also see what we 'think' we see – and of how our art or writing can show us a reality beyond that and in excess of our wildest dreams. From learning that A.A.Milne (author of *Winnie the Pooh*, etc) would take forty mile walks with his brother, staying overnight at inns when they were six and seven years old. And from realising that the saying 'be careful what you wish for' is perfectly true.

THINKING PRE-SCHOOL

GETTING THE RIGHT IDEAS FOR THE 0–5 AGE RANGE

Books for pre-schoolers need discipline, and 'hidden' subjects and themes to help the child make sense of the world and feel secure, as well as introduce learning. Richard Powell helps us make a start.

RICHARD POWELL

Richard has been making books for pre-school children for twenty or so years, and is co-founder of the small independent publisher Treehouse Children's Books. His own books for children have sold 37 million copies worldwide and have been published in 35 languages.

It's the worst moment. You sit down in front of a blank sheet of paper or new document open on the computer screen, full of enthusiasm to get started, and nothing happens. There isn't the flood of creative ideas you'd expected at the outset of this new venture, no febrile otherworldly issue of fertile thought spilling down onto the page. Instead there is nothing. Not a bean. The paper stays blank, the cursor blinks impatiently at you from the top left corner of the screen.

So what do you do? You can either carry on just sitting and staring in increasing panic, or take steps to cajole the brain into activity. I find that often the problem is lack of focus. Suddenly you are aware of the enormous possibilities, the huge spectrum of subjects and scenarios that are possible and to pin one down decisively seems impossible. You worry that if you make a decision you might cut off the arrival of a better idea, as yet unborn. What you need are boundaries, categories, a framework to work within that will discipline your thoughts.

TITLES THAT SELL

A quick survey of baby and pre-school titles on publishers' websites will confirm that on the whole there are a comparatively few subjects that crop up again and again. Certain subjects simply sell better than others, however worthy those others may be. Just look at how many books about farm animals are out there at any one time. Books about farm animals almost always outsell any other. If you can make an original farm animal book that entertains, makes the reader giggle and cunningly introduces a bit of early learning then everyone will be happy – parent, child, publisher, bookseller. Of course, not every book can be about farm animals, simply for the sake of sanity, so here's my method for giving the muse a kick.

Start with the premise that there are six elements to be considered when making a pre-school children's book: age group (baby 0–12 months), toddler (18–30 months, or pre-school (3–5 years); subject; setting; format; character (the hero); and early learning themes.

If you select one choice from each of these elements you might come up with something like: Age group: toddler 18–30 months; Format: flap book; Setting: farmyard; Subject: animal babies; Character: puppy; Early Learning: counting.

There you have the beginnings of a framework. Any of the above elements could provide the starting point for your framework, but the age group is a good one to start with because it is the one that tends to determine how the other categories are applied. By considering each category and its parameters and imagining how they might be used in conjunction with one another, by mixing and matching, I find little questions popping up in my mind, trains of thought developing and throwing up images and from there the whole paper chase of one idea leading to another develops – the mental blockage becomes cleared and that fretful state of mind which allows ideas to bump, collide, amalgamate and grow takes over. You will probably end up with something that bears no relation to the ideas you started with, but you will have been set on the road. Of course, whether anything worthwhile comes out of it is another matter and all down to chance. It's a bit like stepping outside Bilbo's front door.

BOOK CHOICES

Here are some notes to help you make your choices. Children develop alarmingly fast (nearly 50% of a child's learning occurs in the first four years of life), and the rates vary considerably from one individual to another, so any attempt at age ranging has to be taken with a pinch of salt.

BOOKS FOR BABIES (0–12 MONTHS)

Babies like tactile cloth books or simple bath books with bright pictures. They love small board books that they can hold themselves. These should include pictures of things they know – babies, toys, animals or experiences they have such as at bath or meal times. Babies love the sound of a parent's voice, so play with words that cry out to be read out loud with expression and feeling.

SUBJECTS

Simple stories for babies could be about loving relationships, characters on a simple quest ('Where's Mummy?'), or parents and children playing games together. All these portray affection, give reassurance and can be the vehicles for the positive images these books need. A quick look at what is out there in the shops shows the most often used editorials outside simple stories feature first words and pictures – things to point to and name – simple, clear, bright pictures of high contrast with a single word naming them, which help create a visual familiarity with text. Art style and format are what distinguish one title from another. Subjects include familiar items around the home the child might see everyday: clothes, toys, animals, stuff they might see out and about or other images they might see regularly.

Books that explore contrasts and patterns that researchers say stimulate the very small baby are popular, as are books that feature big smiley faces and pictures of other babies, whether drawn or photographic. And of course every baby likes to play peekaboo, so try and work that into a book, too. Books that involve parent and baby in a game are perfect. Whatever you choose to do strive to make each page make their little eyes open wide.

SETTINGS

Settings for babies are centred around home and family and include scenes inside the house, in the garden, perhaps in the town, on the farm, and environments encountered on a walk – park and countryside maybe.

FORMAT

The physical aspect of books for babies can be as important as the content in how they communicate and stimulate, so in addition to the list of perennial favourite subjects for content should be added physical content: texture (cuddly cloth books, squidgy plastic bath books, added 'touch and feel' elements); sound (squeakers, rattles, even electronic sound modules), movement (stout card flaps), light (highly reflective holographic foils). Think of shaping books so that they can easily be grasped.

CHARACTER

If you have a main character which carries the editorial along then it is usually best if this is a baby/toddler character or characters, human, or more often as not, animal, with whom our young readers can empathise, whether the editorial is a story or just requires a character to introduce the early learning themes

BOOKS FOR TODDLERS (18–30 MONTHS)

Toddlers enjoy simple word and picture books, storybooks with clear pictures and just a few words. Books with flaps, tabs to pull, pop-ups, peepholes and different textiles and materials are perfect for this age group. At this age their language is developing at a rate so give them grist for their mill – rhythmic and rhyming language, catchphrases to repeat, stuff that just sounds good to say out loud and that the reader can introduce different voices to. They like to be asked and answer questions, so flaps and pull-tabs that reveal answers are ideal. Have a look at the boxes on the next page for some formats and settings to you going.

CHARACTER

The characters in books for toddlers are the same as for those introduced for babies. Toddlers love characters they can become attached to, interact with, laugh with and with whom they can explore and recognise the moods and problems that they experience themselves. So these characters need to do what toddlers do. Good non-peer group characters are grandparents; loving, wise, and with all the time toddlers need.

BOOKS FOR PRE-SCHOOLERS (3–5 YEARS)

Again we have the overlap from the toddler stage, much of which is relevant to this age group. Now we can add a bit of complexity, and enter more fully the gloriously imaginative world of the picture book.

> ## THE HUMAN BRAIN DEVELOPS FASTER BETWEEN BIRTH AND SIX YEARS THAN AT ANY OTHER TIME IN YOUR LIFE – AND BRAIN DEVELOPMENT IS LARGELY A FUNCTION OF STIMULUS

SUBJECTS, SETTINGS AND FORMATS

Pre-schoolers like funny stories or ones where things get muddled up. They also enjoy make-believe, so particular, varied and even invented settings can be used as their imaginations begin to soar (provided they retain their own logic).

Children of three and four like poems, songs, jokes and early learning books on letters, numbers, animals (including dinosaurs), vehicles, and books with lots of pictures. The human brain develops faster between birth and six years than at any other time in your life – and brain development is largely a function of stimulus – that is to say, at this early age children simply soak up new information. They can't get enough of it; the more the better. They also love repetition and knowing what is going to happen next.

> ## "CHILDREN DEVELOP AN UNDERSTANDING OF MATHS THROUGH STORIES, SONGS, GAMES AND IMAGINATIVE PLAY"

Stories can be about friendships, fears, adventures, love, loss and discovery. Subjects can look at the arrival of new siblings, coming to terms with new places, learning about differences, sharing and interacting with peers. With this age group we enter the chief realm of the picture book and first non-fiction or information books, where board novelty is largely left behind, as are pop-ups, fold-outs and flaps and other paper engineered bits and pieces. We are edging into the world of school and the widening of horizons. Animal titles based on habitat might add forest, mountain and desert, and could look at different animal families: birds, mammals, insects, reptiles and amphibians, fish and plants. Look at life cycles, and home in on a themed approach: the biggest, fiercest, smallest, fastest. You might find fun ways to introduce early science.

THE EARLY LEARNING DIMENSION

Early years workers often refer to the six areas of learning which underpin the foundation stage in the national curriculum. Based on how a child develops, they are very useful points of reference for the creator of the pre-school book. So add an educational slant to the framework of possibilities by considering these brief descriptions of the areas of learning as they might apply to pre-school books.

PERSONAL, SOCIAL AND EMOTIONAL DEVELOPMENT

This refers to things like the child developing self-confidence and a sense of self-worth, empathy with others, taking an interest in things, knowing what their own needs are, learning to look after themselves – dressing, bathing, eating, learning to be self-confident, learning about right and wrong, about relationships and good and bad behaviour. All subjects that books can reinforce.

COMMUNICATION, LANGUAGE AND LITERACY

This is about children learning to talk confidently and clearly, enjoying stories, songs and poems, hearing and saying sounds, and linking them to the alphabet and recognising that words on a page have sound and meaning.

MATHEMATICAL DEVELOPMENT

Children develop an understanding of maths through stories, songs, games and imaginative play. We are not talking about times tables or equations but being comfortable with numbers and with ideas

POSSIBLE SETTINGS FOR TODDLERS

- **Animals:** farm animals, baby animals, pets, ocean animals, garden animals, creepy crawlies

- **Animals by habitat:** seaside, countryside, farm, jungle

- **Early learning:** pairs, patterns, opposites, counting, shapes, go-togethers, odd one out, textures, sounds, actions, parts of the body, senses

- **Situations:** baby's day, playtime, bedtime, bath time, meal time, getting dressed, first experiences

- **Environments:** town, home, park, playschool

- **Transport:** tractors, trains, boats, diggers, planes

- **Family and friends:** routines, relationships, emotions, right/wrong such as 'heavier than' or 'bigger', sorting, matching and sequencing, and being aware of shapes and space.

KNOWLEDGE AND UNDERSTANDING OF THE WORLD

Children learn more and more about the world around them as they grow, and ask questions about it. Books can help introduce them to the wider world and prompt questions, provide answers, and provide experiences outside their immediate familiar environment.

PHYSICAL DEVELOPMENT

Handling books and using novelty books helps develop hand/eye co-ordination and fine motor movement, and subjects can inspire children to try physical activities.

CREATIVE DEVELOPMENT

Books can help children explore colours and shapes, and try out movements through copying, making things, telling stories and dramatising stories.

A SATISFYING END

That's it. Once you have picked your ingredients, remember: a book for a pre-school child should be simple and clear, it should present a logical sequence of pictures and end with a positive twist or satisfying roundup or conclusion to what has gone before. It should bring a smile to your face. Pictures, story and words should all pull together, and any novelty element should be a part and parcel of the whole with a definite editorial or design function.

This rough and ready overview of possibilities is far from exhaustive, and by now you may be saying 'But what about?' and 'What if?' and 'Could you?' in which case I suggest this article has done its job and stimulated a little creative juice.

So, now I can go and revisit my children's novel that never seems to get beyond the first chapter…

A LIST OF POSSIBLE FORMATS FOR TODDLERS

- **Flap books:** lift-the-flap books are a staple diet now – perfect for hide-and-seek editorials

- **Movement books:** these have sliding panels or simple pop-ups on their pages, or levers and tabs to pull that animate the pictures or reveal hidden pictures, peekaboo-style

- **Sound books:** books with bits that rattle or squeak, or have electronic sound modules

- **Books plus plush:** books that have finger puppets or soft toys built into them

- **Books plus:** board books with custom-built plastic or wood parts such as a plastic rattle, a simple abacus, a snow dome etc.

- **Jigsaw-puzzle books:** books that have simple push-out playtray jigsaws included among their pages

- **Pop-ups:** card books with paper engineered 3D pictures can be very simple and effective, or mind-boggingly complex and delicate. For these age groups simple and stout are best

- **Touch and feel:** books that include different materials – plush lambs' wool, slippery plastic, rough textures and so on

- **Electronic books:** with sound modules that provide lights, sounds and voiceovers which may even electronically interact with each page, perhaps being set off by touch

- **Activity board books:** with drawing tools, stencils and re-usable, wipe-clean surfaces

THE PUBLISHING PROCESS

HOW DO BOOKS GET FROM CONCEPTION TO PRINTED WORKS IN THE BOOKSHOP?

We take you through the stages in a theoretical (and simplified) publishing house, and we provide practical advice for you along the way.

▶ Every publisher has its own unique way of working, and often its own jargon to describe what is going on. As is the way with jargon, there is usually an assumption that you will understand what is being said. If you don't understand then you must ask at once, since publishing jargon frequently has implications about key processes and possibly also about your own relationship with the publisher. As Duncan Cameron suggests in his article on page 26, it's a great idea to keep a list of all this terminology.

When you submit your work to a publisher it will usually eventually arrive in the in-tray of a senior publishing manager unless you have addressed it to a specific person. In the *Writer's Market* books we try to provide you with a name to write to. You should also look at the website of the publisher you are targeting to see if you can find a named person to contact. The more you try to pin down exactly who to address your proposal to, the better your chances of a favourable reception. Editors will respond much better if you have written to them specifically – it shows you've done your homework, and it tickles their egos, which is always a good thing to do! Also, if it has their name on it, the onus is on them to reply to you. A letter addressed simply to 'The Publisher' is an easy one to ignore, and editorial offices are usually very busy, so excuses not to do something are jumped on.

If your submission does end up with a senior manager they will most likely simply push it down the pecking order, and it will keep going until it ends up on the desk of someone who has no choice but to take some responsibility for it. By now several weeks may already have passed.

'FROM THE DESK OF...'

Editors are always busy. Many publishers run as tight a ship as they can (tighter if they can get away with it) so people are not sitting around waiting for your (or anybody else's) submission.

If your letter or submission is messy, vague or illiterate you might just as well forget it. Most editors in receipt of such things will give it the priority it deserves, which is none.

If you've written a good letter and have a good book or idea and it is appropriate to the publisher, then you may get a fast reply (all the faster if you provide an email address – most editors prefer email as their main communication tool).

It will usually be a holding reply, perhaps saying that the editor thinks it is a good idea but that she needs to discuss it with colleagues before a decision can be made. These days, such discussion is most likely to be with the sales team or teams.

If your book idea is suitable only for the UK book trade (as is often the case with non-fiction) then the UK sales manager will be approached. Most publishers also operate in international markets, and so look for ideas that will work in both the UK and beyond. If your idea might be suitable for an international market, then the international sales team will be asked for their opinion. They might give an immediate response, but more likely they will ask key publishing partners in other countries; they might even delay their decision until they have taken the idea to one of the big international book fairs, the most important of which is in Frankfurt, held every October. Be prepared to submit more information and sometimes material for this, even if the publisher hasn't committed to the idea yet. Bookfairs are the place where they find out if the international markets are interested in the idea, and publishers sometimes also use this as an indicator of how heavily to invest in the idea. Book fairs can make or break a project, so be prepared to do some really good presentation work, if asked – but beware, the book may well be adapted, changed or developed significantly from what is shown at the fairs, and almost certainly from your original idea.

By now several more weeks, even months, may have passed since you wrote, and still no decision has been made.

With fiction, much the same process is likely, except that the publisher, other editors, and possibly 'readers' (experts whose opinion is valued) may be part of the decision-making team.

If all of this sounds like publishing by committee, that's because it is. Publishing is a risky business (it always was) and these days there are few houses where any one person will make the decision to publish. But there are some houses where powerful commissioning editors, editorial managers, and even the legendary 'Publisher' have enough clout, influence and sheer guts to push an idea through.

HOW MUCH WILL IT COST?

Even supposing the idea gets a thumbs-up from some or even all of the above, there is more work to be done before the decision to publish is made. Essentially this is costing the project. For fiction, this is a reasonably simple equation: how many copies do publishers think it can sell set against how much it will cost to make (author costs, editorial costs, design costs, production costs, printing costs,

> ## "MOST PUBLISHERS ALSO OPERATE IN INTERNATIONAL MARKETS, SO LOOK FOR IDEAS THAT WILL WORK IN THE UK AND BEYOND"

distribution costs, promotional costs, company overheads) and therefore how much money can be made? What will the ROI (return on investment) be?

Doesn't sound very romantic or creative, does it? It's not – it's a business, much like any other. And it can be hugely stressful for the editor or editorial team trying to get their precious ideas through this process.

Non-fiction is more complex, especially for big, illustrated books. Cost is an enormous factor. A typical 'coffee table' book: A4-ish in size, with 256 pages and photographs and/or illustrations on every page, might cost anywhere between £40,000 and £100,000 and beyond just to create. And then there is printing, shipping, distribution and so forth on top of that. You need to sell a lot of books to get a decent return on that investment. Commissioning editors spend many hours trying to make these costings work, balancing all of the outgoings to try to reach a good figure that everyone is happy to commit to, and to convince senior management to invest in the idea. And this is where having an international market for the book can give the figures that extra 'push'.

TIMING AND SCHEDULES

If your idea survives this protracted process, and by now many months may have passed, (read the articles by Duncan Cameron on page 26 and by Caroline Buckingham on page 35 for real-life examples of all this) the next step is to build a realistic schedule.

Schedules have to 'factor in' lots of things. How I ong will it take you to write the manuscript? How long will it take any artworks to be done? Will material have to be created and photographed for the book (technical art and craft books, for example, have to factor in a lot of time for the actual projects to be created). How long will the pages take to be designed – a complex, intricate design will take longer to lay out than a text-only fiction book, but probably less time that a coffee table book. How long will it take to print? Where is it being printed? How long will it take to ship to the appropriate destination(s)? When would be the best time to publish? How does that fit with the 'call cycles' that the sales force (the people who sell the books into the bookshops) work to? (Call cycles are essentially a way of the booksellers managing the publishing stream so that all books and their associated costs don't arrive at the same time.)

This is also the point at which you should tell the publisher if you have any plans for going away for prolonged periods (on an expedition to the Himalayas, for example), or have any period during which you will be unable to work. These factors can all affect the schedule and need to be accounted for.

That can take a lot of working out. But eventually, all of the costs are gathered and agreed (often after a great deal of haggling), the schedule is set, and the book is formally signed off.

Then, and usually only then, will you – the author – be sent a contract. Depending on the size of the project the contract can vary from a very simple one-page document for a one-off fee, through to a full blown Author Contract.

CONTRACTS

Whether your contract is the traditional 'advance against royalty' sort or the more modern (and often preferred by non-fiction publishers) 'one-off' fee will depend on the publisher, and possibly on the author to an extent. Famous or top-selling authors will most often only work to a royalty-based agreement. 'Jobbing' authors will very often accept a one-time payment, with all the rights going to the publisher. First-time authors might think they are lucky to get a deal of any kind, and will generally be very grateful!

Polite haggling can sometimes work wonders. It will usually be the editor who does any such negotiating with the author or the author's agent. Behind the editor will be the senior management

SHOULD I SELF-PUBLISH?

Probably not.

But if you know exactly what kind of deal you are getting into with the company concerned, then you might consider it if you have a particular reason to do so.

That reason might simply be that no traditional publisher will take your work but you still want it published.

In which case, fair enough, but look on the internet for the stories of those who have been left with garages full of unsaleable books, or those who have been landed with huge bills for printing because they did not read the small print in the agreement, or those who have simply been cheated by the self- or vanity publisher. You must go into it with your

eyes open, and make sure someone other than just you reads that all-important agreement. And then reads it again.

We at *Writer's Market* have heard success stories about self-published books that sold thousands, or that went on to be picked up by the mainstream publishing industry. But such stories must be balanced against the negative stories, and the balance is not in favour of self publishing.

You might consider doing it yourself – in other words doing everything a traditional publisher does. But you'll need perseverance, good book-keeping skills, a strong will, and, probably, a sturdy car to distribute the books. It can be done and this can be a good way forward, especially for regional or speciality books.

and the publisher's legal team or advisors. It is the legal experts who will agree or reject any changes to a standard contract, or who will draw up a special contract. If there is to be negotiation over the contract more time will pass of course, since the hard-pressed editor will have dozens of other books that they are working on. And contracts are a pain, so they may well let it slip down the priority list. A nudge from the author can help clear this particular blip in the proceedings.

While the idea of haggling for weeks over another 1% royalty, additional free copies, a higher advance or some such niggly detail may seem incredibly appealing, it can delay proceedings massively, as the delivery date will generally not change to accommodate all of this to-ing and fro-ing. It may also irritate the publisher/editor if you are deemed to be making unreasonable demands or splitting hairs. Be realistic about your requests, and if in doubt over any aspect of your contract make sure you talk them through with the editor, or seek professional advice from one of the numerous consultancies listed in the *Writer's Market* books.

BOOK CREATION AND PRODUCTION

Contract safely signed and delivered, the job of actually putting the book together can begin at last.

Simple books have simple designs and simple schedules – well, in theory at least. Complex books with many pages, lots of illustrative material and so forth can take months and even years to create. A typical 'coffee table' book takes around 18 months from project start up to final files sent to the production department. During that time a mix that might include editors, designers, picture researchers, verifiers, proofreaders, indexers, cartographers, illustrators, photographers, stylists, and other experts could be involved. No wonder such books are so costly, and no wonder they take so long to make.

Once the final digital book files are ready and approved, then off they go to the production department who check them, and send them either direct to the printer, or to a 'repro' (reproduction) house for the book to be turned into print-ready files. The repro house will send back to the publisher colour proofs if appropriate. These are checked

with care (often with a set going out to the author), marked up with colour corrections and any last-minute vital text corrections (usually the publisher will provide new text-only files with such amends on), and sent back to the repro house.

The files are then converted into PDFs (Portable Document Format), which can't be edited, and are sent to the printer who might be anywhere in the world. China and the Far East are favoured both for cost and for quality, but eastern Europe is catching up, and there are still some quality printers in western Europe.

SHIPPING AND DISTRIBUTION

Once printed, the books need to reach their publishing place. For reasons of cost, books printed in the Far East and China will be sent to the UK (or wherever) by ship, which takes weeks. 'Advance' copies for senior managers, sales people, the press (and the author if they are lucky) will be airmailed.

When the full book shipments reach their proper destination they end up in the distribution warehouses of companies that specialise in such things. From there they eventually reach the bookshops.

And that is where, months or even years after you submitted your idea, you can stand and glow inwardly as you pick up your book, before putting it back down at the front of the display (don't worry, we all do it!).

SELLING YOUR BOOK

Of course, you want other people to pick up your book, too, and buy it.

That involves the publisher's PR and marketing departments (who may have come up with a cunning sales plan), possibly bookshops, maybe local radio, perhaps local press and very rarely, TV. Authors can help a lot here: shyness and a retiring nature do not sell books – if you are asked to do radio or press interviews swallow hard and get on with it. Be professional, be positive, and project confidence, but never arrogance.

Now you just have to wait and see if that hard work pays off…

MIC CADY

FEATURE

GETTING YOUR SUBMISSION RIGHT

HOW TO CONTACT A PUBLISHER, AND WHAT TO SAY

First impressions count, so getting it right first time is key

▶ There are two simple and clear tips that all writers should heed when approaching a publisher – one: do your research first; two: presentation is key.

RESEARCH

There is no point approaching a publisher who does not publish the kind of thing you write. Publishing houses that do illustrated non-fiction won't be interested in your novel or your poems, just as publishers of poetry will have no use for your *Model Making Made Easy* idea.

So, don't waste your time or theirs: check publisher details in this book and on the website; check the publisher's website. If you are still in doubt, phone up and find out whether they publish in your area.

Make sure you have checked for any submission guidelines they may have, again either by looking at the company listing in this book, or on the publisher's website. Some publishers also list submission details – including details of any areas in which they're looking to publish and likewise are not currently accepting – on the website, so it's definitely worth being as familiar with it as possible.

PRESENTATION

Poorly presented work or a shoddily presented letter will result in almost certain failure. Use clean, white, A4 paper. Type using a standard, non-fussy, typeface, single spaced.

> ## "MAKE SURE YOU HAVE CHECKED FOR ANY SUBMISSION GUIDELINES THE PUBLISHER MAY HAVE"

Put the letter or submission in a clean, neat, envelope (in these conservation-minded days a re-used outer envelope will probably be OK, but make sure you package it as neatly as you can).

THE LETTER

Whether a query letter or a submission letter the rules are the same – keep it short (no more than one sheet of A4), keep it to the point, make it crystal clear what you are saying, and make the first paragraph compelling so the editor will read on. Remember that editors are bombarded with submissions, the majority of which will be rejected, so if you want to be in the minority that make it past the first hurdle, spend time on that letter.

THE EMAIL

If you approach the publisher by email, do so formally in the first instance, outlining your idea in brief and asking if they'd like to know more about your work. Don't include attachments unless invited to do so, as the publisher may not accept such

> ## IF YOU APPROACH THE PUBLISHER BY EMAIL, DO SO FORMALLY IN THE FIRST INSTANCE

things, or the editor may prefer to see it all on paper – they will almost invariably print out everything you send in any case.

THE PHONE CALL

Most editors would prefer it if this was not the way you approached them for the first time. If you do phone keep it simple and keep it short. Do not leave a rambling voicemail message – chances are you'll never get a return call if you do. Give them the option of replying to you by email as well as phone. And remember that editors are busy; the days of leisurely, gentlemanly publishing are long gone, by and large. If the first impression you leave is that you are going to use up more of their time than you are worth, then you will fail.

Most editors will be cautious of anyone who sounds like they might be too high maintenance, so be wary of making yourself sound too eccentric or quirky – at the first introduction, anyway!

ILLUSTRATORS

Illustrators can approach publishers in similar ways to writers. It is worth sending a letter, along with copies of your work (or a disc). It is also a good idea to try to arrange a meeting with the art editor, to show them your work. Here you should show a **portfolio** of your work, either digitally, as prints or originals (if you're doing it in person and taking it home again). The work should show off your skills in the broadest possible way, unless you (or the publisher) have a specific project or story in mind.

Never, ever, send original work through the post unless you've been commissioned to do so, or the recipient is expecting it. Even in this instance, you should copy the work in case you need to re-do it if it's lost. Prospective submissions should always be copies or digital files. Again, avoid emailing images until invited to do so.

Another good way of showcasing your work is to set up a website, and contact the publisher with the link. There are also forums (listed in this book) where illustrators and writers can meet to brainstorm ideas and potentially work together.

THE SUBMISSION PACKAGE

Regardless of the genre, this will include the following three elements:

1) A covering letter
2) A synopsis or concept document
3) Samples of work

The **covering letter** should, as discussed above, be no more than one sheet of A4. It should say who you are, what your idea/story is, and what makes it such a unique, brilliant idea.

The **synopsis**, or in the case of a lot of non-fiction, the 'concept' document, should do several things: explain the idea in more detail, explain who the idea is for and how and where it might sell, and, if appropriate, provide a complete breakdown of what is to go in.

'Dos'

Be short, sharp, focused and polite
Make it look professional
Consider what the recipient will think
of your email/phone message/letter
Get someone to check your proposal for mistakes

'Don'ts'

Ramble
Mention money in the first instance
Say you've copyrighted the work
Say this is the best book ever written
Try to make your submission look fancy; chances
are it will simply look naff

TOP TEN TIPS FOR LETTER WRITING SUCCESS

1. **Take the letter as seriously as the work itself.**
2. **Ask someone else to read your letter objectively** before you send it to anyone, and ensure it doesn't have any mistakes.
3. **Always try to find a contact name** to address your letter to.
4. **Familiarise yourself with the company's website and latest publications** – there is no point approaching them with an idea if they don't publish in that area, or if they aren't taking submissions. You can find out a lot about the publisher from their website.
5. **Paragraph 1: Grab the reader's attention.** Tell them what is special about your idea, how many words it comes to and what your proposed title is (make it punchy!).
6. **Paragraph 2: Go into more detail about the idea** in a calm and structured way. Explain any particularly noteworthy or unusual aspects of your idea, who would want to read it and why.
7. **Paragraph 3: Discuss any realistic marketing ideas** you may have, and any events that will boost publicity (such as festivals, anniversaries, film releases etc).
8. **Paragraph 4: Present your credentials**, and show that you are familiar with the work of the publisher.
9. **Sign off by thanking the reader** for their time and consideration, and ensure you have enclosed your contact details, should they want more information.
10. **If you use email, be formal in the first instance** and only send attachments with prior permission.

The **samples** depend on what you are submitting: in fiction it is traditionally the first three chapters (and you should have completed the rest!); in non-fiction it should be as broad a selection possible of what you intend, from across the book. Non-fiction authors will usually recommend that you don't need to have completed your book. Poetry should include a selection of completed poems.

HOW LONG DO YOU WAIT FOR A REPLY?

Most publishers are overwhelmed with submissions. The post can be dreaded: not more brown envelopes full of unpublishable ramblings, surely? That is one of the reasons why submissions might go unanswered for months. Another is that the editor can't decide whether the idea is any good or not. The worst is that the editor is so appalled by what he has received he does not know how to respond. Realistically, wait for a minimum of a month before reminding the publisher about your submission. And be aware it is not unknown for submissions still to be lurking in the famous slush pile six months after submission, so don't take offence or get angry if you still don't hear from them.

And even supposing the publisher does get back to you and makes encouraging if cautious noises, then you've still got all the negotiating to do…

MULTIPLE SUBMISSIONS

You can do this, but let each publisher you write to know that you have approached others. You should probably ask them to write back ASAP if they are interested. Will it work? Maybe.

> " EVEN IF THE PUBLISHER DOES GET BACK TO YOU AND MAKES ENCOURAGING NOISES, YOU'VE STILL GOT ALL THE NEGOTIATING TO DO… "

LITERARY AGENTS: SOME PROS AND CONS

DO YOU NEED AN AGENT?

Here we look at both sides of the argument

Many writers worry about whether they should have an agent or not. Most top writers have them, but not all do. You can make your way perfectly well in the literary world without, but…

First things first: you are more likely to need an agent if you write fiction than if you write non-fiction. Also, if you are writing in a specialist field you are as likely to have the same kinds of contacts as an agent. If you specialise in short articles, then the chances are an agent would simply not be worth the fees or the bother.

And here is a big caveat: you are much more likely to be accepted by an agent if you are already published. The agent can then see that you are a potential commercial prospect – after all the agent is there to make money at the end of the day.

You might want to be wary of an agent who seems keen to snap you up out of the blue, just like that. Successful agents are busy agents, so you would not usually expect to take on an unknown without some thought.

THE PROS

• They open doors for you; a good agent will get you noticed by publishers
• Many publishers will not work with unagented authors (or at least they say they won't), so you have to have an agent
• They might get a much better deal than you could negotiate
• They will understand the gobbledegook in the contract and weed out any nasty clauses
• They will do all of the financial haggling on your behalf, leaving you to have an entirely creative relationship with the publisher
• The more successful you are as an author, the more clout your agent has, and it is in her interest to negotiate better and better deals for you

THE CONS

• They take up to 20% of your advance and royalty in some cases, though the norm is more like 10%
• Although they negotiate the contract on your behalf with the publisher, the agreed changes may actually make you no better off
• Some editors prefer not to work via agents

HOW DO AGENTS MAKE THEIR MONEY?

All monies paid to you by the publisher go via the agent, who will deduct her percentage and send you a cheque for the difference. That is the normal way of working for all reputable UK and Irish agents. You should not normally pay an agent any money yourself, and you should be suspicious of an agent who does want money upfront. Some agencies do charge a reading fee.

HOW DO I FIND AN AGENT?

Look in the *Writer's Market* books, where all relevant UK and Irish agents are listed. Look on the website of the Association of Authors Agents (www. agentsassoc.co.uk) as this lists most established UK agents. And ask friends and other writers if they have an agent they know and trust.

BOOKS

A&C Black Publishers Ltd
38 Soho Square, London, W1D 3HB
- 020 7758 0200
- 020 7758 0222
- enquiries@acblack.com
- www.acblack.com/children

Parent Company Bloomsbury Publishing Plc
Contact Chairman/Chief Executive, Bloomsbury, Nigel Newton; Managing Director, A&C Black, Jill Coleman
Established 1807
Imprint(s) Andrew Brodie Publications
Insider Info Publishes approximately 85 children's titles per year. Receives approximately 3,000 queries and 650 manuscripts per year. Five per cent of books published are from first time authors and 70 per cent are from unagented authors. Offers an advance. Average lead time is nine months with simultaneous submissions accepted. Aims to respond within two months to proposals and manuscripts. Catalogue is free on request and available online.
Non-Fiction Publishes Children's Non-fiction, Educational and Reference titles on a range of subjects.
Submission Guidelines Accept submissions by post with SAE. No emailed submissions.
Fiction Publishes Children's fiction and Plays.
 * Age groups are 4–7, 8–11 and 12–14.
Submission Guidelines Accept submissions by post with SAE. No emailed submissions. Enquire about current seasonal themes and directions before submitting fiction.
Poetry Publishes Children's Poetry.
Submission Guidelines Accept submissions by post with SAE. No emailed submissions.
Recent Title(s) *Creative Thinking*, Ann Barker (Educational); *Mouldylocks and the Three Clares*, Sally Grindley (Fiction); *The Ultimate Teen Book Guide* (Reference)
Tips Explore the website or obtain the catalogue, as these give good indicators as to the current trends in A&C Black's lists. Particularly with fiction submissions, an initial enquiry as to the style of the list would be advisable before submitting.

Abbey Home Media
435–437 Edgware Road, London, W2 1TH
- 020 7563 3910
- 020 7563 3911
- james.harding@abbeyhomemedia.com
- www.abbeyhomemedia.com

Contact Managing Director, Licensing, James Harding
Insider Info Catalogue available online.
Non-Fiction Publishes Children's Non-fiction, Educational and Reference titles based on licensed characters.
Fiction Publishes Children's fiction and Picture books based on licensed brands.
 * Brands include *Superted* and *Teddy Trucks*
Recent Title(s) *Learn About Sheep* (Picture board book); *Jingle Bells* (Seasonal board book)
Tips Abbey Home Media produce CDs, DVDs and other resources for children, as well as their book publishing programme. Note that most ranges are linked in some way to characters or brands either created and licensed themselves, or bought from other licence holders.

Academy of Light
Unit 1c, Delta Centre, Mount Pleasant, Wembley, Middlesex, HA0 1UX
- 020 8795 2695
- 020 8903 3748
- info@academyoflight.co.uk
- www.academyoflight.co.uk

Contact Managing Director, Dr. Yubraj Sharma
Established 2000
Non-Fiction Publishes Children's Illustrated Reference titles on the following subjects: Alternative Lifestyles, Art/Architecture, Health/Medicine, New Age, Spirituality.
Tips Academy of Light is a specialist book publisher on homoeopathy and spirituality that mainly publishes adult titles. It aims to integrate the many fields of alternative medicine into a holistic system of new age medicine.

BOOKS

PUBLISHERS

LISTINGS

55

Acair Ltd

7 James Street, Stornoway, Isle of Lewis, HS1 2QN

- 01851 703020
- 01851 703294
- info@acairbooks.com
- www.acairbooks.com

Established 1975

Insider Info Authors paid by royalty. Catalogue available online.

Non-Fiction Publishes Illustrated Children's Educational and Reference titles on the following subjects:

Gaelic primary school education.

Fiction Publishes Picture books, Board books, Children's, Young Adult and Gaelic fiction titles.

* Age ranges are typically pre-school, 5–7 and 8–12.

Recent Title(s) *Facail agus Dealbhan*, (Pre-school, Educational); *Leum Suas air an Sguaib*, Julia Donaldson (Illustrated Fiction, 5–7); *Ceitidh Mòrag agus an Dà Sheanmhair*, Mairi Hedderwick (Illustrated Gaelic Translation, Fiction)

Tips Acair is a bilingual publisher, printing books in both English and Gaelic languages, and targeted mainly at Gaelic primary school education. About 50 per cent of books are published in the Gaelic language, including translations of English texts. Looking to the future, Acair are keen to carry on producing quality Scottish books, and in order to do that are keen to promote talent from the Western Isles in particular, and Scotland in general. Also publish adult non-fiction.

African Books Collective

Unit 13, King's Meadow, Ferry Hinksey Road, Oxford, OX2 0DP

- 01869 349110
- 01869 349110
- abc@africanbookscollective.com
- www.africanbookscollective.com

Contact Mary Jay

Established 1989

Insider Info Catalogue available online. Only accepts manuscripts from participating African publishers.

Fiction Publishes Children's and Young Adult's, Multicultural, Translation, Novels and Short Story titles.

Recent Title(s) *The Frog's Band*, Akua Opokua Ohene (African fiction)

Tips African Books Collective (ABC), founded, owned and governed by African publishers, seeks to strengthen indigenous African publishing through collective action, and to increase the visibility and accessibility of the wealth of African scholarship and culture. The collective is open to genuinely autonomous and independent African publishers, and ABC actively seeks suitable titles for distribution outside Africa. Note that the list of children's books published is small and not very current, as the organisation focuses mainly on adult publishing (non-fiction as well as fiction).

Allegra Publishing Ltd

15 Quayside Lodge, William Morris Way, London, SW6 2UZ

- 020 7384 3348
- 020 7384 3327
- felicia@allegrapublishing.com
- www.allegrapublishing.com

Contact Publisher, Felicia Law; Managing Editor, Karen Foster

Established 2002

Insider Info Catalogue available online.

Non-Fiction Publishes Children's Non-fiction, Educational and Activity titles.

Fiction Publishes Children's fiction and Picture books.

Recent Title(s) *Rumble's Cave*, (Set of Educational Resources)

Tips Titles and resources are aimed at children between the ages of 0 and 14, with education and entertainment being the primary aims. They also produce audio visual products, and gifts and activity packs alongside their books. Allegra Publishing own the copyright to a range of children's brands that are licensed out to worldwide media companies.

Alligator Books

Gadd House, Arcadia Avenue, London, N3 2JU

- 020 8371 6622
- 020 8371 6633
- sales@alligatorbooks.co.uk
- www.alligatorbooks.co.uk

Contact Managing Directors, Neil Rodol and Andrew Rabin

Established 1999

Imprint(s) Pinwheel Limited (division)

Insider Info Catalogue available online.

Non-Fiction Publishes Children's Non-fiction and Activity titles based on licensed characters.

Fiction Publishes Children's fiction and Picture books based on licensed brands.

* Brands include *Barbie* and *Batman*.

Tips Specialises in film, television and magazine tie-ins. Produces activity packs, work books, stickers and other gifts, as well as more traditional picture books. Recently acquired Pinwheel Limited (see separate entry).

Andersen Press Ltd
20 Vauxhall Bridge Road, London SW1V 2SA
- 020 7840 8701
- 020 7233 6263
- anderseneditorial@randomhouse.co.uk
- www.andersenpress.co.uk

Contact Fiction Editor, Liz Maude (Children's Fiction); Editorial Director, Rona Selby (Children's Books)
Established 1976
Insider Info Publishes 64 titles per year. Receives approximately 200 queries and 500 manuscripts per year. 25 per cent of books published are from first-time authors and 30 per cent of books published are from unagented authors. Payment is via royalty (on retail price), with 0.075 (per £) minimum and 0.125 (per £) maximum. The advance offered is £2,000. Aims to respond to proposals within two months. Catalogue is free on request, and available online. Manuscript guidelines are free on request.
Non-Fiction Publishes Young Adult and Children's titles.
 * Publishes very little non-fiction.
Submission Guidelines Accepts proposal package (including outline, one sample chapter, author biography and SAE) and artworks/images (send digital files as jpegs or other formats). No emailed submissions.
Fiction Publishes Children's Picture book titles and Young Adult novels.
Submission Guidelines Accepts proposal package (including outline, one sample chapter and SAE). Illustrators should send photocopied samples of artwork or sketches. Never send originals. No emailed submissions.
Recent Title(s) *I Want a Cat*, Tony Ross (Picture book); *This is What I Did*, Ann Dee Ellis (Young Adult novel)
Tips Andersen Press' readership is children and young adults, between the ages of one and eighteen. The press publish mainly picture books, for which the required text is under 1,000 words, a series of early readers fiction called *Tigers,* which are about 3–5,000 words long, and older fiction texts at about 15–50,000 words. Books are sold in conjunction with Random House Children's books.

Andromeda Children's Books
Winchester House, 259–269 Old Marylebone Road, London, NW1 5XJ
- 020 7616 7200
- 020 7616 7201
- -
- www.pinwheel.co.uk

Parent Company Pinwheel Limited (division of Alligator Books)
Insider Info Catalogue available online. As part of Pinwheel (now owned by Alligator Books), the Andromeda imprint focuses on the three to twelve year old age group.
Non-Fiction Publishes Children's Cloth, Novelty, Gift and Illustrated titles on the following subjects: Children's and Baby's Early Learning.
Fiction Publishes Children's Picture book titles.
Recent Title(s) *Secrets of the Master Magician* (Activity Pack); *The Beautiful Butterfly Book* (Illustrated Non-fiction)
Tips Typical titles include wipe clean books for pre-schoolers and novelty series such as *Beautiful Bugs*. Any picture book submissions should be directed to Gullane Children's Books (another imprint of Pinwheel) and not Andromeda.

Anness Publishing
Hermes House, 88–89 Blackfriars Road, London, SE1 8HA
- 020 7401 2077
- 020 7633 9499
- info@anness.com
- www.annesspublishing.com

Contact Chairman/Managing Director, Paul Anness; Publisher/Partner, Joanna Lorenz (Creative Issues)
Established 1988
Imprint(s) Lorenz Books
 Southwater
 Hermes House
 Peony Press
Insider Info Publish 300 titles (including adult books) per year. Catalogue available online. The company has embarked on a major forestry project by managing and planting trees to replace the ones used in producing their books.
Non-Fiction Publishes Children's Illustrated Non-fiction titles on the following subjects: Cooking/Foods/Nutrition, History, Crafts, Nature, Hobbies, Animals, Sports, Food and Drink, Pets.
 * The Lorenz Books and Southwater imprints publish traditionally across the range of non-fiction topics, whereas Hermes House and Peony Press deal

with non-trade sales, promotional sales and customised publishing for major customers.

Recent Title(s) *Step Into: Aztec and Maya World*, Fiona MacDonald (Southwater, Illustrated history)

Tips Anness' children's lists are relatively small compared to the adult programme.

Anova Books Company Ltd
151 Freston Road, London, W10 6TH
- 020 7314 1400
- 020 7314 1588
- websales@chrysalisbooks.com
- www.anovabooks.com

Established 2005

Imprint(s) Batsford
Robson
Pavilion
Conway Maritime Press
Portico
Collins & Brown
National Trust Books
Chrysalis Children's Books

Insider Info Publishes 150 titles per year (including adult books). Receives approximately 40 queries and 200 manuscripts per year. 50 per cent of books published are from first-time authors and 50 per cent of books published are from unagented authors. Payment is via royalty (on retail price), with 0.075 (per £) maximum, or outright purchase. Advance offered will be up to £10,000. Average lead time is seven months, with simultaneous submissions not accepted. Submissions accompanied by SAE will be returned. Aims to respond to queries within one week, proposals within two weeks, and manuscripts within five weeks. Catalogue is free on request, and available online.

Non-Fiction Publishes Children's Non-fiction titles on the following subjects:
Art/Architecture, Cooking/Foods/Nutrition, Crafts, Nature, History, Animals.

Submission Guidelines Agented submissions only for children's books.

Fiction Children's Illustrated fiction titles.

Submission Guidelines Agented submissions only for children's books.

Recent Title(s) *Lifesize Reptiles*, Hannah Wilson (Illustrated non-fiction); *After the War was Over*, Michael Foreman (Picture Book)

Antique Collector's Club
Sandy Lane, Old Martlesham, Woodbridge, IP12 4SD

- 01394 389950
- 01394 389999
- sales@antique-acc.com
- www.antique-acc.com

Contact Managing Director, Diana Steel

Established 1966

Insider Info Catalogue free on request, or available online.

Fiction Publishes Children's Illustrated titles.
* Only publishes reprints of childhood classics. No new titles.

Poetry Publishes Children's Poetry.
* Only publishes reprints of childhood classics. No new titles.

Recent Title(s) *Nonsense Verse*, Edward Lear, illustrated by Jonathan Bentley (Picture book of Poetry)

Apex Publishing Ltd
PO Box 7086, Clacton on Sea, Essex, CO15 5WN
- 01255 428500
- 0870 046 6536
- enquiry@apexpublishing.co.uk
- www.apexpublishing.co.uk

Contact Managing Editor, Susan Kidby; Production Manager, Chris Cowlin; Marketing Manager, Jackie Bright

Established 2002

Insider Info Publishes 20 titles per year (including adult books). Receives approximately 500 queries and 500 manuscripts per year. 60 per cent of books published are from first-time authors and 90 per cent of books published are from unagented authors. 50 per cent of books published are author subsidy published, based on potential sales. Payment is via royalty (on retail price). Average lead time is nine months, with simultaneous submissions accepted. Submissions accompanied by SAE will be returned. Aims to respond to queries within seven days, proposals within 14 days, manuscripts within 21 days, and any other enquiry within seven days. Catalogue and manuscript guidelines are free on request, and available online or by email.

Non-Fiction Publishes Children's Non-fiction titles on a variety of subjects.

Submission Guidelines Accepts query with SAE or completed manuscript (including publishing history, clips, author biography and SAE) and artworks/images (send photocopies or digital files as jpegs).

Fiction Publishes Children's fiction and Picture book titles.

Submission Guidelines Accepts query with SAE or completed manuscript (including publishing history, clips, author biography and SAE).

Tips Mainly publish adult books. The publishers warn that saturated markets, such as children's books, may well be steered down the subsidy publishing route. Research all options thoroughly before committing.

Arcturus Publishers Ltd
26/27 Bickels Yard, 151-153 Bermondsey Street, London, SE1 3HA
- 020 7407 9400
- 020 7407 9444
- info@arcturuspublishing.com
- www.arcturuspublishing.com

Parent Company Foulsham Publishers
Insider Info Catalogue is free on request and available online.
Non-Fiction Publishes Children's Illustrated Reference and Activity titles on he following subjects:
History, Puzzles and Games, Entertainment.
Submission Guidelines Accepts proposal package (including outline, author biography, SAE, information on the market position of the book, its competitors and its readership).
Fiction Publishes Children's titles.
Recent Title(s) *Time Soldiers - Rex*, Kathleen Duey (Illustrated adventure fiction); *Little Giants - Mind Bending Mazes*, (Puzzle book)
Tips Will not accept emailed submissions.

Ashley Drake Publishing Ltd
PO Box 733, Cardiff, CF14 7ZY
- 07803 940867
- 0870 705 2582
- post@ashleydrake.com
- www.ashleydrake.com

Contact Managing Director, Ashley Drake
Established 1994
Imprint(s) Welsh Academic Press
St. David's Press
Welsh Educational Press
Y Ddraig Fach (The Little Dragon)
Insider Info Publishes five titles per year (including adult books). Receives approximately ten queries per year and ten manuscripts per year. Three per cent of books published are from first-time authors and 100 per cent of books published are from unagented authors. Payment is via royalty on net receipts. Average lead time is one year, with simultaneous submissions not accepted. Submissions accompanied by SAE will be returned. Aims to respond to queries within five days, and proposals and manuscripts within one month. Catalogue is

free on request, and available online or by email. Manuscript guidelines are available online.
Non-Fiction Publishes Children's Illustrated titles.
 * Note that the children's publishing programme is extremely small and titles are released infrequently. The main focus is on the adult programme.
Submission Guidelines Not currently accepting any proposals or manuscripts.
Tips Writers should ensure that their subject matter is relevant to Ashley Drake's list, by checking on their website. If your work is a departure from their usual editorial policy, do not submit your proposal. The few children's books that have been published are mostly Welsh language titles.

Ashmolean Museum Publications
Ashmolean Museum, Beaumont Street, Oxford, OX1 2PH
- 01865 278010
- 01865 278018
- publications@ashmus.ox.ac.uk
- www.ashmolean.org

Contact Publications Manager, Declan McCarthy; Publications Deputy Manager, Emily Jolliffe; Picture Library Manager, Amanda Turner
Insider Info Catalogue available online.
Non-Fiction Publishes Children's titles on the following subjects:
Anthropology/Archaeology, Art/Architecture, Crafts, Education, History, Photography, Science.
Tips The publications department supports the Ashmolean's mission to disseminate information and educate the public through its collection. Only books directly concerned with the museum's own collections are published and most of these are adult titles. Most of the authors are staff at the Ashmolean Museum, although sometimes an academic from another institution is appointed to write a book, if they are an expert on the particular subject. Authors are not generally encouraged to submit manuscripts.

Atom
Brettenham House, Lancaster Place, London, WC2E 7EN
- 020 7911 8000
- 020 7911 8100
- atom.uk@twbg.co.uk
- www.atombooks.co.uk

Parent Company Little, Brown Book Group
Contact Publishing Director, Tim Holman; Editorial Director, Darren Nash
Established 2002

Insider Info Submissions accompanied by SAE will be returned. Aims to respond to proposals within 12 weeks. Catalogue available online.

Fiction Publishes Young Adult/Teenage fiction, including historical adventure, fantasy, science fiction and high school adventures.

 * Only able to read unsolicited submissions for novels in the science fiction genre. No other genres, short stories or poetry.

Submission Guidelines Send an outline and no more than 30 pages of double spaced text, and SAE.

Recent Title(s) *The Extraordinary and Unusual Adventures of Horatio Lyle*, Catherine Webb

Tips Writers are recommended to browse through some author websites for personal insights on writing for teenagers. No email submissions.

Aurora Metro Publications

2 Oriel Court, The Green, Twickenham, TW2 5AG

☏ 020 8898 4488

🖷 020 8898 0735

✉ info@aurorametro.com

🌐 www.aurorametro.com

Contact Publisher, Cheryl Robson (Drama, Fiction, Biography)

Established 1989

Imprint(s) Amp Books

Insider Info Publishes eight titles per year (including adult titles). Receives approximately 100 queries and 25 manuscripts per year. Ten per cent of books published are from first-time authors and 50 per cent of books published are from unagented authors. 20 per cent of books published are author-subsidy published, based on funding available from the Arts Council. Payment is via royalty (on retail price) or outright purchase. Average lead time is one year, with simultaneous submissions accepted. Submissions will not be returned. Aims to respond to queries within ten days, proposals within four months, and manuscripts within six months. Catalogue is free on request, or available by email.

Fiction Publishes Young Adult plays.

Submission Guidelines Accepts proposal package (including outline, synopsis, three sample chapters, author biography and reviews). No unsolicited manuscripts.

Recent Title(s) *Coming Back*, David Hill (Young Adult)

Tips Aurora Metro specialises in theatre and play scripts, and often seeks subsidies from the Arts Council for projects that fall within their funding criteria, e.g. translations.

Authentic Media

9 Holdom Avenue, Bletchley, Milton Keynes, MK1 1QR

☏ 01908 364213

🖷 01908 648592

✉ firstname.lastname@authenticmedia.co.uk

🌐 www.authenticmedia.co.uk

Contact Publishing Co-ordinator, Kath Williams (Authentic); Robin Parry, Commissioning Editor (Paternoster)

Established 1962

Imprint(s) Authentic
 Paternoster Press

Insider Info Publishes 50 titles per year (including adult titles). Catalogue available online.

Non-Fiction Children's Non-fiction and Biography titles on the following subjects:
 Religion, Spirituality.

Submission Guidelines Accepts proposals via post or email, addressed to the editor.

Fiction Publishes Religious Children's and Young Adult titles.

Submission Guidelines Accepts proposals via post or email, addressed to the editor.

Recent Title(s) *Amrac and the Paraclete*, John Glass (Christian fantasy); *Cry of the Tiger*, Angela Little (Biography)

Tips Publishes Christian books to help all types of Christians, wherever they are on their spiritual journey. Does not publish poetry.

Autumn Publishing

Appledram Barns, Birdham Road, Chichester, West Sussex, PO20 7EQ

☏ 01243 531660

🖷 01243 774433

✉ autumn@autumnpublishing.co.uk

🌐 www.autumnpublishing.co.uk

Contact Editorial Director, Lyn Coutts

Established 1976

Imprint(s) Byeway Books

Insider Info Publishes 200 titles per year. Submissions will not be not returned. Catalogue available online.

Non-Fiction Publishes Children's Illustrated books and Activity books.

Submission Guidelines Email editorial submissions to anna@autumnpublishing.co.uk
 Email illustrations to maria@ autumnpublishing.co.uk

Fiction Publishes Children's and Picture books.

Submission Guidelines Email editorial submissions to anna@autumnpublishing.co.uk

Email illustrations to maria@
autumnpublishing.co.uk

Recent Title(s) *Bumper Star Learning Diploma; Bath Time Books; Big Dots for Tiny Tots*

Tips All books are published under the Byeway Books imprint. Titles are aimed at giving children the chance to enjoy learning while they play. The creative teams work hard to ensure that the books are at the forefront of current trends, and that the range is always fresh and vibrant. Focuses on younger children's and infant's activity books, which are often in high demand.

Award Publications
The Old Riding School, The Welbeck Estate, Worksop, Nottinghamshire, S80 3LR
- 01909 478170
- 01909 484632
- info@awardpublications.co.uk
- www.awardpublications.co.uk

Established 1972

Insider Info Catalogue available online. Manuscript guidelines available online.

Non-Fiction Publishes Children's and Reference titles on the following subjects:
Crafts, Creative Non-fiction, Education, Entertainment/Games, Dictionaries.

Submission Guidelines Accepts query with SAE/ proposal package (including outline, one to two sample chapters and SAE), and artwork/images via email or post.

Fiction Publishes Children's Picture books, Religious titles, Short story collections, Novelty books and General titles.

Submission Guidelines Accepts query with SAE/ proposal package (including outline, one to two sample chapters and SAE). Illustrators interested in working with Award Publications should send in a samples of their work via email.

Recent Title(s) *Billy Brown Mouse Won't Go To Sleep* (Picture Book); *On the Farm* (Activity Book)

Tips Titles are aimed at children and infants, and parents. Award Publications are always on the lookout for talent, particularly for new illustrators and designers, so please send sample work.

Barefoot Books Ltd
124 Walcot Street, Bath, Somerset, BA1 5BG
- 01225 322400
- 01225 322499
- info@barefootbooks.co.uk
- www.barefootbooks.com

Contact Editor in Chief, Tessa Strickland (Picture books, Young Fiction)

Established 1993

Insider Info Publishes 16 titles per year, 15 per cent of books published are from first-time authors and 75 per cent of books published are from unagented authors. Payment is via royalty (on wholesale price) with 0.025 (per £) minimum and 0.05 (per £) maximum. Advance offered is variable. Average lead time is over 18 months, with simultaneous submissions accepted. Submissions will not be returned. Aims to respond to queries within eight weeks. Catalogue is free on request, and available online. Manuscript guidelines are available online.

Non-Fiction Publishes Children's Illustrated titles on the following subjects:
Multicultural, Nature/Environment, Spirituality, Travel.

Submission Guidelines Accepts query with SAE, or send completed manuscript by post. Illustrators should send photocopied samples by post.

Fiction Publishes Illustrated Children's fiction.

Submission Guidelines Accepts query with SAE, or send completed manuscript by post. Illustrators should send photocopied samples by post.

Tips Titles should be designed to introduce children to other cultures in a positive way.

Barn Owl Books
157 Fortis Green Road, London, N10 3LX
- ann@barnowlbooks.com
- www.barnowlbooks.com

Contact Ann Jungman

Insider Info Catalogue available online.

Non-Fiction Publishes Out-of-print Children's titles.

Fiction Publishes Out-of-print Children's titles.

Tips Publishes reprints only, no new titles.

Barny Books
The Cottage, Hough on the Mill, Grantham, Lincolnshire, NG32 2BB
- 01400 250246
- 01400 251737
- barnybooks@hotmail.com
- www.barnybooks.biz

Contact Managing Director, Molly Burkett

Established 1980

Insider Info Catalogue available online. Barny Books are too small to accept unsolicited manuscripts. Manuscript guidelines are not available.

Non-Fiction Publishes some Children's General Non-fiction titles.

Submission Guidelines Accepts query with SAE but no full manuscripts.

Fiction Publishes Children's fiction titles.

* Fiction is aimed at children from the age of seven upwards.

Submission Guidelines Accepts query with SAE, but no full manuscripts.

Recent Title(s) *Enjoying Life*, Sue Ricks (Health/Spirituality); *Operation Firewall*, Glenda Abramson (Military)

Tips Aims to help and support authors from the writing stage, all the way through to publication. The writer is taken through the process of getting a book into print, advising on how their book should look, and discussing the best places to sell their end product. This process can also include translation when the author's first language is not English, and help for those who are dyslexic, handicapped or the elderly. Although they cannot accept any unsolicited manuscripts due to their small size, Barny Books offer professional critiquing and editing services, as well as some self-publishing facilities. Any service that requires the author to pay a fee should be researched thoroughly.

Barrington Stoke
18 Walker Street, Edinburgh, EH3 7LP
- 0131 225 4113
- 0131 225 4140
- barrington@barringtonstoke.co.uk
- www.barringtonstoke.co.uk

Contact Publishing Administrator, Fiona Brown

Established 1998

Insider Info Catalogue available online or with SAE. Manuscript guidelines not available.

Non-Fiction Publishes Children's and Young Adult's Educational and Dictionary titles.

Submission Guidelines Does not accept unsolicited manuscripts, only queries.

Submission details to: fiona.brown@barringtonstoke.co.uk

Fiction Publishes Children's Picture books, Short story collections, and Young Adult titles.

Submission Guidelines Does not accept unsolicited manuscripts, only queries.

Submission details to: fiona.brown@barringtonstoke.co.uk

Recent Title(s) *Assassin!*, Tony Bradman (Children's Fiction); *Kiss of Death*, Charles Butler (Young Adult Fiction)

Tips Titles are aimed at children and young adults who are struggling readers, and children with dyslexia or a learning difficulty. Texts must be subtly adapted so that these children do not feel

patronised or short changed. Accessible language, a fast moving and unambiguous plot, and clear presentation are essential.

BBC Children's Books
80 Strand, London, WC2R 0RL
- 020 7010 3000
- 020 7010 6060
- customer.service@penguin.co.uk
- www.penguin.co.uk

Parent Company Penguin Group UK

Contact Managing Director, Sally Floyer

Established 2004

Insider Info Catalogue available online.

Non-Fiction Publishes Children's, General Non-fiction, Illustrated, Activity, Novelty and Television tie-in titles.

Submission Guidelines Agented submissions only.

Fiction Publishes Children's Television tie-in and Activity titles.

Submission Guidelines Agented submissions only.

Recent Title(s) *Doctor Who Activity Pack*; *CBeebies Little Library*

Tips BBC Children's books publishes illustrated titles ranging from pre-school to older children. Most books and products are linked to BBC children's programmes. No unsolicited submissions.

Black & White Publishing
99 Giles Street, Edinburgh, EH6 6BZ
- 0131 625 4500
- 0131 625 4501
- mail@blackandwhitepublishing.com
- matthew@itchy-coo.com
- www.blackandwhitepublishing.com
- www.itchy-coo.com

Contact Managing Director, Campbell Brown; Editor (Itchy Coo), James Robertson; National Schools and Communities Scots Language Development Officer (Itchy Coo), Matthew Fitt

Established 1990

Imprint(s) Chroma

Itchy Coo

Insider Info Submissions accompanied with SAE will be returned. Aims to respond to queries and manuscript queries within three months. Catalogue and manuscript guidelines are available online.

Fiction Children's Picture books, Young Adult titles, Scottish language and Scottish interest titles.

* Scottish language children's books are published through the Itchy Coo imprint.

Submission Guidelines Accepts query with SAE/proposal package (including outline, sample chapter(s), 30 pages maximum, contact details and SAE).

Poetry Publishes Children's Poetry.

Submission Guidelines No unsolicited proposals or manuscripts accepted at present.

Recent Title(s) *Rosie's Wish*, Isla Dewar (Picture book); *The Thing that Mattered Most*, Diana Hendry and Hamish Whyte (Eds.), (Poetry anthology)

Tips Titles are are aimed at anyone, especially Scottish children. Proposals are accepted, but do not send complete manuscripts. Many books published through Itchy Coo have an educational slant, despite being predominantly fictional.

Bloomsbury Publishing Plc

36 Soho Square, London, W1D 3QY

- 020 7494 2111
- 020 7434 0151
- csm@bloomsbury.com
- www.bloomsbury.com/childrens

Contact Chairman/Chief Executive, Nigel Newton; Publishing Director (Book Division), Liz Calder (Fiction); Editorial Director, Sarah Odedina (Children's Books); Editor in Chief, Alexandra Pringle

Established 1986

Imprint(s) A&C Black Publishers Ltd
Peter Collin Publishing Ltd
Berlin Verlag GmbH (German Division)
Bloomsbury USA (US Division)
Walker & Company (US Division)

Insider Info Payment is via royalties. Aims to respond to proposals within three months. Catalogue and manuscript guidelines are available online.

Non-Fiction Children's Illustrated titles.

Submission Guidelines No unsolicited submissions for children's titles.

Fiction Publishes Children's Picture book and Young Adult titles.

Submission Guidelines No unsolicited submissions for children's titles.

Poetry Publishes Children's Poetry titles.

Recent Title(s) *Notes From the Teenage Underground,* Simmone Howell (Young Adult novel); *Bathtime with Woof*, Caroline Jayne Church (Picture book)

Tips Bloomsbury is a major publisher, perhaps best known for its publishing phenomenon, J.K. Rowling's *Harry Potter* books. Bloomsbury, and its various divisions, publishes a wide range of children's books, both fiction and non-fiction. Currently Bloomsbury is not accepting unsolicited submissions for children's titles. The Bloomsbury website has a writers' area which holds a wealth of advice and links for aspiring authors. Aside from its UK imprints, Bloomsbury also has a division in America and owns the American publisher Walker & Company, and the German company Berlin Verlag GmbH.

Book Guild Publishing Ltd

Pavilion View, 19 New Road, Brighton, East Sussex, BN1 1UF

- 01273 720900
- 01273 723122
- info@bookguild.co.uk
- www.bookguild.co.uk

Contact Managing Director, Carol Biss; Managing Editor, Joanna Bentley

Established 1982

Insider Info Publishes 100 titles per year (including adult titles). 60 per cent of books published are from first-time authors. Payment is via royalties. Aims to respond to proposals and manuscripts within one month. Catalogue and manuscript guidelines are available online.

Non-Fiction Publishes Children's and Young Adult's General and Illustrated Non-fiction titles.

Submission Guidelines Accepts query with SAE/proposal package (including outline, two sample chapters, your publishing history, author biography and SAE).
Submission details to: joanna@bookguild.co.uk

Fiction Publishes Children's Picture book and Young Adult fiction titles.
* Wishes to publish engaging novels and stories for adult and child readers.

Submission Guidelines Accepts query with SAE/proposal package (including outline and two sample chapters).
Submission details to: joanna@bookguild.co.uk

Recent Title(s) *Larry Dilworth and the Legends of Football*, Ron Carlton-Gwilliam (Fiction); *The Itsy-Bitsy Family*, Robert Fallon

Tips The Book Guild is an independent publisher and most material is conventionally published, but 'Joint Venture' services, where the author contributes costs as well as other production services, are offered for a fee. This option should be researched thoroughly.

Bookmart Ltd

Blaby Road, Wigston, Leicester, LE18 4SE

- 0116 275 9060
- 0116 275 9060
- books@bookmart.co.uk
- www.bookmart.co.uk

Insider Info Catalogue available online. Accepts queries via email or online form.
Non-Fiction Publishes Children's Educational, Activity, Novelty and General non-fiction titles.
Fiction Publishes Children's fiction and Picture books.
Poetry Publishes Children's poetry titles.
Recent Title(s) *Bathtime Baby* (Flap book); *Fun With French* (Educational)
Tips Titles are aimed at children of all ages, from babies, toddlers and pre-schoolers, to paperback fiction for older readers up to the age of 15.

Boxer Books
101 Turnmill Street, London, EC1M 5QP
- 020 7017 8980
- 020 7608 2314
- info@boxerbooks.com
- www.boxerbooksltd.co.uk

Contact Creative Director, Dave Bennett
Insider Info Submissions accompanied by SAE will be returned. Catalogue available online.
Fiction Publishes Children's Picture books.
Submission Guidelines Accepts entire manuscript and colour artwork, if sent by post to the Submissions Editor. Does not accept email submissions. All artwork and manuscript must be copies, not originals.
Recent Title(s) *Big Smelly Bear*, Britta Teckentrup; *Chicky Chicky Chook Chook*, Cathy MacLennan
Tips Titles are aimed at children aged 0–6. Boxer Books are keen to publish first-time authors and have done so in the past.

The British Museum Press
38 Russell Square, London, WC1B 3QQ
- 020 7323 1234
- 020 7436 7315
- pressmarketing@britishmuseum.co.uk
- www.britishmuseum.co.uk

Parent Company The British Museum
Contact Managing Director, Andrew Thatcher
Established 1973
Insider Info Catalogue is available online.
Non-Fiction Publishes Children's, Illustrated, Activity and Gift titles on the following subjects:
Religion, History, Archaeology, Arts.
Recent Title(s) *Kings & Queens of Britain*, Katherine Hoare; *The Vikings Activity Book*, David Wilson

Brown Watson
The Old Mill, 76 Fleckney Road, Kibworth Beauchamp, Leicestershire, LE8 OHG
- 0116 279 6333
- books@brownwatson.co.uk
- www.brownwatson.co.uk

Non-Fiction Publishes Children's General non-fiction and Picture book titles.
Fiction Publishes General Children's fiction.
Tips Brown Watson is a small, family owned children's book publisher and distributor.

Bryntirion Press
Bryntirion, Bridgend, CF31 4DX
- 01656 655886
- 01656 665919
- office@emw.org.uk
- www.emw.org.uk/books/bryntirionpress/default.htm

Contact Press Manager, Huw Kinsey
Established 1955
Insider Info Catalogue free on request and online.
Non-Fiction Publishes Children's and Young Adult titles on the following subjects:
Religion, Spirituality, Christianity.
Tips Titles are aimed at the Evangelical/Welsh reader. Also publishes Christian books and magazines in the Welsh language, although many books published are for adults. Welsh language writers are in generally more in demand.

b Small Publishing
The Book Shed, 36 Leybourne Park, Kew, Richmond, Surrey, TW9 3HA
- 020 8948 2884
- 020 8948 6458
- info@bsmall.co.uk
- www.bsmall.co.uk

Contact Publisher, Catherine Bruzzone; Editorial Contact, Susan Martineau
Insider Info Catalogue available online.
Non-fiction Publishes Children's Educational, Activity and Reference titles on the following subjects:
Languages, Activities, Science, Puzzles, Art, Craft, History and Animals.
Submission Guidelines No unsolicited proposals, as all books are created in-house.
Tips b Small create most of their books with a small stable of writers and illustrators, details of whom appear on the website.

Buster Books

16 Lion Yard, Tremadoc Road, London, SW4 7NQ

- ☎ 020 7720 8643
- 🖷 020 7627 8953
- ✉ enquiries@mombooks.com
- ✉ firstname.lastname@mombooks.com
- 🌐 www.mombooks.com/busterbooks

Parent Company Michael O'Mara Books

Contact Managing Director, Lesley O'Mara; Publishing Director, Philippa Wingate; Managing Editor, David Sinden

Established 1985

Insider Info Average lead time is six months, with simultaneous submissions accepted. Submissions accompanied by SAE will be returned. Catalogue is available with SAE. Manuscript guidelines are available online.

Non-Fiction Publishes Children's Educational and General non-fiction.

 * Most educational non-fiction is aimed at children aged 8–12.

Submission Guidelines Accepts proposal package (including outline, two to three sample chapters, your publishing history, author biography and SAE) and artworks/images (send photocopies). Do not send original artworks or whole manuscripts.

Fiction Publishes Children's Board books and Picture book titles.

Submission Guidelines Does not accept fiction submissions.

Cadogan Guides

New Holland Publishers, Garfield House, 86–88 Edgeware Road, London, W2 2EA

- ☎ 020 7724 7773
- 🖷 020 7258 1293
- ✉ info@cadoganguides.co.uk
- 🌐 www.cadoganguides.com

Parent Company The Globe Pequot Press (Morris Communications Corporation)

Insider Info Catalogue is available online.

Non-Fiction Publishes Children's Guidebook, Activity and Reference titles on the following subjects:

 Travel destinations.

Recent Title(s) *Pick Your Brain About France*, Marian Pashley (Children's Travel); *There and Back Again: In the footsteps of J.R.R. Tolkien,* Matthew Lyons (Travel Literature)

Tips Cadogan Guides is part of The Globe Pequot Press book division of Morris Communications Corporation, an American multimedia business. They publish a wide range of books for adults and children and the children's titles tend to be bright, colourful and designed to engage young people, whilst travelling both at home and abroad.

Campbell Books

20 New Wharf Road, London, N1 9RR

- ☎ 020 7014 6000
- 🖷 020 7014 6001
- 🌐 www.panmacmillan.com

Parent Company Pan Macmillan

Insider Info Catalogue available online.

Fiction Publishes Picture books and Children's Interactive, Moving and Textured books.

Submission Guidelines Agented submissions only.

Recent Title(s) *Mini Magic Drawing Books: My Animal Drawing Book*, Rachel Fuller (Board Book); *Noisy Jungle Babies: Little Zebra*, Rebecca Harry (Picture book with noise)

Tips Founded by Rod Campbell, the creator of the toddler classic, *Dear Zoo*. The imprint is a front-runner in the specialist pre-school market. No unsolicited submissions.

Carlton Publishing Group

20 Mortimer Street, London, W1T 3JW

- ☎ 020 7612 0400
- 🖷 020 7612 0401
- ✉ enquiries@carltonbooks.co.uk
- 🌐 www.carltonbooks.co.uk

Contact Managing Director, Jonathan Goodman

Established 1992

Imprint(s) Carlton Books

 Andre Deutsch

 Prion

Insider Info Aims to respond to proposals within four weeks. Catalogue is available online.

Non-Fiction Publishes Children's Illustrated, Activity, Reference and Gift titles

Submission Guidelines Does not accept proposals for children's books

Fiction Publishes Children's Illustrated fiction.

Submission Guidelines Does not accept proposals for children's fiction.

Recent Title(s) *Extreme Dinosaurs*, Robert Mash (Illustrated); *Santa*, Rod Green (Illustrated); *The Complete Book of Witches and Wizards*, Time Dedopulos

Tips Proposals are only accepted for adult titles.

Caterpillar Press

1 The Coda Centre, 189 Munster Road, London, SW6 6AW

📞 020 7386 6705/07721 887080
📞 020 7610 3353
📧 jasher@caterpillarbooks.co.uk
🌐 www.littletigerpress.com/caterpillar/
Parent Company Magi Publications
Contact Publisher, Jamie Asher
Fiction Publishes Picture and Novelty book titles for the 0–3 age group.
Tips Caterpillar specialises in novelty books, such as board and cloth books for pre-schoolers. Contact Jamie Asher for more information. See Little Tiger Press for Magi Publications' imprint for slightly older children.

Catnip Publishing Ltd
Islington Business Centre, 3–5 Islington High Street, London, N1 9LQ
📞 01206 233333
📧 martin@catnippublishing.co.uk
🌐 www.catnippublishing.co.uk
Contact Martin West (Editorial/Foreign Rights)
Insider Info Catalogue available online. Accepts queries by email, phone or post.
Fiction Publishes Out-of-print Children's titles and New Children's fiction.
  * Publishes illustrated and non-illustrated books.
Recent Title(s) *Children of Winter*, Berlie Doherty (Reprint); *Fairy Charm: The Pesky Spell*, Emily Rodda
Tips Although some new titles are published, the main emphasis of Catnip is on reprints.

Chicken House Publishing
2 Palmer Street, Frome, Somerset, BA11 1DS
📞 01373 454488
📞 01373 454499
📧 chickenhouse@doublecluck.com
🌐 www.doublecluck.com/index.php
Contact Publisher/Managing Director, Barry Cunningham; Deputy Managing Director, Rachel Hickman; Fiction Editor, Imogen Cooper
Established 2000
Insider Info Aims to respond to proposals and manuscripts within three months. Catalogue and manuscript guidelines are available online.
Fiction Publishes Teenage titles, Picture books, and Children's titles.
  * Does not publish board books, pop-up books or activity titles.
Submission Guidelines Accepts query with SAE/proposal package (including outline and three sample chapters). No email submissions. There is no need to send illustrations with picture books unless you have already arranged them. Novels should be a

minimum of 15,000 words and picture books should not exceed 1,500 words.
Recent Title(s) *When Santa Fell to Earth*, Cornelia Funke (Picture book); *The Wright Three*, Blue Balliet (Novel)
Tips The Chicken House is a 'plucky', highly individual, children's book publishing company with an enthusiasm for finding new writers, artists and ideas. Books are aimed at children, parents, teachers and librarians.

Child's Play (International)
Ashworth Road, Bridgemead, Swindon, Wiltshire, SN5 7YD
📞 01793 616286
🌐 www.childs-play.com
Contact Chief Executive, Neil Burden
Insider Info Catalogue is free on request and available online or by email.
Non-Fiction Publishes Children's Illustrated and Educational titles.
Fiction Publishes Picture books, Board books and Children's titles.
Recent Title(s) *Bear and Turtle and the Great Lake Race*, Andrew Fusek Peters (Picture book); *The Ding Dong Bag*, Jess Stockham (Picture book)
Tips Child's Play is an independent publisher specialising in learning through play, with a range of books, games, toys and other resources (aimed at Key Stage 1 and 2). Company products also support minority groups and languages.

Christian Education
1020 Bristol Road, Selly Oak, Birmingham, B29 6LB
📞 0121 472 4242
📞 0121 472 7575
📧 editorial@christianeducation.org.uk
🌐 www.christianeducation.org.uk
Contact Senior Editor, Anstice Hughes
Insider Info Catalogue is available online.
Non-Fiction Publishes Illustrated Children's Educational titles on Religion.
Fiction Publishes Illustrated Children's Religious titles.
Tips Christian Education (CE) provides advice, resources and opportunities for teaching and learning in the school, the church and the family group, carrying forward the work of the National Christian Education Council (NCEC, formerly the National Sunday School Union) and the Christian Education Movement (CEM). The two organisations are now joining together to maximise their delivery

of high quality training and resources for Christian educators, and for teachers of Religious Education in schools. Children's titles are a relatively small proportion of the list and include illustrated books for very young children.

Christian Focus Publications
Geanies House, Fearn by Tain, Ross-shire, IV20 1TW
- 01862 871011
- 01862 871699
- Catherine.Mackenzie@christianfocus.com
- www.christianfocus.com

Contact Children's Editor, Catherine Mackenzie
Imprint(s) CF4Kids
 Christian Heritage
 Mentor
Insider Info Aims to respond to proposals within six months. Proposals accompanied with SAE will be returned. Catalogue and manuscript guidelines are available online.
Non-Fiction Publishes Children's Illustrated Religious titles.
Submission Guidelines Query with SAE/proposal package (including outline, three sample chapters, author biography, author information sheet [online] and SAE). Details of all series styles are on the website and should be read thoroughly before submitting.
Fiction Publishes Children's Illustrated religious titles.
Recent Title(s) My 1st Book of Bible Prayers, Philip Ross (Illustrated Non-fiction); Kiwi Adventures, Bartha Hill (Fiction)
Tips Titles are aimed at all ages and abilities. Christian Focus Publications (CFP) has been producing Christian books since the early 1970s, originally starting as a publisher of classic Scottish authors. It is a conservative, evangelical publishing house and comes from a non-denominational, reformed background. Although it is not insisted that all authors call themselves reformed, anything that would be a polemic against the reformed faith would not be considered. CFP are committed to the historic foundations of the faith, the inerrancy of Scripture in its original manuscripts, the deity of Christ, his uniqueness as a means of salvation and the existence of hell. It is recommended that you browse the online catalogue to make sure that your title would fit in with the general ethos.

Chrysalis Children's Books
151 Freston Road, London, W10 6TH
- 020 7314 1400
- 020 7314 1401
- www.anovabooks.com

Parent Company Anova Books Company Ltd
Contact Catalogue available online.
Non-fiction Publishes Children's Illustrated reference titles.
Fiction Publishes Children's Picture Book, Novelty and Classic titles.
Recent Title(s) Billy the Kid, Michael Morpurgo (Novel)
Tips Chrysalis Children's Books are published within the Anova Books Company and are separated into three divisions: Pre-school and Fiction; Education, and Non-fiction. The age range covered is from infants to ten years plus.

Compendium Publishing
43 Frith Street, London, W1D 4SA
- 020 7287 4570
- 020 7494 0583
- compendiumpub@aol.com

Contact Managing Director, Alan Greene; Editorial Director, Simon Forty
Established 1996
Non-Fiction Publishes Children's Illustrated and Educational books on the following subjects:
 Education, History, Hobbies, Transportation.
Submission Guidelines Accepts brief proposal with SAE. No unsolicited manuscripts.
Tips Compendium Publishing have a fast growing programme of high quality, illustrated non-fiction titles for the general trade, and educational and reference materials for schools and colleges. Generally publishes and packages for international publishing companies.

Corgi Children's Books
61–63 Uxbridge Road, London, W5 5SA
- 020 8231 6439
- 020 8231 6767
- childrenseditorial@randomhouse.co.uk
- www.randomhouse.co.uk/childrens

Parent Company Random House Children's Books
Insider Info Catalogue is available online.
Fiction Publishes Children's and Teenage novels in paperback.
Submission Guidelines Accepts proposal package (including outline and one sample chapter).

Photocopies of images and illustrations are accepted.

Recent Title(s) *The Medici Seal*, Theresa Breslin; *The Intruders*, E.E. Richardson

Tips Agented submissions are strongly preferred.

Crossbridge Books

Tree Shadow, Berrow Green, Martley, WR6 6PL

- ☎ 01886 821128
- 📠 01886 821128
- ✉ crossbridgebooks@btinternet.com
- 🌐 www.crossbridgebooks.com

Contact Managing Director, Eileen Mohr

Established 1995

Imprint(s) Mohr Books

Insider Info Catalogue is available online.

Non-Fiction Publishes Children's Illustrated books on Religion.

Fiction Publishes Religious titles.

Recent Title(s) *A Kentle-Shaddy Knows Something*, E.M. Mohr

Tips Titles are aimed at a predominantly Christian readership and the children's list is a relatively small part of the programme. Most books are inspirational or spiritual in nature and it is anticipated that all future books will be of strong Christian interest.

David Fickling Books

31 Beaumont Street, Oxford, OX1 2NP

- ☎ 01865 339000
- 📠 01865 339009
- ✉ dfickling@randomhouse.co.uk
- 🌐 www.davidficklingbooks.co.uk

Parent Company Random House Children's Division

Contact Publisher, David Fickling; Senior Editor, Bella Pearson

Insider Info Approximately 30 per cent of books published are from first-time authors. Catalogue available online.

Fiction Publish Children's Picture books and Novels.

Submission Guidelines Strongly prefer agented submissions.

Recent Title(s) *Before I Die*, Jenny Downham (Novel)

Tips David Fickling Books are a very small imprint within Random House, but they publish some very commercially successful authors. They are the first bicontinental children's publisher with books publishing simultaneously in the US and the UK.

Day Books

Orchard Piece, Crawborough, Charlbury, Oxfordshire, OX7 3TX

- ☎ 01608 811196
- 📠 01608 811196
- ✉ lives@day-books.com
- 🌐 www.day-books.com

Contact Managing Editor, James Sanderson

Established 1997

Imprint(s) Charlbury Press
Leo Children's Books

Insider Info Receives approximately 200 queries and 100 manuscripts per year (including for adult books). Ten per cent of books published are from first-time authors and 80 per cent are from unagented authors. Payment is via royalty (on wholesale price) with 0.1 (per £) maximum. Average lead time is one year, with simultaneous submissions accepted. Aims to respond to proposals and manuscripts within one month.

Fiction Publishes Children's titles.

 * A limited number of children's books are published under the Leo Children's Book imprint.

Submission Guidelines Accepts query with SAE.

Recent Title(s) *Zoot*, Alan Fraser (Children's Fiction)

Tips Day Books is an independent publishing company, established to publish a series of 'great diaries from around the world'. Since then they've branched out to include children's books, among other things, but this list is still relatively small. The company can only respond to those who include return postage, or provide an email address.

Dorling Kindersley

80 Strand, London, WC2R 0RL

- ☎ 020 7010 3000
- 📠 020 7010 6060
- ✉ childreneditorial@uk.dk.com
- 🌐 www.dorlingkindersley-uk.co.uk

Parent Company Penguin Group (UK)

Contact CEO, Gary June; Global Managing Director, Andrew Welham

Established 1974

Insider Info Catalogue available as a pdf online.

Non-Fiction Publishes Children's Illustrated, Educational, Multimedia, Encyclopedia and Reference titles on the following subjects:
 Animals, Art, Comics, Crafts, Dictionaries, Dinosaurs, Encyclopedias, Entertainment/Games, Graphic Novels, History, Hobbies, Language/Literature, Nature, Science, Sports, Young Adult, Film and Television.

Submission Guidelines No unsolicited submissions, agented submissions only.
Recent Title(s) *History Dudes: Ancient Egypt*, Laura Buller (Illustrated Reference)
Tips Dorling Kindersley is the world leader in illustrated reference books. Books aim to inspire and teach people of all ages by using design, illustration and photography to make ideas come alive.

Dublar Scripts
204 Mercer Way, Romsey, Hampshire SO51 7QJ
- 01794 501377
- 01794 502538
- scripts@dublar.freeserve.co.uk
- www.dublar.co.uk

Contact Managing Director, Bob Heather
Established 1994
Imprint(s) Sleepy Hollow Pantomimes
Fiction Publishes Family Pantomime titles.
Recent Title(s) *The King's New Clothes*, Bob Heather (Pantomime)
Tips Produces and publishes several pantomimes, performed all over Great Britain, Canada, Australia, and New Zealand, and a few in Malta, Poland, Spain and France. Traditional family pantomimes only.

Edgewell Publishing
5a Front Street, Prudhoe, Northumberland, NE42 5HJ
- 01661 835330
- 01661 835330
- keith@tynedale-languages.co.uk
- www.tynedale-languages.co.uk

Contact Editor, Keith Minton
Established 2005
Insider Info Submissions accompanied by SAE will be returned. Manuscript guidelines are available by email and online.
Non-Fiction Publishes Children's and Young Adult's Educational and Multicultural Reference titles.
Submission Guidelines Accepts queries by phone or email.
Fiction Publishes Children's Multicultural Short story collections, Translations and Young Adult titles.
Submission Guidelines Accepts queries with SAE.
Poetry Publish Children's and Young Adult's Poetry titles.
Submission Guidelines Accepts queries by phone or email.
Recent Title(s) *LIVELY TALES Magazine*, (Short story magazine)
Tips Titles are aimed at foreign language students/immigrants, and young or new writers. Edgewell

Publishing also offers a basic critiquing service which can then lead to work being published in *LIVELY TALES Magazine*, or as a stand alone book.

Egmont Books
239 Kensington High Street, London, W8 6SA
- 020 7761 3500
- 020 7761 3510
- info@egmont.co.uk
- www.egmont.co.uk

Contact Publishing Director, David Riley
Established 1878
Insider Info Publishes 500 titles per year. Catalogue available online. Manuscript guidelines are also available online.
Non-Fiction Publishes Gift books and Children's titles.
Submission Guidelines No unsolicited manuscripts.
Fiction Picture books and Children's titles.
Submission Guidelines No unsolicited manuscripts.
Recent Title(s) *Thomas & Friends: Sing-Along Song Book*
Tips Egmont Books aim is to turn writers into successful authors and children into passionate readers, producing books that enrich and entertain. Due to a huge backlog, they are unable to accept unsolicited manuscripts and recommend first seeking a literary agent.

Eilish Press
4 Collegiate Crescent, Broomhall Park, Sheffield, S10 2BA
- 07973 353964
- eilishpress@hotmail.co.uk

Contact Dr. Suzi Kapadia (Women's Issues, Human Rights, Anti-Racism)
Established 2006
Insider Info Publishes five titles per year (including adult books). Receives approximately 30 queries and five manuscripts per year. 100 per cent of books published are from unagented authors. Payment is via royalty (on wholesale price), or outright purchase. Catalogue available online or by email.
Non-Fiction Publishes Children's and Young Adult's titles on the following subjects:
 Ethnicity, Health/Medicine, History, Women's Issues/Studies, Human Rights.
 * Eilish Press only accepts email proposals for children's non-fiction titles with human rights or anti-racism themes.

Submission Guidelines Accepts query by email. All unsolicited manuscripts are returned unopened. Accepts artworks/images (send digital files as jpegs).
Fiction Publishes Young Adult titles.
  * Eilish Press only accepts email proposals for fiction titles with human rights or anti-racism themes.
Submission Guidelines Accepts query by email. All unsolicited manuscripts are returned unopened. Accepts artworks/images (send digital files as jpegs).
Tips Eilish Press only publishes works for children that have non-sexist, non-racist, humanitarian themes.

Emma Treehouse Ltd
Little Orchard House, Mill Lane, Beckington, Somerset, BA11 6SN
- 01373 831215
- 01373 831216
- info@emmatreehouse.com
- www.emmatreehouse.com

Contact Director, David Bailey; Creative and Editorial Director, Richard Powell
Established 1992
Imprints Treehouse Children's Books
Insider Info Catalogue is available online.
Non-Fiction Publishes Children's Activity and Gift titles.
Submission Guidelines Accepts query with SAE, or via email.
Fiction Publishes Children's Board books and Activity titles.
Submission Guidelines Accepts query with SAE, or via email.
Recent Title(s) *Big Bath Book*, Illustrated by Ana Martin-Larranaga (Plastic Bath Book); *Best Friends*, Illustrated by Gerald Hawksley (Novelty Board Book)
Tips A specialist creator of books for children aged from 0–5 years. Emma Treehouse have a worldwide audience and international recognition for their innovative concepts. Novelty, Cloth, Feel, Flap and books with a sound concept are included in the company's list. Publishes in the UK as Treehouse Children's Books and acts as a packager for international co-editions (see entry under Packagers). Do not send unsolicited manuscript submissions, and contact via email with ideas only.

Everyman's Library
Northborough House, 10 Northborough Street, London, EC1V 0AT
- 020 7566 6350
- 020 7490 3708
- books@everyman.uk.com

- www.randomhouse.com/knopf/classics/
Parent Company The Random House Group Ltd
Contact Publisher, David Campbell
Established 1906
Fiction Publishes Children's classic titles.
  * No new titles, only publishes classic reprints.
Submission Guidelines Does not accept submissions.
Tips Titles aimed at anyone (children and adults) interested in classic literature/world writing. Submissions cannot be accepted since titles are mainly reprints of 'classic' literature.

Faber & Faber Ltd
3 Queen Square, London, WC1N 3AU
- 020 7465 0045
- 020 7465 0034
- gachildren@faber.co.uk
- www.faber.co.uk

Contact Chief Executive, Stephen Page; Editorial Director (Children's), Julia Wells
Established 1929
Insider Info Publishes 300 titles per year (including adult books). Payment is via royalty, along with varying advances. Submissions accompanied by SAE will be returned. Aim to respond to manuscripts within 12 weeks (submissions for adult titles only). Catalogue is available online and via email to: gacatalogue@faber.co.uk
Non-Fiction Publishes Children's and Young Adult titles on the following subjects:
  Art, Creative Non-fiction, Entertainment/Games, History, Humanities, Multicultural, Music/Dance, Recreation, Science, Sports, Travel, Film, Music.
Submission Guidelines Accepts agented submissions only for text. Illustrators may send electronic samples to gadesign@faber.co.uk
Fiction Publishes Children's and Young Adult's novels and drama titles.
Submission Guidelines Accepts agented submissions only for text. Illustrators may send electronic samples to gadesign@faber.co.uk
Poetry Publishes Children's Poetry titles.
Recent Title(s) *Forbidden Truths*, Herbie Brennan (History/Archaeology); *Do the Creepy Thing*, Graham Joyce (Teenage Novel); *The Books of Whispers*, Julie O'Callaghan (Poetry)
Tips Although Faber & Faber accept submissions for adult poetry, they do not accept any children's submissions at all.

Fidra Books

60 Craignook Road, Edinburgh, EH3 3PJ
- 0131 343 3118
- info@fidrabooks.co.uk
- www.fidrabooks.co.uk

Contact Vanessa Robertson
Insider Info Catalogue is available online.
Fiction Publishes Children's and Young Adult titles.
  * Reprints of children's fiction only.
Submission Guidelines Accepts query with SAE.
Recent Title(s) *Run Away Home*, Elinor Lyon
Tips Fidra Books is a new publishing company, specialising in reprinting some of the best children's fiction from the 20th Century. Please only approach Fidra if you are interested in reissuing a work of children's fiction. A background in book selling provides the publisher with an awareness of authors that are in demand, yet whose books are hard to find. There is a definite policy of only publishing books that the publisher likes.

Flame Tree Publishing

Crabtree Hall, Crabtree Lane, London, SW6 6TY
- 020 7386 4700
- 020 7386 4701
- info@flametreepublishing.com
- www.flametreepublishing.com

Parent Company The Foundry Creative Media Company Ltd
Contact Publisher/Creative Director, Nick Wells
Established 1992
Insider Info Catalogue is available online.
Non-Fiction Children's Gift books and Activity titles on the following subjects:
  Art, Education, History, Hobbies, Animals.
Recent Title(s) *Enchanted Jigsaw Book* (Illustrated Activity); *Fantastic Press-Out Racing Cars* (Illustrated)
Tips Also publishes stationary items and other gifts for children (and adults).

Floris Books

15 Harrison Gardens, Edinburgh, EH11 1SH
- 0131 337 2372
- 0131 347 9919
- floris@florisbooks.co.uk
- www.florisbooks.co.uk

Contact Managing Director, Christian Maclean; Children's Editor, Gale Winskill
Established 1977
Imprint(s) Flyways
  Kelpies

Insider Info Payment is via royalties. Catalogue and manuscript guidelines are available online.
Non-Fiction Publishes Children's Illustrated books and Activity titles on the following subjects:
  Art, Crafts, General Activities.
Submission Guidelines Accepts query with SAE/ proposal package (including outline, three sample chapters and SAE). No email submissions. Freelance illustrators may send samples in, but are not guaranteed a reply.
Fiction Publishes Historical, Children's, Regional and Scottish titles.
  * All fiction is for children under 12. The *Kelpies* series are Scottish novels, for either 7–10 or 9–12 year olds.
Submission Guidelines Accepts query with SAE/ proposal package (including outline, three sample chapters and SAE). No email submissions. No children's picture book submissions. Freelance illustrators may send samples in but are not guaranteed to receive a reply. Specific details on how to submit a proposal for the Kelpies series are on the website.
Recent Title(s) *Bees and Honey, from Flower to Jar*, Michael Weiler; *Story of the Wind Children*, Sibylle von Olfers (Picture Book)
Tips Floris Books publishes books for children and adults, including fiction and non-fiction books in which the subject matter is predominantly Scottish in content. Research has found that there is a huge demand for books encompassing modern settings, with contemporary situations and characters to which today's children can relate. That does not rule out historical fiction, but more modern titles are currently being prioritised.

Forward Press

Remus House, Coltsfoot Drive, Woodston, Peterborough, PE2 9JX
- 01733 898099
- 01733 313524
- info@forwardpress.co.uk
- www.forwardpress.co.uk

Established 1989
Imprint(s) Poetry Now
  Anchor Books
  Triumph House
  Need2Know
  New Fiction
  Spotlight Poets
  Writers' Bookshop
  Pond View

Insider Info Average lead time is three months.
Non-fiction Publishes Children's Educational guides.

71

Fiction Publishes Children's Picture books and Educational fiction.

Poetry Publishes Children's Poetry titles.

 * The website details specific calls for submissions under particular themes, these change regularly.

Submission Guidelines Submit two sample poems by email. Poems submitted for the monthly themes may be sent by post or email. If posting, write your name and address on each piece separately. If emailing, enter the theme name in the subject box.

Recent Title(s) *Dan the Handyman and Betty Busy's Cottage*, Philip Demonte (Picture book);

Tips Forward Press are the largest publisher of new poetry for both children and adults in the world. All poets published by Forward Press or any of its imprints, are automatically entered into the Top 100 Poets of the Year competition. Forward Press also publishes short stories (New Fiction imprint, launched 1992), biographies, educational titles, general non-fiction (Pond View Books imprint), books for writers, and a series of books which address the problems/situations that ordinary people encounter in their everyday lives (Need2Know imprint). The main remit of the company however, remains to publish poetry.

Foulsham Publishers (W Foulsham & Co Ltd)

The Publishing House, Bennetts Close, Slough, Berkshire, SL1 5AP

- 01753 526769
- 01753 535003
- marketing@foulsham.com
- www.foulsham.com

Contact Publisher/Managing Director, B.A.R. Belasco

Established 1819

Imprint(s) Quantum
 Arcturus Publishers Ltd

Insider Info Submissions accompanied by SAE will be returned. Catalogue available free on request and online. Manuscript guidelines available online (see 'Contact' for authors' information).

Non-Fiction Publishes Children's Illustrated titles on the following subjects:
 Entertainment, History, Animals.

Submission Guidelines Accepts query with SAE/ proposal package addressed to the Editorial Department (including outline, sample chapter(s), chapter breakdown showing proposed structure, consumer profile defining target market, information on other books in same area, explaining how your title is different, and your author biography). No email submissions are accepted and material is not returned unless SAE is enclosed.

Recent Title(s) *1001 Gruesome Facts*, Helen Otway

Tips The children's list is extremely small compared to the adult list, and there may be limited opportunities in this area.

Frances Lincoln

4 Torriano Mews, Torriano Avenue, London, NW5 2RZ

- 020 7284 4009
- 020 7485 0490
- flcb@frances-lincoln.com
- www.franceslincoln.com

Contact Managing Director, John Nicoll

Established 1977

Insider Info Publishes 100 titles per year (including adult books), Catalogue available online.

Non-Fiction Publishes Illustrated Children's titles on the following subjects:
 Animals, Crafts, History, Education, Outdoors, Environment, General Reference topics, Activities.

Submission Guidelines Submit completed manuscript. Will review artwork photos as part of the manuscript package.

Fiction Publishes Children's Picture books and Young Adult titles.

Submission Guidelines Submit completed manuscript.

Recent Title(s) *Noko's Suprise Party*, Fiona Moodie (Picture Book); *Colours: A First Art Book*, Lucy Micklethwait (Young Children's Non-Fiction)

Tips Frances Lincoln publish high quality illustrated books, with special emphasis on the world around us and its diversity.

Gairm Publications

29 Waterloo Street, Glasgow, G2 6BZ

- 0141 221 1971
- 0141 221 1971

Non-Fiction Publishes Children's and Young Adult's Illustrated Gaelic titles.

 * Texts are in Gaelic language only.

Fiction Publishes Children's and Young Adult's Gaelic titles.

 * Texts are in Gaelic language only.

Tips Titles are aimed at fluent Gaelic readers and students.

Geddes & Grosset

David Dale House, New Lanark, ML11 9DJ

- 01555 665000
- 01555 665694
- ron@gandg.sol.co.uk

⊕ www.geddesandgrosset.co.uk
Contact Publisher, Ron Grosset
Established 1989
Non-Fiction Publishes Children's Reference titles.
Submission Guidelines Accepts query with SAE.
Submit completed manuscript.
Fiction Publishes Children's titles.
Submission Guidelines Accepts query with SAE.
Submit completed manuscript.
Tips Unsolicited submissions will be accepted only with correct SAE. Scottish titles are of particular interest.

Glowworm Books Ltd
Broxburn, EH52 5LH
⊕ www.glowwormbooks.co.uk
Contact Ann Jungman
Established 1999
Non-Fiction Publishes Children's titles.
Submission Guidelines Queries only, no unsolicited manuscripts.
Fiction Publishes Children's titles.
Submission Guidelines Queries only, no unsolicited manuscripts.
Recent Title(s) *The History of Scotland*, Judy Paterson
Tips Formed by the merger of Glowworm Books and the Amaising Publishing house, known for its *Maisie* books. Glowworm continues to publish the *Maisie* titles, but has since branched out into other areas such as children's history, and works with a few different authors.

Gomer Press/Gwasg Gomer
Llandysul Enterprise Park, Llandysul, Ceredigion, SA44 4JL
☎ 01559 362371
🖷 01559 363758
✉ children@gomer.co.uk
⊕ www.gomer.co.uk
Contact Publishing Director, Mairwen Prys Jones; Editor, Viv Sayer (English Books for Children, Pont Books); Editor, Sioned Lleinau (Welsh Books for Primary School Children); Editor, Helen Evans (Welsh Books for Secondary School Children); Editor, Rhiannon Davies (Welsh Educational Resources for Children)
Established 1892
Imprint(s) Gomer
 Pont Books
Insider Info Publishes 120 titles per year (including adult books). Aims to respond to proposals and

manuscripts within one month. Catalogue and manuscript guidelines available online.
Non-Fiction Publishes Textbooks and Educational titles on the following subjects:
 Primary and Secondary Education
 * Many texts are in Welsh language.
Submission Guidelines Accepts query with SAE, or via email, with proposal package (including outline, one sample chapter and your author biography).
Fiction Publishes Children's Picture books and Young Adults' Welsh titles.
Poetry Publishes Children's Welsh Poetry collections.
Submission Guidelines Accepts query with SAE, or via email, with proposal package (including outline, one sample chapter and your author biography).
Recent Title(s) *Anifeiliad Aaron: 2 Carla*, Emily Huws (Children's Fiction); *Bywyd Am Fywyd*, Mair Wynn Hughes (Teenage Fiction)
Tips Gomer Press is Wales' largest independent publisher, publishing books from Wales, about Wales. They work in Welsh and in English, for children and adults. Do not send whole manuscripts to an editor, a sample chapter and a synopsis will be sufficient to start. It would also be useful to include a CV and an outline of the sales strengths of the proposal. As the publisher receives a large number of manuscripts for consideration every week, they advise authors to be patient.

Gullane Children's Books
Winchester House, 259–269 Old Marylebone Road, London, NW1 5XJ
☎ 020 7616 7200
🖷 020 7616 7201
⊕ www.pinwheel.co.uk
Parent Company Pinwheel Limited (division of Alligator Books)
Insider Info Catalogue available online.
Non-Fiction Publishes Children's/Juvenile and Illustrated titles.
Submission Guidelines Accepts entire manuscript with SAE for children's picture books (up to 800 words).
Fiction Publishes Children's Picture books and Illustrated fiction titles.
Submission Guidelines Accepts entire manuscript with SAE for children's picture books (up to 800 words).
Recent Title(s) *Ten in the Bed,* Jane Cabrera (Picture Book); *The Human Body*, Janet Sack (Non-Fiction)
Tips Within Pinwheel, a specialist children's publisher, the Gullane imprint publishes fairly traditional picture books for which submissions are

sought. Titles submitted for consideration should be pitched at children aged seven or younger.

Gwasg Pantycelyn
Lon Dewi, Caernarfon, Gwynedd, LL55 1ER
☎ 01268 672081
✆ 01268 677823
✉ gwasgpantycelyn@ukonline.co.uk
Non-Fiction Publishes Children's Welsh and English language titles.
Fiction Publishes Children's Welsh and English language Fiction titles.
Tips Has published a collection of around 150 books for adults and children. Books tend to reflect the social and cultural history of Wales.

Hachette Livre UK
338 Euston Road, London, NW1 3BH
☎ 020 7873 6000
✆ 020 7873 6024
🌐 www.hachette.com
Parent Company Hachette Livre Publishing Group
Contact CEO, Tim Hely Hutchinson
Established 1993
Imprint(s) Divisions:
 Hachette Children's
 Hachette Livre Australia
 Hachette Livre Ireland
 Hachette Livre Scotland
 Headline
 Hodder Education
 Hodder & Stoughton General
 Hodder & Stoughton Religious
 John Murray
 Little, Brown Book Group
 Octopus Publishing Group
 Orion Publishing Group Ltd
 Chambers Harrap Publishers Ltd
 The Watts Publishing Group
Tips See the entries for Hachette Children's Books; Hodder Education; Hodder & Stoughton Religious; Little, Brown; Octopus Publishing Group and The Watts Publishing Group for more information on children's publishing at Hachette Livre.

Hachette Children's Books
338 Euston Road, London, NW1 3BH
☎ 020 7873 6000
✆ 020 7873 6024
🌐 www.hodderheadline.co.uk
Parent Company Hachette Livre UK
Contact Managing Director, Marlene Johnson

Established 2005
Imprint(s) Franklin Watts
 Orchard Books
 Wayland
Insider Info Catalogue available online (see www.wattspublishing.co.uk for Franklin Watts and Orchard Books imprints).
Non-Fiction Publishes Children's Gift and Reference titles on the following subjects:
 Animals, Crafts, History, Hobbies, Science, General Information, including Special Needs, Reading Development, Citizenship and PSHE.
Submission Guidelines Agented submissions only.
Fiction Publishes Picture book and Novelty titles.
Submission Guidelines Agented submissions only.
Tips Now reports directly to Hachette Livre UK, following the closure of Hodder Headline.

Haldane Mason Ltd
PO Box 34196, London, NW10 3YB
☎ 020 8459 2131
✆ 020 8728 1216
✉ info@haldanemason.com
🌐 www.haldanemason.com
Contact Director, Sydney Francis; Director, Ron Samuel
Established 1995
Imprint(s) Red Kite Books
Non-Fiction Publishes Children's Illustrated Gift titles.
 * Children's books are published under the Red Kite imprint
Submission Guidelines Accepts query with SAE to Sydney Francis. Submit proposal package (including outline, and sample chapter(s)).
Tips Currently commissioning in the area of illustrated non-fiction for children. All submissions must be accompanied by SAE if material is to be returned.

HarperCollins Publishers Ltd
77–85 Fulham Palace Road, Hammersmith, London, W6 8JB
☎ 020 8741 7070
✆ 020 8307 4440
✉ info@harpercollins.co.uk
🌐 www.harpercollins.co.uk
Parent Company HarperCollins Worldwide (Division of News Corporation)
Contact Chief Executive and Publisher, Victoria Barnsley
Established 1819
Imprint(s) Collins (Division)

General Books (Division)
Press Books (Division)

Insider Info Publishes 1,500 titles per year (including adult titles). Catalogue and manuscript guidelines available online.

Non-Fiction Publishes Children's and Young Adult's Illustrated, Multimedia and Reference titles, and Dictionaries on the following subjects:
 Alternative Lifestyles, Art, Contemporary Culture, Cooking/Foods/Nutrition, Education, Entertainment/ Games, History, Hobbies, Humanities, Language/ Literature, Music/Dance, Nature/Environment, Recreation, Science, Sports, Travel, Film and Television tie-ins.

Submission Guidelines Agented submissions only.
Fiction Publishes Children's and Young Adult's novels and Picture books.

Submission Guidelines Agented submissions only.
Recent Title(s) *How to Catch a Star*, Oliver Jeffers (Picture Book); *Alone on a Wide Wide Sea,* Michael Morpurgo (Novel)

Tips HarperCollins only accepts submissions from literary agents, or previously published authors, but may consider submissions that are accompanied by a positive assessment from a manuscript assessment agency.

HarperCollins Publishers Ltd – General Books Division
77–85 Fulham Palace Road, Hammersmith, London, W6 8JB
- 020 8741 7070
- 020 8307 4440
- customerservice@harpercollins.co.uk
- www.harpercollins.co.uk

Parent Company HarperCollins Publishers Ltd
Contact Managing Director, Amanda Ridout
Imprint(s) HarperCollins Children's Books
 HarperFiction
 HarperCollins
 Voyager
 HarperThorsons
 HarperElement
 HarperEntertainment
 HarperSport
 Tolkien and Estates
 HarperCollins Crime & Thrillers
 HarperCollins Audio

Insider Info Catalogue available online at: www.harpercollinschildrensbooks.co.uk
Non-Fiction Publishes Children's and Young Adult's Illustrated, Multimedia and Reference titles, and Dictionaries on the following subjects:

 Alternative Lifestyles, Art, Contemporary Culture, Cooking/Foods/Nutrition, Education, Entertainment/ Games, History, Hobbies, Humanities, Language/ Literature, Music/Dance, Nature/Environment, Recreation, Science, Sports, Travel, Film and Television tie-ins.

Submission Guidelines Agented submissions only.
Fiction Publishes Children's and Young Adult's novels and Picture books.

 * Books published under license include: *Mary-Kate and Ashley, Noddy, The Hulk, Spiderman, The Simpsons, The Magic Roundabout, Dr Seuss* and *Paddington Bear.*

Submission Guidelines Agented submissions only.
Tips HarperCollins Children's Books is a division within the General Books division of HarperCollins Publishers Ltd. They only accept submissions from literary agents or previously published authors, but may consider submissions that are accompanied by a positive assessment from a manuscript assessment agency.

HarperCollins Children's Books
77–85 Fulham Palace Road, Hammersmith, London, W6 8JB
- 020 8741 7070
- 020 8307 4440
- enquiries@harpercollinschildrensbooks.co.uk
- www.harpercollinschildrensbooks.co.uk

Parent Company HarperCollins Publishers Ltd – General Books Division
Contact Publishing Director, Gillie Russel (Fiction); Publishing Director, Sue Buswell (Picture Books)
Insider Info Catalogue available online.
Non-Fiction Publishes Children's and Young Adult's Illustrated, Multimedia and Reference titles, and Dictionaries on the following subjects:
 Alternative Lifestyles, Art, Contemporary Culture, Cooking/Foods/Nutrition, Education, Entertainment/ Games, History, Hobbies, Humanities, Language/ Literature, Music/Dance, Nature/Environment, Recreation, Science, Sports, Travel, Film and Television tie-ins.

Submission Guidelines Agented submissions only.
Fiction Publishes Children's and Young Adult's novels and Picture books.

Submission Guidelines Agented submissions only.
Recent Title(s) *Have a Crazy Christmas with Dr. Seuss!*; *Across the Wall*, Garth Nix (Teen Fantasy)
Tips HarperCollins Children's Books is a division within HarperCollins General Books, itself a division of HarperCollins Publishers Ltd. They publish fiction, picture books and audiobooks for children of all ages, including young adults. Various intellectual

properties are also published under licence by the imprint including *Spiderman, Paddington Bear* and *The Simpsons*. HarperCollins only accepts submissions from literary agents or previously published authors, but may consider submissions that are accompanied by a positive assessment from a manuscript assessment agency.

HarperEntertainment
77–85 Fulham Palace Road, Hammersmith, London, W6 8JB
- 020 8741 7070
- 020 8307 4440
- customerservice@harpercollins.co.uk
- www.harpercollins.co.uk

Parent Company HarperCollins Publishers Ltd – General Books Division
Contact Managing Director, Amanda Ridout
Imprint(s) HarperCollins Audio
 HarperCollins Entertainment
 HarperSport
Insider Info Catalogue available online.
Non-Fiction Publishes Children's Audio cassettes, Illustrated and Multimedia titles on the following subjects:
 Entertainment/Games, Sports, Film/Television tie-ins.
Submission Guidelines Agented submissions only.
Fiction Publishes Children's and Film/Television tie-in titles, Comic books and Audio books.
Submission Guidelines Agented submissions only.
Recent Title(s) *Peter Jackson: A Film-maker's Journey*, Brian Sibley (Biography); *That Hideous Strength*, C.S. Lewis (Novel)
Tips HarperCollins Entertainment publishes humour and media related non-fiction books, from film companions to autobiographies, to various types of television and cinema tie-ins for children and adults. HarperSport publishes sporting guides, biographies of athletes and sporting figures and general interest sports titles. HarperCollins Audio publishes recordings of HarperCollins fiction and non-fiction titles, for both children and adults. HarperCollins as a whole only accepts submissions from literary agents or previously published authors, but may consider submissions that are accompanied by a positive assessment from a manuscript assessment agency.

Hodder & Stoughton Religious
338 Euston Road, London, NW1 3BH
- 020 7873 6051
- 020 7873 6059
- religious-sales@hodder.co.uk

- www.hodderheadline.co.uk

Parent Company Hachette Livre UK
Contact Managing Director, Jamie Hodder-Williams; Publishing Director, Judith Longman; Editorial Director, David Moloney
Established 1868
Imprint(s) Hodder Christian Books
Insider Info Catalogue available free online on request.
Non-Fiction Publishes Children's titles on the following subjects:
 Guidance, Health/Medicine, Religion, Spirituality.
Submission Guidelines Accepts proposal package (including outline, sample chapter(s), author biography, SAE and marketing and/or publicity information, if available).
Fiction Publishes Spiritual and Religious Children's titles.
Tips Hodder Christian Books publishes various Christian books and bibles for children and adults, as well as religious teaching resources. Hodder & Stoughton Religious accepts unsolicited manuscripts, ideally with in-depth market research of similar titles and a brief author biography and publishing history. Full details are available on the website. Now reports directly to Hachette Livre UK, following the closure of Hodder Headline.

Honno Welsh Women's Press
Canolfan Merched y Wawr, Vulcan Street, Aberystwyth, SY23 1JH
- 01970 623150
- 01970 623150
- post@honno.co.uk
- www.honno.co.uk

Contact Publishing Manager, Lindsay Ashford; Editor, Caroline Oakley
Established 1986
Insider Info Publishes eight titles per year (including adult books). Payment is via royalties. Aims to respond to proposals and manuscripts within three months. Catalogue available online on request. Manuscript guidelines available online via the website.
Fiction Publishes Children's and Young Adult's Novels, Short Story Collections, Translation, and Welsh Fiction titles.
Submission Guidelines Accepts proposal package (including outline and 50 pages) but please note that they are not actively seeking to publish children's or teenage work at the moment.
Recent Title(s) *Who's Afraid of the Bwgan Wood?*, Anne Lewis (Children's Fantasy)

Tips Honno is an independent co-operative press run by women and committed to publishing the best in Welsh women's writing for adults and children. Most of Honno's titles are written in English, but it also publishes books in Welsh. Honno only considers for publication the work of women who are Welsh, living in Wales, or have a significant Welsh connection. Please call if you are unsure if you meet this requirement, and they can advise you.

House of Lochar
Isle of Colonsay, Argyll, PA61 7YR
- 01951 200323
- 01951 200323
- lochar@colonsay.org.uk
- www.houseoflochar.com

Contact Chairman, Kevin Byrne; Managing Director, Georgina Hobhouse
Established 1995
Imprint(s) Colonsay Books
 West Highland Series
Insider Info Payment is via royalties. Catalogue available online. Manuscript guidelines are available on the website.
Fiction Publishes Children's, Regional and Scottish titles.
Submission Guidelines Accepts query with SAE and proposal package (including outline and sample chapter(s)), addressed to the 'Marketing Agents' at: Highland Media, Taigh na h-Alba, 35 High Street, South Queensferry, EH30 9HN, or telephone: 0131 331 2700.
Recent Title(s) *The Stone Men*, Murray Herbert (Novel)
Tips House of Lochar is a specialist Scottish publisher with a particular remit to print quality books on a number of subjects, including Scottish history, traditions and other titles of general Scottish interest. The children's list, however, is very small compared to the rest of the programme, which is made up mainly of adult non-fiction.

Hutchinson Children's Books
61–63 Uxbridge Road, London, W5 5SA
- 020 7840 8648
- 020 7233 6058
- childrenseditorial@randomhouse.co.uk
- www.randomhouse.co.uk/childrens

Parent Company Random House Children's Books
Insider Info Catalogue is available online.
Fiction Publishes Children's and Activity titles.
Submission Guidelines Accepts proposal package (including outline and one sample chapter).

Recent Title(s) *More and More Rabbits*, Nicholas Allen (Picture Book); *Little Red Train Magnetic Playbook*, Benedict Blathwayt (Activity Book).
Tips Specialise in hardback children's books.

Icon Books Ltd
The Old Dairy, Brook Road, Thriplow, Cambridge, SG8 7RG
- 01763 208008
- 01763 208080
- info@iconbooks.co.uk
- firstname.lastname@iconbooks.co.uk
- www.iconbooks.co.uk

Contact Managing Director, Peter Pugh; Publishing Director, Simon Flynn; Editorial Director, Duncan Heath; Editor, Lucy Leonhardt
Established 1991
Imprints Wizard Books
Non-Fiction Publishes Children's and Young Adult's titles on the following subjects:
 Sport, History, Science, Games, Activities.
Submission Guidelines Query with SAE. Send submission proposals only, not full manuscripts.
Fiction Publishes Children's Fiction titles for ages seven and upwards.
 * Children's books are largely published by the Wizard Books imprint (see separate entry).
Submission Guidelines Query with SAE.
Recent Title(s) *Fighting Fantasy: The Beast is Loose*, Steve Jackson and Ian Livingstone (Fantasy Novel)
Tips Icon Books is a small independent British publisher specialising in thought provoking books for both children and adults. Having tended to publish in series, Icon is now increasingly publishing individual titles.

The Islamic Foundation
Markfield Conference Centre, Ratby Lane, Markfield, Leicestershire, LE67 9SY
- 01530 244944
- 01530 244946
- i.foundation@islamic-foundation.org.uk
- www.islamic-foundation.org.uk

Insider Info Catalogue available online.
Non-Fiction Publishes Children's titles on Islam.
Tips The Islamic Foundation was established as a centre for education, training, research and publication. The foundation promotes the highest standards of publications for children and adults, related to Islam, and publish only on subjects relating to Islam.

Ivy Publications

72 Hyperion House, Somers Road, London, SW2 1HZ

☎ 020 8671 6872

🖷 020 8671 3391

Contact Proprietor, Ian Burton-Simmonds

Established 1989

Insider Info Authors paid by royalty.

Non-Fiction Publishes Children's Non-fiction on the following subjects:

Education, History, Science, Travel.

* No Gardening or Cookery

Submission Guidelines Accepts query with SAE. Submit proposal package (including outline, two sample chapters and SAE).

Fiction Publishes Children's Fiction titles.

* No Science Fiction

Submission Guidelines Accepts query with SAE. Submit proposal package (including outline, two sample chapters and SAE).

Tips Proposals are preferable to full manuscripts.

Jane Nissen Books

Swan House, Chiswick Mall, London, W4 2PS

✉ jane@nissen.demon.co.uk

🌐 www.janenissenbooks.co.uk

Contact Jane Nissen

Insider Info Publishes approximately four titles per year. Catalogue available online.

Non-Fiction Publishes out of print Children's titles.

Fiction Publishes out of print Children's Fiction.

Poetry Publishes out of print Children's Poetry.

Tips Publishes reprints of out of print children's books only, no new titles. Suggestions for 'forgotten classics' are welcome.

Jonathan Cape Children's Books

61–63 Uxbridge Road, London, W5 5SA

☎ 020 7840 8648

🖷 020 7233 6058

✉ childrenseditorial@randomhouse.co.uk

🌐 www.randomhouse.co.uk/childrens

Parent Company Random House Children's Books

Insider Info Catalogue is available online.

Non-fiction Publishes Children's and Young Adult Entertainment and Activity titles.

Fiction Publishes Children's and Young Adult novels.

Submission Guidelines Accepts proposal package (including outline and one sample chapter). Accepts photocopied samples of illustrations.

Recent Title(s) *Roald Dahl Address Book 2007*

Tips Agented submissions are strongly preferred.

Kevin Mayhew Publishers

Buxhall, Stowmarket, Suffolk, IP14 3BW

☎ 01449 737978

🖷 01449 737834

✉ info@kevinmayhewltd.com

🌐 www.kevinmayhewltd.com

Contact Chairman/Commissioning Editor, Kevin Mayhew

Established 1976

Imprint(s) Palmtree Press

Insider Info Payment is via royalties. Catalogue free on request, online. Manuscript guidelines available online.

Non-Fiction Publishes Children's titles on the following subjects:

Music/Dance (Sacred/Religious Music), Hymns, Religion.

Submission Guidelines Accepts query with SAE/ proposal package (including outline, one sample chapter and SAE).

Recent Title(s) *C Mail*, Tony Bower; *Boring Bible: New Testament Heroes*, Andy Robb

Tips The company holds a unique position, in that its products are targeted in equal measure to members of all Christian denominations. Whilst they continue to strive and pray for unity within the Church, Kevin Mayhew Publishers believe that it is possible to serve the whole Church of God. Many of their products, for children and adults, enjoy broad appeal across the many streams. Please note that online submissions are not accepted, and a hard copy of all manuscripts is required, together with a one page synopsis.

Kingfisher Publications Plc

New Penderel House, 283–288 High Holborn, London, WC1V 7HZ

☎ 020 7903 9999

🖷 020 7903 4979

🌐 www.kingfisherpub.com

Parent Company Houghton Mifflin Co (see entry under European & International Publishers)

Established 1973

Insider Info Catalogue available online or by email.

Non-Fiction Publishes Children's Encyclopedias, Activity books and Reference titles on the following subjects:

History, Language/Literature, Nature/Environment, Religion, Science, Maths, Technology.

Fiction Publishes Humour, Children's Picture books, Pre-school, Toddler and Gift titles.
Poetry Publishes Children's Poetry.
Recent Title(s) *The Fire Thief Fights Back*, Terry Deary (Novel); *Ask Dr K Fisher about Animals* (Illustrated Reference)
Tips Kingfisher is part of the Boston based publisher Houghton Mifflin Co. It is well known for its children's educational reference titles and picture books. Kingfisher does not accept unsolicited material.

Kinglake Publishing
16 B Praed Street, London, W2 1NS
- online form
- www.kinglakepublishing.co.uk

Contact Commissioning Editor, R.S. Byram (Non-Fiction); Commissioning Editor, H.L. Byram (Fiction & Educational)
Established 2004
Imprint(s) Kinglake Non-Fiction
 Kinglake Religion
 Kinglake Fiction
Insider Info Publishes 30 titles per year (including adult books). Receives approximately 250 queries and 80 manuscripts per year. Five per cent of books published are from first-time authors, ten per cent of books published are from unagented authors. Five per cent of books published are author subsidy-published, based on an estimation of market reach. Payment is via royalty (on retail price), with 0.08 (per £) minimum and 0.12 (per £) maximum. Does not offer an advance. Average lead time is six months, with simultaneous submissions not accepted. Submissions accompanied by SAE will be returned. Aims to respond to queries within two days, proposals within five days and manuscripts within 14 days. Catalogue is available with SAE, or by email. Manuscript guidelines are available by email.
Non-Fiction Publishes Children's and Young Adult's Educational Textbooks.
Submission Guidelines Accepts initial queries by email only (including outline and short letter).
Fiction Publishes Young Adult's Science Fiction, Adventure and Romance titles.
 * Kinglake looks for quality in narrative and dialogue.
Submission Guidelines Accepts initial queries by email only (including outline and short letter).
Tips Kinglake publishes books for a popular/general readership, or a carefully worked out niche market. Initial queries must be by email. Research all author subsidy publishing options carefully before committing.

Ladybird Books
80 Strand, London, WC2R 0RL
- 020 7010 3000
- 020 7010 6060
- ladybird@uk.penguingroup.com
- www.ladybird.co.uk

Parent Company Penguin Group (UK)
Insider Info Submissions accompanied by SAE will be returned. Catalogue and manuscript guidelines are available online.
Non-Fiction Publishes Children's Illustrated books with an emphasis on key skills and home learning.
Submission Guidelines Accepts queries with SAE or completed manuscripts. Will accept artworks/images (send digital files as jpegs).
Fiction Publishes Children's and Picture book titles, including classic tales.
 * Most Ladybird story titles tend to be part of an already established series.
Submission Guidelines Accepts query with SAE or submit completed manuscript.
Recent Title(s) *Noisy, Noisy Fairies*, Emma Dodd (Illustrator)
Tips The well known Ladybird list covers illustrated books for children aged 0–8 years old, with an emphasis on key skills and home learning. The list also encompasses classic children's stories and children's favourites, such as *Meg and Mog*, and *Angelina Ballerina*.

Lion Hudson Plc
Wilkinson House, Jordan Hill Road, Oxford, OX2 8DR
- 01865 302750
- 01865 302757
- enquiries@lionhudson.com
- www.lionhudson.com

Contact Commissioning Editor, Lois Rock (Children's Books); Commissioning Editor, Carol Jones (Children's Books)
Established 1971
Imprint(s) Lion
 Lion Children's Books
 Candle
 Monarch
Insider Info Publishes 160 titles per year (including adult books). Receives approximately 1,000 queries and 500 manuscripts per year. Three per cent of books published are from first-time authors, 90 per cent of books published are from unagented authors. Payment is via royalty (on wholesale price), or outright purchase. Average lead time is one year, with simultaneous submissions accepted.

Submissions accompanied by SAE will be returned. Aims to respond to queries within one week, proposals within two months and manuscripts within three months. Catalogue is free on request and available online. Manuscript guidelines are available online.

Non-Fiction Publishes Children's and Young Adult's Christian themed Illustrated titles.

Submission Guidelines Submit a synopsis and covering letter by mail, clearly stating which imprint you are submitting to (details of which may be found on the website). For children's books this is likely to be Lion Children's. Illustrators should send 72dpi colour jpegs or PDFs addressed to the Art Director, to: webmaster@lionhudson.com.

Tips All Lion Hudson books are written by people who are happy to be called Christians and reflect a Christian world view.

Little, Brown Book Group

Brettenham House, Lancaster Place, London, WC2E 7EN
- ☎ 020 7911 8000
- ☎ 020 7911 8100
- ✉ info@littlebrown.co.uk
- 🌐 www.littlebrown.co.uk

Parent Company Hachette Livre UK
Contact CEO and Publisher, Ursula Mackenzie
Established 1988
Imprint(s) Abacus
Atom
Little, Brown
Orbit
Sphere
Virago Press

Insider Info Submissions accompanied by SAE will be returned. Aims to respond to proposals within eight weeks. Catalogue available online.

Fiction Publishes Children's Science Fiction and Fantasy titles.

* Children's Fiction is published through the Atom imprint.

Submission Guidelines Accepts query with SAE/ proposal package (including outline, three sample chapters, and covering letter).

Tips Formerly known as The Time Warner Book Group, Little, Brown reverted to its original name following purchase by Hachette Livre UK. The company publishes a wide range of paperback and hardcover fiction and non-fiction across its many imprints. See the Atom entry for more details on its children's list.

Little Tiger Press

1 The Coda Centre, 189 Munster Road, London, SW6 6AW
- ☎ 020 7385 6333
- ☎ 020 7385 7333
- ✉ info@littletiger.co.uk
- 🌐 www.littletigerpress.com

Parent Company Magi Publications
Contact Editorial, Jude Evans and Stefanie Stansbie
Insider Info Aims to respond to manuscripts within two months. Catalogue and manuscript guidelines are available online.

Fiction Publishes Picture and Novelty book titles for the 0–7 age group.

Submission Guidelines Accepts completed manuscripts by post with SAE. Manuscripts must be no longer than 750 words. Accepts colour photocopied illustrations, never originals.

Recent Title(s) *Ted, Bo and Diz*, Jason Chapman (Picture Book); *Can't you Sleep Dotty?*, Tim Warnes (Picture Book)

Tips Little Tiger Books focus on contemporary and innovative books for young children (Key Stage 1) that are also fun for adults. They publish board books, picture books, character books, gift books, home learning and books suitable for use in schools and pre-schools.

Lorenz Books

Hermes House, 88–89 Blackfriars Road, London, SE1 8HA
- ☎ 020 7401 2077
- ☎ 020 7633 9499
- 🌐 www.lorenzbooks.com

Parent Company Anness Publishing
Contact Chairman/Managing Director, Paul Anness; Publisher/Partner, Joanna Lorenz (Creative Issues)
Established 1994
Insider Info Publishes 140 titles each year (including adult books). Catalogue available online.

Non-Fiction Publishes Children's Illustrated titles on the following subjects:
History, Nature/Environment, Recreation, Sports.

Recent Titles *The Deadly World of Bugs, Snakes, Spiders, Crocodiles and Hundreds of other Amazing Reptiles and Insects*

Tips Lorenz Books is the trade sales imprint for new hardback titles at Anness Publishing Ltd. It includes the Aquamarine list of upmarket lifestyle directories. Its children's list is relatively small compared to the adult programme.

The Lutterworth Press

PO Box 60, Cambridge, CB1 2NT

☎ 01223 350865

📠 01223 366951

✉ publishing@lutterworth.com

🌐 www.lutterworth.com

Established 1700s

Imprint(s) James Clarke & Co.
 Acorn Editions

Insider Info Catalogue and manuscript guidelines are available online.

Non-Fiction Publishes Children's and Young Adult's Illustrated Reference and Textbook titles on the following subjects:
 Art, Crafts, Education, Literature, Sports, Leisure, History, Nature/Environment, Religion.
 * The Lutterworth Press specialise in adult and children's religious titles, alongside their general and scholarly non-fiction lists.

Submission Guidelines No children's submissions accepted.

Fiction Publishes Children's Picture books, Novels and Short stories.

Submission Guidelines No submissions for children's fiction accepted.

Poetry Publishes Children's Poetry.

Recent Title(s) *Lost People of Malplaquet*, Andrew Dalton (Children's Fiction)

Tips The company ethos is still to provide high quality publishing for children (and adults) with an emphasis on moral values. No manuscripts are accepted for any children's books, whether fiction or non-fiction.

Macmillan Publishers Ltd

Brunel Road, Houndmills, Basingstoke, Hampshire, RG21 6XS

✉ fiction@macmillan.co.uk/nonfiction@macmillan.co.uk

🌐 www.macmillan.com

Parent Company Verlagsgruppe Georg von Holtzbrink GmbH

Contact Chief Executive, Richard Charkin

Established 1843

Imprint(s) Macmillan Education (Division)
 Palgrave Macmillan (Division)
 Pan Macmillan Publishers (Division)
 Nature Publishing (Subsidiary)

Non-Fiction Publishes Children's and Young Adult Textbooks, Reference and Scholarly titles.

Fiction Publishes Children's General Fiction titles.

Tips The Macmillan Group and its divisions cover: education publishing, including English language teaching (ELT); academic publishing, including reference, science, technological and medical; fiction and non-fiction book publishing (for both children and adults); and publishing services including distribution and production. For more information, see the individual division entries.

Macmillan Children's Books

20 New Wharf Road, London, N1 9RR

☎ 020 7014 6000

📠 020 7014 6001

✉ children@macmillan.co.uk

🌐 www.panmacmillan.com

Parent Company Pan Macmillan Publishers (Macmillan Publishers Ltd)

Insider Info Catalogue available online.

Non-Fiction Publishes Children's and Young Adult's Illustrated titles.

Submission Guidelines Does not accept unsolicited submissions. Accepts agented submissions only.

Fiction Publishes Picture books, Young Adult's and Children's titles.

Submission Guidelines Accepts agented submissions only.

Poetry Publishes Children's Poetry titles.

Submission Guidelines Accepts agented submissions only.

Recent Title(s) *Tyrannosaurus Drip*, Julia Donaldson, David Roberts (Picture Book); *Crusade*, Elizabeth Laird (Novel); *Wow! Events that changed the world*, Philip Ardagh (Educational)

Tips Macmillan Children's Books produce a diverse and quality list of fiction and non-fiction, aimed at children aged 0–16 years.

Magi Publications

1 The Coda Centre, 189 Munster Road, London, SW6 6AW

☎ 020 7385 6333

📠 020 7385 7333

✉ info@littletiger.co.uk

🌐 www.littletigerpress.com

Contact Editorial, Jude Evans and Stefanie Stansbie

Imprint(s) Little Tiger Press
 Caterpillar Books

Insider Info Aims to respond to manuscripts within two months. Catalogue and manuscript guidelines are available online.

Fiction Publishes Picture and Novelty book titles for the 0–7 age group.

Submission Guidelines Accepts completed manuscripts by post with SAE. Manuscripts must be no longer than 750 words. Accepts photocopied samples of artwork/images.

Recent Title(s) *1,2,3 Little Fish* (Board Book); *Shhh!*, Julia Sykes and Tim Warnes (Character Book)

Tips Magi Press publish solely under their two imprints. Little Tiger focus on books for children aged up to seven, whereas Caterpillar mainly focus on books for children aged up to three (see separate entries).

Mantra Lingua

Global House, 303 Ballards Lane, London, N12 8NP

- ☎ 020 8445 5123
- 🖷 020 8446 7745
- ✉ sales@mantralingua.com
- 🌐 www.mantralingua.com

Contact Managing Director, M. Chatterji; Commissioning Editor, Henriette Barkow

Established 1984

Insider Info Aims to respond to proposals and manuscripts within two months. Catalogue available online. Manuscript guidelines are available online.

Non-Fiction Publishes Children's Gift books and Multimedia titles.

Fiction Publishes Children's Multimedia, Picture books, Translation and Young Adult titles.

Submission Guidelines Accepts query with SAE or via email with proposal package (including a 250 word synopsis and sample chapter(s)), or completed manuscript. Manuscripts should be no longer than 1,200 words for picture books and 2,500 words for junior fiction.

Submission details to: mishti@mantralingua.com

Recent Title(s) *Sahir Goes to the Dentist* (Chris Petty); *Floppy's Friends*, Guido Van Genechten

Tips MantraLingua is a UK based publishing house that supplies bilingual resources around the world, focusing on connecting languages for children. With increased mobility of populations across the globe, e.g. Brazilians in Japan, Malis in Sweden, and Indians in Gambia, MantraLingua aim to develop titles that encourage integration of new communities in various societies. Calls for submissions for particular series are advertised on the website.

Marion Boyars Publishers Ltd

24 Lacy Road, London, SW15 1NL

- ☎ 020 8788 9522
- 🖷 020 8789 8122
- ✉ catheryn@marionboyars.com
- 🌐 www.marionboyars.co.uk

Contact Director, Catheryn Kilgarriff; Editor, Rebecca Gillieron (Fiction)

Established 1960s

Insider Info Catalogue and manuscript guidelines available online.

Fiction Publishes Children's Picture book titles.

Submission Guidelines Agented submissions only.

Recent Title(s) *Zoe and her Zany Animals*, Illlustated by Marjorie Dumortier

Tips A literary, independent publishing house based in South West London. Renowned for being adventurous and sometimes controversial, they mainly publish adult titles in the areas of new fiction and non-fiction in the fields of film, music, social theory, philosophy and feminism. Review the children's list in the catalogue for an idea of the types of books published.

Meadowside Children's Books

185 Fleet Street, London, EC4A 2HS

- ☎ 020 7400 1092
- 🖷 020 7400 1037
- ✉ info@meadowsidebooks.com
- 🌐 www.meadowsidebooks.com

Parent Company DC Thomson

Established 2003

Insider Info Publishes 100 titles per year. Receives approximately 2,000 queries and 2,000 manuscripts per year. 50 per cent of books published are from first-time authors, 25 per cent of books published are from unagented authors. Payment is via royalty (on retail price). Average lead time is six months, with simultaneous submissions accepted. Submissions accompanied by SAE will be returned. Aims to respond to queries within three months. Catalogue is available with SAE, or by email. Manuscript guidelines are available online.

Fiction Publishes Children's Picture books, Novelty books and Young Adult titles.

Submission Guidelines Accepts proposal package (including outline, and three sample chapters) by email if possible (although a hard copy back-up is appreciated). Illustration samples should be supplied digitally.

Poetry Publishes Children's Poetry.

Submission Guidelines Accepts proposal package (including outline and three sample poems) by email if possible (although a hard copy back-up is appreciated).

Mercier Press Ltd

Mercier Press, Douglas, Cork, Republic of Ireland

- ☎ 00353 21 489 0621

☎ 00353 21 489 9887

✉ info@mercierpress.ie

🌐 www.mercierpress.ie

Contact Commissioning Editor, Eoin Purcell

Established 1944

Imprint(s) Marino Books

Insider Info Aim to respond to proposals within two months. Catalogue available online. Manuscript guidelines available online.

Non-Fiction Publishes Children's Humorous Irish interest titles.

Submission Guidelines Accepts query with SAE, or via email with proposal package (including outline, sample chapter(s), author biography).
Submission details to: commissioning@mercierpress.ie

Fiction Publishes Children's Picture books, Short Story collections and Novels.

Recent Title(s) *Irish Legends for the Very Young* , Niamh Sharkey (Picture Book); *Stories of Old Ireland for Children,* Eddie Lenihan (Short Stories)

Tips Mercier Press is Ireland's oldest independent publishing house, based in Cork. Today they focus mainly on history, folklore and politics for adults, although not exclusively, and they do have a children's list. Please bear in mind that they publish mainly for the Irish market, and as such the list focuses on Irish interest titles.

Michael O'Mara Books Ltd

16 Lion Yard, Tremadoc Road, London, SW4 7NQ

☎ 020 7720 8643

📠 020 7627 8953

✉ enquiries@mombooks.com

✉ firstname.lastname@mombooks.com

🌐 www.mombooks.com

Contact Director (Commissioning), Lindsay Davies; Director (Editorial), Toby Buchan

Established 1985

Imprint(s) Buster Books (Children's)

Insider Info Publishes 70 titles per year (including adult titles). Average lead time is six months, with simultaneous submissions accepted. Submissions accompanied by SAE will be returned. Catalogue is available with SAE. Manuscript guidelines are available online.

Non-Fiction Publishes Children's Gift, Illustrated, Educational and Novelty titles.
 * Children's titles are published by Buster Books (see separate entry).

Submission Guidelines Accepts proposal package (including outline, two to three sample chapters, your publishing history, author biography and SAE) and artworks/images (send photocopies).

Fiction Publishes Children's Board books and Picture book titles.
 * Children's titles are published by Buster Books (see separate entry).

Submission Guidelines Does not accept fiction submissions.

Miles Kelly Publishing Ltd

The Bardfield Centre, Great Bardfield, Essex, CM7 4SL

☎ 01371 811309

📠 01371 811393

✉ info@mileskelly.net

🌐 www.mileskelly.net

Contact Publisher, Jim Miles; Publisher, Gerard Kelly

Established 1996

Imprint(s) Miles Kelly
 Bardfield Press

Insider Info Publishes 100 titles per year. Catalogue available online and via email.

Non-Fiction Publishes Children's Gift book and Reference titles.

Submission Guidelines No unsolicited manuscripts.

Fiction Publishes Children's Illustrated titles.

Submission Guidelines No unsolicited manuscripts.

Poetry Publishes Children's Illustrated Poetry.

Submission Guidelines No unsolicited manuscripts.

Recent Title(s) *100 Great Poems*, Various (Poetry collection); *100 Things You Should Know About Ancient Egypt*, Jane Walker (Reference)

Tips Above all, Miles Kelly's aim has been to make top quality books that are enjoyable, attractive and useful, with fresh and innovative features that appeal to a wide readership. Also packages books for other publishers (see entry under Packagers).

National Trust Books

151 Freston Road, London, W10 6TH

☎ 020 7314 1400

📠 020 7314 1401

🌐 www.anovabooks.com

Parent Company Anova Books Company Ltd

Established 2005 (became an imprint of Anova)

Insider Info Catalogue available online.

Non-Fiction Publishes Children's Gift books, Activity books and Illustrated titles on the following subjects: Heritage, Gardening, Craft, Cooking, History, Nature/Environment, Regional, Science.
 * Books may reflect works done by the trust to preserve and protect coastline, countryside and

buildings, and aim to educate people about the importance of the environment and of preserving our heritage for future generations.

Recent Title(s) *Arts & Crafts Needlepoint*, Beth Russell

Nightingale Books

Sheraton House, Castle Park, Cambridge, CB3 OAX

✆ 01223 370012

✉ 01223 370040

✉ editors@pegasuspublishers.com

🌐 www.pegasuspublishers.com

Parent Company Pegasus Elliot MacKenzie Publishers Ltd

Insider Info Catalogue and manuscript guidelines available online.

Non-Fiction Publishes Children's Illustrated Reference and Educational titles.

Submission Guidelines Submit proposal package (including outline and two sample chapters).

Fiction Publishes Multimedia, Fables and Myths, Picture books, Teenage Literature and 'Chick Lit'.

Submission Guidelines Submit proposal package (including two sample chapters).

Poetry Publishes Contemporary Poetry titles.

Submission Guidelines Accepts queries.

Tips Specialises in children's fiction and educational resources. Detailed guidelines, hints and tips are available on the website, and should be read thoroughly before submitting any material.

O Books

The Bothy, Deershot Lodge, Park Lane, Ropley, Hants, SO24 0BE

✆ 01962 773768

✉ 01962 773769

✉ john.hunt@o-books.net

🌐 www.o-books.com

Parent Company John Hunt Publishing Ltd

Contact Publisher, John Hunt (MBS, Religion, History, Psychology)

Established 2003

Insider Info Publishes 80 titles per year (including adult books). Receives approximately 1,000 queries and 500 manuscripts per year. 20 per cent of books published are from first-time authors, 80 per cent of books published are from unagented authors. Five per cent of books published are author subsidy published, depending on sales prospects and category of publishing. Payment is via royalty (on wholesale price), with 0.1 (per £) minimum and 0.25 (per £) maximum. Average lead time is 14 months, with simultaneous submissions not accepted.

Submissions accompanied by SAE will be returned. Aims to respond to queries, proposals and manuscripts within two weeks. Catalogue and manuscript guidelines are free on request.

Non-Fiction Publishes Children's Illustrated titles on the following subjects:

Faith, Religion.

Submission Guidelines Accepts complete manuscripts (including outline, your publishing history and author biography).

Fiction Publishes Children's Picture books and Board books.

* Children's fiction normally relates to the Bible, Christianity, other faiths or spirituality either directly or indirectly.

Submission Guidelines Query with SAE.

Tips O Books publish books for people of all faiths, including those who have no faith, although most titles have a spiritual or religious connection. The vast majority of the list (including the adult books) focuses on non-fiction, very little fiction or poetry is published.

The O'Brien Press

12 Terenure Road East, Rathgar, Dublin 6, Republic of Ireland

✆ 00353 1 492 3333

✉ 00353 1 492 2777

✉ books@obrien.ie

🌐 www.obrien.ie

Contact Managing Director, Michael O'Brien; Editorial Administrator, Sarah Bredin

Established 1974

Insider Info Payment is via royalties. Aims to respond to proposals and manuscripts within eight weeks. Catalogue and manuscript guidelines available online.

Non-Fiction Publishes Children's Illustrated Reference titles on the following subjects:

Art, Crafts, History, Nature, Animals.

Submission Guidelines Accepts query with SAE/ proposal package (including outline and two sample chapters). Will review artwork/photos as part of the manuscript package, but only send photocopies.

Fiction Publishes Children's Picture book and Young Adult titles.

Submission Guidelines Accepts query with SAE/ proposal package (including outline and sample chapter(s)).

Recent Title(s) *Castles of Ireland*, Mairéad Ashe FitzGerald; *Shamrock Sean Goes Fishing*, Brian Gogarty, (Children's)

Tips The O'Brien Press is Ireland's leading general publisher of both children's and adult's books. Their list covers a huge range and they are constantly expanding into new and exciting areas. They generally do not publish any children's or adult poetry. The publishers will only accept submissions/proposals/artwork via the post, email submissions will not be considered. Due to the high level of submissions they receive, unsolicited manuscripts will not be returned.

Octopus Publishing Group
2–4 Heron Quays, London, E14 4JP
- 020 7531 8400
- info@octopus-publishing.co.uk
- www.octopus-publishing.co.uk

Parent Company Hachette Livre UK
Contact CEO, Alison Goff
Established Early 1970s
Imprint(s) Bounty Books
Cassell Illustrated
Conran Octopus
Hamlyn
Mitchell Beazley
Philip's
Insider Info Catalogue available online.
Non-Fiction Publishes Children's Illustrated, Multimedia and Educational titles on the following subjects:
Food and Drink, Maps and Cartography, General Reference, Education, History, Crafts, Activities
Recent Title(s) *Outdoor Fun and Games for Kids*, Jane Kemp and Clare Walters
Tips A major cross-platform illustrated publisher for children and adults, however the children's list is extremely small compared to the adults' and there tend to be more books for adults about children, rather than directly for children.

Onlywomen Press
C/O Onlywomen, 40 St. Lawrence Terrace, London, W10 5ST
- 020 8354 0796
- onlywomenpress@btconnect.com
- www.onlywomenpress.com

Contact Lilian Mohin
Established 1974
Insider Info Publishes four titles per year (including adult books). 98 per cent of books published are from first-time authors, 100 per cent of books published are from unagented authors. Payment is via royalty (on retail price). Average lead time is one year, with simultaneous submissions not accepted. Submissions accompanied by SAE will be returned. Aims to respond to queries within one month and

proposals and manuscripts within three months. Catalogue is free on request. Manuscript guidelines are available with SAE, or available online or by email.
Fiction Publishes Children's Picture book titles.
Submission Guidelines Accepts proposal package (including outline, sample pages, your publishing history, author biography and SAE).
Recent Titles *If I had 100 mummies*, Vanda Carter
Tips Publish mainly adult titles (both fiction and non-fiction), with a small backlist of children's titles written by women. Only accepts submissions from female authors. Priority is given to lesbian authors.

Orchard Books
338 Euston Road, London, NW1 3BH
- 020 7873 6000
- 020 7873 6024
- www.wattspublishing.co.uk

Parent Company Hachette Children's Books
Insider Info Catalogue available online.
Fiction Publishes Children's Picture book and Young Adult titles.
Submission Guidelines Agented submissions only.
Tips Titles are aimed at encouraging children of all ages to become avid readers.

Orion Publishing Group Ltd
Orion House, 5 Upper St Martins Lane, London, WC2H 9EA
- 020 7240 3444
- 020 7240 4822
- www.orionbooks.co.uk

Parent Company Hachette Livre UK
Contact Chairman, Armand Nourry; Chief Executive, Peter Roche
Established 1992
Imprint(s) Everyman Classics
Orion
Gollancz
Weidenfeld & Nicholson
Tips Publish books for adults as well as children. The children's list can largely be found under the Orion imprint, through Orion Children's Books (see separate entry).

Orion
Orion House, 5 Upper St Martins Lane, London, WC2H 9EA
- 020 7240 3444
- 020 7240 4822
- www.orionbooks.co.uk

Parent Company Orion Publishing Group Ltd
Contact Managing Director, Lisa Milton; Managing Director - Orion Paperback Division, Susan Lamb
Established 1992
Imprint(s) Orion Fiction
 Orion Children's Books
 Orion Paperback (division)
Insider Info Catalogue available online, download a pdf or use online request form. Also available via email on request.
Non-Fiction Publishes Children's Illustrated Reference titles on the following subjects:
 History, Activities.
Submission Guidelines Accepts agented submissions only.
Fiction Publishes Children's Picture books, Novels and Young Adult titles.
Submission Guidelines Accepts agented submissions only. Illustrators may send in photocopied samples of their work by post to the 'Design Department'. No email submissions. Alternatively, drop originals off at the offices on any Tuesday (you do not have to telephone before or afterwards), at 2.00pm and pick-up after 5.00pm. The Art Director will take your work into the department meeting, look through it and discuss it.
Recent Title(s) *Grizzly Tales 1: Nasty Little Beasts*, Jamie Rix (Children's Illustrated); *My Swordhand is Singing*, Marcus Sedgwick (Novel); *The Second Roman Mysteries Quiz Book*, Caroline Lawrence (Activity Book)

Orion Children's Books
Orion House, 5 Upper St Martins Lane, London, WC2H 9EA
 020 7240 3444
 020 7240 4822
 www.orionbooks.co.uk
Parent Company Orion (Orion Publishing Group)
Contact Publisher, Fiona Kennedy
Established 1992
Insider Info Catalogue available online via request form, or as a downloadable pdf.
Non-Fiction Publishes Children's Illustrated titles on the following subjects:
 Activities, History.
Submission Guidelines Accepts agented submissions only. Illustrators may send in photocopied samples of their work by post to the 'Design Department'. No email submissions. Alternatively, drop originals off at the offices on any Tuesday (you do not have to telephone before or afterwards), at 2.00pm and pick-up after 5.00pm. The

Art Director will take your work into the department meeting, look through it and discuss it.
Fiction Publishes Children's Multimedia, Picture books, Young Adult and General Fiction titles.
 *Children's characters include *Asterix* and *Horrid Henry*.
Submission Guidelines Accepts agented submissions only. Illustrators may send in photocopied samples of their work by post to the 'Design Department'. No email submissions. Alternatively, drop originals off at the offices on any Tuesday (you do not have to telephone before or afterwards), at 2.00pm and pick-up after 5.00pm. The Art Director will take your work into the department meeting, look through it and discuss it.
Recent Title(s) *King Ocean's Flute*, Lucy Coats (Picture Book); *Soul Eater*, Michelle Paver (Novel)
Tips Orion Children's Books publish fiction and non-fiction books for the children's and young adult markets, as well as audio and multimedia material. They do not accept submissions from unknown authors unless they are submitted through a literary agent.

Pan Macmillan Publishers
20 New Wharf Road, London, N1 9RR
 020 7014 6000
 020 7014 6001
 nonfiction@macmillan.co.uk
 fiction@macmillan.co.uk
 children@macmillan.co.uk
 www.panmacmillan.com
Parent Company Macmillan Publishers Ltd
Contact Managing Director, David North
Established 1843
Imprint(s) Boxtree
 Campbell Books
 Macmillan
 Macmillan Children's Books
 Macmillan New Writing
 Pan
 Picador
 Sidgwick & Jackson
 Think Books
 Tor
 Young Picador
Insider Info Catalogue available online via downloadable pdf.
Fiction Publishes Children's Picture books, Novels and Young Adult titles.
Submission Guidelines Accepts agented submissions only.
Poetry Publishes Children's Poetry.

Recent Title(s) *Freddy and the French Fries 2*, David Baldacci (Children's Comedy); *The Harsh Cry of the Heron*, Lian Hearn (Novel)

Tips Although Pan Macmillan does not accept unsolicited/unagented manuscripts there is still a good deal of information for aspiring authors on the website. Please note that the Macmillan New Writing imprint, which is a good way for new writers to get noticed by Macmillan, is not open to writers of children's or young adult books. Please see the entries for Campbell Books, Macmillan Children's Books and Young Picador as these are the major children's imprints within Pan Macmillan.

Pegasus Elliot MacKenzie Publishers Ltd

Sheraton House, Castle Park, Cambridge, CB3 0AX
- 01223 370012
- 01223 370040
- editors@pegasuspublishers.com
- www.pegasuspublishers.com

Contact Senior Editor, D.W. Stern; Editor, R. Sabir
Imprint(s) Vanguard Press
Pegasus
Nightingale Books
Chimera

Insider Info Payment is via royalties. Catalogue available online. Manuscript guidelines available online via the website.
Non-fiction Publishes Children's Illustrated Educational books for pre-schoolers.
Submission Guidelines Accepts query with SAE and proposal package (including outline, two sample chapters, author biography and SAE).
Fiction Publishes Children's and Young Adult titles.
 * Published through the Nightingale Books imprint
Submission Guidelines Accepts query with SAE and proposal package (including outline, two sample chapters, author biography and SAE).
Recent Title(s) *Asteroid*, Mark Cooke (Novel); *Eric And The Secrets Of Egerton*, Anne Worship (Novel)
Tips Concentrates on fiction from international writers, who can bring different talents and cultural experiences to their work for both children and adults. Submissions from new writers are welcomed. Authors may be required to contribute to production costs and this should be researched very thoroughly before committing.

Penguin Group (UK)

80 Strand, London, WC2R 0RL
- 020 7010 3000

- 020 7010 6060
- customer.service@penguin.co.uk
- www.penguin.co.uk

Parent Company Pearson Plc
Contact Group Chairman and Chief Executive, John Makinson; Managing Director, Helen Fraser
Established 1936
Imprint(s) Penguin Press (division)
Penguin General (division)
Penguin Ireland
Penguin Audiobooks
ePenguin
Dorling Kindersley
Puffin
Ladybird Books
Rough Guides
Warne

Insider Info Publishes approximately 4,000 titles per year. Catalogue is available online.
Non-Fiction Publishes Children's Illustrated Reference titles on the following subjects: Astrology, Cooking, Entertainment/Games, History, Language, Nature/Environment, Recreation, Science, Sports, Travel, Film and Television Tie-ins.
Submission Guidelines Accepts agented submissions only.
Fiction Publishes Children's Picture books, Short Story Collections and Young Adult titles.
Submission Guidelines Accepts agented submissions only.
Poetry Publishes a wide selection of Children's Poetry titles.
Submission Guidelines Accepts agented submissions only.
Recent Title(s) *Half Moon Investiagtions*, Eoin Colfer (Novel); *Peekaboo Baby! Mini Gift Book*, Mandy Ross (Board Book)
Tips The group as a whole published 250 first-time writers (including books for adults) in 2005 and although the Penguin Group does not accept unagented submissions, it does have some good information for authors on its website, including advice for aspiring children's fiction authors. See individual entries for Ladybird, Puffin and Dorling Kindersley and Warne for more information on the children's lists.

Pennine Pens

32 Windsor Road, Hebden Bridge, West Yorkshire, HX7 8LF
- 01422 843724
- info@penninepens.co.uk
- www.penninepens.co.uk

Established 1995

Insider Info Catalogue available online.
Non-Fiction Publishes Children's titles on the following subjects:
History, Regional/Local Interest.
Fiction Publishes Children's titles.
Poetry Publishes Children's Poetry.
Recent Title(s) *Animal Antics*, Debjani Chatterjee (Poetry)
Tips Pennine Pens started as a small press for children's and adults' books, and still publishes books by local authors. They were one of the early pioneers of the e-book and continue to mostly publish adult's local interest titles.

Peter Haddock Publishing Ltd
Pinfold Lane Industrial Estate, Bridlington, East Yorkshire, YO16 6BT
☎ 01262 678121
📠 01262 400043
✉ pat.hornby@phpublishing.com
🌐 www.phpublishing.co.uk
Parent Company DC Thompson & Co.
Contact Publisher, Pat Hornby; Creative Director, Jo Ross
Established 1952
Insider Info Catalogue and manuscript guidelines are available online, via the website.
Non-Fiction Publishes Children's Illustrated and Multimedia titles.
Submission Guidelines Send manuscripts, ideas or illustrations either via recorded delivery, addressed to the publisher, or via the online enquiry form as an attachment.
Fiction Publishes Picture books and Children's titles.
Submission Guidelines Send manuscripts, ideas or illustrations either via recorded delivery, addressed to the publisher, or via the online enquiry form as an attachment.

Piccadilly Press
5 Castle Road, London, NW1 8PR
☎ 020 7267 4492
📠 020 7267 4493
✉ books@piccadillypress.co.uk
🌐 www.piccadillypress.co.uk
Contact Publisher/Managing Director, Brenda Gardner
Established 1983
Insider Info Publishes 30 titles per year. Payment is via royalties. Aim to respond to proposals within six weeks. Catalogue and manuscript guidelines are available online.

Non-Fiction Publishes Children's and Young Adult Non-fiction titles on the following subjects:
Child Guidance/Parenting, Teenage Issues.
Submission Guidelines Accepts query with SAE and proposal package (including outline and two sample chapters). Will accept artworks/images (send photocopies).
Fiction Publishes Picture books, Children's and Young Adult's novels.
Submission Guidelines Accepts query with SAE and proposal package (including outline and two sample chapters). Picture books should be 500–1,000 words long (no novelty books). Teenage novels should be between 25,000 to 35,000 words. Accepts artworks/illustrations, but only copies.
Recent Title(s) *Girl Writer: Sleuths and Truths*, Ros Asquith (Novel); *Fergus in the Park*, Tony Maddus (Picture Book)
Tips Piccadilly Press is an independent publisher, specialising in teenage fiction and non–fiction, 'tween' fiction, picture books and parenting books by highly acclaimed authors and illustrators. They publish a range of titles, but there are three strands of publishing on which they focus when commissioning new titles: picture books, teenage fiction, and teenage non-fiction. Check the website for further details.

Picthall and Gunzi
21a Widmore Road, Bromley, Kent, BR1 1RW
☎ 020 8460 4032
📠 020 8460 4021
✉ chris@picthallandgunzi.demon.co.uk
🌐 www.picthallandgunzi.com
Contact Managing Director, Chez Picthall; Publisher and Editorial Director, Christiane Gunzi
Insider Info Catalogue available via email to: sales@picthallandgunzi.com
Non-Fiction Publishes Children's Activity, Board and Picture books.
Tips All titles are aimed at pre-schoolers and are photographically illustrated.

Pinwheel Limited
Winchester House, 259–269 Old Marylebone Road, London, NW1 5XJ
☎ 020 7616 7200
📠 020 7616 7201
🌐 www.pinwheel.co.uk
Parent Company Alligator Books
Contact Managing Director, Andrew Flatt
Imprint(s) Pinwheel Children's Books
Andromeda Children's Books

Gullane Children's Books
Insider Info Catalogue available online.
Non-Fiction Publishes Children's, Cloth, Novelty, Gift, Illustrated, Reference, Dictionary and General Non-fiction titles on the following subjects:
 Baby and Child's Early Learning, Religion, Natural History.
Submission Guidelines Accepts entire manuscript with SAE for children's non-fiction picture books (up to 800 words). Submissions should be addressed to: The Commissioning Editor, Gullane Children's Books.
Fiction Publishes Children's Picture books and Illustrated fiction titles.
Submission Guidelines Accepts entire manuscript with SAE for children's fiction picture books (up to 800 words). Submissions should be addressed to: The Commissioning Editor, Gullane Children's Books.
Recent Title(s) *Cuddle Me Christmas: Reindeer Games*, Melanie Mitchell (Board Book); *Amazing Weather*, Heather Maisner (Non-Fiction)
Tips Specialises entirely in children's publishing. Within the company, Pinwheel Children's imprint concentrates on packaging novelty books (see entry under Packagers), and Andromeda focuses on the 3–12 year old age group, with gift books. Gullane publishes the more traditional picture books, for which submissions are sought. Titles submitted for consideration should be pitched at children aged seven or younger.

Pipers' Ash Ltd
Church Road, Christian Malford, Chippenham, Wiltshire, SN15 4BW
 01249 720563
 0870 056 8916
 pipersash@supamasu.co.uk
 www.supamasu.co.uk
Contact The Manuscript Evaluation Desk (All subjects)
Established 1976
Insider Info Publishes 15 titles per year (including adult titles). Receives 1,200 queries and 800 manuscripts per year. 90 per cent of books published are from first-time authors and 100 per cent are from unagented authors. Payment is via royalty (on retail price) of 0.1 (per £). No advance is offered. Average lead time is six months, with simultaneous submissions not accepted. Submissions accompanied by SAE will be returned. Aims to respond to queries within seven days, proposals within five weeks, and manuscripts within two months. Catalogue and manuscript guidelines are available online.

Non-Fiction Publishes Educational and Textbook titles on the following subjects:
 Creative Non-fiction, History, Humanities, Language/Literature, Marine Subjects, Memoirs, Military/War, Multicultural, Philosophy, Psychology, Recreation, Regional, Sport, Translation (well known classics), Young Adult, Science Fiction (realistic), Local Histories, Stagecraft, True Life 'Problem' Stories.
 * Potential authors should study the market, visit the website, read the guidelines, and beg, borrow or buy sample copies.
Submission Guidelines Accepts query with SAE, or via a telephone call. Will not accept artworks/images.
Fiction Publishes Children's Chapbook Short story titles.
 * Potential authors should study the market thoroughly.
Submission Guidelines Accepts query with SAE, or via a telephone call.
Recent Title(s) *Cubs with a Difference*, Stephen Andrews (Chapbook of bedtime stories)
Tips Titles are aimed at a worldwide readership (mainly adults). Visit the website and read the Pipers' Ash published authors, who have set the high standards for others to follow.

The Playwrights Publishing Company
70 Nottingham Road, Burton Joyce, Nottingham, Nottinghamshire, NG14 5AL
 0115 931 3356
 playwrightspublishingco@yahoo.com
 www.geocities.com/playwrightspublishingco
Contact Partner, Tony Breeze (Drama); Partner, Elizabeth Breeze (Drama)
Established 1990
Insider Info Publish 12 titles per year (including adult titles). Payment is via royalty (on retail price) and performance rights. Simultaneous submissions are not accepted. Submissions accompanied by SAE will be returned. Aims to respond to queries within one day and manuscripts within four weeks. Catalogue is free on request, and available via A4 SAE, online or email. Author guidelines are free on request and available via email.
Fiction Publishes Plays and Drama titles for theatre companies and schools.
 * A template for good scripts is *The Writer's Journey* by Christopher Vogler.
Submission Guidelines Accepts proposal package (including SAE, reading fee of £15 for one act, £30 for full length). Submit completed manuscripts via email. Will not accept artwork/images.
Tips It is strongly recommended that writers read and digest *The Writer's Journey*.

Poolbeg Press

123 Grange Hill, Baldoyle Industrial Estate, Baldoyle, Dublin 13, Republic of Ireland
- 00353 1 832 1477
- 00353 1 832 1430
- info@poolbeg.com
- www.poolbeg.com

Contact Publishing Director, Paula Campbell; Managing Director, Kieran Devlin
Established 1976
Insider Info Catalogue available online.
Non-Fiction Publishes Children's titles on the following subjects:
History, World Affairs, Drugs, Self-help
Fiction Publishes Children's, Young Adult and Irish interest titles.
Recent Title(s) *The Connemara Champion*, Ann Henning (Novel); *Battle of the Somme*, Arthur McKeown (History)
Tips Poolbeg is Ireland's premier popular fiction publishing company and publishes mainly new Irish writers. In terms of children's publishing, the fiction lists are much bigger than the non-fiction lists.

Praxis Books

Crossways Cottage, Walterstone, Herefordshire, HR2 0DX
- 01873 890695
- author@rebeccatope.fsnet.co.uk
- www.rebeccatope.com/praxisbooks.asp

Contact Proprietor, Rebecca Smith
Established 1992
Insider Info Catalogue and manuscript guidelines are available online.
Submission Guidelines Accepts query with SAE.
Fiction Has published one Children's title.
Submission Guidelines Accepts query with SAE.
Tips Praxis Books is a small press, mainly dedicated to the re-issue of the novels of Sabine Baring-Gould. They will also occasionally consider approaches from authors, the door is never completely closed, despite limited cash flow. They have only ever published one children's title, however, and this was a fantasy story.

Prestel Publishing Ltd

4 Bloomsbury Place, London, WC1A 2QA
- 020 7323 5004
- 020 7636 8004
- sales@prestel-uk.co.uk
- www.prestel.com

Contact Commissioning Editor, Philippa Hurd

Established 1924
Insider Info Catalogue available online.
Non-Fiction Publishes Children's Illustrated books on Art.
Submission Guidelines Accepts query with SAE/proposal package (including outline, sample chapter(s) and SAE). Will accept artwork/images.
Recent Title(s) *Where is Jasper Johns?*, Debra Perlman
Tips Although Prestel publish a wider range of non-fiction for adults, the only type of book published for children are educational art books. Titles are published in both English and German.

Priddy Books

4 Crinan Street, London, N1 9XW
- 020 7418 5515
- 020 7418 85507
- website@priddybooks.com
- www.priddybooks.com

Contact Publisher, Roger Priddy
Insider Info Catalogue available online.
Non-fiction Publishes Illustrated Novelty Children's titles.
Fiction Publishes Picture Books and Young Children's fiction.
Recent Title(s) *Dino IQ* (age 5+); *Alien Al* (Novelty Book)
Tips Priddy Books specialise in novelty books, such as cloth books and board books for young children. Books should be designed to stimulate a child's mind and raise awareness of the world around it.

Puffin

80 Strand, London, WC2R 0RL
- 020 7010 3000
- 020 7010 6060
- customer.service@penguin.co.uk
- www.puffin.co.uk

Parent Company Penguin Group (UK)
Contact Managing Director, Francesca Dow; Publishing Director, Fiction, Sarah Hughes; Associate Publisher, Gifts and Novelties, Mandy Suhr; Editorial Director, Picture Books, Louise Bolongaro; Senior Editor, Picture Books, Janice Thompson
Established 1940
Insider Info Catalogue is available online.
Non-Fiction Publishes Children's Gift, Illustrated and Novelty titles on the following subjects:
Film, Popular Culture, Television tie-ins.
* Puffin publishes non-fiction for very young readers, through to teenagers.
Submission Guidelines Agented submissions only.

Fiction Publishes Children's, Humour, Mystery, Novelty, Picture, Teenage and Young Adult titles.
Submission Guidelines Agented submissions only.
Poetry Publishes collections of Poetry for Children and Young Adult readers.
Submission Guidelines Agented submissions only.
Recent Title(s) *Charlie and Lola: My Picnic Sticker Book*, Lauren Child (Novelty Book); *Wild Magic*, Cat Weatherill (Novel)
Tips Puffin is the UK's leading publisher of children's books. It aims its fiction and non-fiction titles at a range of age groups, from younger children, through to teenage and young adult readers.

Ragged Bears Publishing Ltd
Unit 14a Bennett's Field, Southgate Road, Wincanton, Somerset, BA9 9DT
☎ 01963 824184
☎ 01963 31147
✉ info@raggedbears.co.uk
🌐 www.raggedbears.co.uk
Contact Managing Director, Henrietta Stickland; Submissions Editor, Barbara Lamb
Established 1994
Insider Info Publishes up to ten titles per year. Aims to respond to submissions within four months. Catalogue available online.
Non-fiction Publishes Illustrated Novelty Children's titles.
Submission Guidelines Accepts entire manuscript with SAE. Also accepts copies of artworks, no originals.
Fiction Publish Children's Picture Books.
Submission Guidelines Accepts entire manuscript with SAE. Also accepts copies of artworks, no originals.
Recent Title(s) *The Christmas Bear*, Henrietta Stickland; *Battle of the Beasts*, Diz Wallace
Tips Also publish children's greetings cards, activity packs and other gift items.

Random House Children's Books
61–63 Uxbridge Road, London, W5 5SA
☎ 020 8231 6800
☎ 020 8231 6767
✉ childrenseditorial@randomhouse.co.uk
🌐 www.randomhouse.co.uk
Parent Company The Random House Group Ltd
Contact Managing Director, Philippa Dickinson
Imprint(s) The Bodley Head
Corgi Children's Books
David Fickling Books
Doubleday Children's Books
Hutchinson Children's Books
Jonathan Cape Children's Books
Red Fox
Insider Info Catalogue available online.
Non-Fiction Publishes Children's and Young Adult's titles.
Submission Guidelines Accepts agented submissions only. Accepts photocopied artworks/illustrations.
Fiction Publishes Children's Fiction and Picture book titles for children from 0 to 12 plus years.
Submission Guidelines Agented submissions only. Accepts photocopied artworks/illustrations.
Poetry Publishes Children's Poetry.
Submission Guidelines Agented submissions only.
Recent Title(s) *Tiger Ways*, Kes Gray (Author), Nick Sharratt (Illustrator) (Picture Book); *The Spook's Battle*, Joseph Delaney (Novel)
Tips Random House Children's Division merged with Transworld Publishers children's list in 2001, to form Random House Children's Books, and now ranks among the top five children's book publishers in the UK. Although unsolicited manuscripts are not accepted, there is some helpful submission advice on the children's division website.

Ransom Publishing
51 Southgate Street, Winchester, Hampshire, SO23 9EH
☎ 01962 862307
✉ ransom@ransom.co.uk
🌐 http://actinic.thwd.co.uk/
Contact Managing Director, Jenny Ertle (Literacy for ages five to adult)
Established 1995
Insider Info Publishes 50 titles per year. Receives approximately 200 queries and 150 manuscripts per year. Ten per cent of books published are from first-time authors and 90 per cent are from unagented authors. Payment is via royalty (on retail price) with 0.1 (per £) minimum. Average lead time is six months with simultaneous submissions accepted. Submissions accompanied by SAE will be returned. Aims to respond to queries within one week, proposals within two weeks and manuscripts within two months. Catalogue and manuscript guidelines are free on request and available online.
Non-Fiction Publishes Children's titles on the following subjects:
Education (Literacy), Young Adult (Easy Reads), Various topics suitable for Children and Young Adults.
* Ransom specialise in books for reluctant and struggling readers, and in adult literacy.

Submission Guidelines Accept queries via email. Will accept artworks/images (send digital files as jpegs).
Fiction Publishes anything suitable for reluctant and struggling readers.

* Ransom publish very little general children's fiction. They are interested primarily in books for reluctant or very poor readers, ages six up to adult.
Submission Guidelines Accepts queries via email. Will accept artworks/images (send digital files as jpegs).
Recent Title(s) *The Boy, The Witch and the Blobber*, Frances Cross; *Boffin Boy and the Invaders from Space*, David Orme
Tips Ransom titles are aimed at children and young adults who are reluctant, or struggling readers, as well as teachers of literacy and special educational needs teachers. Only submit proposals applicable to these areas of interest. Email first to see if the proposal is of interest. When sending materials, always include SAE.

Reader's Digest Association
11 Westferry Circus, Canary Wharf, London, E14 4HE
- 020 7715 8000
- 020 7715 8181
- www.readersdigest.co.uk

Insider Info Catalogue available online.
Non-Fiction Publishes Children's Illustrated and Reference titles on the following subjects:
 Cooking/Foods/Nutrition, Crafts, History, Photography, Travel, General Knowledge.
 * Also publishes magazines, videos and CDs.
Fiction Publishes Children's Classic Fiction and Short Stories.
Tips The main editorial office for Reader's Digest is based in the US.

Reardon Publishing
PO Box 919, Cheltenham, Gloucestershire, GL50 9AN
- 01242 231800
- reardon@bigfoot.com
- www.reardon.co.uk

Contact Director, Nicholas Reardon (All subjects)
Established 1976
Insider Info Publish 15 titles per year (including adult books). Receives approximately 20 queries and ten manuscripts per year. 75 per cent of books published are by first-time authors, 100 per cent are by unagented authors and 50 per cent are author-subsidy published. Payment is via royalty (on retail

price). Average lead time is six months, with simultaneous submissions accepted. Submissions accompanied by SAE will be returned. Aims to respond to queries, proposals and manuscripts within two weeks. Catalogue available online. Manuscript guidelines available via email.
Non-Fiction Publish Children's titles on the following subjects:
 Arts, Crafts, Activities.
Submission Guidelines Accepts query with SAE. Will accept artworks/images (send photocopies or digital files as jpegs).
Fiction Publishes Children's and Young Adult's titles.
Submission Guidelines Accepts query with SAE.
Recent Title(s) *Design and Make for Active Youngsters*, Robert Shayler (Booklet)
Tips Many titles are published in pamphlet or booklet form and a very small percentage of titles are aimed at children (the rest of the programme is made up of the adult list). Research the author-subsidy publishing route thoroughly before committing.

Red Bird Press
Kiln Farm, Brightlingsea, Colchester, Essex, CO7 0SX
- 01206 303525
- 01206 304545
- info@red-bird.co.uk
- www.red-bird.co.uk

Insider Info Catalogue available online.
Fiction Publishes Picture books and Children's Illustrated Fiction titles.
Tips Red Bird specialise in distinctive children's formats featuring 3D vision, glow in the dark, hidden pictures and other special effects. Books are often based on international licensed characters, including those from Disney, Hasbro, Mirage and Fox Kids.

Red Fox
61–63 Uxbridge Road, London, W5 5SA
- 020 7840 8640
- 020 7233 6058
- childrenseditorial@randomhouse.co.uk
- www.randomhouse.co.uk/childrens

Parent Company Random House Children's Books
Insider Info Catalogue available online.
Fiction Publishes Picture books and Children's Fiction titles.
Submission Guidelines Accepts proposal package (including outline, sample chapter(s)). Accepts artworks/images (send photocopies, never originals).

Recent Title(s) *More and More Rabbits*, Nicholas Allan (Picture Book); *Dinosaur Chase!* Benedict Blathwayt (Picture Book)

Tips Agented submissions are strongly preferred, but unagented proposals are considered. The focus of Red Fox tends to be on illustrated books for young children.

Rockpool Children's Books
15 North Street, Marton, CV23 9RJ
- ☎ 01926 633114
- ✉ info@rockpoolchildrensbooks.com
- ⊕ www.rockpoolchildrensbooks.com

Contact Artistic Director, Stuart Trotter
Established 2006
Insider Info Catalogue available online.
Fiction Publishes Picture book titles.
Recent Title(s) *Big Bully Hippo*, Stuart Trotter; *Greedy Grumpy Hippo*, Stuart Trotter

Tips Rockpool is a very new company, and as such only has four books in its current list, all by Artistic Director, Stuart Trotter. More books are planned for the future.

Salariya Book Company Ltd
Book House, 25 Marlborough Place, Brighton, BN1 1UB
- ☎ 01273 603306
- ☎ 01273 693857
- ✉ salariya@salariya.com
- ✉ david.salariya@salariya.com
- ⊕ www.salariya.com

Contact Director, David Salariya
Established 1989
Imprint(s) Book House
Insider Info Catalogue available online.
Non-Fiction Publishes Illustrated and Children's titles.
Recent Title(s) *Scary Creatures: Sharks*, Penny Clarke

Tips Specialises in illustrated information books with a unique appeal for the younger reader. Many Salariya books are aimed at the international market and translated into multiple languages. New titles for the UK are published under the Book House imprint. The publishers do not have submission guidelines, as they commission the vast majority of their titles.

Scholastic Ltd
Villiers House, Clarendon Avenue, Leamington Spa, CV32 5PR
- ☎ 01926 887799
- ☎ 01926 883331
- ✉ enquiries@scholastic.co.uk
- ⊕ www.scholastic.co.uk

Parent Company Scholastic Inc (see entry under European & International Publishers)
Contact Chairman and Chief Executive Officer (USA), Richard Robinson; Manging Director, Miles Stevens-Hoare (Book Fair Division and Book Clubs); Publishing Director, Anne Peel (Education)
Established 1920
Imprint(s) Scholastic Children's Books
Scholastic Educational Publishing
Insider Info Catalogue available online.
Non-Fiction Publishes Children's Illustrated, Multimedia, Reference and Scholarly titles on the following subjects:
Contemporary Culture, Education, History, Nature/Environment, Science and Teaching Materials.
Fiction Publishes Children's books, Picture books and Young Adult titles.
Recent Title(s) *My First Bible Stories*, Eva Moore (Illustrated); *Flora Sugunda*, Ysabeau Wilce (Novel)
Tips Scholastic Ltd publishes fiction, non-fiction and picture books for children and young adults under the Children's Division, which includes Scholastic Children's Books. The Educational Division publishes a wide range of educational and teaching material for primary school teachers, in addition to related magazines. The Direct Marketing Division handles Scholastic book fairs and the children's book clubs.

Scholastic Children's Books
Euston House, 24 Eversholt Street, London, NW1 1DB
- ☎ 020 7756 7756
- ✉ SCBenquiries@scholastic.co.uk
- ⊕ www.scholastic.co.uk

Parent Company Scholastic Ltd
Contact Editorial Director, Caroline Gott (Pre-School); Editorial Director, Charlie Cousins (Non-Fiction); Editorial Director, Kristen Skidmore (Fiction)
Imprint(s) Hippo
Point
Scholastic Fiction
Scholastic Non-Fiction
Scholastic Press
Insider Info Payment is via royalties. Aims to respond to proposals within six months. Catalogue available online.
Non-Fiction Publishes Children's Illustrated, Multimedia and Reference titles on the following subjects:

Contemporary Culture, Education, History, Nature/Environment, Science, Sports and Television/Film tie-ins.

Submission Guidelines Accepts hard copy manuscripts sent to the Editorial Department.

Fiction Publishes Children's Picture books, Television/Film tie-ins and Young Adult's titles.

Submission Guidelines Accepts hard copy manuscripts sent to the Editorial Department.

Recent Title(s) *Alex and the Wigpowder Treasure*, Adrienne Kress

Tips Scholastic Children's Books publish a wide range of fiction, non-fiction, picture and activity books for children of all ages. The Hippo imprint publishes paperback fiction for younger children, whereas the Point imprint specialises in paperback fiction for older children and young adults, including the work of Philip Pullman. Scholastic Press is a specialist hardback imprint.

SCM-Canterbury Press Ltd
13–17 Long Lane, London, EC1A 9PN
- 020 7776 7540
- 020 7776 7556
- admin@scm-canterburypress.co.uk
- firstname@scm-canterburypress.co.uk.uk
- www.scm-canterburypress.co

Contact Publishing Director, Canterbury Press, Christine Smith; Senior Commissioning Editor, SCM Press, Barbara Laing

Established 1986 – SCM Press was acquired by The Canterbury Press Norwich in 1997

Imprint(s) Canterbury Press
SCM Press
Religious and Moral Education Press (RMEP)
Epworth Press

Insider Info Catalogue available free on request and online.

Non-Fiction Publishes Children's and Young Adult's Educational titles on the following subjects: Religion, Spirituality, Translation, Lifestyle, Contemporary Issues, History, Philosophy, Theology, Academic Theology, Poetry, Science, World Religions, and Jewish Studies.

Submission Guidelines Submission and manuscript information available online. Submission details to: barbara@scm-canterburypress.co.uk

Tips SCM Press is the UK's best known publisher of academic theology and provides accessible and rigorous textbooks, reference books and other resources aimed at young people, students and clergy.

Scottish Cultural Press & Scottish Children's Press
Unit 6, Newbattle Abbey Business Park, Newbattle Road, Dalkeith, EH22 3LJ
- 0131 660 4757 (children's)
- 0131 660 6366 (children's)
- info@scottishbooks.com
- www.scottishbooks.com

Contact Directors, Avril Gray and Brian Pugh

Established 1992

Insider Info Payment is via royalties. Aims to respond to proposals within six months. Catalogue and manuscript guidelines are available online.

Non-Fiction Publishes Children's Reference and Educational titles on the following subjects: Activities, Cooking, History, Language/Literature, Regional and Scottish Interest.

Submission Guidelines Accepts query with SAE/proposal package (including outline, one sample chapter, intended market and readership). Will accept artworks/images (send photocopies).

Fiction Publishes Children's Picture books and Young Adult's titles.

Submission Guidelines Not accepting fiction submissions at this time.

Poetry Publishes Children's and Young Adult's Poetry titles.

Submission Guidelines Not accepting poetry submissions at this time.

Recent Title(s) *Discover Scotland's History*, A.D. Cameron (Non-Fiction); *My Mums a Punk*, Various (Poetry)

Tips Scottish Cultural Press is one of the foremost publishers in Scotland, specialising in quality books with a Scottish interest, or connection that goes deeper than simply being set in Scotland. Scottish Children's Press publishes quality Scottish interest books for children of all ages, from graded readers to teacher's resource books, fun and games, to young fiction. Titles are written for, about and by Scottish children, and they aim to encompass Scots, English and Gaelic. As the publishers receive a great quantity of manuscripts, they recommend that prospective authors should phone first to discuss the suitability of the manuscript before sending any work.

Scripture Union
207–209 Queensway, Bletchley, Milton Keynes, Buckinghamshire, MK2 2EB
- 01908 856000
- 01908 856111
- info@scriptureunion.org.uk
- www.scriptureunion.org.uk

Contact Publishing Director, Terry Clutterham
Established 1867
Insider Info Catalogue and manuscript guidelines available online.
Non-Fiction Publishes Children's Multimedia, Reference and Scholarly titles on the following subjects:
 Religion (including Christian faith resources) and Spirituality.
Submission Guidelines Accepts query with SAE/ proposal package (including outline and one sample chapter).
Fiction Publishes Children's Religious (including Bible Stories) and Young Adult titles.
Tips Scripture Union is a non-denominational, Christ-centred international movement, working in partnership with individuals and churches across the world. Their aim is to use the Bible to inspire children, young people and adults to discover God. All books must be sympathetic to the Christian faith. Scripture Union publish very few unsolicited manuscripts.

Serendipity
First Floor, 37–39 Victoria Road, Darlington, DL1 5SF
- 0845 130 2434
- info@serendipitypublishers.com
- www.serendipitypublishers.com

Established 2001
Insider Info Publishes 40 titles per year (including adult titles). Average lead time is six months, with simultaneous submissions accepted. Submissions accompanied by SAE will be returned. Aims to respond to queries within two days and manuscripts within three weeks. Catalogue and manuscript guidelines are free on request.
Non-Fiction Publishes Children's and Young Adult Illustrated Reference titles on the following subjects:
 Education, History, Humanities, Marine Subjects, Nature/Environment, Recreation, Regional, Religion, Science.
Submission Guidelines Accepts query with SAE, or via email. Also accepts completed manuscripts. Will accept artworks/images (send photocopies or digital files as jpegs).
Fiction Publishes Children's and Young Adult Adventure, Ethnic, Fantasy, Humour, Multicultural, Mystery, Picture book, Religious and Science Fiction titles, and Short story collections.
Submission Guidelines Accepts query with SAE, or via email. Also accepts completed manuscripts.
Poetry Publishes Poetry and Poetry in Translation.

Submission Guidelines Accepts query with SAE, or via email (include five sample poems). Also accepts completed manuscripts.

Short Books
3a Exmouth House, Pine Street, Exmouth Market, London, EC1R 0JH
- 020 7833 9429
- 020 7833 9500
- emily@shortbooks.biz
- www.shortbooks.co.uk

Contact Editorial Director, Aurea Carpenter; Editorial Director, Rebecca Nicholson
Established 2000
Insider Info Catalogue and manuscript guidelines available online.
Non-Fiction Publishes Children's Educational and Humour titles on the following subjects:
 Literature, History and Teaching Resources.
 * Short Books strives to bridge the gap between publishing and journalism. They publish general non-fiction titles for adults and children, and offer teaching resources to support classroom orientated books.
Submission Guidelines Accepts query with SAE/ proposal package including outline and two sample chapters. Proposals and chapters must be emailed as attachments.
Fiction Publishes Children's novels.
Recent Title(s) *Who Was... King Henry VIII*, Emma Craigie (History); *Rubies in the Snow*, Kate Hubbard (Novel)
Tips All prospective authors should bear in mind that Short Books are a small company which is inundated with book proposals and manuscripts. They should follow the submissions policy detailed above and should not send unsolicited manuscripts. The publisher will respond by email.

Simon & Schuster UK Ltd
Africa House, 64–78 Kingsway, London, WC2B 6AH
- 020 7316 1900
- 020 7316 0332
- enquiries@simonandschuster.co.uk
- www.simonsays.co.uk

Contact CEO/Managing Director, Ian Stewart Chapman
Established 1924
Imprint(s) Free Press
 Martin Books
 Pocket Books
 Scribner

Simon & Schuster Children's Books (division)
Insider Info Catalogue available online.
Non-Fiction Publishes Children's Gift, Humour, Illustrated, Reference, Educational and Media tie-in titles on the following subjects:
 Contemporary Culture, Cooking/Foods/Nutrition, Creative Non-fiction, History, Language/Literature, Science, Spirituality, Sports, and Travel
Submission Guidelines Accepts agented submissions only.
Fiction Publishes Children's Picture books, Novels and Young Adult's titles.
Submission Guidelines Accepts agented submissions only.
Recent Title(s) *Vampirates: Blood Captain*, Justin Somper (Young Adult Novel); *Dora's River Race* (Nickelodeon Picture Book)
Tips Simon and Schuster has a stable of bestselling international authors. The company publishes a broad range of non-fiction and fiction, for both adults and children. No unsolicited manuscripts are accepted.

Simon & Schuster Children's Books
Africa House, 64–78 Kingsway, London, WC2B 6AH
- 020 7316 1900
- 020 7316 0332
- editorial.enquiries@simonandschuster.co.uk
- www.simonsays.co.uk
Parent Company Simon & Schuster UK Ltd
Contact Publishing Director, Ingrid Selberg
Established 1998
Non-fiction Publishes Children's Illustrated titles and Media tie-ins.
Submission Guidelines Accepts agented submissions only.
Fiction Publishes Children's and Young Adult's Novels and Picture book titles.
Submissions Guidelines Accepts agented submissions only.
Recent Title(s) *The Great Escape*, Natalie Haynes (Children's Fiction); *Pirate Treasure* (Nickelodeon Picture Book)

The Society for Promoting Christian Knowledge (SPCK)
36 Causton Street, London, SW1P 4ST
- 020 7592 3900
- 020 7592 3939
- spck@spck.org.uk
- www.spck.org.uk
Imprint(s) Azure

Sheldon Press
Insider Info Catalogue available online.
Non-Fiction Publishes Children's titles on the following subjects:
 Religion, Spirituality, Biblical Studies, Church History
Submission Guidelines Accepts proposal package (including outline and two sample chapters). Address to Editorial Department (Submissions).
Recent Title(s) *Being Confirmed*, Nick Aitken
Tips Publishes work for both adults and children; students and teachers of theology, lay Christians, spiritual seekers, and a general readership with an interest in Christianity. The list covers a diversity of Christian traditions, from the Evangelical to the Catholic, the conservative to the liberal. The children's titles are aimed at either ages six to eleven, or eleven plus

Southwater
Hermes House, 88–89 Blackfriars Road, London, SE1 8HA
- 020 7401 2077
- 020 7633 9499
- info@anness.com
- www.annesspublishing.com
Parent Company Anness Publishing Ltd
Contact Chairman/Managing Director, Paul Anness; Publisher/Partner, Joanna Lorenz (Creative Issues)
Established 1999
Insider Info Publishes 150 titles per year (including adult books). Catalogue available online.
Non-Fiction Publishes Children's Illustrated titles on the following subjects:
 Cooking/Foods/Nutrition, Crafts, Gardening, History, Recreation, Spirituality and Sports.
Recent Title(s) *Step Into: Aztec and Maya World*, Fiona MacDonald
Tips Southwater is the trade paperback imprint for Anness Publishing Ltd. Its current children's titles tend to focus on history, especially ancient history.

Souvenir Press Ltd
43 Great Russell Street, London, WC1B 3PD
- 020 7580 9307
- 020 7580 5064
- sp.trade@ukonline.co.uk
Contact Managing Director, Ernest Hecht
Imprint(s) Condor
Insider Info Publishes 50 titles per year (including adult titles). Payment is via royalties. Catalogue available free on request and via email.
Non-Fiction Publishes Children's Illustrated and Scholarly titles on the following subjects:

Anthropology/Archaeology, Art/Architecture, Astrology/Psychic, Cooking/Foods/Nutrition, Crafts, Education, History, Hobbies, Nature/Environment, Sports, Theatre, and Magic and the Occult

Submission Guidelines Accepts query with SAE/ proposal package (including outline and two sample chapters).

Fiction Publishes Children's and Young Adult's titles.

Submission Guidelines Accepts query with SAE/ proposal package (including outline and two sample chapters).

Poetry Publishes Poetry titles.

Submission Guidelines Submit sample poems.

Tips Souvenir Press covers a wide range of academic and general non-fiction topics, specialising in spiritual and mystical titles. Fiction and poetry lists are limited in comparison to the non-fiction list, as are children's titles.

Stacey International

128 Kensington Church Street, London, W8 4BH
- 020 7221 7166
- 020 7792 9288
- info@stacey-international.co.uk
- www.stacey-international.co.uk

Contact Editor, Christopher Ind

Established 1973

Insider Info Catalogue available online.

Non-Fiction Publishes Children's Illustrated titles.

* Stacey International publish a range of books to help develop intercontinental relationships and travels. In terms of children's publishing this means illustrated reference books on travel and foreign countries.

Submission Guidelines Accept proposal package, via post or email (including sample chapter, covering letter, market research, intended book specifications and proposed schedule and SAE).

Fiction Publishes Children's Picture books.

Submission Guidelines Accept proposal package, via post or email (including sample chapter, covering letter, market research, intended book specifications and proposed schedule and SAE).

Recent Title(s) *The Illustrated Encyclopaedia of Arabia,* Mary Beardwood; *The First Dog to be Somebody's Best Friend: A Likely Story in Two Bits and a Decide,* Tom Stacey (Picture Book)

Tips In terms of children's publishing, books linked in some way to the Middle East are currently of particular interest.

Storysack

Resource House, Kay Street, Bury, BL9 6BU
- 0161 763 6232
- 0161 763 5366
- hello@resourcehouse.co.uk
- www.storysack.com

Established 1999

Insider Info Catalogue available via online form.

Fiction Publishes Picture books with accompanying Fact books, Parent's guides and Games.

Tips The packages of books and games are highly illustrated and presented in cloth sacks. Titles are aimed at children aged 3+.

St. Pauls Publishing

187 Battersea Bridge Road, London, SW11 3AS
- 020 7978 4300
- 020 7978 4370
- editions@stpauls.org.uk
- www.stpauls.org.uk

Contact Publisher, Andrew Pudussery

Established 1914

Insider Info Publishes 30 titles per year (including adult titles). Catalogue available online.

Non-Fiction Publishes Children's Illustrated and Multimedia titles on the following subjects: Religion, Spirituality and Prayer.

* Through books, magazines, journals, film, radio, television, video and the internet, the Society of St. Paul aims to continue the vision of its founder, James Alberione. That is, to follow in the missionary footsteps of St. Paul the Apostle, by bringing news of Jesus Christ to the world.

Submission Guidelines Accepts query with SAE/ proposal package (including outline) or submit completed manuscript.

Recent Title(s) *Bible Stories for Growing Kids,* Francine Rivers

Tips All proposals should relate to the Catholic faith.

Tamarind Ltd

PO Box 52, Northwood, Middlesex, HA6 1UN
- 020 8866 8808
- 020 8866 5627
- contact@tamarindbooks.co.uk
- www.tamarindbooks.co.uk

Contact Managing Editor, Verna Allette Wilkins

Established 1987

Insider Info Catalogue is available free on request, online, or via email to: catalogues@ tamarindbooks.co.uk

Non-Fiction Publishes Children's and Illustrated titles on the following subjects:
 Education, Ethnic and Multicultural.

Fiction Publishes Children's and Picture book titles.

Recent Title(s) *The Life of Stephen Lawrence*, Verna Allette Wilkins (Biography); *Choices, Choices*, Dawne Allette (Picture Book)

Tips Tamarind publishes multicultural children's books for a multicultural world. Both fiction and non-fiction books are typically picture books, with an age range of two to twelve years. Books are published for both the trade and educational markets, and scope exists for teaching reference material, or classroom aids promoting a positive multicultural image.

Tango Books Ltd

PO Box 32595, London, W4 5YD

- 020 8996 9970
- 020 8996 9977
- sales@tangobooks.co.uk
- www.tangobooks.co.uk

Contact Director, Sheri Safran (Children's Fiction, Non-Fiction)

Established 1982

Insider Info Publishes 20 titles per year. Receives approximately 500 queries and 200 manuscripts per year. 80 per cent of books published are from first-time authors and 90 per cent are from unagented authors. Payment is via royalty (on retail price), or via outright purchase. Average lead time is nine months with simultaneous submissions accepted. Submissions accompanied by SAE will be returned. Aims to respond to queries within 14 days, proposals within 21 days and manuscripts within 30 days. Catalogue is available free on request and online. Manuscript guidelines are free on request, and available online or via email.

Non-Fiction Publishes Children's titles on a wide variety of subjects.
 * Books must be suitable for quality novelty book publication, and suitable for children from the ages of one to fifteen.

Submission Guidelines Accepts query with SAE, or via email. Will accept artworks/images (send digital files as jpegs or copies in the post).

Fiction Publishes Novelty titles.
 * No poetry or rhyming stories. Strong stories are the most important element, novelty elements can be created at a later stage if the book lends itself to them. Must be suitable for a child between the ages of one to eight.

Submission Guidelines Accepts query with SAE or via email. Also accepts completed manuscripts. Will accept artworks/images (send digital files as jpegs, or copies in the post).

Tips Titles are aimed at children, from babies up to age fifteen, as well as schools and specialist markets (particularly in diverse and multicultural areas). Books usually contain no more than 1,000 words and illustrations tend to be unusual and quirky, with Tango not tending to work with 'traditional' children's illustrators. Also acts as a co-edition packager (see entry under Packagers).

Tarquin Publications

99 Hatfield Road, St. Albans, Hertfordshire, AL1 4JL

- 01727 833866
- 0845 456 6385
- info@tarquinbooks.com
- www.tarquinbooks.com

Contact Managing Editor, Andrew Griffin

Established 1970

Insider Info Publishes five titles per year (including adult titles). Payment is via royalties. Catalogue available free on request and online.

Non-Fiction Publishes Children's Education, Multimedia and Scholarly titles on the following subjects:
 Crafts, Hobbies, Science, Optical Illusions, Mirror Reflections, Costume, History and Paper Engineering.
 * Also publishes do-it-yourself pop-up books, and collections of colourful mobiles and gift boxes.

Submission Guidelines Accepts query with SAE/ proposal package (including outline).

Tips Tarquin specialise in papercraft and modelling for both children and adults, but will consider publishing in other areas if there is a strong connection to papercraft. Browse the backlist to get a feel for the specialist books and other products produced by Tarquin.

Templar Publishing

The Granary, North Street, Dorking, RH4 1DN

- 01306 876361
- info@templarco.co.uk
- firstname.lastname@templarco.co.uk
- www.templarpublishing.co.uk

Contact UK Publishing Manager, Rebecca Elliott; Art Director, Mike Jolly

Insider Info Catalogue available online.

Non-Fiction Publishes Children's, Illustrated and Multimedia titles.

* Templar publishes illustrated and interactive books for children of all ages, including the hugely successful *Ologies* series.

Fiction Publishes Children's Multimedia and Picture titles.

* Many of Templar's books have interactive elements such as puppets, pop-outs and unconventional design.

Recent Title(s) *Slam!*, Adam Stower

Tips Virtually all of Templar's books are highly illustrated or interactive in some way, and many are concept driven. For prospective authors, a background in art and design would be helpful.

Ticktock

Unit 2 Orchard Business Centre, North Farm Road, Tunbridge Wells, Kent, TN2 3XF

☎ 01892 509400

✉ editorial@ticktock.co.uk

🌐 www.ticktock.co.uk

Contact Publishing Director, Ruth Owen; Managing Editor, Sophie Furse; Creative Manager, Graham Rich

Established 2002

Imprints Little Ticktock

Insider Info Catalogue available free on request, online and via email to: info@ticktock.co.uk

Non-Fiction Publishes Children's Illustrated books and Educational titles on a variety of National Curriculum and General subjects.

Fiction Publishes Children's Picture books and Novelty books.

Tips All Ticktock books are produced in-house, but the team do work with freelance authors and editors. Most titles are aimed at either the trade or school markets. The Little Ticktock imprint was launched in 2007 and deals with books for pre-schoolers. To contact a member of the editorial team, use firstname_lastname@ticktock.co.uk.

Titan Books

Titan Books, 144 Southwark Street, London, SE1 0UP

☎ 020 7620 0200

📠 020 7803 1990

✉ editorial@titanemail.com

🌐 www.titanbooks.com

Parent Company Titan Publishing Group

Contact Editorial Director, Katy Wild (Film, Television, Graphic Novels)

Established 1981

Insider Info Publishes 220 titles per year (including adult books). Receives approximately 100 queries and 50 manuscripts per year. 15 per cent of books published are from first-time authors. Payment is via royalty (on retail price), or an outright purchase. Simultaneous submissions are accepted. Submissions accompanied by SAE will be returned. Aims to respond in one week to queries, one month to proposals, and three months to manuscripts. Catalogue and author guidelines are free on request.

Fiction Publishes Illustrated Comic, Film and Television tie-in books.

Submission Guidelines No fiction or comic book proposals will be accepted.

Recent Title(s) *Wallace and Gromit: Plots in Space; The Simpson's Big Beastly Book of Bart*

Tips Titan's book publishing output is split between adult non-fiction related to film and television, adult fiction, and illustrated comic and media tie-in books. No children's proposals are accepted, but adult submissions are welcomed, see website for details.

Top That! Publishing Plc

Marine House, Tide Mill Way, Woodbridge, Suffolk, IP12 1AP

☎ 01394 386651

☎ 01394 386011

✉ info@topthatpublishing.com

🌐 www.topthatpublishing.com

Contact Managing Director, Barrie Henderson; Creative Director, Simon Couchman; Editorial Director, Daniel Graham

Established 1999

Imprint(s) Top That! Kids

KUDOS

Tide Mill Press

Insider info Publish approximately 150 children's titles per year. Catalogue available online.

Non-Fiction Publishes Children's General Non-fiction, Gift, Humour and Illustrated titles on the following subjects:

Cooking/Foods/Nutrition, Crafts, Creative Non-fiction, Entertainment/Games, Hobbies.

Submission Guidelines Accepts query via phone before sending in any material.

Fiction Publishes Children's and Multimedia titles and Picture books.

Submission Guidelines Accepts query via phone before sending in any material.

Recent Title(s) *Millie the Millipede*, Erin Ranson

Tips Titles are designed to challenge and stimulate young minds. Most books in the children's ranges are highly illustrated, so it is important to send sample illustrations with any submission. Children's titles are mainly published through the Tide Mill Press and Top That! Kids imprints.

Usborne Publishing Ltd

Usborne House, 83–85 Saffron Hill, London, EC1N 8RT

- ☎ 020 7430 2800
- ✆ 020 8636 3758/020 7242 0974 (Illustrations)
- ✉ mail@usborne.co.uk
- ✉ firstnamelastinitial@usborne.co.uk
- 🌐 www.usborne.co.uk

Contact Managing Director, Peter Usborne; Director, Robert Jones; Art Director, Mary Cartwright

Established 1975

Insider Info Publishes 250 titles per year. Payment via royalty. Aims to respond to manuscripts within six months. Catalogue and manuscript guidelines available online.

Non-Fiction Publishes Illustrated Children's Reference titles on the following subjects: Art/Architecture, Crafts, Entertainment/Games, Hobbies, Language/Literature, Music/Dance, Sports, Puzzle Books.

Submission Guidelines All unsolicited manuscripts will be returned unopened.

Fiction Publishes Children's and Early Years titles, and Picture and Baby Books.

Submission Guidelines Submit proposal package (including outline and three sample chapters) for fiction for children up to twelve years, address to 'Fiction Submissions'. See the detailed manuscript guidelines, available to download from the website, for specific age ranges. Will not accept picture book proposals or manuscripts, however they are always on the lookout for freelance illustrators. Send copies of your work (no originals) to the Art Director at the above address.

Recent Title(s) *True Stories: Survival*, Paul Dowswell (Non-Fiction); *The Gingerbread Man*, illustrated by Elena Temporin (Picture Book)

Tips Usborne is a major independent UK publishing company. Their list includes almost every type of children's book, for babies to young teenagers, and covering a wide range of topics. Usborne will only accept submissions for new children's fiction, not for picture books or non-fiction, as these are commissioned in-house.

Veritas

7–8 Lower Abbey Street, Dublin 1, Republic of Ireland

- ☎ 00353 1 878 8177
- ✆ 00353 1 878 6507
- ✉ sales@veritas.ie
- ✉ firstname.lastname@veritas.ie
- 🌐 www.veritas.ie

Parent Company Veritas Communications

Contact Managing Editor, Ruth Garvey; Commissioning Editor, Donna Doherty

Established 1969

Insider Info Publishes 30 titles per year (including adult books). Payment is via royalty. Aims to respond to proposals and manuscripts within six weeks. Catalogue and manuscript guidelines are available online.

Non-Fiction Publishes Children's titles on the following subjects: Religion, Spirituality, Bible Study.

Submission Guidelines Accepts query with SAE. Submit proposal package (including outline, three sample chapters and author biography). Accepts either printed proposals, or those saved on disk, addressed to Donna Doherty.

Fiction Publishes Illustrated Children's Fiction (often linked to Christianity or Christian values).

Submission Guidelines Accepts query with SAE. Submit proposal package (including outline, three sample chapters and author biography). Accepts either printed proposals, or those saved on disk, addressed to Donna Doherty.

Recent Title(s) *Can I Play Too?*, Noel Lambert (Picture Book)

Tips Veritas is not solely a children's publisher, they also publish religious, spiritual and social resources for adults, all with Christian overtones.

Walker Books

87 Vauxhall Walk, London, SE11 5HJ

- ☎ 020 7793 0909
- ✉ editorial@walker.co.uk
- 🌐 www.walkerbooks.co.uk

Contact Publisher, Jane Winterbotham

Established 1978

Insider Info Aims to respond to queries within three months. Catalogue available online.

Non-Fiction Publishes Children's and Young Adult's, Gift, Illustrated, Audio cassettes and Reference titles. Also Big books, Board books, Character books, and Novelty/Activity books on the following subjects: Early Learning, Activity, Hobby and Craft, Biography, History, Arts, Life Issues, Animals, Environment and Conservation, Feelings, Language, Football, First Concepts.

Submission Guidelines Approach with query in the first instance. Mainly accepts agented submissions. For illustrators, send in sample copies of eight to ten pieces of work, with a typed or dummy manuscript if applicable. Address illustrations to: 'Illustrator Submission, Art Department' and include SAE.

Fiction Publishes Children's and Young Adult's Adventure, Humour, and Science Fiction titles. Also publishes Short Story Collections, Anthologies and Traditional Tales.

Submission Guidelines No fiction or picture book submissions, agented submissions only. For illustrators, send in sample copies of eight to ten pieces of work, with a typed or dummy manuscript if applicable. Address illustrations to: 'Illustrator Submission, Art Department' and include SAE.

Poetry Publishes Children's Poetry titles.

Recent Title(s) *The Robe of Skulls*, Vivien French (Junior Fiction); *Beans on Toast,* Paul Dowling (Early Learning); *Where's Wally*, *Alex Rider*, *Maisy*, and *Curious George* (Walker Character Books)

Tips Due to the huge amount of interest, Walker are no longer accepting unsolicited manuscripts for fiction or picture books. However, they still accept queries for non-fiction titles and continue to invite freelance illustrators to approach them with work (aimed at either fiction or non-fiction).

Warne

80 Strand, London, WC2R 0RL

- 📞 020 7010 3000
- 📠 020 7010 6060
- ✉ customer.service@penguin.co.uk
- 🌐 www.penguin.co.uk

Parent Company Penguin Group (UK)

Contact Managing Director, Sally Floyer

Established 1865 (acquired by Penguin in 1983)

Insider Info Catalogue available online. Manages character licences from classic children's literature. Does not publish brand new titles.

Fiction Publishes Children's Illustrated and Picture book titles.

Recent Title(s) *The Tale of Peter Rabbit*, Beatrix Potter (Board Book)

Tips Warne specialises in book-based children's character properties, including the Beatrix Potter titles and other classic children's titles such as the *Flower Fairies* and *Orlando the Marmalade Cat*. As such, they cannot accept unsolicited proposals. For the main children's publishing programme at Penguin, see the entries for Puffin and Ladybird Books.

The Watts Publishing Group

338 Euston Road, London, NW1 3BH

- 📞 020 7873 6000
- 📠 020 7873 6225
- 🌐 www.wattspublishing.co.uk

Parent Company Hachette Livre UK

Established 1972

Imprint(s) Franklin Watts
Orchard Books
Cat's Whiskers

Insider Info Catalogue available online.

Non-Fiction Publishes Teacher Resources, Young Adult, Big books and Children's titles on the following subjects:
Citizenship and PHSE, Special Needs, Religious Education, Geography - People and Environment, History through story, Social History, Science, Technology, Art, Craft and Music, Hobbies and Pets.
* Education titles are published through the Franklin Watts imprint.

Submission Guidelines Agented submissions only.

Fiction Publishes Children's Picture books, Gift books, Novelty books, Board books, Graded Reading books and Children's classics.

Submission Guidelines Agented submissions only.

Poetry Publishes Children's Poetry titles.

Recent Title(s) *Sex, Puberty and All That Stuff* (age 9–16); *Faraway Farm*, Ian Whybrow

WF Graham

2 Pondwood Close, Moulton Park, Northampton, NN3 6RT

- 📞 01604 645537
- 📠 01604 648414
- ✉ books@wfgraham.co.uk
- 🌐 www.wfgraham.co.uk

Non-Fiction Publishes Children's Colouring and Activity titles.

Recent Title(s) *Birds to Colour; My First Colouring Book*

Tips WF Graham only publish colouring books and related items, therefore they will not accept submissions from children's writers.

Willow Bank Publishers Ltd

16a Bunters Road, Wickhambrook, Newmarket, Suffolk, CB8 8XY

- 📞 0800 731 5258
- ✉ editorial@willowbankpublishers.co.uk
- 🌐 www.willowbankpublishers.co.uk

Contact Christopher Sims

Imprint(s) Willow Books
Derringer Books
Butterfly Books
Fen Books

Insider Info Payment is via royalties. Catalogue and manuscript guidelines are available online.

Non-Fiction Publishes Children's Non-fiction titles.

Submission Guidelines Accepts query with SAE. Submit proposal package (including outline, two sample chapters and SAE).
Fiction Publishes Children's titles.
Submission Guidelines Accepts query with SAE. Submit proposal package (including outline and two sample chapters).
Poetry Publishes Children's Poetry.
Recent Title(s) *White Roads to Akyab*, James Meridew
Tips The Butterfly Books imprint publishes children's non-fiction, fiction and poetry. Willow Bank Publishers may choose to offer either a traditional, or author-funded publishing agreement. Author-funded publishing is for those authors whose work meets the required standard set by their publishing panel, but whose commercial viability is not quite strong enough.

Wizard Books

The Old Dairy, Brook Road, Thriplow, Cambridge, SG8 7RG
- ☎ 01763 208008
- ☎ 01763 208080
- ✉ wizard@iconbooks.co.uk
- 🌐 www.iconbooks.co.uk/wizard

Parent Company Icon Books
Contact Managing Director, Peter Pugh; Publishing Director, Simon Flynn; Editorial Director, Duncan Heath
Established 2002
Insider Info Publishes around four titles per year.
Non-Fiction Publishes Illustrated Children's titles for ages eight to thirteen.
Submission Guidelines Query with SAE. Include a detailed proposal (for what to include in this section, see the website), synopsis, table of contents, sample of writing and CV (listing any relevant previous publications), or author biography.
Fiction Publishes Children's Fiction titles for ages eight to thirteen.
Submission Guidelines Query with SAE. Include a detailed proposal (for what to include in this section, see the website), synopsis, table of contents, sample of writing and CV (listing any relevant previous publications), or author biography.
Recent Title(s) *The Toxic Toadburger Conspiracy*, Ian Hills
Tips Specialises in children's fantasy gaming books. For detailed submission guidelines, visit the website. The current emphasis is for books aimed at children aged nine and older.

Wolfhound Press

Newmarket Hall, Cork Street, Dublin 8, Republic of Ireland
- ☎ 00353 1 453 5866
- ☎ 00353 1 453 5930
- ✉ publishing@merlin.ie
- 🌐 www.merlinwolfhound.com

Parent Company Merlin Publishing
Contact Editorial Manager, Aoife Barrett
Established 1974
Insider Info Catalogue and manuscript guidelines are available online.
Non-Fiction Publishes Children's and General Non-fiction (Irish Interest) titles.
Submission Guidelines Accepts proposal package (including outline, synopsis, one sample chapter, marketing information, author biography and SAE, or IRC for overseas replies). Will accept artworks/images (send photocopies or digital files as jpegs). Send submissions by post or email.
  Submission details to: aoife@merlin.ie
Fiction Publishes Children's Picture books and Novels.
Submission Guidelines Will not be publishing any new children's fiction for the near future.
Poetry Publishes Children's Poetry.
Recent Title(s) *What You See Is What You Get*, Rosemary Furber
Tips Wolfhound Press is well known for producing high quality books of Irish interest, for both adults and children, along with a range of children's books.

The Women's Press

27 Goodge Street, London, W1T 2LD
- ☎ 020 7636 3992
- ☎ 020 7637 1866
- ✉ sales@the-womens-press.com
- 🌐 www.the-womens-press.com

Contact Managing Director, Stella Kane
Established 1978
Imprint(s) Women's Press Classics
  Livewire Books for Teenagers
Insider Info Payment is via royalties. Catalogue available online.
Non-fiction Publish Young Adult/Teenage titles on the following subjects:
  Women's Studies/Issues, Feminism, Relationships, Lifestyle.
Submission Guidelines Agented submissions only.
Fiction Publishes Young Adult/Teenage titles.
Submission Guidelines Agented submissions only.
Recent Title(s) *Perfectly Safe to Eat?*, Vicki Hird; *Those Bones Are Not My Child*, Toni Cade Bambara

Tips A series of up-front, contemporary, issue driven works of fiction and non-fiction for young women are published in the Livewire list. The Women's Press also publishes incisive feminist fiction and non-fiction by outstanding women writers from all round the world. They will only publish books written by women and even then, only if there is a female protagonist, or the book deals with women's issues.

Wordsworth Editions Ltd
8b East Street, Ware, Hertfordshire, SG12 9HJ
- 01920 465167
- 01920 462267
- dennis.hart@wordsworth-editions.com
- www.wordsworth-editions.com

Contact Managing Director, Helen Trayler (Production, Editorial); Director, Derek Wright (Accounts, IT)
Established 1986
Insider Info Publishes 20 titles per year (including adult books). Receives approximately five to ten queries, and six manuscripts from writers each year. 100 per cent of books are from unagented authors. Payment is via outright purchase. Submissions accompanied by SAE will be returned. Catalogue is free on request, and available online and via email. Manuscript guidelines are not available.
Fiction Publish Classic Children's titles.
  * Does not publish living authors of fiction.
Tips Although Wordsworth editions do publish some new non-fiction work for adults, all its children's output is made up of reprints.

Working White Ltd
Chancery Court, Lincolns Inn, Lincolns Road, High Wycombe, Buckinghamshire, HP12 3RE
- 01494 429318
- 01494 429317
- info@workingwhite.co.uk
- www.workingwhite.co.uk

Contact Erica Filler
Imprint(s) Poppy Red
Insider Info Catalogue is available free on request and via email: sales@workingwhite.co.uk
Non-Fiction Publishes Children's Illustrated and Activity titles.
Fiction Publishes Children's titles.
Tips Working White is an independent publisher of co-edition children's books for the international market. Titles are aimed at children of pre-school age, through to young teenagers. Poppy Red is the sister company, which publishes and distributes the books solely in the UK. Working White children's

books are always illustrated and informative, and usually have an extra 'interactive' component such as pop-up, touch and feel sections, or kit-books.

The X Press
PO Box 25694, London, N17 6FP
- 020 8801 2100
- 020 8885 1322
- vibes@xpress.co.uk
- www.xpress.co.uk

Contact Editorial Director, Dotun Adebayo; Publisher, Steve Pope
Established 1992
Imprint(s) Black Classics
  Nia
  20/20
Insider Info Publishes 25 titles per year (including adult titles). Catalogue available online.
Fiction Publishes Children's/Teenage Black interest novels.
Submission Guidelines Submit completed manuscript.
Recent Title(s) *Age Aint Nothin' but a Number*, Yinka Adebayo (Novel)
Tips The X Press has grown into Europe's largest publisher of black interest books. As well as many adult titles, the X Press publishes general black fiction aimed at a younger audience, and aims to take black writing into a new era. Prefers full manuscript submissions rather than proposals, and preferably black interest popular fiction, from black writers.

Y Lolfa Cyf
Talybont, Ceredigion, Wales, SY24 5AP
- 01970 832304
- 01970 832782
- ylolfa@ylolfa.com
- www.ylolfa.com

Contact Managing Director, Garmon Gruffudd; Chief Editor, Lefi Gruffudd
Established 1967
Imprint(s) Dinas
Insider Info Publishes 50 titles per year (including adult titles). Payment is via royalties. Catalogue available online.
Non-Fiction Publishes Children's titles on the following subjects:
  History and Welsh interest.
Fiction Publishes Children's Picture book and Fiction titles.
Recent Title(s) *Dragon and Mousie*, Andrew Fusek Peters and Gini Wade (Picture Book)

Tips Y Lolfa is an independent Welsh publisher specialising in fiction and non-fiction for both children and adults, from, or about Wales. They print in both Welsh and English and also offer services as a commercial print company. The Dinas imprint is a part author subsidised press, for unusual and non-mainstream Welsh interest books. Its aim is to produce interesting and original books, which enhance the variety of books published in Wales.

Young Picador
20 New Wharf Road, London, N1 9RR
- 020 7014 6000
- 020 7014 6001
- www.panmacmillan.com

Parent Company Pan Macmillan Publishers
Established 2002
Insider Info Downloadable pdf and catalogue are available online.
Non-Fiction Young Adult and Teenage titles.
Submission Guidelines Agented submissions only.
Fiction Young Adult and Teenage titles.
Submission Guidelines Agented submissions only.
Poetry Publishes a small amount of Young Adult Poetry.
Submission Guidelines Agented submissions only.
Recent Title(s) *Roundabout*, Rhiannon Lassiter
Tips Concentrates mainly on teenage fiction. The non-fiction and poetry sections of the list are extremely small. No unsolicited submissions.

EDUCATIONAL

Andrew Brodie Publications
38 Soho Square, London, W1D 3HB
- 020 7758 0200
- 020 7758 0222
- childrens@acblack.com
- www.acblack.com

Parent Company A&C Black Publishers Ltd
Insider Info Publishes approximately 20 titles per year. Catalogue available online.
Non-Fiction Publishes Children's Illustrated Educational and Multimedia titles.
 * Titles are aimed at primary and secondary schools and are for children aged between four and fourteen.
Submission Guidelines Accepts postal submissions. Aims to respond to proposals within two months
Recent Title(s) *Get Ready for Starting School*, Andrew Brodie, Judy Richardson
Tips Andrew Brodie Publications publishes reference and education material for children of all ages covering all curriculum subjects. Books are practical in nature including activities and tasks, and easily photocopiable for use as teaching materials.

Anglia Young Books
PO Box 120, 4 Balloo Avenue, County Down, BT19 7BX
- 0800 731 2837
- 0800 027 2833
- info@millpublishing.co.uk
- www.millpublishing.com

Parent Company Mill Publishing
Insider Info Catalogue available online or via email to info@motivationinlearning.com
Non-Fiction Publishes Educational Resources on the following subjects:
 National Curriculum Key Stage 2, History, Reading, Writing.
Submission Guidelines Will accept ideas for new titles, particularly from teachers. Send a brief synopsis. Accepts images/artworks.
Fiction Publishes Children's Historical titles.
 * Should be educational and aimed at Key Stage 2 children.
Tips The editorial office for Anglia Young Books is based in Cambridge, although they can be contacted through the head office, in Northern Ireland.

Atlantic Europe Publishing Co. Ltd
Greys Court Farm, Greys Court, Henley on Thames, Oxfordshire, RG9 4PG
- 01491 628188
- 01491 628189
- enquiries@atlanticeurope.com
- www.atlanticeurope.com

Established 1990
Insider Info Accepts queries via email. Catalogues available online. Publishes the 'Curriculum Vision' Series, quality resources for teachers and students that cover all major curriculum subjects.
Non-Fiction Publishes Children's Educational and Reference titles on the following subjects:

Science, Maths, History, Technology, Geography, English, Spelling, Citizenship and R.E.

Recent Titles *Curriculum Vision: The Ancient Egyptians*, Dr Brian Knopp, Student Workbook

Submission Guidelines Accept emailed submissions only.

Tips Prefer authors with relevant qualifications, such as teachers and other education professionals.

Badger Publishing
15 Wedgwood Gate, Pin Green Industrial Estate, Stevenage, Hertfordshire, SG1 4SU

☎ 01438 356907

🖷 01438 747015

✉ info@badger-publishing.co.uk

🌐 www.badger-publishing.co.uk

Established 1989

Insider Info Catalogue available online. Publishes educational books for foundation stage to year 9.

Non-fiction Publishes Children's Educational and Reference titles on the following subjects:
 All curriculum subjects from foundation to year nine.

Recent Titles *Christian Beliefs and Issues,* one of a series of books covering the 6 major world religions for key stage 3, Michael Keene

Tips Badger Publishing started by selling educational books to schools, but over recent years has developed a publishing programme of its own. Books are aimed at both pupils and teachers.

BBC Active
Edinburgh Gate, Harlow, Essex, CM20 2JE

☎ 01279 623623

🖷 01279 414130

✉ emma.shackleton@pearson.com

🌐 www.bbcactive.com

Parent Company Pearson Education

Contact Editor, Emma Shackleton

Insider Info Catalogue and manuscript guidelines are available online.

Non-Fiction Publishes Children's Multimedia, Scholarly and Textbooks titles on the following subjects:
 Education, Home Learning, Language/Literature and BBC TV Tie-Ins.

Submission Guidelines Accepts proposal package (including synopsis, sample chapters, market research, your publishing history and author biography).

Recent Title(s) *Get Into Spanish*, BBC Active (Language/Multimedia)

*Japanese Language and People,*features a course book, DVD and activity book

Tips BBC Active publishes learning resources for children at home, school and college. The imprint has developed a wide range of innovative and interactive ways of learning to suit all styles, with DVDs, CD-ROMs and online products. Resources cover the school curriculum across modern foreign languages, plus a variety of other skills. Also publish learning resources for adults.

BIS Publications
PO Box 14918, London, N17 8WJ

☎ 020 8880 4066

🖷 020 8880 4067

✉ info@bispublications.com

🌐 www.bispublications.com

Insider Info Catalogue available online.

Non-fiction Publishes Educational titles for children of African descent.

Recent Title(s) *True Friends*, Susan Fayinka; *Mr & Mrs Ken – The Numbers 1 to 10*, Michael Williams and Natalie White

Tips Titles need to inspire black children, many stories feature strong black characters overcoming difficulties.

Brilliant Publications
Unit 10, Sparrow Hall Farm, Edlesborough, Dunstable, Bedfordshire, LU6 2ES

☎ 01525 222292

🖷 01525 222720

✉ priscilla@brilliantpublications.co.uk

🌐 www.brilliantpublications.co.uk

Contact Publisher, Priscilla Hannaford

Established 1993

Insider Info Publishes 12 titles per year. Submissions accompanied by SAE will be returned. Catalogue and manuscript guidelines are free on request, and available online.

Non-Fiction Publishes Children's Reference, Scholarly and Textbook titles on the following subjects:
 Education, Teaching (all school subjects).
 * Does not publish children's picture books.

Submission Guidelines Accepts query with SAE and proposal package (including outline, two sample chapters, author biography, market research, and intended audience).

Recent Title(s) *Jouons Tous Ensemble*, Kathy Williams (French language)

Tips Specialise in producing high quality, well designed materials that make teaching and learning enjoyable and rewarding, for both teachers and pupils. Brilliant Publications are always looking for new book ideas, including book series. Writers should try to sell both themselves and their book strongly in the proposal, and include plenty of information on what makes their book, or series, distinct.

Cambridge University Press
The Edinburgh Building, Shaftesbury Road, Cambridge, CB2 8RU
- 01223 312393
- 01223 315052
- information@cambridge.org
- www.cambridge.org

Contact Chief Executive, Stephen R.R. Bourne; Managing Director - Europe, Middle East & Africa, Andrew Gilfillan; Managing Director – Academic Publishing, Andrew Brown; Publishing Director, Richard Fisher (Humanities & Social Sciences); Publishing Director, Richard Barling (Science, Technology & Medicine); Managing Director - Cambridge Learning, Hanri Pieterse
Established 1534
Insider Info Publishes 1,200 titles per year (including adult academic books). Payment is via royalties. Catalogue available online. Manuscript guidelines are available online.
Non-Fiction Publishes Reference, Scholarly and Technical titles for school children and students on the following subjects:
 Anthropology/Archaeology, Business/Economics, Education, Government/Politics, Health/Medicine, History, Language/Literature, Law, Multicultural, Music/Dance, Nature/Environment, Philosophy, Psychology, Religion, Reading, Writing, Maths, School Curriculum, Science, Transportation.
Submission Guidelines Accepts query with SAE/proposal package (including outline, two sample chapters, your publishing history, author biography).
Recent Title(s) *What a Wreck! Guided Reading Multipack*, John Parker (Literacy)
Tips CUP publishes the finest academic and educational writing from around the world. As a department of the University of Cambridge, its purpose is to further the University's objective of advancing knowledge, education, learning, and research. They do not publish new fiction, poetry or other forms of creative writing, autobiography or memoir, overtly devotional or religious tracts (except for the Bible), political polemic, cookbooks, car handbooks or DIY manuals, or highly illustrated books for the general reader. Everything they do publish must have some educational and/or scholarly value.

CJ Fallon
Ground Floor, Block B, Liffey Valley Office Campus, Dublin, Republic of Ireland
- 00353 1 616 6400
- 00353 1 616 6499
- editorial@cjfallon.ie
- www.cjfallon.ie

Contact Managing Director, H.J. McNicholas; Editorial Director, N. White
Established 1927
Non-Fiction Publishes Educational material for Irish children.

Claire Publications
Unit 8, Tey Brook Craft Centre, Great Tey, Colchester, Essex, CO6 1JE
- 01206 211020
- 01206 212755
- mail@clairepublications.com
- www.clairepublications.com

Established 1980
Insider Info Catalogue available online
Non-Fiction Publishes Primary and Secondary Educational Resources on the following subjects:
 Maths, English, PSHE, Science, Languages, Design and Technology.
Submission Guidelines Will accept ideas for new products.
Tips As well as books, Claire Publications produce other classroom resources including games, activity packs and gifts. Products are mostly aimed at schools.

Collins Education
77–85 Fulham Palace Road, Hammersmith, London, W6 8JB
- 020 8741 7070
- 020 8307 4440
- editorial@collinseducation.com
- www.collinseducation.com

Parent Company Collins (HarperCollins Publishers Ltd)
Contact Managing Director, Jim Green; Publishing Director, Paul Cherry (Education)
Insider Info Catalogue is available online.
Non-Fiction Publishes Children's General and Multimedia Educational titles.
Submission Guidelines Accepts queries and proposals from academic authors for educational

books or materials. Contact by email with ideas in the first instance.

Recent Title(s) *Exam Practice: GCSE English (Series)*, John Reynolds (Education)

Tips Collins Education publishes books and electronic materials, including CD-ROMs and online resources for schools, colleges and universities, as well as students of any age, and home learners.

Colourpoint Books

Colourpoint House, Jubilee Business Park, 21 Jubilee Road, Newtownards, BT23 4YH, Northern Ireland

- 028 9182 0505
- 028 9182 1900
- info@colourpoint.co.uk
- www.colourpoint.co.uk

Contact Partner, Sheila Johnston (Educational); Partner, Norman Johnston (Transportation/General); Partner, Malcolm Johnston; Partner, Wesley Johnston

Established 1993

Insider Info Publishes 25 titles per year (including adult non-fiction titles). Aims to respond to proposals and manuscripts within two months. Catalogue and submission details are available online.

Non-Fiction Publishes Children's Textbooks and Educational titles on the following subjects: Geography, RE, English, HE, ICT, Maths, Politics and PE.

Submission Guidelines Accepts query with SAE/proposal package (including outline, sample chapter(s), and your publishing history). Will accept emailed queries.

Submissions details to: sheila@colourpoint.co.uk (write 'submissions query' as the subject line).

Recent Title(s) *Talking and Listening: GCSE English*, Evelyn Shaw

Tips Titles are mainly aimed at students and teachers, or anyone involved with the Northern Ireland education system. Before approaching the publisher with a proposal, be sure that it fits with the Colourpoint list, which as well as children's educational titles, is made up of non-fiction titles on the military, and transport.

The Continuum International Publishing Group

The Tower Building, 11 York Road, London, SE1 7NX

- 020 7922 0880
- 020 7922 0881

- firstinitiallastname@continuumbooks.com
- www.continuumbooks.com

Contact Publisher, Alexandra Webster (Education); Commissioning Editor, Joanne Allcock (Academic Division, Teacher Education); Commissioning Editor, Christina Garbutt (Education)

Established 1999

Imprint(s) Burns & Oates
Thoemmes Continuum
T & T Clark

Insider Info Publishes over 500 titles per year (including adult books). Catalogue and manuscript guidelines are available online.

Non-Fiction Publishes Educational, Reference and Scholarly titles on the following subjects: Primary, Secondary and Higher Education.

Submission Guidelines Accepts proposal package (including outline, your publishing history, author biography and market research). Send no more than four A4 sheets.

Tips Send submissions directly to the relevant editorial contact. See the company website for full contact details, downloads and submission guidelines.

Coordination Group Publications (CGP)

Kirkby in Furness, Cumbria, LA17 7WZ

- 01229 715714
- 0870 750 1292
- carolinebatten@cgpbooks.co.uk
- www.cgpbooks.co.uk

Contact Caroline Batten

Insider Info Accept queries by email or phone. Catalogue available online.

Non-fiction Publishes Children's Educational titles and Revision guides on the following subjects: All Curriculum subjects including Maths, English, Science, Technology, Languages and Humanities from Key Stage 1 to A2 level.

Tips CGP titles are written by educational professionals, and although they do not advertise for book proposals, they are on the look out for teachers who are interested in contributing to, or proofreading, their range of upcoming titles. Contact Caroline Batten for more details.

David Fulton Publishers

2 Park Square, Milton Park, Abingdon, Oxford, OX14 4RN

- 020 7017 6000
- 020 7017 6699
- tf.enquiries@informa.com

www.routledge.com
Parent Company Routledge Education (Taylor & Francis Group)
Insider Info Manuscript guidelines available online.
Non-fiction Publishes Reference, Scholarly and Textbook titles on the following subjects:
Education, Teaching Resources.
Submission Guidelines Accepts proposal package (including outline, sample chapters, your publishing history and author biography).
Tips David Fulton Publishers publishes books for teacher training and continuing professional development. They also produce a comprehensive range of resources for SENCOs, and teachers working with special needs.

Dramatic Lines
PO Box 201, Twickenham, TW2 5RQ
020 8296 9502
020 8296 9503
mail@dramaticlines.co.uk
www.dramaticlines.co.uk
Contact Managing Editor, John Nicholas
Non-Fiction Publishes Children's Reference and Scholarly titles on the following subjects:
Education, Drama.
Submission Guidelines Queries should include SAE.
Tips Specialises in educational texts for both children and adults concerning varying aspects of drama and plays. Titles are aimed at school children and teachers.

Dref Wen
28 Church Road, Whitchurch, Cardiff, CFI4 2EA
029 2061 7860
029 2061 0507
gwilym@drefwen.com
Contact Managing Director, G. Boore
Established 1970
Non-Fiction Publishes Children's Educational Welsh language titles.
Fiction Publishes Children's (Welsh language/ bilingual) Fiction titles.
Tips Titles aimed at Welsh language learners.

The Educational Company of Ireland
Ballymount Road, Walkinstown, Dublin 12, Republic of Ireland
00353 1 450 0611
00353 1 450 0993
info@edco.ie

www.edco.ie
Contact Chief Executive, Frank Maguire; Publisher, Frank Fahy
Established 1910
Insider Info Catalogue and manuscript guidelines available online.
Non-Fiction Publishes Children's Reference, Scholarly and Textbook titles on the following subjects:
Irish Primary and Post Primary Curriculum.
Submission Guidelines Accepts proposal package (including outline, contents and a sample chapter). Address to Frank Fahy.
Recent Title(s) *Edco Oxford English Dictionary*; *Bon Travail! 1* (Post Primary French)
Tips Publishes educational books and teaching resources on all subjects in both English and Irish. It is worth bearing in mind that educational publishers must keep an eye on the number of students taking a particular subject, in order to ensure that any publishing proposal is commercially viable.

Educational Explorers
PO Box 3391, Wokingham, RG41 5ZD
0118 978 9680
0118 978 2335
explorers@cuisenaire.co.uk
www.cuisenaire.co.uk
Contact Director, M.J. Hollyfield; Director. D.M. Gattegno
Established 1962
Non-Fiction Publishes Textbook and Educational titles on the following subjects:
Literacy, Numeracy, Maths, Languages.
Submission Guidelines No unsolicited manuscripts.

Evans Brothers Ltd
2a Portman Mansions, Chiltern Street, London, W1U 6NR
020 7487 0920
020 7487 0921
sales@evansbrothers.co.uk
www.evansbooks.co.uk
Contact Managing Director, Stephen Pawley; Publisher, Su Swallow
Established 1908
Imprint(s) Cherrytree Books
Zero to Ten
Insider Info Publishes 120 titles per year. Payment is via royalties (annually). Catalogue is available online. Discounts are available for schools.

Non-Fiction Publishes Children's Educational Textbooks and Picture books on the following subjects:
Education, Translation, Foreign languages.
Fiction Publishes Young Adult's and Children's Fiction.
* Fiction published has an educational purpose.
Recent Title(s) *Animal Worlds*, Paul Hess (Educational Picture book); *Witness*, Anne Cassidy (Young Adult Novel)
Tips Titles are aimed at a wide range of children, from early years to secondary school pupils. The publisher is committed to providing children, teachers and carers with books that help deliver key areas of the curriculum, whilst instilling a lifelong love of reading and learning in children and young people. Publishes children's education books only.

First and Best in Education

Earlstrees Court, Earlstrees Road, Corby, Northamptonshire, NN17 4HH
- 01536 399005
- 01536 399012
- info@firstandbest.co.uk
- www.firstandbest.co.uk

Contact Publisher, Tony Attwood; Editor, Anne Cockburn
Established 1992
Imprint(s) School Improvement Reports
Insider Info Payment via royalties. Catalogue and submission guidelines are available online.
Non-Fiction Publishes Reference, Textbook and Scholarly titles on the following subjects:
Drama, History, DT, PSHE and Religious Studies, Special Needs and Behaviour Management materials
* Books must be photocopiable.
Submission Guidelines Accepts query with SAE/ proposal package (including outline, two to four sample chapters and SAE). At this moment the publisher cannot consider any fiction or primary texts.
Recent Title(s) *Ofsted Buster Departmental Handbook*, Francis Stapleton (Copiable book)
Tips Publishes photocopiable books and books on disk for teachers and parents. First and Best is interested in publishing the following types of educational books: materials for teachers, lesson materials, special needs and behaviour management materials, and information for school administrators.

Folens Ltd

Waterslade House, Thame Road, Haddenham, Buckinghamshire, HP17 8NT
- 0870 609 1235
- 0870 609 1236
- folens@folens.com
- www.folens.com

Contact Senior Publisher, Peter Burton
Established 1987
Imprint(s) Belair
Insider Info Publishes 150 titles per year. Catalogue and manuscript guidelines are available online.
Non-Fiction Publishes Educational Textbook and Scholarly titles.
Submission Guidelines Accepts query with SAE, or via email, with proposal package (including outline, three sample chapters, market research, your author biography, and SAE).
Submission details to: pburton@folens.com
Recent Title(s) *Art Through Music,* Belair (Textbook)
Tips Folens are one of the leading publishers of primary and secondary educational texts, classroom resources and software for both students and teaching professionals. The publishers are pleased to receive suggestions for publications from teachers, or others involved in education. Please check the website for manuscript submission guidelines.

Folens Publishers

Hibernian Industrial Estate, Greenhills Road, Tallaght, Dublin 24, Republic of Ireland
- 00353 1 413 7200
- 00353 1 413 7280
- info@folens.ie
- www.folens.ie

Contact Managing Director, John O'Connor
Established 1956
Imprint(s) Blackwater Press
Magic Emerald
Insider Info Catalogue available online.
Non-Fiction Publishes Children's Educational titles on the following subjects:
Irish Curriculum subjects.
Fiction Publishes Children's Irish interest titles.
Recent Title(s) *Disappeared*, Seamus McKendry
Tips Publishes books for both primary and post primary Irish school children.

Franklin Watts

338 Euston Road, London, NW1 3BH
- 020 7873 6000
- 020 7873 6225

© www.wattspublishing.co.uk
Parent Company Hachette Children's Books
Established 1972
Insider Info Catalogue available online.
Non-Fiction Publishes Children's Educational titles, on the following subjects:
  All aspects of the National Curriculum.
Submission Guidelines Agented submissions only.
Tips Publishes children's information books, designed to engage, stimulate and entertain the more reluctant reader, and generally encourage a positive response to discovering the world around us.

Galore Park
19–21 Sayers Lane, Tenterden, Kent, TN30 6BW
✆ 0870 234 2304
✆ 0870 234 2305
✉ info@galorepark.co.uk
© www.galorepark.co.uk
Contact Managing Director, Nicholas Oulton (Classics, English, History, Languages); Director, Louise Martine (Science, Maths)
Established 1999
Insider Info Publishes 15 titles per year. Catalogue available free on request, online and via email.
Non-Fiction Publishes Textbooks on the following subjects:
  Maths, Science, English, Spanish and French.
  * Galore Park's textbooks are tailored to the preparatory school market and are endorsed by the ISEB. Non-preparatory school material is not published.
Tips Galore Park titles must be aimed specifically at preparatory school students.

Gardner Education
168e High Street, Egham, Surrey, TW20 9HP
✆ 01784 477470
✉ info@gardnereducation.com
© www.gardnereducation.com
Insider Info Catalogue available online and in hard copy via an online form, or by a phone call to: 0845 230 0775.
Non-Fiction Publishes Children's Educational and Textbook titles.
Tips Formerly known as Horwitz Gardner, Gardner Education is an independent publisher of learning materials for both pupils and teachers. Most publications are linked to the UK National Literacy Strategy, and are designed to help children achieve results within the classroom in terms of literacy, as well as subject knowledge.

Ginn and Co
Halley Court, Jordan Hill, Oxford, OX2 8EJ
✆ 01865 311366
✆ 01865 314641
✉ enquiries@harcourt.co.uk
© www.harcourt.co.uk
Parent Company Harcourt Education Ltd
Non-Fiction Publishes Children's Reference, Textbook and Scholarly titles.
Tips Ginn has a strong tradition for publishing quality educational resources, mainly for children aged three to twelve, including the UK's most successful maths scheme, *Abacus*, and the new *Abacus Evolve*. Its literacy and science materials are also popular with teachers internationally.

Harcourt Education
Halley Court, Jordan Hill, Oxford, OX2 8EJ
✆ 01865 888084
✆ 01865 314641
✉ uk.school@harcourteducation.co.uk
© www.harcourteducation.co.uk
Parent Company Reed Elsevier Group Plc
Contact Chief Executive, Chris Jones
Established 2001
Imprint(s) Heinemann Educational
  Ginn & Co
  Rigby
Insider Info Payment is via royalties. Catalogue available online.
Non-Fiction Publish Reference, Scholarly and Textbook titles.
Tips Harcourt Education is an international publishing group with operations in the UK, Australia, New Zealand, Southern Africa and South East Asia. Titles are aimed at school pupils all over the world, and also for educators of all kinds. Only educational textbooks are published. See individual imprint entries for more details.

Heinemann Educational
Halley Court, Jordan Hill, Oxford, OX2 8EJ
✆ 01865 311366
✆ 01865 314641
✉ enquiries@harcourt.co.uk
© www.heinemann.co.uk
Parent Company Harcourt Education
Non-fiction Publishes Children's Scholarly and Textbook titles.
Tips Publishes educational titles aimed at primary and secondary school children, vocational and further education students, and library users and

professionals. Publications must fit with appropriate curriculum guidelines.

Hodder Education
338 Euston Road, London, NW1 3BH
- 020 7873 6000
- 020 7873 6299
- educationenquiries@hodder.co.uk
- www.hoddereducation.co.uk

Parent Company Hachette Livre UK
Contact Managing Director, Philip Walters; Publishing Director, Lis Tribe (School Textbooks and Learning Materials); Publishing Director, John Mitchell (Scottish School Textbooks and Learning Materials); Publishing Director, Alexia Chan (College and University Textbooks and Learning Materials, Reference); Publishing Director, Katie Roden (Self-Improvement and Home Learning Materials); Publishing Director, Joanna Koster (Health Sciences Textbooks, Reference and Other Learning Materials)
Established 2001
Imprint(s) Hodder Arnold
 Hodder Murray
 Hodder Gibson
 Philip Allan Updates
Insider Info Catalogue available online, free on request.
Non-Fiction Publishes Reference, Scholarly and Textbook titles on the following subjects: Computers/Electronics, Education/Curriculum, Health/Medicine, History, Humanities, Science, Home Learning, Self-Improvement.
Submission Guidelines Accepts proposal package (including outline, sample chapter(s), market research, publishing history, author biography and SAE).
Recent Title(s) *Hodder Graphics: A Kestrel for a Knave*, Phil Page (Graphic Text)
Tips Now reports directly to Hachette Livre UK, following the closure of Hodder Headline. Of the individual imprints, Hodder Arnold publishes books and digital materials for the Further Education, Higher Education, Health Sciences and Consumer Education markets. It comprises Hodder Arnold Further & Higher Education, Hodder Arnold Consumer Education, and Hodder Arnold Health Sciences. It also publishes the popular *Teach Yourself* series. Hodder Murray publishes books, resources, digital materials and assessment for the schools market and is the second largest publisher for secondary education in the UK. Hodder Gibson publishes educational books and digital materials in Scotland. Philip Allan Updates runs conferences and courses, as well as publishing subject specific

material for GCSE and A-Level studies across the UK. Hodder Education is always keen to hear from qualified writers with new educational books. Send a proposal along with market research and some personal information, including publishing history, to the relevant publishing contact (see website).

Hopscotch Educational Publishing Ltd
Office 9, Fiveways House, Fiveways Industrial Estate, Corsham, Wiltshire, SN13 9RG
- 01249 812649
- 01249 812773
- sales@hopscotchbooks.com
- www.hopscotchbooks.com

Contact Editorial Director, Margot O'Keeffe; Creative Director, Frances Mackay
Established 1997
Insider Info Catalogue available free on request and online. Manuscript guidelines are available online via the website.
Non-Fiction Publishes Reference, Scholarly and Textbook titles on the following subjects: Literacy, Numeracy, Science, ICT, History, Geography, PSHE/Citizenship, Thinking Skills.
Submission Guidelines Accepts query with SAE, or by telephone. Alternatively, submit completed manuscript.
Recent Title(s) *Pick Up A Play – Plays for Primary Schools – Ages 7–8*; *Curriculum Focus – History – Famous Events KS1*
Tips Hopscotch exist to produce high quality, value for money resources that enable teachers to teach with confidence. The aim of the books is to enable children to have fun and success in their learning. They do accept manuscripts and ideas from first-time authors. The in-house team of experts will guide writers through the publishing process. Please call the editorial department for further information, or simply send in the manuscript. Never send original or valuable products through the post.

Jolly Learning Ltd
Tailours House, High Road, Chigwell, Essex, IG7 6DL
- 020 8501 0405
- 020 8500 1696
- info@jollylearning.co.uk
- www.jollylearning.co.uk

Established 1987
Imprints Jolly Phonique
 Jolly Phonics
 Jolly Readers

Jolly Grammar

Insider Info Publishes approximately 25 titles per year. Catalogue available online.

Non-Fiction Publishes Children's Educational Resources on the following subjects:
 Reading, English and Grammar

Submission Guidelines Will accept ideas for products that are add-ons to existing ranges. No unsolicited submissions or brand new ideas.

Tips Jolly Learning products are based around a teaching method called phonics, developed by the two primary authors; Sue Lloyd and Sara Wernham. Phonics teaches children to hear and identify the sounds in words at the same time as they are being taught the letter sounds. As well as books, Jolly Learning produces activity packs, gifts and other learning materials, all highly illustrated. A more detailed explanation of the principles behind Jolly Learning is available on the website.

Kingscourt/McGraw-Hill
Shoppenhangers Road, Maidenhead, Berkshire, SL6 2QL
- 0800 317 457
- 0870 241 6398
- enquiries@kingscourt.co.uk
- www.mcgraw-hill.co.uk/kingscourt

Established 1988

Insider Info Catalogue and sales presentation available online.

Non-Fiction Publishes Children's Educational and Textbook titles for Key Stages 1–3 on the following subjects:
 Literacy, Numeracy, Software/Interactive, Special Needs and PSHE.

Tips Titles are aimed at schools in both the UK and Ireland. They support the National Literacy and Numeracy Strategies, the Scottish Guidelines 5–14, the Northern Ireland Curriculum and Curriculum 2000 in Wales.

Learning Matters Ltd
33 Southernhay East, Exeter, EX1 1NX
- 01392 215560
- 01392 215561
- info@learningmatters.co.uk
- www.learningmatters.co.uk

Contact Julia Morris (Education); Di Page (Social Work)

Insider Info Catalogue available online. Manuscript guidelines available online.

Non-Fiction Publishes Textbook and Scholarly titles on the following subjects:

Counselling/Career, Education, Law, Social Service.

Submission Guidelines Accepts query with SAE or via email, with a proposal package (including outline).
 Submission details to: editor@learningmatters.co.uk

Recent Title(s) *Inspiring Primary Teaching*, Denis Hayes (Educational)

Tips As publishers, particularly in the field of teacher training, Learning Matters primarily supply books for education and social services. As a new company they are keen to talk to authors with ideas for new books. Writers will be encouraged to help with the marketing of their book. They take the stance that often authors will know where and how the book can be promoted better than they will. Therefore they are pleased when authors phone and ask whether they have made the most of every possible opportunity.

Leckie & Leckie
4 Queen Street, Edinburgh, EH2 1JF
- 0131 220 6831
- 0131 225 9987
- enquiries@leckieandleckie.co.uk
- www.leckieandleckie.co.uk

Parent Company Huveaux

Contact Publishing Director, Sarah Mitchell (Secondary Education); Assistant Publisher, John MacPherson (Secondary Education); Publishing Assistant, Fiona McGlade

Established 1989

Insider Info Publishes 250 titles per year. Receives approximately 30 queries and 30 manuscripts per year. Five per cent of books published are from first-time authors, 100 per cent of books published are from unagented authors. Payment is via royalty (on wholesale price). Advance offered is from £500 to £2,000. Average lead time is nine months, with simultaneous submissions accepted. Submissions accompanied by SAE will be returned. Aims to respond to queries within five days and to proposals and manuscripts within four weeks. Catalogue is free on request and available online, or by email.

Non-Fiction Publishes Scholarly and Textbook titles on the following subjects:
 Education (Scottish specific), Scottish Secondary and Further Education.

Submission Guidelines Accepts proposal package (including outline, one sample chapter, a proposal rationale, your publishing history and SAE), and artworks/images (send photocopies).
 Submission details to: fiona.mcglade@leckieandleckie.co.uk

Submissions must be specifically tailored to fit with the Scottish education system. Audiences will include Scottish secondary school teachers and students.

Letts Educational

4 Grosvenor Place, London, SW1X 7DL
☎ 01539 564911
✉ mail@lettsed.co.uk
🌐 www.lettsed.co.uk
Contact Publishing Director, Wayne Davies
Established 1979
Insider Info Catalogue available online, website http://shop.letts-successzone.com
Non-Fiction Publishes Children's Textbook and Scholarly titles on the following subjects: Education, Revision/Study guides.
Recent Title(s) *Premier Quick Tests English 10–11 Years*, Letts (Study Books)
Tips Letts Education is the UK's market leader in study and revision guides. Titles are aimed at all ages, from pre-school to A-Level.

Longman

FREEPOST ANG2041, Harlow, Essex, CM20 2YF
☎ 0800 579 579
☎ 0870 850 5255
🌐 www.longman.co.uk
Parent Company Pearson Education
Insider Info Catalogue and manuscript guidelines are available online
Non-Fiction Publishes Multimedia, Reference, Scholarly and Textbook titles on the following subjects: ELT, Primary Education (Literacy, Numeracy, Science), Secondary Education (Psychology, Sociology, Business, Economics), Language/Literature, Law, Humanities, Social Sciences.
Submission Guidelines Accepts proposal package (including synopsis, sample chapters, market research, your publishing history and author biography).
Recent Title(s) *The Pack*, Tom Pow (Teaching Guide); *Longman School Atlas*
Tips Longman, the world's oldest commercial imprint, is a leading publisher of educational materials for schools and English Language Teaching (ELT). Audiences include primary and secondary pupils, adult learners and students taking English exams, as well as users of dictionaries and reference titles. For students in higher education, Longman publishes textbooks for law, humanities and social sciences.

Macmillan Education

Macmillan Oxford, Between Towns Road, Oxford, OX4 3PP
☎ 01865 405700
☎ 01865 405701
✉ elt@macmillan.com
✉ firstinitial.lastname@macmillan.com
🌐 www.macmillaneducation.com
Parent Company Macmillan Publishers Ltd
Contact Managing Director, Chris Harrison; Publisher, Sue Bale; Publishing Director Educational, Alison Hubert
Insider Info Catalogue is available online.
Non-Fiction Publishes Textbooks, Online resources, Children's Reference and Scholarly titles on the following subjects: Language/Literature, English Language teaching and Curriculum materials for schools.
Tips Macmillan Education operates in 40 countries, publishing school and learning materials. Most resources, both print and online, are developed in conjunction with teachers and other education professionals. Materials are always in line with the relevant curriculum. The three main areas are; Macmillan English (English language teaching), Macmillan Caribbean (books for and about the Caribbean) and Macmillan Africa (educational text books for African schools).

Marshall Cavendish Ltd

5th Floor, 32/38 Saffron Hill, London, EC1N 8FH
☎ 020 7421 8120
☎ 020 7421 8121
✉ info@marshallcavendish.co.uk
🌐 www.marshallcavendish.co.uk
Contact Clive Gregory
Insider Info Catalogue available online.
Non-Fiction Publishes Children's Partworks, Reference and Educational titles on the following subjects: English Language Teaching, General Educational and Reference topics.
Submission Guidelines Accepts query with SAE.
Recent Title(s) *Young Learners Go!*, Frances Bates-Treloar, Jane Thompson and Steve Thompson (Educational)
Tips Titles are aimed at enriching life through knowledge, and transcend boundaries of geography and culture. In line with this vision, products for both children and adults reach across the globe in 13 languages, and the publishing network spans Asia, Europe and the US. Marshall Cavendish's illustrated reference and non-fiction titles for schools and

libraries are aimed at enhancing the educational experiences of students at all levels.

Mentor Books
43 Furze Road, Sandyford Industrial Estate, Dublin 18, Republic of Ireland
- 00353 1 295 2112
- 00353 1 295 2114
- admin@mentorbooks.ie
- www.mentorbooks.ie

Insider Info Catalogue is available online.
Non-Fiction Publishes Children's Textbook, Educational and Reference titles.
Fiction Publishes Children's Fiction titles.
Recent Title(s) *Trapdoor to Treachery*, Kieran Fanning (Novel 9–13 years); *PE Workout*, Jason Carey (Educational)
Tips Children's fiction is written by a few authors and tends to be in series (see website for examples). Also publishes adult non-fiction.

Mill Publishing
PO Box 120, 4 Balloo Avenue, County Down, BT19 7BX
- 0800 318 192
- 0800 027 2833
- info@millpublishing.co.uk
- www.millpublishing.com

Parent Company Motivation in Learning Ltd
Imprint(s) Anglia Young Books
Insider Info Catalogue available online, or via email to info@motivationinlearning.com
Non-Fiction Publishes Educational Resources on the following subjects:
National Curriculum at all stages.
Submission Guidelines Will accept ideas for new titles, particularly from teachers. Send a brief synopsis. Accept images/artworks.
Fiction Publishes Children's Historical titles.
* Fiction is published through the Anglia Young Books imprint (see separate entry). Historical fiction is aimed at Key Stage 2 children.
Tips Mill Publishing produce several series, including *Skill Builder* and *Write into History*. These series have specific characteristics, details of which are on the website. See the Anglia Young Books entry for more information on this imprint.

National Association for the Teaching of English (NATE)
50 Broadfield Road, Sheffield, S8 0XJ
- 0114 255 5419
- 0114 255 5296
- info@nate.org.uk
- www.nate.org.uk

Contact Publications Manager, Anne Fairhall; Publications Coordinator, Julie Selwood
Established 1963
Insider Info Publishes approximately four titles per year, as well as a journal.
Non-Fiction Publishes Primary, Secondary and Tertiary Educational and Teaching Resources on the following subjects:
English, Drama and Media
Submission Guidelines Will accept ideas for new publications from teachers.
Tips NATE is a voluntary association. All publication ideas will go through an editorial board.

Neate Publishing
Hedgerows, 33 Downside Road, Winchester, SO22 5LT
- 01962 841479
- 01962 841743
- bobbie@neatepublishing.co.uk
- www.neatepublishing.co.uk

Contact Managing Director, Bobbie Neate
Established 1999
Insider Info Catalogue available online.
Non-Fiction Publishes Children's Textbook and Scholarly titles on Educational subjects.
Submission Guidelines The best way to get in touch is by post. Do not send emails with attachments, they will not be opened.
Recent Title(s) *Colours Around Us*, Carole Roberts and Ann Langram (Education/Reference)
Tips Specialise in non-fiction books, role play and the teaching of 'notemaking' and 'notetaking' for schools and pupils. All ideas for publishing are welcome. Of particular interest are titles for primary age children and the publishers would like to hear from any potential authors. Particularly welcome are ideas for new role play packs.

Nelson Thornes Ltd
Delta Place, 27 Bath Road, Cheltenham, Gloucestershire, GL53 7TH
- 01242 267100
- 01242 221914
- cservices@nelsonthornes.com
- http://aa.nelsonthornes.com

Parent Company Wolters Kluwer Group
Contact Managing Director, Mary O'Connor

Established Formed in 2000 with the merger of Thomas Nelson and Stanley Thornes publishing companies

Insider Info Catalogue is free on request and available online, by email, or by telephone, 01242 267382

Non-Fiction Publishes Illustrated, CD-ROM, Electronic Teaching and Learning Resource titles on the following subjects:
  Primary and Secondary Education, Nursing, Health Sciences, Teacher Training, CPD.

nferNelson

The Chiswick Centre, 414 Chiswick High Road, London, W4 5TF
- 020 8996 8445
- 020 8996 3660
- www.nfer-nelson.co.uk

Established 1981

Insider Info Catalogue available online and by email.

Non-fiction Publishes Educational and Scholarly materials.

Tips nferNelson specialise in electronic and paper based tests and assessments for the educational market (largely focusing on ages up to 14, but also up to age 19), covering knowledge, understanding and progress, ability, special needs, personal development testing, and assessment.

NMS Enterprises Limited-Publishing

National Museums Scotland, Chambers Street, Edinburgh, EH1 1JF
- 0131 247 4026
- 0131 247 4012
- publishing@nms.ac.uk
- firstinitial.lastname@nms.ac.uk
- www.nms.ac.uk

Contact Director of Publishing, Lesley A. Taylor; Publishing Administrator, Rajeev Jose

Established 1987

Insider Info Payment is via royalties.

Non-Fiction Publishes Children's Illustrated Reference and Educational titles on the following subjects:
  Anthropology/Archaeology, Art/Architecture, History, Nature/Environment, Science.

Submission Guidelines Accepts query by email, or with SAE/proposal package (including outline, sample chapter(s)).

Recent Title(s) *Scottish Castles*, Gordon Jarvie (Reference/Picture Book)

Tips Books published by National Museums Scotland reflect the range and international importance of their collections. As well as children's books, publications vary from full colour exhibition catalogues, academic monographs, biography and souvenir booklets. Themes include applied art, archaeology, natural history, conservation, and Scottish history and culture. The list of titles represents collections from all their museums and they are only interested in proposals that concern National Museum of Scotland collections.

Oxford Education

Great Clarendon Street, Oxford, OX2 6DP
- 01865 556767
- 01865 556646
- webenquiry.uk@oup.com
- www.oup.com/oxed

Parent Company Oxford University Press

Contact Editorial Director, Antonia Owen; Managing Director of the Education and Children's Division, Kate Harris; Children's Publisher, Liz Cross (Fiction and Picture Books); Publisher, Modern Foreign Languages, Dick Capel-Davies; Publisher, Science and Maths, Elspeth Boardley

Established 1907

Insider Info Payment is by royalties. Catalogue available online.

Non-Fiction Publishes General Non-fiction, Reference, Scholarly and Textbook titles for Teenagers and Children on the following subjects:
  National Curriculum subjects, Dictionaries, Atlases and General reference topics.

Submission Guidelines Accepts query with SAE/proposal package (including outline, two sample chapters, author biography and SAE).

Fiction Publishes Children's Fiction and Picture book titles.
  * Key age ranges are 5–7, 8–12 and Teenagers.

Poetry Publishes Children's Poetry.

Recent Title(s) *Bunker 10*, J. A Henderson (Teenage fiction); *Peter Pan in Scarlet*, Valerie Thomas and Korky Paul (Picture Book); *Oxford Illustrated Computer Dictionary*

Tips Titles and materials are aimed at children from birth to teenage. Markets include primary schools, secondary schools, FE colleges, international schools and pre-school children.

Oxford University Press

Great Clarendon Street, Oxford, OX2 6DP
- 01865 556767
- 01865 556646

○ webenquiry.uk@oup.com
ⓦ www.oup.co.uk
Contact Editorial Director, Antonia Owen;
Commissioning Editor, David Musson (Academic
and Professional Books)
Established 1478
Imprints Oxford Education (including Oxford
Children's Books)
Insider Info Publishes 6,000 titles per year. Payment
is by royalties. Catalogue available online.
Manuscript guidelines available online via
the website.
Non-Fiction Publishes General Non-fiction,
Reference, Scholarly, Technical and Textbook titles
for Adults and Children on the following subjects:
Education, Government/Politics, Health/Medicine,
History, Language/Literature, Literary Criticism,
Music/Dance, Philosophy, Religion, Science and
Social Sciences, National Curriculum, Health,
Relationships
Submission Guidelines Accepts query with SAE/
proposal package (including outline, two sample
chapters, author biography and SAE).
Fiction Publishes Children's Picture book and
Fiction titles.
Recent Title(s) *The Diary of a Teenage Health Freak*,
Aidan Macfarlane, Ann McPherson, John Astrop
(Teenage Reference); *Peter Pan in Scarlet*, Geraldine
McCaughrean (Children's Book)
Tips Oxford University Press (OUP) is a department
of the University of Oxford. It furthers the University's
objective of excellence in research, scholarship, and
education by publishing worldwide. It publishes in
many countries, in a variety of different languages,
for all levels, and across virtually the whole range of
academic disciplines. With the acquisition of
Blackstone Press, OUP is now one of the leading Law
publishers. Please note that Oxford University Press
is obliged by its charter to have all books published
ratified by the University. As a rule, the press don't
publish works of fiction, unless it forms part of an
educational course or examination. The main criteria
when evaluating a new title is its quality, and the
contribution it will make to the furtherance of
scholarship and education. Oxford Education (see
separate entry) deals with all children's fiction, non-
fiction and educational titles.

PCET Publishing
27 Kirchen Road, London, W13 0UD
○ 020 8567 9206
ⓕ 020 8566 5120
○ info@pcet.co.uk
ⓦ www.pcet.co.uk

Established 1964
Insider Info Catalogue available online or via an
online form.
Non-fiction Publishes Children's Primary and
Secondary Educational Resources and
Activity books.
Tips As well as books, PCET produce illustrated wall
charts and other classroom accessories based
around key texts and aspects of the National
Curriculum. Also provides funding and teaching
resources for the developing world.

Pearson Education
Edinburgh Gate, Harlow, Essex, CM20 2JE
○ 01279 623623
ⓕ 01279 414130
○ elizabeth.kelly@pearson.com
ⓦ www.pearsoned.co.uk
Parent Company Pearson Plc
Contact CEO Pearson Education (Asia, Europe,
Middle East and Africa), John Fallon; Editorial
Assistant, Elizabeth Kelly
Established 1998
Imprint(s) Addison-Wesley
Allyn & Bacon
BBC Active
Benjamin Cummings
Cisco Press
FT Prentice Hall
Longman
New Riders
Peachpit Press
Pengin Longman
QUE Publishing
SAMS Publishing
Wharton
York Notes
Insider Info Payment is via royalties. Catalogue and
manuscript guidelines are available online.
Non-Fiction Publishes Multimedia, Reference,
Scholarly, Technical and Textbook titles on the
following subjects:
Business/Economics, Children's Education,
Humanities, Language/Literature, Science,
Technology
Submission Guidelines Accepts query with SAE, or
proposal package (including outline, sample
chapters, market research, your publishing history
author biography).
Tips Pearson Education is always looking for exciting
new projects to work on and new authors to work
with. A project proposal can be submitted by post or
email; check the website for a full list of editorial
contacts and their interests. Alternatively contact

one of Pearson Education's various imprints with suitable projects. See the entries for BBC Active, Longman, Penguin Longman and York Notes for more information on children's publishing at Pearson Education.

Penguin Longman
Edinburgh Gate, Harlow, Essex, CM20 2JE
☎ 01279 623623
☎ 01279 414130
🌐 www.pearsoned.co.uk/Imprints/ PenguinLongman
Parent Company Pearson Education
Insider Info Catalogue and manuscript guidelines are available online.
Non-Fiction Publishes Reference and Textbook titles on the following subjects:
 Education, English Language Teaching (ELT), Language/Literature, Teaching Guides.
Submission Guidelines Accepts proposal package (including synopsis, sample chapters, market research, your publishing history and author biography).
Recent Title(s) *A New Zealand Adventure*, Jan Thorburn (Penguin Reader)
Tips Specialists in the field of English Language Teaching and reading/supplementary materials for ELT students. The Penguin Readers series publishes reading guides of classic literary and popular fiction and media tie-ins. The Penguin English Series provides teachers with guides and resources to supplement lessons. See website for a full list of submissions contacts.

Portland Press Ltd
3rd Floor, Eagle House, 16 Procter Street, London, WC1V 6NX
☎ 020 7280 4110
☎ 020 7280 4169
✉ editorial@portlandpress.com
🌐 www.portlandpress.com
Contact Managing Director, Rhonda Oliver; Managing Editor, Pauline Starley; Acquisitions Editor, Roheena Anand
Established 1990
Insider Info Publishes four titles per year (including adult titles). Payment is via royalties. Catalogue and manuscript guidelines are available online.
Non-Fiction Publish Children's Reference titles on Biomedical Sciences.
Submission Guidelines Accepts query with SAE.
Tips Portland Press is a not for profit publisher of journals and books in the cellular and molecular life

sciences. Titles are aimed largely at graduate, postgraduate and research students. The children's book publishing programme falls within the biomedical sciences field, in the *Making Sense of Science Children's Books* series. They do not normally accept unsolicited proposals, unless they could potentially form a volume of the *Essays* series.

Prim-Ed Publishing
PO Box 2840, Coventry, CV6 5ZY
☎ 0870 876 0151
☎ 0870 876 0152
✉ authors@prim-ed.com
🌐 www.prim-ed.com
Insider Info Catalogue available online. Accept queries via email.
Non-Fiction Publishes Primary and Special Educational Needs, and Lower Secondary School Educational Resources.
Tips All texts are photocopiable and are called *Copymasters*. Although there is no official submissions policy, Prim-Ed are always looking for qualified teachers to undertake contract writing. Email for further details.

QED Publishing
226 City Road, London, EC1V 2TT
☎ 020 7812 8600
☎ 020 7253 4370
✉ qedpublishing@quarto.com
🌐 www.qed-publishing.co.uk
Parent Company The Quarto Group
Contact Publisher, Steve Evans; Editorial Director, Jean Coppendale; Editor, Hannah Ray; Art Director, Zeta Davies
Established 2003
Insider Info Payment is via an outright fee. Catalogue free on request and available online.
Non-Fiction Publishes Children's Educational and Reference titles on the following subjects:
 Education, History, Nature/Environment, Art and Design, ICT, Geography, Science, Maths and Literacy.
 *Books are specially devised to support children's curriculum learning.
Submission Guidelines Accepts query with SAE.
Recent Title(s) *Communicate Online*, Anne Rooney (Educational)
Tips Authors for children's educational books should be experts in their field.

Rigby

Halley Court, Jordan Hill, Oxford, OX2 8EJ

☎ 01865 311366

🖷 01865 314641

✉ enquiries@harcourt.co.uk

🌐 www.harcourt.co.uk

Parent Company Harcourt Education

Non-Fiction Publishes Children's Reference, Educational and Textbook titles.

Tips Rigby publish titles that are designed to provide flexible support for teachers, and challenging materials for school pupils; mainly aged from three to twelve years.

Robinswood Press Ltd

South Avenue, Stourbridge, West Midlands, DY8 3XY

☎ 01384 397475

🖷 01384 440443

✉ info@robinswoodpress.com

🌐 www.robinswoodpress.com

Contact Managing Editor, Chris Marshall; General Manager (Sales), Tracy Cooper

Established 1985

Insider Info Publishes 15 titles per year. Payment is via royalties. Catalogue and manuscript guidelines are available online

Non-Fiction Publishes Children's Illustrated, Multimedia and Scholarly titles on the following subjects:

Child Guidance/Parenting, Education and Teacher Resources.

* Books should contribute to a particular objective, to foster a love of reading and writing, especially where students need to overcome difficulties with words and literacy.

Submission Guidelines Accepts query with SAE/proposal package (including outline, one sample chapter, your publishing history, and author biography).

Submission details to: cm@robinswoodpress.com

Fiction Publishes Picture books, and Young Adult's and Children's novels.

Submission Guidelines Accepts query with SAE/proposal package (including outline, one sample chapter, your publishing history, and author biography).

Submission details to: cm@robinswoodpress.com

Recent Title(s) *Avalanche*, Paul Kropp (Young Adult Novel); *Bruno*, Guy Halifax (Picture Book)

Tips Authors usually have an established reputation in some aspect of teaching or work with children. Books should fit into the Robinswood objectives of

encouraging reading and writing, and helping overcome difficulties in these areas.

Routledge

2 Park Square, Milton Park, Abingdon, Oxford, OX14 4RN

☎ 020 7017 6000

🖷 020 7017 6699

✉ jon.manley@tandf.co.uk

🌐 www.routledge.com

Parent Company Taylor and Francis Group

Contact Managing Editor, Jon Manley

Imprint(s) Routledge-Cavendish

Routledge Education

Insider Info Publishes over 1,000 titles per year (including adult and academic titles). Catalogue and manuscript guidelines are available online.

Routledge maintains the following series: Routledge Asian & Middle East Studies; Routledge Classics; Routledge Mental Health; Routledge Politics & International Relations; Routledge Reference; Routledge Sport & Leisure Studies; Routledge Military & Strategic Studies.

Non-Fiction Publishes Journals, Reference, Scholarly and Textbook titles on the following subjects: Art, History, Leisure, Literature/Language, Military/War, Religion, Science, Social Sciences, Sport, Children's Educational topics.

Submission Guidelines Accepts proposal package (including outline, synopsis, one to two sample chapters, market research and CV).

Tips Routledge is a multi-disciplinary publisher of leading academic and reference titles. The main bulk of their children's publishing (excluding young adults in further education) is through the Routledge Education imprint (see separate entry for further details). Submissions should be directed towards the appropriate list/series; full editorial contacts are available on the website.

Routledge Education

2 Park Square, Milton Park, Abingdon, Oxford, OX14 4RN

☎ 020 7017 6248

🖷 020 7017 6699

✉ anna.clarkson@tandf.co.uk

🌐 www.routledge.com/education

Parent Company Routledge (Taylor & Francis Group)

Contact Publisher, Anna Clarkson (Primary Education, Secondary Education, School Management and Leadership, Foundation Subjects and Classroom Issues); Senior Editor, Alison Foyle

(Early Years, Childhood Studies, Special Educational Needs, Literacy); Senior Editor, Philip Mudd (Study Guides, Adult Education, Research Methods, General Books); Senior Editor, David Fulton (Textbooks); Senior Editor, Bruce Roberts (Primary and Secondary Education)

Imprint(s) David Fulton Publishers
Lawrence Erlbaum Associates

Insider Info Catalogue and manuscript guidelines are available online.

Non-Fiction Publishes Practical, Reference, Scholarly and Textbook titles on the following subjects: Education (Primary, Secondary and Higher), Open and Distance Learning, Psychology, Special Needs Education, Teacher Training, Teaching Resources.

Submission Guidelines Accepts proposal package (including outline, synopsis, one to two sample chapters, market research and CV).

Recent Title(s) *Observing, Assessing and Planning for Children in the Early Years*, Sandra Smidt (Education)

Tips Routledge Education publishes books aimed at professionals in education at any level, textbooks for trainee teachers, books for classroom practitioners and research books for international academics. The Routledge Education list now includes David Fulton Publishers, and also Lawrence Erlbaum Associates, an international academic publisher of books and journals in education and psychology.

Saint Andrew Press
121 George Street, Edinburgh, EH2 4YN
- 0131 225 5722
- 0131 220 3113
- standrewpress@cofscotland.org.uk
- www.churchofscotland.org.uk/shop/index.htm

Contact Head of Publishing, Ann Crawford
Established 1954
Insider Info Publishes 20 titles per year (including adult titles). Payment is via royalties.
Non-Fiction Publishes Children's Reference titles on Religion.
Submission Guidelines Accepts query with SAE.
Tips Saint Andrew Press is owned by the Church of Scotland and publishes books on religion and general faith. Both its children's and adult's books are aimed at both local and international trade markets.

Schofield & Sims Ltd
Dogley Mill, Fenay Bridge, Huddersfield, HD8 0NQ
- 01484 607080
- 01484 606815
- post@schofieldandsims.co.uk

- www.schofieldandsims.co.uk

Contact Chairman, C.N. Platts
Established 1901
Insider Info Catalogue available online and free on request.
Non-Fiction Publishes Children's Multimedia, Scholarly, Textbook, Dictionaries, Posters and Educational Workbooks on the following subjects: Geography, History, Literacy, Numeracy, Puzzles, Languages
Recent Title(s) *Understanding Maths*, Steve Mills and Hilary Koll (Textbook Series); *Nursery Activity*, Kathryn Linaker (Set of six nursery books)
Tips Titles are aimed at home tutors, schools, nurseries and playgroups. Most products are created by classroom teachers.

Scholastic Educational Publishing
Villiers House, Clarendon Avenue, Leamington Spa, Warwickshire, CV32 5PR
- 01926 887799
- 01926 883881
- www.scholastic.co.uk

Parent Company Scholastic Ltd
Contact Managing Director, Denise Cripps
Insider Info Payment is via royalties. Catalogue available online. Aims to respond to proposals within six months.
Non-Fiction Publishes Educational Resources and Classroom materials for schools.
 * Focuses on primary education.
Submission Guidelines Accepts proposal package (including synopsis, sample chapters, author biography and SAE). Outline should be no longer than one side of A4 paper and should be typed.
Tips Do not accept proposals via email, or on disk. Including any relevant teaching qualifications and experience in your author biography may help. Scholastic also publish the magazines; *Child Education, Junior Education, Nursery Education, Literacy Time, Junior Focus* and *Child Education Topics*.

Smart Learning
PO Box 321, Cambridge, CB1 2XU
- 01223 477550
- 01223 477551
- admin@smart-learning.co.uk
- www.smart-learning.co.uk

Contact Sarah Baron (Foundation to Key Stage 2); Sam Watkins (Key Stage 3)
Insider Info Catalogue available online. Accept queries via email.

Non-Fiction Publishes Classroom resources, Activity books, Educational packs and Photocopiable resources on the following subjects:
 ICT, PSHE, English, Citizenship, Literacy
Submission Guidelines Accepts query via email from people interested in authoring, or evaluating products.
Recent Title(s) *Inspiring Primary Teaching*, Denis Hayes (Educational)
Tips Products are aimed at either Foundation, Key Stage 1, 2 or 3. Smart Learning work with teachers, freelance writers and designers to create books and packs.

Taylor & Francis Group
2 Park Square, Milton Park, Abingdon, Oxfordshire, OX14 4RN
☎ 020 7017 6000
☎ 020 7017 6699
✉ tf.enquiries@tfinforma.com
🌐 www.taylorandfrancis.com
Parent Company T&F Informa Plc
Contact CEO, Roger Horton
Established 1936
Imprint(s) Taylor & Francis
 CRC Press
 Garland Science
 Psychology Press
 Routledge
Insider Info Publishes 1,800 titles per year (including adult titles), and 1,000 journals per year. Catalogue and manuscript guidelines are available online.
Non-Fiction Publishes Multimedia, Reference, Scholarly, Educational, Technical and Textbook titles.
 * Imprints under the Taylor & Francis Group publish academic titles in a broad range of science and humanities subject areas.
Submission Guidelines Accepts proposal package (including outline, synopsis, one to two sample chapters, market research and CV).
Tips Taylor & Francis Group is the academic publishing division of T&F Informa Plc (formerly Informa Plc). Taylor & Francis mainly publishes at University level and its educational publishing is under the Routledge Education imprint, within Routledge. See the individual entries for more details.

Trotman & Co. Ltd
c/o Crimson Publishing, Westminster House, Kew Road, Richmond , Surrey, TW9 2ND
☎ 020 8334 1600
☎ 020 8334 1601

✉ enquiries@trotman.co.uk
🌐 www.trotman.co.uk
Contact Managing Director, Toby Trotman; Editorial Director, Mina Patria; Commissioning Editor, Rachel Lockhart
Established 1970
Insider Info Publishes 60 titles per year. Payment is via royalties. Catalogue available online.
Non-Fiction Publishes Multimedia and Reference titles on the following subjects:
 Business/Economics, Counselling/Career, Education, Training Courses.
Submission Guidelines Complete online form.
 Submission details to: editorial@trotman.co.uk
Recent Title(s) *Choosing Your A levels and Post-16 Options*, Gary Woodward
Tips Trotman Publishing produce products in a wide range of media – including books, photocopiable packs, videos, the internet and CD-ROMs – which cover the areas of higher education, careers information, teaching resources, employment and training.

Ward Lock Educational Co. Ltd
BIC Ling Kee House, 1 Christopher Road, Great East Grinstead, West Sussex, RH19 3BT
☎ 01342 318980
☎ 01342 410980
✉ wle@lingkee.com
🌐 www.wardlockeducational.com
Established 1952
Insider Info Catalogue available online, or on request.
Non-Fiction Publishes Primary and Secondary Educational Resources on the following subjects:
 English, Reading, Drama, Science, Music, Teaching, Maths.
Recent Title(s) *The Primary Performance Handbook*, Gaynor Davies (Drama)
Tips Titles are mainly aimed at Key Stages 1 to 4. Also publish resource materials for the Numeracy Hour and the Literacy Hour.

Wayland
338 Euston Road, London, NW1 3BH
☎ 020 7873 6000
☎ 020 7873 6024
🌐 www.wattspublishing.co.uk
Parent Company Hachette Children's Books
Established 1972
Insider Info Catalogue available online.
Non-Fiction Publishes Children's Illustrated, Educational titles.

Submission Guidelines Agented submissions only.
Tips Titles must have quality educational content, and an up to date, appealing, child friendly approach to design.

York Notes
Edinburgh Gate, Harlow, Essex, CM20 2JE
✆ 01279 623623
✆ 01279 414130
🖳 www.pearsoned.co.uk/imprints/yorknotes/
Parent Company Pearson Education
Insider Info Catalogue and manuscript guidelines are available online.
Non-Fiction Publishes Textbook (Study guide) titles on the following subjects:
  Film, Language/Literature, Literary Criticism.
  * York Notes provides three main series, catering for different ages groups: 11–14 years, 14–16 years and 16–18 years and undergraduates. Each series covers the main curriculum texts studied at that level.
Submission Guidelines Accepts proposal package (including synopsis, sample chapters, market research, your publishing history and author biography).

Recent Title(s) *The Handmaid's Tale (York Notes Advanced)*, Neil McEwan (Study Guide)
Tips York Notes publishes comprehensive literature guides to help students gain a better understanding of a curriculum text. Each title aims to help students form their own ideas and opinions, and help them to success in examinations. See the website for full list of submissions contacts.

ZooBooKoo
4 Gurdon Road, Grundisburgh, Woodbridge, Suffolk, IP13 6XA
✆ 01473 735346
✆ 01206 212755
✉ sales@zoobookoo.com
Insider Info Catalogue available online.
Non-Fiction Publishes Illustrated, Educational folding cube books and mats.
Tips ZooBooKoo products are all highly illustrated, and are aimed at making education fun for children by changing the traditional book format into a 3D folding cube, or an activity mat.

POETRY

POETRY PUBLISHERS

A&C Black Publishers Ltd
See entry under Book Publishers

Antique Collector's Club
See entry under Book Publishers

Black & White Publishing
See entry under Book Publishers

Bloomsbury Publishing Plc
See entry under Book Publishers

Bookmart Ltd
See entry under Book Publishers

Edgewell Publishing
See entry under Book Publishers

Faber & Faber Ltd
See entry under Book Publishers

Forward Press
See entry under Book Publishers

Gomer Press/Gwasg Gomer
See entry under Book Publishers

Hands Up Books
1 New Spout Hill Cottages, Brantingham, East Yorkshire, HU15 1QW
✉ handsup@handsup.karoo.co.uk
🖳 www.handsup.karoo.net
Contact Graham Denton
Established 2002
Insider Info Accepts queries by email. Catalogue available online.
Poetry Publishes Children's Illustrated Poetry titles.
Recent Title(s) *A Bag of Stars*, Collected by Graham Denton (Poetry Collection)

Tips A very small press that is focused solely on publishing fun poetry for children, particularly young children.

Jane Nissen Books
See entry under Book Publishers

Kingfisher Publications Plc
See entry under Book Publishers

The King's England Press
Cambertown House, Commercial Road, Goldthorpe, Rotherham, S63 9BL
- 01484 663790
- 01484 663790
- sales@kingsengland.com
- www.kingsengland.com

Established 1989
Insider Info Submissions accompanied by SAE will be returned. Catalogue and manuscript guidelines available online.
Poetry Publishes Children's Illustrated Poetry titles. * Publishes the *Potty Poetry* series only (A5, 64-page books, illustrated by black and white line drawings for children).
Submission Guidelines No unsolicited manuscripts will be accepted prior to 2008.
Recent Title(s) *The Armadillo Under My Pillow: Potty Poems for a Barmy Bedtime*, Chris White (Poetry collection)
Tips Also publish non-fiction books for adults. Detailed guidelines as to how to submit manuscripts are available on the website, which will also announce when they will start accepting manuscripts again (2008 at the earliest).

Luath Press Ltd
543/2 Castlehill, The Royal Mile, Edinburgh, Lothian, EH1 2ND
- 0131 225 4326
- 0131 225 4324
- gavin.macdougall@luath.co.uk
- www.luath.co.uk

Contact Director, Gavin McDougall
Established 1981
Insider Info Publishes 30 titles per year (including adult books). Receives less than 1,000 queries and less than 1,000 manuscripts per year. 10 to 50 per cent of books published are from first-time authors, more than 90 per cent of books published are from unagented authors. Payment is via royalty.

Submissions accompanied by SAE will be returned. Catalogue is free on request and available online. Manuscript guidelines are available online.
Poetry Publishes Children's Illustrated poetry.
Submission Guidelines Accepts complete manuscripts, proposals, or queries with SAE, by mail only. No emailed submissions and no artworks will be accepted.
Recent Title(s) *Septimus Pitt and The Grumbleoids*, Brian Whittingham (Children's Poetry)
Tips Most, but not all of Luath Press books have a Scottish connection, and the majority of the programme is made up of adult fiction and non-fiction.

The Lutterworth Press
See entry under Book Publishers

Macmillan Children's Books
See entry under Book Publishers

Meadowside Children's Books
See entry under Book Publishers

Miles Kelly Publishing Ltd
See entry under Book Publishers

Nightingale Books
See entry under Book Publishers

Oxford Education
See entry under Book Publishers

Pan Macmillan Publishers
See entry under Book Publishers

Penguin Group (UK)
See entry under Book Publishers

Pennine Pens
See entry under Book Publishers

Puffin
See entry under Book Publishers

The Random House Group Ltd
See entry under Book Publishers

Random House Children's Books
See entry under Book Publishers

Scottish Cultural Press & Scottish Children's Press
See entry under Book Publishers

Serendipity
See entry under Book Publishers

Souvenir Press Ltd
See entry under Book Publishers

Walker Books
See entry under Book Publishers

The Watts Publishing Group
See entry under Book Publishers

Willow Bank Publishers Ltd
See entry under Book Publishers

Wolfhound Press
See entry under Book Publishers

Young Picador
See entry under Book Publishers

POETRY ORGANISATIONS

Apples and Snakes
Battersea Arts Centre, Lavender Hill, London, SW11 5TN
- info@applesandsnakes.org
- www.applesandsnakes.org

Contact Director, Geraldine Collinge; Education Manager, Lisa Mead; Programme Manager, Sarah Ellis

About An organisation covering the whole of the country, staffed with regional coordinators, designed to encourage and facilitate performance poetry. Also runs an educational programme for children of all ages.

British Haiku Society
38 Wayside Avenue, Hornchurch, Essex
- www.britishhaikusociety.org

About Actively promotes the teaching of haiku to children in schools and colleges. Also runs competitions and can provide workshops on haiku.

Children's Poetry
- www.poetry-online.org/childrens_poetry_resource_index.htm

About An online library of many children's poems, both classic and more contemporary, categorised into subjects. Also contains some resources on writing poetry, as well as useful quotes from poems.

Children's Poetry Archive
- www.poetryarchive.org/childrensarchive

About A website dedicated to the appreciation of children's poetry, including Q&A sessions with poets, and live recordings of the poems themselves.

Children's Poetry Bookshelf
Poetry Book Society, 4th Floor, 2 Tavistock Place, London, WC1H 9RA
- 020 7833 9247
- 020 7833 5990
- info@poetrybooks.co.uk
- www.childrenspoetrybookshelf.co.uk

About A book club for children aged 7–11 who love poetry. Contains puzzles, games, links, readers' poems and the opportunity to buy books. Children may also send in their poems to be published on the site, with a parent or teacher's permission.

Football Poetry
FootballPoets.org, c/o 18 Bisley Road, Stroud, Gloucestershire, GL5 1HE
- editors@footballpoets.org
- www.footballpoets.org/schools

About An organisation aiming to encourage young people to write poetry about football. Schools can submit poems written by pupils for publication on the site. Also facilitates workshops within schools based around football-themed poetry, and kicking racism out of football.

Giggle Poetry

o info@meadowbrookpress.com
ⓦ www.gigglepoetry.com
About A US based website dedicated to humorous children's poetry, run by Meadowbrook Press. Contains hundreds of children's poetry to read and comment on, as well as interviews with children's poets and many other resources such as the ability to book author visits (these are limited to the US though).

Man in the Moon

o webmaster@maninthemoon.co.uk
ⓦ www.maninthemoon.co.uk/menu.html
About A website dedicated to poetry written by children, with inspiration, ideas, examples of poetry, games and poetry for children by adult poets. Currently unable to accept submissions, however this may change in the future.

Mini Mushaira

o info@simonfletcher.net
ⓦ www.simonfletcher.net/mm.html
Contact Simon Fletcher
About Set up in 1997 to promote interest in multicultural arts through poetry events and readings. Aims to involve youth groups and schools in particular. The group is made up of poets from a variety of backgrounds.

National Association of Writers in Education

PO Box 1, Sheriff Hutton, York, YO60 7YU
o 01653 618429
o paul@nawe.co.uk
ⓦ www.nawe.co.uk
Contact Director, Paul Munden; Project Manager, Liz Fincham
About Focuses on the need for children and adults in education to have the input of practising writers. Runs programmes in schools, colleges and adult learning centres, designed to encourage the development of creative writing, including poetry. Members are writers and teachers, who benefit from the professional development programmes.

Northern Poetry Library

County Library, The Willows, Morpeth, Northumberland, NE61 1TA
o 01670 534524

About A specialist library covering all types of poetry from all over the country, as well as the local area, in the form of books and magazines. A useful resource for anyone living in the local areas of Cumbria, Cleveland, Tyne and Wear, Durham and Northumberland.

Poetry Class

o poetryclass@poetrysociety.org.uk
ⓦ www.poetryclass.net/kids.htm
About Part of the Poetry Society, Poetry Class is an organisation dedicated to improving the teaching of poetry in schools. Visitors to the site can read through potential lesson plans, build their own poetry libraries, read interviews with poets and find links to other relevant sites.

Poetry Ireland

2 Prouds Lane, off St Stephen's Green, Dublin 2
o 00353 1 478 9974
o 00353 1 478 0205
o poetry@iol.ie
ⓦ www.poetryireland.ie
Contact Acting Director, Jane O'Hanlan; Education Officer, Moira Cardiff; Writers in Schools Development Officer, Anna Boner
About A national resource and information organisation for anyone in Ireland who has an interest in poetry, whether it be students, writers, academics or members of the public. Also runs a 'Writers in Schools' scheme involving poets visiting schools and hosting workshops and readings. Looks to maximise opportunities for poets and poetry in Ireland.

Poetry Library Children's Zone

Poetry Library, Level Five, Royal Festival Hall, London, SE1 8XX
o 020 7921 0943/020 7921 0664
ⓦ www.poetrylibrary.org.uk/education/children/
About The children's branch of the Poetry Library. News, reviews, advice and competitions for young poets.

The Poetry Society

22 Betterton Street, London, WC2H 9BX
o 020 7420 9880
o 020 7240 4818
o info@poetrysociety.org.uk
ⓦ www.poetrysociety.org.uk
Contact President, Jo Shapcott

About A membership based, registered charity, whose members include many professional poets, as well as students, academics, journalists, librarians and teachers, and those who simply enjoy poetry. Publishes the magazine *Poetry Review*, as well as a newsletter, *Poetry News*, and runs and promotes National Poetry Day. Also hosts events, readings and workshops around the country. Members enjoy many benefits, including Poetry Prescription, an appraisal service that is offered at a discounted rate for members. Membership is open to both children and schools, as well as adults.

The Poetry Zone

- poems@pzone.freeserve.co.uk
- www.poetryzone.ndirect.co.uk

About A website for poetry written by children, with the facility to submit poems for publication. Children must send the poem in the body of an email and keep it under 20 lines, and include their name and age. The site also contains reviews, competitions, activities and interviews, all aimed at young people.

Scottish Poetry Library

Crichton's Close, Canongate, Edinburgh, EH8 8DT

- 0131 557 2876
- 0131 557 8393
- reception@spl.org.uk

- www.spl.org.uk

Contact Director, Robyn Marsack; Education Officer, Lorna Irvine

About A specialist library and organisation to be used as a resource for readers, writers, academics and casual browsers alike. Features a large collection of poetry, including poetry for children, specialising (not exclusively) in Scottish and Gaelic poetry. As well as traditional library services, the library also runs an education programme and regular poetry related events.

The Seamus Heaney Centre for Poetry

c/o School of English, Queen's University Belfast, Belfast, BT7 1NN

- 028 9097 1070
- shc@qub.ac.uk
- www.qub.ac.uk/schools/SeamusHeaneyCentreforPoetry

Contact Director, Professor Ciaran Carson

About A research centre for poetry in Northern Ireland, used as a central point for a wide range of local and international poets, creative writing students, and academics. The centre holds an extensive poetry library, runs courses, workshops and events, and produces a number of poetry publications. Although the centre is largely academic, it may still hold useful resources for poets of all kinds.

INTERNATIONAL BOOKS

ABC Melody

16 rue Charlemagne, 75004 Paris, France

- 0033 1 44 78 92 43
- 0033 1 48 87 67 07
- info@abcmelody.com
- www.abcmelody.com

Contact Director, M. Stéphane Husar

Categories Publishes Illustrated books and CDs that introduce children to languages and cultures using fun songs and pictures.

Insider Info ABC Melody is an innovative and successful educational publisher of *Sing & Learn* books for children aged three and upwards. Each *Sing & Learn* title contains a 24 page illustrated book, and a CD with songs performed by native artists. The books reflect the work of artists and children across the world.

Recent Titles *Sing & Learn: French*

Sing & Learn: Spanish

Future titles for 2008 are *Sing & Learn: Arabic and Chinese*

Tips The company has distribution rights in Europe, USA, Canada and parts of Asia. ABC participates in international book fairs

Abingdon Press

201 Eighth Avenue South, Nashville, Tennessee, 37203, USA

- 001 615 749 6000
- 001 615 749 6512
- www.abingdonpress.com

Parent Company The United Methodist Publishing House

Contact President and Publisher, Neil M. Alexander; Senior Editor, Robert Ratcliff; Senior Editor, Ron Kidd

Imprint(s) Abingdon Press
Cokesbury
Dimensions for Living

Categories Publishes Children's Bible Picture books, General Picture books, Games and Crafts, General Picture Books, Miscellaneous, Religious Fiction, Religious Non-Fiction, Pop-Up book, Religious Youth books and Adult titles.

Insider Info Publishes 120 titles per year including adult titles. Pays 7.5 per cent royalty on retail price. Receives 3,000 queries per year. Receives 250 manuscripts per year. Average lead time is two years. Book catalogue available free on request.

Submission Guidelines Accepts unsolicited manuscripts and proposals. Does not accept simultaneous submissions.

Recent Title(s) *God Gave Me;* Wade Hudson (Board Book)

Tips Abingdon also produces various multimedia products, including audiobooks and computer software.

Absey & Company Inc

23011 Northcrest Drive, Spring, Texas 77389, USA

☏ 001 212 277 8028

✉ info@absey.biz

🌐 www.absey.com

Contact Editor in Chief, Edward Wilson

Established 1996

Categories Publishes Children's Fiction and Non-Fiction, Picture books, Young readers, Poetry, Language Arts and Educational books.

Insider Info An award winning company that specialises in poetry and language arts.

Submission Guidelines Send a brief covering letter and sample chapters, also include any publishing credits to date and a SAE. No email submissions.

Recent Title(s) *Regular Lu* (Children's fiction); *Stealing a Million Kisses*, Jennifer Skaggs (Author) Lesa Scott (Photography) (Board book)

Actes Sud Junior

13 quai de Conti, 75006 Paris, France

☏ 0033 1 55 42 63 12

☏ 0033 1 55 42 09 19

✉ contact@actes-sud.fr

🌐 www.actes-sud.fr

Contact President and Director, Madame Johanna Brock Lacassin; Children's Editor, Isabelle Rémond

Parent Actes Sud

Categories Publishes Children's Dramatic Fiction, Adventure Fiction, Young Fiction, Illustrated books

and Non-fiction titles on the following subjects: History, Documentaries, Arts and Crafts, Art, Nature and Animals, Sociology, Tales and Legends and IT

Insider Info A successful publisher with offices throughout France. Also publishes high quality adult, education titles and comics.

Submission Guidelines No email submissions. Aims to respond to manuscripts in four months. Accepts samples of illustrations but do not send any original work. To check the status of a manuscript, email: manuscrits@actes-sud.fr

Recent Titles *Camille Clarisse,* Robert Bigot (Adventure Fiction)
La mythologie romaine, Florence Noiville (Author) Serge Ceccarelli (Illustrator) (Ancient Mythology)

Tips Does not accepts poetry or autobiographical submissions.

Action Publishing LLC

PO Box 391, Glendale, California, 91209

☏ 001 323 478 1667

☏ 001 323 478 1767

🌐 www.actionpublishing.com

Contact President and Publisher, Michael Metzler

Established 1996

Categories Publishes Children's Picture books, Children's and Young Adult Fiction and Art and Photographic books.

Insider Info A relatively new publishing company, Action Publishing has enjoyed great success with 'Politicards' a Political humour series by Christopher Smith. Action Publishing ventured into educational and value-orientated children's books, with the successful 'Kuekumber Kids' Series by southern Californian children's author and illustrator Scott Sutton for pre-school through to first grade.

Submission Guidelines Most scripts are acquired through agents or developed in house however they will review unsolicited manuscripts but there is no guarantee as to how long it will take for a response. No email submissions. Please apply standard manuscript formatting. There are many resources online that describe the standard manuscript format.

Recent Title(s) *Margaret,* Jeremy Dubow, *The Family of Ree Series,* Scott E. Sutton

Adriano Salani Publisher S.p.A.

Via Gherardini 10 – 20145 Milan, Italy

☏ 0039 2 3459 7624

☏ 0039 2 3459 7206

✉ info@salani.it

🌐 www.salani.it

Contact President, Luigi Spagnol; General Executive Manager, Guglielmo Tognetti; Publisher, Maria Mazzitelli

Parent Group Mauri Spagnol

Categories Publishes Children's Fiction, Picture books, How-To books, Comics, Gift books, Film/Television Tie-Ins in all genres, including: Fantasy, Fairy Tales, Action, Adventure, Animals and Poetry.

Insider Info Adriano Salani publish bestselling children's book translations such as *Harry Potter* and the *His Dark Materials* trilogy.

Recent Titles *La Bussola D'oro*, Phillip Pullman (Fantasy); *Ucciderà mia madre*, Michela Franco Celani (Fiction)

Aladdin Paperbacks

1230 Avenue of the Americas, New York, NY, 10020, USA

 001 212 698 2808

 001 212 698 4350

 www.simonsayskids.com

Parent Simon and Schuster Inc

Contact Vice President and Publisher, Ellen Kreiger; Executive Editor, Jen Klonsky; Editorial Director, Julia Richardson; Editor, Liesa Abrams

Categories Publishes Children's Fiction and Non-Fiction and Picture books.

Insider Info The majority of Aladdin's list is reprints from their hardcover imprints, including some of the most enduring children's books of the modern era, such as classic picture books like *Chicka Chicka Boom Boom* by Bill Martin Jr. Aladdin's list also includes original series, single titles and a line for beginner readers; *Ready to Read*.

Submission Guidelines Accepts queries, proposals or manuscripts for the attention of the 'Submissions Editor'.

Recent Title(s) *Scaredy-Pants! A Halloween Story (Ant Hill)*, Joan Holub (Author), Will Terry (Illustrator) (Ready to Read Series); *Among the Free-Shadow Children Trilogy*, Margaret Peterson Haddix (Young Novel); *Jay Leno's How to Be the Funniest Kid in the Whole Wide World (or Just in Your World)*, Jay Leno (Author) S.B. Whitehead (Illustrator) (Humour)

Albert Whitman & Company

6340 Oakton Street, Morton Grove, Illinois 60053-2723, USA

 001 847 581 0033

 mail@awhitmanco.com

 www.albertwhitman.com

Contact Editor in Chief, Kathleen Tucker; Art Director, Carol Gildar

Categories Publishes Novels, Picture books, Multicultural books, Seasonal books and Educational books. Also produce Children's Concept books, tackling issues such as Divorce, Bullying and Disability.

Insider Info An independent publisher known for the classic series *The Boxcar Children® Mysteries*.

Submission Guidelines They are interested in picture book manuscripts for ages two to eight; novels and chapter books for ages eight to twelve; non-fiction for ages three to twelve; and art samples showing pictures of children. Picture books must be less than eight pages. For novels send a query letter and three sample chapters, and for non-fiction the entire manuscript is accepted if less than eight pages. Send illustrations for the attention of the 'Art Director'. Accepts simultaneous submissions.

Recent Title(s) *The Super Soybean,* written by award winning author and photographer, Raymond Bial (Educational Book)

Albin Michel

22, rue Huyghens, 75014 Paris, France

 0033 1 42 79 10 00

 0039 1 43 27 21 58

 Online submission form

 www.albin-michel.fr

Contact Foreign Rights Youth, Madame Aurélie Lapautre

Categories Publishes Children's Fiction, Picture books and Non-fiction on the following subjects: Fantasy, Adventure, Family, Geography, Nature, Space, Human Body, Arts and Crafts, Comics, and Television Tie-ins

Insider Info Ranked the number three publisher in France, Albin Michel is an independent family publishing group with an extensive catalogue of over 6,000 titles. Their list covers a wide range of children's categories, to more specialist books for adults, such scholarly legal texts. Publishes 600 new books each year for adults and children. Catalogue is available on request.

Submission Guidelines No email submissions. Aims to respond in one to three months. Receives 500 manuscripts per month, five of which are selected.

Recent Titles *Blanche ou La triple contrainte de l'enfer*, Hervé Jubert (Children's Fiction)
Amanda Crapota: L'apprentie sorcière..., A magical, illustrated story book about a young witch called Amanda Crapota (Picture Book)

Alfred A. Knopf Books for Young Readers

1745 Broadway, New York, NY 10019, USA

☏ 001 212 782 9000

☏ 001 212 302 7985

🌐 www.randomhouse.com

Parent Random House Inc

Established 1915

Contact Senior Editor, Erin Clarke; Editor, Stephanie Lane

Categories Young Fiction for a wide age range, from babies to eighteen year olds.

Insider Info
The imprint publishes between 60–70 new hardcover books each year. Authors and illustrators published by Alfred A. Knopf include Marc Brown, Robert Cormier, Leo and Diane Dillon, Carl Hiaasen, Leo Lionni, Christopher Paolini and Philip Pullman.

Submission Guidelines Accepts unsolicited manuscripts via post. Do not send the only copy of the manuscript. If you are submitting a picture book, please send a covering letter and the full manuscript. If you are submitting a novel, please send a covering letter, a one-page synopsis (outlining the plot), and 25 pages of text. A response is made within six months if they are interested in publishing the script. Address the manuscripts to the 'Submissions Editor'. Send in illustration samples with SAE.

Recent Title(s) *Kindergarten Countdown*, Anna Jane Hays (Young Fiction-Concepts-Counting)

All About Kids Publishing

9333, Benbow Drive, Gilroy, CA 95020, USA

☏ 001 408 578 4026

☏ 001 408 578 4029

✉ lguevara@aakp.com

🌐 www.aakp.com

Contact Publisher, Mike G. Guevara; Editor, Linda L. Guevara

Established 1999

Categories Publishes Children's Fiction and Non-Fiction, Picture books, Chapter books and Educational books.

Insider Info All About Kids strives to publish high quality and innovative children's books with beautiful artwork.

Submission Guidelines Accepts unsolicited manuscripts. Send in full manuscript for picture and chapter book and include SAE and a covering letter. Send illustrations with SAE.

Recent Title(s) *The Flight of The Sunflower*, Melissa Bourbon Ramirez (Author), Nadine Takvorian (Illustrator), (Picture Book); *My Name Is Andrew*, Mary McManus Burke (Author), Donna Ingemanson (Illustrator), (Educational)

Tips Submissions are not being accepted until the end of March 2008.

Allen & Unwin Pty Ltd

406 Albert Street, East Melbourne, VIC 3002, Australia

☏ 0061 2 8425 0100

☏ 0061 2 9906 2218

✉ frontdesk@allenandunwin.com

🌐 www.allenandunwin.com

Contact Publishing Director, Patrick Gallagher; Publisher (Children's Books), Rosalind Price; Editorial Director, Rebecca Kaiser

Categories Publishes Children's Fiction and Non-Fiction, Picture books, Teenage novels, How-To books, Audio books and Film/Television Tie-Ins on a wide range of subjects, including: History, Astronomy, Friendship and Family and Fantasy. Also publishes Educational books for students and lecturers.

Insider Info Allen & Unwin is one of Australia's leading independent publishers and distributors. Publishes 220 titles per year (including adult titles).

Submission Guidelines Seeking outstanding fiction and non-fiction for children at the present time. Length guidelines are as follows:

Junior Fiction: children aged five to eight, word length 5,000–10,000; children aged seven to ten, word length 10,000–30,000; children aged 11–14, word length 30,000–55,000.

Young Adult novels: teenagers aged 13–16, word length 40,000–60,000; mature teenagers aged 15 plus, word length 40,000–100,000.

For non-fiction send a proposal for your idea, a detailed synopsis and three sample chapters.

Recent Title(s) *Bananas in Pyjamas CD Card*, Richard Tulloch (Audio Book/Television Tie-In); *Brian Banana Duck Sunshine Yellow*, Chris McKimmie (Picture Book); *The Cat Kin*, Nick Green

Tips Runs the Iremonger award for a great non-fiction book, the winning entry will receive a cash prize, guaranteed publication, royalties on book sales and editorial support. Visit their website for more details.

Allen & Unwin are not considering picture books, plays, poetry or short story collections at the present time.

Alyson Publishing Inc

PO Box 4371, Los Angeles, CA 90078, USA

☏ 001 323 860 6065

● 001 323 467 0152
● editorialguidelines@alyson.com
● www.alyson.com
Established 1999
Categories Publishes Adult and Children's Fiction and Non-Fiction, dealing with gay/lesbian issues.
Insider Info A leading publisher of gay and lesbian books for adults, teenagers and their families.
Submission Guidelines For young adult books submit synopsis and sample chapters with SAE. Visit website for further submission guidelines.
Recent Title(s) *Daddy's Wedding* Michael Willhoite
Tips Catalogue available on request.

American Girl
8400 Fairway Place, Middleton, WI 53562, USA
● 001 608 831 5210
● 001 323 467 0152
● Online form.
● www.americangirl.com
Established 1986
Categories Publishes Advice and Activity books, Craft books and Non-Fiction specifically for girls.
Insider Info American Girl provides inspiring products for each stage of a young girl's development including books, magazines, toys, clothes and accessories. American Girl first introduced a line of historical characters Kaya, Felicity, Josefina, Kirsten, Addy, Samantha, Kit, and Molly that came to life in their books. These books are developed in-house.
Submission Guidelines Send in a detailed synopsis of the concept and sample chapters, include any published works to date. Full manuscripts are accepted. Aims to respond in 12 to 16 weeks.
Recent Title(s) *School Smarts Homework Survival Guide, The Light in the Cellar: A Molly Mystery*
Tips Visit their website for magazine submissions.

Amethyst House Publishing Inc
Scarborough, Ontario, Toronto, Canada
● 001 416 431 1339
● 001 416 221 8400
● publisher@amethysthouse.com
● www.amethysthouse.com
Established 2004
Categories Publishes Children's Fiction and Non-Fiction, Young Adult novels, and Self-help books.
Insider Info Amethyst is a small up and coming publishing company, which focuses on nurturing new talent and finding a market for authors whose work is yet to receive a favourable reception.

Submission Guidelines Accepts unsolicited manuscripts and proposals. At this time they only accept original manuscripts of unpublished work, or self-published work without a contract. No picture book submissions at the present time. Submissions via email are welcome. Send SAE with illustration samples.
Recent Title(s) *Adrift in the Moonlight*, D.F. Lemna (Young fiction); *Sofia's Pink Balloon*, Zanita DiSalle (Author) Nadine Dennis (Illustrator) (Picture book)
Tips Amethyst will publish books from unrecognised and undiscovered authors who have talent. Previous authors include a successful journalist, an artist, an ex-military officer and a psychic.

Amistad Press
10 East 53rd Street, New York, New York, 10022, USA
● 001 212 261 6500
● 001 212 207 6927
● www.harpercollins.com
Parent Company HarperCollins Children's Books
Contact Editorial Director, Alix Reid; Senior Editor, Ruth Katcher; Editors Clarissa Hutton, Barbara Lalicki, Antonia Markiet, Maria Modugno, Robin Benjamin, Susan Rich; Editorial Director Phoebe Yeh; Executive Editor Abby McAden
Insider Info Amistad Press is an imprint of Harper Collins publishing company. It publishes works by and about people of African descent on subjects and themes that have significant influence on the intellectual, cultural, and historical perspectives of a world audience.
Submission Guidelines Only accepts agented submissions.
Recent Title(s) *Harriet Tubman*, Ann Petry

Annick Press
15 Patricia Avenue, Toronto, Ontario, M2M 1H9, Canada
● 001 416 221 4802
● 001 416 221 8400
● annickpress@annickpress.com
● www.annickpress.com
Contact Publishing Director, Rick Wilks; Associate Publisher, Colleen MacMillan
Established 1975
Categories Publishes Children's Fiction, Children's Non-Fiction, Picture books, Young Adult, 'Annikins' Series (small pocket sized children's books).
Insider Info Publishes 30 titles per year. Authors paid by royalty, with advance offered. Receives 5,000

queries and 3,000 manuscripts per year. 80–85 per cent of books are from unagented writers. 20 per cent of books are from first-time authors. Aims to respond to manuscripts in three months. Average lead time is two years.

Submission Guidelines Accepts unsolicited manuscripts and proposals. Send in a synopsis, a sample chapter, a covering letter and SAE. No submissions via email or fax. Picture book manuscripts are not accepted at the present time. Send in illustration samples to the 'Art Director' and include a SAE. Annick Press is committed to publishing Canadian children's writers and cannot accept submissions from outside of Canada.

Recent Title(s) *The Big Book of Pop Culture*, Hal Niedzviecki (Non-fiction); *Generals Die in Bed*, Charles Yale Harrison (Fiction); *The List*, Hazel Hutchins (Author), Maria van Lieshout (Illustrator) (Picture book)

Tips Publishes the successful "Annikins" series, which are small pocket sized books for children.

Arnoldo Mondadori Editore
Mondadori Libri per Ragazzi, Via Mondadori 15, 37131 Verona, Italy
- 0039 2 75421
- 0039 2 75422302
- mondojunior@mondadori.it
- www.mondadori.it

Contact Chairman, Marina Berlusconi; Deputy, Maurizio Costa

Imprint(s) Mondadori Books
 Edizioni EL
 Piemme Publishing Group
 Edumond Le Monnier

Categories Publishes Contemporary Fiction, Classics, Paperbacks and Children's books including Movie/TV Tie-Ins, Fiction, Picture books and Board books.

Insider Info Mondadori Group's book publishing activities cover a wide range of cultural interest and reading needs. A publisher of books and magazines, In 2004 Arnoldo Mondadori Editore, including all its imprints published 2,240 books for adults and children.

Tips Mondadori Group's Book Division also operates in sectors with considerable development potential, such as arts books, educational publishing, tourist guides and professional titles.

Atelier du poisson soluble
35, boulevard Carnot, 43000 Le-Puy-en-Velay, France

- 0033 4 73 94 90 70
- 0033 4 73 94 90 70
- www.poissonsoluble.com

Contact Director, M. Olivier Belhomme; Assistant Director, M. Stéphane Queyriaux

Categories Publishes Children's Fiction on the following subjects: Animals, Family, Adventure, Romance, and Fantasy. Publishes Non-fiction on the following subjects: Nature and the World, Space, Geography, How-To and Arts and Crafts. Also publishes Baby books and Picture books

Insider Info A successful publisher, with offices throughout France, Switzerland, Belgium and Canada.

Submission Guidelines Visit their website for submission guidelines

Recent Titles *Le Grand Gentil Loup* (The Large Gentle Wolf Picture Book), Ben Lebègue (Author and Illustrator)

Atheneum Books for Young Readers
1230 Avenue of the Americas, New York, NY, 10020
- 001 212 698 2808
- 001 212 698 4350
- www.simonsayskids.com

Parent Simon and Schuster Inc

Contact Editorial Directors, Ginee Seo and Caitlyn Dlouhy; Editor, Susan Burke; Associate Editor, Jordan Brown

Established 1961

Categories Publishes Children's Fiction and Non-Fiction and Young Adult novels.

Insider Info Atheneum publishes literary fiction and fine picture books for pre-schoolers through to young adults. Atheneum has begun to publish high-end novelty books, the first being the bestselling *Pirates* by John Matthews.

Submission Guidelines Accepts queries, proposals or manuscripts for the attention of the 'Submissions Editor'. Approximately ten per cent of books published are by first-time authors.

Recent Title(s) *The Legend of Sleepy Hollow*, Washington Irving (Author), Gris Grimly (Illustrator)

August House Publishing
3500 Piedmont Road, NE, Suite 310, Atlanta, GA 30305, USA
- 001 501 372 5450
- 001 501 372 5579
- graham@augusthouse.com
- www.augusthouse.com

Contact Chief Executive Officer, Steve Floyd; Editor, Liz Parkhurst

Established 1970

Categories Publishes Folktales, Picture books, Resource books, Audio.

Insider Info August House is an award-winning multimedia publisher of children's stories for young children, their families, teachers and librarians. August House offers an online learning centre for children and teachers, which features additional curriculum resources that will help engage young learners and emerging readers in a variety of ways. August House publishes *Story Cove,* classroom sets that includes copies of an educational book, a lesson plan and an audio CD for classroom use.

Submission Guidelines Accepts unsolicited manuscripts. They will only respond to submissions or queries if they wish to pursue the script. Aims to respond within four to twelve weeks. For their general trade line, they are interested in acquiring books pertaining to folklore, folktales, and the art and application of storytelling. For picture books they are seeking single story manuscripts that feature traditional folktales.

Recent Title(s) *When Turtle Grew Feathers*, Tim Tingle (Author), Stacey Schuett (Illustrator); *Anansi and the Tug o'War*, Bobby Norfolk and Sherry Norfolk (Author), Baird Hoffmire (Illustrator) (Story Cove Picture book)

Australian Council for Educational Research (ACER)

19 Prospect Hill Rd, Camberwell, VIC, 3124, Australia

- 0061 3 9277 5555
- 0061 3 9277 5500
- sales@acer.edu.au
- www.acer.edu.au

Categories Publishes Books, Assessment instruments, Kits and Periodicals on the following subjects: Education (covering most school subjects), Human Resources, Psychology, Parent Education and Mental Health, Speech Pathology and Autism Spectrum Disorders.

Insider Info ACER is a non-governmental educational research organisation based in Camberwell, Victoria, which researches and develops educational products across Australia. Its publishing arm, ACER Press, publishes and distributes books, tests and resources.

Submission Guidelines All submitted proposals or manuscripts should be evidence or research-based. Visit their website for full details.

Recent Title(s)
Action Literacy, Student Workbook for Middle Primary
Tips Visit the website to download the book and product catalogues.

Au Vent des Iles

BP 5670, 98716 Tahiti - Polynésie, France

- 0033 6 89 50 95 95
- 0033 6 89 50 95 97
- christian@auventdesiles.pf
- www.auventdesiles.pf

Contact Director, M. Christian Robert

Categories Publishes Children's Adventure Fiction and Dramatic Fiction, Comics and Picture Books

Submission Guidelines Visit website for submission guidelines.

Recent Titles *La téte á Coco*, Catherine Villadier (Author), Nicolas Bernier (Illustrator)
Fa'a'amu le petit secret de la nuit (The Small Secrets of the Night), Roxane Marie Galliez (Author), Nicolas Bernier (Illustrator) (Dramatic Fiction)

Balivernes

16, rue de la Doulline, 69340 Francheville, France

- 0033 6 76 21 32 10
- 0033 4 26 29 90 34
- online submission form
- www.balivernes.com

Contact Director, M. Pierre Crooks

Categories Publishes Children's Picture Books on many subjects and Young Novels

Insider Info A specialist publisher of beautiful, illustrated children's books. Publishes a number of popular series; *Le Monde Animaginaire* features animal illustrations for children aged three to six; *Collection Calembredaines* for children aged four to seven; *Collection Fariboles* for children aged seven to ten; and *Hors Collection* for books that do not correspond to an age bracket.

Submission Guidelines Include SAE.

Recent Titles *A l'orée des fées* (Who are the Fairies?), Lenia Major (Poet), Cathy Delanssay (Illustrator)

Baloon Books

Generaal Lemanstraat 27, 2018 Antwerpen, Belgium

- 0032 3 309 17 10
- 0032 3 309 17 90
- info@balloonbooks.be
- www.balloonbooks.be

Contact Director, M. Laurent Schmidt

Parent Group Mauri Spagnol

Categories Publishes Children's Activity, Sticker, Drawing, Games, and Arts and Crafts books. Also produces Educational books for very young children, on subjects including: Science, Maths, Dictionaries and Encyclopedias, 'Mezzanine' Comics Series and Picture books.
Recent Titles *Le dictionnaire de Titou* (Board Book) *Les tables de multiplication,* ages seven to eight (Educational Illustrated Book)

Barefoot Books
2067 Massachusetts Avenue, Cambridge, MA 02140, USA
- 001 617 576 0660
- 001 617 576 0049
- www.barefoot-books.com

Established 1970
Categories Publishes Young Children's books, Non-Fiction, Educational, Picture books, Gift products, Audio, Anthologies and Spanish Children's books.
Insider Info Barefoot offers products that are thoughtfully written, beautifully designed and illustrated, and have high educational value; which encourages children to read deeper and embrace their own creative abilities.
Submission Guidelines Accepts unsolicited manuscripts. Barefoot prefers entire manuscripts with SAE. A response is made if they wish to pursue the script.
Recent Title(s) *I Wish I Were a Pilot*, Stella Blackstone (Author) Max Grover (Illustrator); *Indian Tales-A Barefoot Collection*, Retold by Shenaaz Nanji, Christopher Corr (Illustrator)
Tips Inspiration for Barefoot's books come from themes that embrace cultural diversity.

Baron Perché
91 bis, rue du Cherche-midi, 75006 Paris, France
- 0033 1 44 59 92 00
- 0033 1 53 10 02 88
- online submission form
- www.vilo-groupe.com

Contact Editor, Mme. Maylis de Kerangal
Parent Vilo Groupe
Categories Publishes Children's Picture books, Illustrated books, Fiction, Documentaries and Short novels.
Insider Info An imprint that publishes books for 9–11 year olds.
Recent Titles *Charlepogne et Poilenfrac,* A tale about Kings and Knights by Roland Fuentès (Historical Fiction)

Le petit inconnu au Baloon (Small Unknown Balloon) (Illustrated Book)

Barron's Educational Series Inc
250 Wireless Blvd, Hauppauge, NY 11788
- 001 800 645 3476
- 001 631 434 3723
- barrons@barronseduc.com
- www.barronseduc.com

Contact Chief Executive Officer, Manuek H. Barron, President and Publisher, Ellen Sibley
Established 1941
Categories Publishes Children's Fiction and Non-Fiction, Test Preparation Manuals including SAT and ACT Test Preparation books, Foreign language learning books, Crafts & Hobbies and Adult titles.
Insider Info Barron publishes more than 300 titles annually and maintains an extensive backlist of well over 2,000 titles. Pays 12–14 per cent royalty on net receipts, with an advance offered. Receives 75 per cent of books from unagented writers and 25 per cent of books from first-time authors. Also provides online test material for children.
Submission Guidelines Accepts unsolicited manuscripts. To initiate any proceedings send a query letter with a SAE, if the response is positive then send in a full manuscript. Unsolicited submissions may take up to eight months for a response. Accepts simultaneous submissions.
Recent Title(s) *The Big Book of Magic Fun*, Ian Keable (Magic Tricks Non-fiction); *Everyday Witch*, Sandra Forrester (Fiction/Fantasy)

Bayard Jeunesse
3, rue Bayard, 75 008, Paris, France
- 0033 1 44 35 60 60
- 0033 1 44 35 61 61
- M.deJenlis@bayard.be
- www.bayard-jeunesse.com

Parent Bayard Communications
Contact Director, Maxime de Jenlis
Categories Publishes Children's general, Educational books, Magazines, Religious titles and CD-ROMS.
Insider Info Bayard is a global publishing, press and multimedia company with operations in America, Canada, Asia and Europe. The European arm of the company publishes children's educational books, successful magazines and a daily newspaper *Le Croix*. They have an extensive catalogue of over 4,000 products for adults and children and a book list of 1,500 titles for children. Bayard also publish religious books (they are the number one Catholic

press group in France), and multimedia products such as CD-ROMS.

Recent Titles *Victor Hugo,* Benoît Marchon (Author), Pierre Mazan and Séverine Cordier (Illustrators) (Educational Book, *Dans la même* Series)
Clic d'Api: Le journal d'actvities, features fun activities (CD-ROM)
Muze, teenage magazine for 16 year olds
Tips For information on the operations in America, Canada and Asia visit their website.

Beasco
Travessera de Gràcia 47–49, 08021 Barcelona, Spain
- 0034 93 366 03 00
- 0034 93 366 04 49
- www.randomhousemondadori.es
Parent Random House Mandadori
Categories Publishes Picture books, Children's Fiction and Adventure books aimed at children aged up to six years old.
Insider Info The imprint was a pioneer of 'libros vivos' (live books): adventurous books of extraordinary quality. Some of its popular characters include 'Barbapapa', the entire Disney family, the popular Spanish 'Los Lunnis' and the renowned Fisher Price series of playbooks.
Tips Beasco's books are distributed in 35 countries, including all of its Random House territories.

Bebop Books
95 Madison Avenue, NY 10016, USA
- 001 212 779 4400
- 001 212 683 894
- editors@bebopbooks.com
- www.bebopbooks.com
Contact Contact Editor, Jennifer Fox
Established 2000
Parent Lee & Low Books Inc
Categories Publishes Children's Multicultural books in English and Spanish.
Insider Info Bebop books aims to publish books that help improve and encourage reading for children. They provide multicultural content for beginner readers, with guided reading and intervention settings.
Submission Guidelines Detailed submission guidelines are contained on their website.
Tips At the present time Bebop are not accepting submissions, however their website contains up to date information regarding the submission process.

Berlin Verlag
Greifswalder Strasse 207, 10405, Berlin, Germany
- 0049 30 44 38450
- 0049 30 44 384595
- info@berlinverlag.de
- www.berlinverlag.de
Parent Company Bloomsbury Publishing Plc (see entry under UK & Irish Book Publishers)
Contact Managing Director, Kathy Rooney
Categories Publishes Children's Non-Fiction, Fiction and Translation titles.
Insider Info Publishes 120 titles per year.
Recent Title(s) *Ruhelos,* William Boyd
Tips Berlin Verlag, owned by Bloomsbury Publishing Plc, is one of the leading literary publishers in Germany and focuses mainly on literary fiction for the adult market. Berlin Verlag will accept proposals in either German or English language.

Bertelsmann
Verlagsgruppe Random House, Neumarkter Strasse 28, 41360, Munich, Germany
- 0049 89 41360
- 0049 89 41363333
- kundenservice@randomhouse.de
- www.randomhouse.de
Parent Company Random House Group Inc
Categories Publishes Children's Non-Fiction and Fiction titles.
Insider Info Average lead time is six months.
Submission Guidelines Accepts unsolicited manuscripts and proposals.
Recent Title(s) *Swamp Blooms,* Carl Hiaasens
Tips Bertelsmann accepts unsolicited submissions by post only, not by email.

Bick Publishing House
307 Neck Road, Madison, CT 06443, USA
- 001 203 245 0073
- 001 203 245 5990
- bickpubhse@aol.com
- www.bickpubhouse.com
Contact Author and Editor, Dale Carlson
Established 1993
Parent Lee & Low Books Inc
Categories Publishes Fiction for Young Adults and Teenagers, Books on Living for Teens, Wildlife and Adult titles.
Insider Info Publishes self-help and health books for young adults.

Recent Titles *TALK:Teen Art of Communication*, Dale Carlson (Teen Living), *Teen Relationships: To Oneself, To Others, To the World*, J. Krishnamurti (Author), Dale Carlson (Editor)

Tips Titles are developed in-house by author Dale Carlson and associates.

Bloomsbury USA Children
175 Fifth Avenue, 3rd Floor, New York, 10010, USA
- 001 212 780 0115
- 001 212 727 0984
- bloomsbury.kids@bloomsburyusa.com
- www.bloomsburyusa.com

Parent Company Bloomsbury Publishing Plc (see entry under Book Publishers)

Contact Executive Editor, Jill Davis; Editorial Director, Melanie Cecka; Editor, Sarah Odedina; Editor, Ele Fountain

Established 1998

Categories Publishes Children's Fiction, Picture books, Young Adult novels, Series Fiction, Poetry, Fantasy, Easy Reads and Non-Fiction.

Insider Info Publishes 40 titles per year and has 80 in print.

Submission Guidelines Accepts unsolicited manuscripts, but they will only respond if they are interested in pursuing the manuscript. Do not send SAE. They welcome picture book manuscripts and queries for longer works, whether fiction or non-fiction. Send illustration samples to the art department. Does not accept simultaneous submissions.

Recent Title(s) *Dragon Slippers*, Jessica Day George (Fantasy); *Princess Academy* Shannon Hale (Young Novel)

Tips Bloomsbury Children offers reading group guides available to download from their website, which accompanies their successful books.

Boyds Mills Press
815 Church Street Honesdale, Pennsylvania 18431, USA
- 001 800 490 5111
- 001 501 372 5579
- contact@boydsmillspress.com
- www.boydsmillspress.com

Contact Editorial Director, Larry Rosler

Imprint(s) Calkin Creek Books
Front Street (Children)
Wordsong (Children's Poetry)

Established 1991

Categories Publishes Activity books, Picture books, Craft books, Children's Fiction, Non-Fiction and Poetry for under 18's.

Insider Info Publishes approximately 70 titles annually.

Submission Guidelines Accepts unsolicited manuscripts or queries. They are interested in imaginative picture book manuscripts. For fiction submit three sample chapters. For non-fiction send a detailed synopsis outlining what the books is about.

Recent Title(s) *Arctic Thaw* Peter Lourie (Author), Peter Lourie (Photographer)

Brown Barn Books
119 Kettle Creek Road, Weston CT 06883, USA
- 001 203 227 3387
- 001 203 222 9673
- editorial@brownbarnbooks.com
- www.brownbarnbooks.com

Parent Company Pictures of Record Inc

Contact Editor, Nancy Hammerslough

Established 1852

Categories Publishes Young Adult Fiction in the following subjects: Romance, Fantasy, Adventure and Humour.

Insider Info A division of Picture Records, an academic publishing company, Brown Barn Books specialises in exceptional young fiction for children aged 12 and upwards.

Submission Guidelines Send a query in the first instance, and then send the full manuscript on request. Emails are accepted, however they do not open attachments, so the query must be in the body of the email.

Recent Title(s) *The Twilight Box: Tales of Terre II*, Troon Harrison; *Northlander: Tales of the Borderlands*, Book I, Meg Burden

Tips They rarely publish picture books, poetry, books containing graphic sex or violence, books previously published in any medium, or short stories. They very rarely publish books for children under 12, or very short novels (fewer than about 30,000 words).

Cambridge University Press South Africa
Lower Ground Floor, Nautica Building, The Water Club, Beach Road, Granger Bay, Cape Town, South Africa
- 0027 21 412 7800
- 0061 21 419 8418
- information@cup.co.za
- www.cambridge.org

Imprint Roedurico Trust

Categories Publishes School Textbooks, Language Courses and Primary Readers for nine African countries in 32 different languages. Also produce Distance Learning material for the IGCSE and HIGSCE examinations offered by Cambridge International Examinations, and supplementary material such as Reading and Life-skills Kits.

Insider Info The African branch of Cambridge University Press is responsible for actively promoting CUP titles in sub-Saharan Africa and the Caribbean.

Submission Guidelines Visit website for full submission details for their different subject areas.

Candlewick Press

2067 Massachusetts Avenue, Cambridge, MA 02140, USA

- 001 617 661 3330
- 001 617 661 0565
- bigbear@candlewick.com
- www.candlewick.com

Contact Editor, Deborah Wayshak; Editor, Karen Lotz; Editor, Elizabeth Bicknell

Established 1991

Categories Publishes Children's Picture books, Easy Readers, Middle Grade and Young Adult Fiction, Non-Fiction, Poetry collections and Novelty and Activity books.

Insider Info Candlewick is one of the largest independent publishers in the US. Approximately five per cent of books are by first-time authors.

Submission Guidelines No unagented submissions. Send illustration samples for the attention of Anne Moore.

Recent Title(s) *The Tail of Emily Windsnap*, Liz Kessler (Author), Sarah Gibb (Illustrator) (Young Fiction Series)

Tips Publishes *Brand New Readers*, a series for young children.

Capstone Press Inc

151 Good Counsel Drive, PO Box 669, Mankato, MN 56002-0669, USA

- 001 800 747 4992
- 001 507 388 1227
- www.capstonepress.com

Parent Company Coughlan Publishing Group

Established 1991

Categories Publishes Children's Non-Fiction, Educational books and Photographic Picture books on the following subjects: Early Concepts, Maths, Science, American History, Social Studies, Curriculum Content books, Spanish & Bilingual books, Basic Facts books, Easy to Read books, and Teenage issues. Also publishes Interactive Multimedia books.

Insider Info Capstone is a leading educational publisher of children's books. Capstone publishes 400 new books per year for grades Pre K-12.

Submission Guidelines No unsolicited manuscripts. Visit their website to download submission guidelines.

Recent Title(s) *Adventures in Sound with Max Axiom, Super Scientist*, Emily Sohn (Author), Anne Timmons (Illustrator) (Interactive Book)

Tips Author payment may vary. Generally authors are paid in two instalments; 20 per cent upon returning the signed contract, and the remaining 80 per cent after the manuscript has been accepted.

Carlsen Verlag

PO Box 50 03 80, 22703 Hamburg, Germany

- 0049 40 398040
- 0049 40 3980 4390
- info@carlsen.de
- www.carlsen.de

Contact Publisher, Klaus Humann

Categories Publishes Children's Fiction and Non-Fiction, Humour, Picture books, Novelty books, Board books and Activity books.

Submission Guidelines Accepts unsolicited manuscripts with SAE. For illustrations, send three sample copies.

Recent Title(s) *Der Goldene Kompass*, Philip Pullman; *Am Rande der Gesellschaft*, Hauck & Bauer (Humour)

Tips Also publishes Comics and Manga.

Caterman Jeunesse

87, quai Panhard et Levassor, 75013, Paris, France

- 0033 1 40 51 31
- 0033 1 46 33 45
- Online form
- www.flammarion.com

Parent Flammarion Group

Categories Publishes Picture books, Early Childhood books, Children's Fiction and Non-fiction, Children's products. Publishes 250 titles annually.

Submission Guidelines Aims to respond to manuscripts in two months. All manuscripts must be typed and double spaced.

Recent Titles *Le petit prince a dit*, Patrice Léo (Early Childhood Book); *Atlas historiques: L'empire romain* (Non-fiction/History)

Charlesbridge Publishing

85 Main Street, Watertown, MA 02472, USA

☎ 001 800 225 3214

☎ 001 800 926 5775

✉ tradeeditorial@charlesbridge.com

🌐 www.charlesbridge.com

Contact President and Publisher, Brent Farmer; Editorial Director, Harold Underdown; Editor, Yolande LeRoy; Editor, Judy O'Malley

Established 1980

Imprint Whispering Coyote Press

Categories Publishes Educational, Resource, Activity books, Picture books, Poetry, Children's Fiction and Non-Fiction, History and Nursery Rhymes.

Insider Info Charlesbridge publishes high quality books for children, with a goal of creating lifelong readers and lifelong learners. Continually strives to find new voices, new visions, and new directions in children's literature.

Submission Guidelines Accepts unsolicited manuscripts submitted exclusively to them. For picture books and young children's books please send a complete manuscript. For fiction and non-fiction books longer than 30 manuscript pages, please send a detailed plot synopsis, a chapter outline, and three chapters of text. Manuscripts should be typed and double-spaced. Include SAE.

Recent Title(s) *Alaska*, Shelley Gill (Author), Patrick J. Endres (Photographer) (Poetry/Historical); *Deep in the Swamp*, Donna M. Bateman (Author) Brian Lies (Illustrator) (Educational Picture Book)

Tips Visit their online blog for up to date information, news and reviews on their books.

Chart Studio Publishing

40 Long Street, Maitland, Cape Town, South Africa

☎ 0027 21 510 7680

☎ 0027 21 511 8797

✉ chartstudio@chartstudio.com

🌐 www.chartstudio.com

Categories Publishes Visual Educational products for Children including: Posters, Flip Charts, Flash Cards, Puzzles and Games and Audio/CD-ROMS on all subjects, including Maths, Science and English.

Insider Info The company creates products that make learning fun for children and teenagers.

Recent Titles *Deluxe Real Science Kits*; *Rhythm and Rhyme*

Chicago Review Press

814 N. Franklin Street Chicago, IL 60610, USA

☎ 001 312 337 0747

☎ 001 312 337 5110

✉ frontdesk@chicagoreviewpress.com

🌐 www.chicagoreviewpress.com

Contact Publisher, Cynthia Sherry

Inprint(s) Lawrence Hill Books
 A Cappella
 Zephyr Press

Established 1973

Categories Publishes General trade, Activity books and Non-Fiction for Children's and Adult titles.

Insider Info Publishes 300 titles of national interest, currently bringing out about 50 new titles a year.

Submission Guidelines Enclose a cover letter describing your book and your credentials. If you want to include a portion of your manuscript, please send no more than the table of contents and one to two sample chapters in double spaced format. See website for imprint submission guidelines.

Recent Titles *Stomp Rockets, Catapults, and Kaleidoscopes*, Curt Gabrielson (Children's Science/Non-Fiction)

Tips Interested in unique educational books.

Chronicle Books

680 Second Street, San Francisco, California 94107, USA

☎ 001 415 537 4200 or 800 722 6657

☎ 001 415 537 460

✉ frontdesk@chroniclebooks.com

🌐 www.chroniclebooks.com

Contact Chief Executive Officer, Nion McEvoy; President and Publisher, Jay Schaefer; Assistant Editor, Melissa Manlove

Established 1967

Categories Publishes Children's Fiction and Non-Fiction, Picture books, Board books, Activity kits, Novelty books and Adult titles.

Insider Info Publishes 60–100 books per year.

Submission Guidelines Accepts queries and unsolicited manuscripts. Picture books should send the entire manuscript. For books aimed at older readers, submit a detailed synopsis and sample chapters. Aims to respond to queries in one month, and manuscripts in three to five months.

Recent Title(s) *Giant Pop-Out Shapes*, Amelia Powers; *Who Loves You, Baby?*, Nina Laden; *Cowboy Stories*, Barry Moser, Peter Glassman (Historical)

Clarion Books

222 Berkeley Street, Boston, Massachusetts, 02116, USA

- 001 617 351 5000
- www.hmco.com

Contact Editor, Virginia Buckley; Assistant Editor, Dinah Stevenson

Parent Company Houghton Mifflin Inc

Established 1965

Insider Info Clarion Books began publishing Children's Fiction and Picture books with a list of six titles. In 1979 it was bought by and became an imprint of Houghton Mifflin Company. Since then the list has expanded to nearly 60 a year and includes Non-fiction as well as Fiction and Picture books.

Submission Guidelines Visit website for detailed submission guidelines.

Recent Title(s) *My Mommy Is Magic*, Carl Norac (Author) Ingrid Godon (Illustrator)

Tips In the picture books area, the editors are looking for active picture book stories with a beginning, middle, and end that deal fully and honestly with children's emotions. In the non-fiction area, the editors are interested in hearing about social studies, science, concept, wordplay, holiday, historical, and biography ideas for all age levels.

Clear Light Books

823 Don Diego Santa Fe, NM 87505, USA

- 001 800 253 2747
- 001 505 989 9519
- market@clearlightbooks.com
- www.clearlightbooks.com

Contact Publisher, Harmon Houghton

Categories Publishes Children's and Adult Non-Fiction and Fiction .

Insider Info Clear Light Publishing specialises in publishing high-quality fiction and non-fiction books in the following areas: American Indian culture, religion and history, Southwestern Americana and Eastern Philosophy.

Submission Guidelines Visit website for detailed submission guidelines.

The Continuum International Publishing Group

80 Maiden Lane, Suite 704, New York, New York, 10038, USA

- 001 212 953 5858
- 001 212 953 5944
- info@continuum-books.com

- www.continuumbooks.com

Contact Editorial Director (US), David Barker; Vice President/Senior Editor, Evander Lomke; Vice President/Senior Editor, Frank Oveis

Imprint(s) Burns & Oates
Continuum
Thoemmes Continuum
T&T Clark

Established 1999

Categories Publishes Non-Fiction on the following subjects: Academic, Biblical Studies, Education, History, Linguistics, Literature, Philosophy, Politics, Religious Studies, Theology, General Religion, Popular Culture.

Insider Info Publishes 500 titles per year. Authors paid by royalty, with advance offered. Catalogue available free on request. Does not accept simultaneous submissions.

Submission Guidelines Accepts unsolicited manuscripts and proposals.

Recent Title(s) *On the Absence and Unknowability of God*, Andrew Louth

Tips Continuum only publishes in areas they are already strong in, so make sure that all submissions are in keeping with guidelines on the website.

Cricket Books

Carus Publishing Company, 30 Grove Street, Suite C, Peterborough, NH 03458, USA

- 001 800 821 0115/001 603 924 7209
- 001 617 661 0565
- mmiklavcic@caruspub.com
- www.cricketbooks.net

Contact Editor, Deborah Wayshak; Editor, Karen Lotz; Editor, Elizabeth Bicknell

Parent Carus Publishing

Imprint Marcato

Established 1999

Categories Publishes Picture books, Chapter books, Poetry, Non-Fiction and Fiction.

Insider Info Cricket Books brings high quality standards of excellence to all its books for children and young adults.

Submission Guidelines No unsolicited manuscripts. Visit website for full submission details.

Recent Title(s) *A Child's Introduction to the Night Sky* (Astronomy)

Tips Publishes magazines for children of all ages who are interested in a wide range of subjects, from writing to science.

PUBLISHERS

LISTINGS

Darby Creek Publishing

7858 Industrial Parkway, Plain City, OH 43064, USA

- 001 614 873 7955
- 001 614 873 7135
- editorial@darbycreekpublishing.com
- www.darbycreekpublishing.com

Established 1991

Categories Publishes Children's Fiction and Non-Fiction.

Insider Info Darby Creek Publishing publishes a small list of high quality children's and young adult books, including the successful Lurlene McDaniel fiction series for children.

Submission Guidelines For short projects, please submit the entire manuscript. For longer works, such as novels, please submit two or three sample chapters, a synopsis, and a brief chapter summary outline. Send submissions to 'Submissions Editor'. Include any publishing credits to date. For illustrations guidelines visit their website.

Recent Title(s) *Albino Animals*, Kelly Milner Halls (Non-Fiction/Science)

Tips DCP is especially interested in seeing non-fiction works for ages eight to fourteen, with themes that relate to sports, science, history, or biography.

David Bateman Ltd

Tarndale Grove, Albany Business Park, Bush Road, Albany, Auckland, 1330, New Zealand

- 0064 9 415 7664
- 0064 9 415 8892
- bateman@bateman.co.nz
- www.bateman.co.nz

Contact Chairman/Publisher, David Bateman

Categories Publishes Non-Fiction, Fiction and Children's titles on the following subjects: Adult books, Architecture, Art, Biography, Business, Children's Fiction, Craft, Education, General Interest, History, How-To, Literary Fiction, Local Interest, Mainstream Fiction, Reference, Science, Self-Help, Travel, Ufology.

Recent Title(s) *Lethal Deliveries*, Ken Benn (Children's Fiction)

Dawn Publications

12402 Britney Springs Road, Nevada City, California, 95959, USA

- 001 800 545 7475
- glenn@dawnpub.com
- www.dawnpub.com

Contact Editor and Co-publisher, Glenn Hovemann; Manager and Co-publisher, Muffy Weaver

Established 1979

Categories Publishes Picture books and Children's Non-Fiction with a focus on Nature, Habitat and Science, Biographies, Seasonal specials and Series.

Insider Info Dawn Publications publishes quality nature books especially targeted at children. It began with the genius of one man, Joseph Cornell, with the publication of *Sharing Nature With Children*, which went on to sell 500,000 copies worldwide and encouraged more of his popular series.

Submission Guidelines Visit website for submission details.

Recent Title(s) *Grandma's Feather Bed,* John Denver (Author), Christopher Canyon (Illustrator) (Picture Book); *Over in the Jungle: A Rainforest Rhyme*, Marianne Berkes (Author), Jeanette Canyon (Illustrator) (Picture Books)

DC Comics

1700 Broadway, New York, 10019, USA

- 001 212 636 5400
- 001 212 636 5975
- www.dccomics.com

Imprint(s) Wildstorm
Vertigo

Categories Publishes Activity books, Board books, Novelty books, Picture books, Painting and Colouring books, Pop-Up books, Fiction, Fairy tales, Film/Television Tie-Ins, Comic gifts and products.

Insider Info DC Comics publishes and licenses comic books in all genres including fantasy, horror and super heroes.

Submission Guidelines Visit website for submission guidelines.

Recent Title(s) *Teen Titans Go!: Titans Together*, J. Torres (Author); *Art*, Mike Norton, Todd Nauck, Larry Stucker and others

Delacorte Press Books for Young Readers

1745 Broadway, New York, NY 10019, USA

- 001 212 782 9000
- 001 212 302 7985
- www.randomhouse.com

Parent Random House Inc

Contact Editor, Emily Jacobs; Editor Meg Ruley

Categories Publishes Children's Fiction and Young Novels, Education and General Interest.

Insider Info
Among the many bestselling authors published by Delacorte Press Books for Young Readers are David

Almond, Ann Brashares, Libba Bray, Caroline Cooney, Robert Cormier, Lurlene McDaniel, Phyllis Reynolds.
Submission Guidelines No unsolicited manuscripts. Agent material only.
Recent Title(s) *Muddle Earth,* Paul Stewart (Author) Chris Riddell (Illustrator)
Tips Delacorte will accept unsolicited manuscripts if they are submitted to either the Delacorte Dell Yearling Contest for a First Middle-Grade Novel or the Delacorte Press Contest for a First Young Adult Novel. Visit website for details.

Destino Infantil y Juvenil
Avenida Diagonal, 662-66408034, Barcelona, Spain
- 0034 93 492 81 55
- 0034 93 496 70 41
- destinojoven@edestino.es
- www.destinojoven.com
Contact Editor, Marta Vilagut
Parent Grupo Planeta
Categories Publishes Picture books, Pop-Up books, Fiction and Alternative Illustrated books for children aged 0–10 years and Teenage novels.
Recent Titles *El maestro de las sombras*, Angela Sommer-Bodenburg (Fantasy)

Deutscher Taschenbuch Verlag
Friedrichstrasse 1a, 80801 Munich, Germany
- 0049 089 381670
- 0049 089 346428
- junior@dtv.de
- www.dtvjunior.de
Parent Company Deutscher Taschenbuch Verlag
Contact Publisher, Anne Schieckel, Editor Gabriele Leja
Categories Publishes Children's Non-Fiction and Fiction on the following subjects; Science Fiction, Action/Adventure, Fantasy, Romance, Family, Animals, Easy Reads, Picture books, Encyclopedias, Series.
Submission Guidelines No email submissions.
Recent Titles *Gelscht*, Marco Art (Science Fiction); *Zutritt erst ab zehn*, Marion Dane Farmer (Fiction/Family)

Dial Books For Young Readers
345 Hudson Street, New York, NY, 10014, USA
- 001 212 366 2000
- 001 416 2124 143394
- www.penguin.com
Parent Company Penguin Group (USA)

Contact President and Publishing, Nancy Paulson; Senior Editor, Cecile Goyette; Art Director, Lily Malcom
Established 1961
Categories Publishes Children's Fiction and Non-Fiction, Picture books, Board books and Interactive books.
Insider Info Publishes 50 titles per year for children of all ages. It has pioneered books for the young, including the first quality board books published in the US, Rosemary Wells's *Very First Books* line.
Submission Guidelines No unsolicited manuscripts. A response is made only if they are interested in publishing the script. Aims to respond in four months. For picture books send the entire manuscript. For longer novels send no more than ten pages along with a covering letter describing the genre and target age range. Send illustration samples to 'Dial Design'. All communication via post should include SAE.
Recent Title(s) *The Old African*, Julius Lester (Author), Jerry Pinkney (Illustrator) (Fiction); *The Twin Princes*, Tedd Arnold (Author and Illustrator) (Picture Book)

Didier Jeunesse
8, rue d'Assas, 75006 Paris, France
- 0033 1 49 54 48 30
- 0033 1 49 54 48 31
- online submission form
- www.didierjeunesse.com
Contact Director, Mme Michéle Moreau; Editor, Emmanuelle Painvin
Categories Publishes Children's Fiction on Fantasy, Humour, and Adventure. Religious books, Cultural books, Illustrated books, Poetry, Early readers series and Musical Picture books featuring an audio CD
Submission Guidelines Include SAE. Aims to respond in three months.
Recent Titles *A l'ombre de l'olivier* (The Shade of the Olive Tree) by Magdeleine Lerasle, Hafida Favret and Nathalie Novi (Music Book)
La nuit des cages (The Night of the Cages) by Simon Hureau (Young Adult)

Doubleday Canada
5900 Finch Avenue East, Scarborough, Ontario, M1B 0A2, Canada
- 001 416 977 7891
- 001 416 977 8707
- www.doubledaycanada.ca
Parent Bertelsmann AG
Random House of Canada Ltd

Contact Chairman, John Neale; Publisher, Maya Mavjee

Established 1942

Categories Publishes General trade, Children's Fiction and Non-fiction, Young Novels and Adult books

Insider Info Doubleday is the premier direct marketer of general interest and speciality book clubs in Canada. Doubleday has a wide variety of children's book clubs, which offer a great selection for every interest.

Recent Title(s) *The Story of the Little Mole Who Went in Search of Whodunit*, Werner Holzwarth (Author), Wolf Erlbruch (Illustrator) (Picture Book); *Outriders: Expedition to Blue Cave & Expedition to Willow Key*, Ed Decter (Children's Fiction Series); *Disney's My First 1000 Words* (Movie Tie-In/Educational)

Dover Publications Inc
31 East 2nd Street, Mineola, New York, 11501, USA
- 001 516 294 7000
- 001 516 873 1401
- info@doverpublications.com
- www.doverpublications.com

Contact Editor-in-Chief, Paul Negri; Editor (Math/Science reprints), John Grafton

Categories Publishes Children's Story books, Activity and Project books, Colouring books, Paper Dolls, Dover Little Activity Books and Children's Classics.

Insider Info Publishes 660 titles per year including the Adult titles. Accepts simultaneous submissions.

Submission Guidelines Accepts unsolicited manuscripts and proposals.

Recent Title(s) *I Love Butterflies*, Cathy Beylon and Nina Barbaresi (Colouring book)

Tips Dover mainly publishes activity books and reprints for children.

The Dundurn Group
3 Church Street, Suite 500, Toronto, Ontario, M5E 1M2, Canada
- 001 416 214 5544
- 001 416 214 5556
- info@dundurn.com
- www.dundurn.com

Contact President and Publisher, Kirk Howard; Editor (Fiction), Barry Jowett; Editor (Non-Fiction), Tony Hawke

Established 1972

Imprint(s) Boardwalk Books
Dundurn Press

Hounslow Press
Simon & Pierre

Categories Publishes Young Adult books on the following subjects: Historical Fiction, Teenage Life, Poetry, Illustrated books, Canadian History and Non-fiction

Insider Info Pays ten percent royalty on net receipts, with advance offered. Receives 600 queries per year. 50 per cent of books come from unagented writers, and 25 per cent of books from first-time authors. Accepts simultaneous submissions. Average lead time of one year.

Submission Guidelines Accepts unsolicited manuscripts and proposals with SAE. No email submissions.

Recent Title(s) *Nobody's Child*, Marsha Forchuk Skrypuch (Fiction)

Dunmore Press Ltd
PO Box 25083, Wellington, 6146, New Zealand
- 0064 4 472 2705
- 0064 4 471 0604
- books@dunmore.co.nz
- www.dunmore.co.nz

Categories Publishes Non-Fiction titles on the following subjects: Business, Economics, Education, Environment, General Interest, Health, History, Law, Media, Politics, Society.

Insider Info Publishes 30 titles per year. Pays ten per cent royalty on retail price. Aims to respond to proposals within three weeks. Average lead time is three months. Authors receive ten free copies of their publication.

Submission Guidelines Accepts unsolicited manuscripts and proposals.

Tips Dunmore Press publishes New Zealand themed non-fiction only.

Dupuis sa
Rue Destrée, 52, 6001 Marcinelle, Belgium
- 0032 71 60 05 00
- 0032 71 60 05 99
- info@dupuis.com
- www.dupuis.com

Contact Director, M. Jérôme Baron

Categories Publishes Children's Comics on Adventure, Family and Humour, Humour books, Science Fiction, Fantasy, Thriller, Action and Heroic tales.

Insider Info Dupuis' catalogue covers nearly 2,000 titles with over 100 series. The works published are sorted into collections covering all the above categories. Visit their website for more details.

Recent Titles *Le Petit Spirou: Fais de beaux rêves*
(13th Book in the Series)
Tips Distributes to France, Switzerland and Canada.
Also a publisher of games and gifts.

Duttons Children's Books
345 Hudson Street, New York, NY, 10014, USA
- 001 212 366 2792
- 001 212 243 6002
- www.penguin.com

Parent Company Penguin Group (USA)
Contact President and Publishing, Stephan Lurie;
Editorial Director, Donna Brooks; Art Director,
Sara Reynolds
Established 1852
Categories Publishes Children's Fiction and Non-Fiction, Young Adult novels and Photographic books
Insider Info Publishes 80 hardcover titles per year
for children of all ages, from babies to young adults.
Half of their published work is fiction mostly in the
young adult age range. The core of Duttons' backlist
is found in the four classic works of A.A. Milne and
Ernest H. Shepard: *Winnie the Pooh, The House at
Pooh Corner, When We Were Very Young*, and *Now We
Are Six*, works that have been in print for over
eighty years.
Submission Guidelines No unsolicited
manuscripts. Send query letter with a SAE. Aims to
respond in four months. Send illustration samples
with a SAE to Dutton's Art Director.
Recent Title(s) *When the Fireflies Come*, Jonathan
London, Teri Weidner (Fiction), *Leonard: Beautiful
Dreamer*, Robert Byrd (Non-Fiction), *Skippyjon Jones*,
Judy Schachner (Picture Book)

Edcon Publishing Group
30 Montauk Boulevard, Oakdale, NY 11769-1399, USA
- 001 631 567 7227
- 001 631 567 8745
- info@edconpublishing.com
- www.edconpublishing.com

Parent A/V Concepts Corp
Contact Editorial Director, Laura Solimene
Categories Publishes Educational books and
Products covering all school subjects and life skills.
Insider Info Edcon publishes high quality learning
materials aimed at children Pre-K-12 and those with
special needs. Their catalogue is available to
order online.
Recent Title(s) *Sharpening Writing Skills Reading
Level 4*

Ediciones SM
**C/Impresores 15, Urb. Prado des Espino, 28660,
Bodilla, Madrid, Spain**
- 0034 91 422 8800
- 0034 91 422616
- editeur@pocket.fr
- www.pocket.fr

Contact Publisher, José Luis Cortes Salinas
Parent Grupo SM
Categories Publishes Children's Fiction, Picture
books, Fiction series, Teenage novels, Novelty books
and Film/Television Tie-Ins.
Insider Info Publishes approximately 200
books a year.
Submission Guidelines Will consider unsolicited
manuscripts; allow six months for a response.
Recent Titles *El caballo de agua* (Children's Fiction
6–8 years)

Éditions Autrement
**77, rue du Faubourg Saint-Antoine, 75011 Paris,
France**
- 0033 1 44 73 80 00
- 0033 1 44 73 00 12
- www.autrement.com

Contact President, M. Henry Dougier; Children's
Editor, M. Christian Demilly
Categories Publishes Children's Fiction on
Adventure, Relationships and Family, and Non-fiction on History, History of France, Culture,
Autobiographies, Human Body, Nature and Sports.
Also publishes Picture books and Dictionaries and
Encyclopedias.
Insider Info Publishes approximately 100 new
titles a year
Recent Titles *Au Loup!*, Sophie Bernard (Author),
Bruno Gilbert (Illustrator) (Picture Book)

Éditions du Poisson Soluble
**35, boulevard Carnot, 43000 Le-Puy-en-Velay,
France**
- 0033 4 73 94 90 70
- 0039 4 73 94 90 70
- poissonsoluble@wanadoo.fr
- www.poissonsoluble.com

Contact Director, M. Olivier Belhomme; Assistant
Director, M. Stéphane Queyriaux
Categories Publishes Children's Fiction on the
following subjects; Romance, Animals, Family and
Fantasy, and Non-fiction on the following subjects;
How-To, Nature, Animals, History, Sports and

Mythology. Also publishes Baby books and Picture books.

Insider Info The company has offices throughout France, Switzerland, Belgium and Canada.

Recent Titles *Le Grand Gentil Loup (The Large Nice Wolf)*, Ben Lebègue (Author and Illustrator) (Picture Book)

Editions Gallimard-Jeunesse

5, rue Sébastien-Bottin, 75328 Paris, Cedex 07, France

- ☎ 0033 1 49 54 42 00
- ☎ 0033 1 45 44 39 46
- ✉ enquiries@gallimard-jeunesse.fr
- 🌐 www.gallimard-jeunesse.fr

Parent Company Gallimard group

Contact Director of Children's Hedwige Pasquet; Publisher, Christine Baker; Editor, Anne de Bouchony

Categories Publishes Children's Fiction, Non-Fiction on Science and History subjects, and Picture books, Board books, Pop-Up books and Novelty books.

Submission Guidelines Only accepts submissions via email. All submissions must be in Word or Adobe Acrobat format. Send submissions to: christian.plezent@gallimard-jeunesse.fr

Recent Titles *Á Pompéi sous l'Empire romain*, Sandrine Mirza (Roman History)
Le Royaume de Thirrin II: Lame de Feu, (The Kingdom of Thirrin II: Blade of Fire) by Stuart Hill Pierre-Marie Valat (Illustrator) (Fiction Series)

Editions Kaliédoscope

11, rue de Sévres, 75006 Paris, France

- ☎ 0033 1 45 44 07 08
- ☎ 0033 1 45 44 53 71
- ✉ infos@editions-kaleidoscope.com
- 🌐 www.editions-kaleidoscope.com

Contact Children's Publisher, Isabel Finkenstaedt; Editors, Stéphanie Jarry and Olivia Egrot

Categories Publishes upmarket Picture books.

Insider Info A small scale publishing company run by three women. It publishes approximately 30 titles a year.

Submission Guidelines Aims to respond to manuscripts and illustrations in three months. All manuscripts must be typed and double spaced.

Recent Titles *Billy se bile,* Anthony Browne (Author and Illustrator) (Picture Book)

Tips Manuscripts must be for children aged 0–6.

Éditions Larousse

21 rue de Montparnasse, 75283 Paris, Cedex 6, France

- ☎ 0033 1 44 39 44 00
- ☎ 0033 1 44 39 43 43
- ✉ Online form
- 🌐 www.larousse.fr

Parent Company Hachette Livre

Imprint(s) Petit Larousse
 Petits Classiques

Categories Publishes Educational, Young Adult and Children's titles on the following subjects: Bilingual Dictionaries, Culture, Encyclopedias, General Interest, Practical Guides, Translations.

Submission Guidelines Accepts unsolicited manuscripts and proposals. See the Hachette website, www.hachette.com for more details (in French only).

Tips Specialises in educational language texts.

Editorial Cruilla

Avenida de la Marina, 54 Polígon Can Calderon, 08830 Sant Boi de Llobregat, Spain

- ☎ 0034 90 212 3336
- ☎ 0034 93 630 8750
- ✉ cruilla_cesma@ediciones-sm.com
- 🌐 www.cruilla.cat

Contact Publisher, Josep Herreco

Categories Publishes Children's Fiction for 5–8 year olds and 9–12 year olds, Teenage novels, Activity books, Picture books, Poetry, Education books and Adult titles.

Insider Info The company publishes approximately 120–130 titles a year.

Recent Titles *Amor, guix i margarides,* Irene Zimmerman

Edizioni El/Einaudi Ragazzi/Emme Edizioni

Via J. Ressel, 5-34018 San Dorligo della Valle TS, Itlay

- ☎ 0039 40 388 0311
- ☎ 0039 40 388 0330
- ✉ edizioniel@edizioniel.it
- 🌐 www.edizioniel.com

Contact Publisher, Orietta Fatucci

Parent Arnoldo Mondadori Editore

Categories Publishes Children's Non-Fiction and Fiction, Activity books, Board books, Picture books, Pop-Up books, Poetry and Fairy tales.

Insider Info The Company comprises of three prestigious publishers; Edizioni EL, Einaudi Ragazzi and Emme Edizioni, with approximately 270 new titles in print each year.

Submission Guidelines Accepts unsolicited manuscripts or sample chapters, however due to the sheer volume of scripts they receive, they are unable to give feedback unless interested in pursuing the book. Aims to respond within six months.

Recent Titles *Favole al telefono*, Rodari Gianni (Author), Altan Francesco (Illustrator)

Eerdmans Books For Young Readers
255 Jefferson Avenue SE, Grand Rapids MI 49503-4554, USA
- 001 616 459 4591
- 001 616 459 6540
- www.eerdmans.com/youngreaders

Parent Eerdmans Publishing Company

Contact President, Judy Zylstra; Art Director, Gayle Brown

Established 1911

Categories Publishes Picture books, Biographies, Bible stories and Young Adult Fiction.

Insider Info Publishes approximately 12–18 books per year. Catalogue is available on request.

Submission Guidelines Eerdmans will only consider exclusive submissions that are clearly marked as such on the outside of the envelope.

Recent Title(s) *Abby's Chairs*, Barbara Santucci (Author), Debrah Santini (Illustrator) (Picture Book); *Angels Among Us*, Leena Lane (Author), Elena Baboni (Illustrator) (Bible Story)

Tips They seek manuscripts that are honest, wise and hopeful, or stories that simply delight with their storyline, characters, or good humour.

Egmont
Vognmagergade 11, DK-1148, Copenhagen, K, Denmark
- 0045 33 305550
- 0045 33 321902
- egmont@egmont.com
- www.egmont.com

Parent Company Egmont International Holdings A/S

Contact President/Chief Executive Officer, Steffen Kragh; Executive Vice President - Egmont Group/ Managing Director - Egmont Books, Tom Harald Jenssen; Editor (Aschehoug), Jeppe Markers

Imprint(s) Aschehoug

Categories Publishes Children's Fiction, Non-Fiction and Magazines, often based around licenced characters.

Submission Guidelines Egmont accept submissions for fiction or non-fiction directed at Aschehoug publishers. See www.aschehoug.dk for details (only available in Danish).

Eos
10 East 53rd Street, New York, New York, 10022, USA
- 001 212 261 6500
- 001 212 207 6927
- www.harpercollins.com

Parent Company HarperCollins Children's Books

Insider Info Eos Books is an imprint of HarperCollins, it publishes the best in science fiction and fantasy for children.

Submission Guidelines Only accepts agented submissions.

Recent Title(s) *Day of the Scarab*, Catherine Fisher

Être Éditions Sarl
56, rue Ramus, 75020 Paris, France
- 0033 1 47 97 44 67
- 0033 1 47 97 44 67
- christianbruel@etre-editions.com
- www.etre-editions.com

Contact Founder and Editor, Christian Bruel; Artistic Director, Richard Takvorian

Categories Publishes beautiful, stylistic illustrated stories for young children and adults, and adaptations of classic texts.

Insider Info Publishes approximately five to seven new books per year. The Editor is a successful, but highly criticised children's author whose books tend to address taboo subjects for children, such as death and sexuality.

Recent Titles *Petits chaperons loups,* a reprint by Christian Bruel, Nicole Claveloux (Illustrator) *Alboum,* Christian Bruel (Author), Nicole Claveloux (Illustrator)

Evan-Moor Educational Publishers
18 Lower Ragsdale Drive, Monterey, CA 93940-5746, USA
- 001 800 714 0971
- 001 831 649 6256
- www.evan-moor.com

Contact President, Linda Hanger; Senior Editor, Marilyn Evans; Art Director, Cheryl Pucket

Established 1979

Categories Publishes Educational Materials (such as Activity books, Textbooks, How-To books, CD-Roms) on all school subjects including Maths, Science,

Social Studies, English, Arts & Craft books for children and teachers.

Insider Info Publishes 50 titles per year with 450 in print.

Submission Guidelines Less than 10 per cent of books are by first time authors. Visit website for submission guidelines.

Recent Title(s) *Building Spelling Skills Daily Practice* (English/Education)

Fabbri Editori

Via Mencenate 91, 20138 Milano, Italy

- ☎ 0039 2 5091
- ☎ 0039 2 5095 2387
- ✉ www.edizionnel.com
- 🌐 www.fabbri.rcslibri.corriere.it

Parent Company RCS Libri S.p.A

Categories Publishes Children's Fiction with a specialist interest in Fantasy, Picture books, and Non-Fiction.

Recent Title(s) *Eragon,* Christopher Paolini; *Randa Ghazy; Oggi forse non ammazzo nessuno*, Sognando Palestina (Non-fiction/Biography)

Facts On File Inc

132 West 31st Street, New York, NY 10001, USA

- ☎ 001 212 967 8800
- ☎ 001 212 967 9196
- ✉ llikoff@factsonfile.com
- 🌐 www.factsonfile.com

Contact Editorial Director (Science, Fashion, Natural History), Laurie Likoff; Senior Editor (Science and Technology, Nature, Reference), Frank Darmstadt; Senior Editor (American History, Women's Studies, Young Adult Reference), Nicole Bowen; Trade Editor (Health, Pop Culture, True Crime, Sports), James Chambers; Acquisitions Editor (Language/Literature), Jeff Soloway

Imprint(s) Checkmark Books

Categories Publishes Educational books on the following subjects: Religion/Mythology, U.S History, Careers, Entertainment, Health, History, Language/Literature, Multicultural, Natural History, Science/Technology, Recreation, Reference, Religion, Sociology and Sports.

Insider Info Publishes 150 titles per year. Pays ten per cent royalty on retail price, with advance offered. 25 per cent of books come from unagented writers. Accepts simultaneous submissions. Book catalogue available free on request.

Recent Title(s) *Career Ideas for Kids Who Like Science, Second Edition*, Diane Lindsey Reeves with Lindsey Clasen (Careers & Education)

Tips Facts On File publishes educational reference material aimed mostly at schools and libraries. Submissions must be directed to the appropriate Editor.

Farrar, Straus and Giroux Books For Young Readers

19 Union Square West, New York, NY 10003, USA

- ☎ 001 212 741 6900
- ☎ 001 212 633 9385
- ✉ childrens.editorial@fsgbooks.com
- 🌐 www.fsgkidsbooks.com

Parent Farrar, Straus and Giroux Inc

Imprints Frances Foster Books
 Melanie Kroupa Books

Contact Editorial Director, Margaret Ferguson; Editor, Wes Adams

Established 1954

Categories Publishes Very Young Children's books, Picture books, Children's Fiction, Teenage Novels.

Insider Info A successful publishing imprint, which publishes high quality children's books in hardback and paperback, with a list from well established children's authors, such as Ruth White and David Small.

Recent Title(s) *Animal Poems*, Valerie Worth (Author), Steve Jenkins (Illustrator) (Picture/Poetry Book)

Submission Guidelines No unsolicited manuscripts. For longer works send a query letter before submitting any work. Manuscripts should be typed and double spaced. There are no fixed lengths for stories. For illustrations send samples not original work. Send submissions to the Children's Editorial Department. Aims to respond in three months.

Firebird

345 Hudson Street, New York, NY 10014, USA

- ☎ 001 212 366 2000
- ✉ firebird@us.penguingroup.com
- 🌐 www.penguin.com/www.firebirdbooks.com

Parent Company Penguin Group (USA)

Contact Editorial Director, Sharyn November

Established 2002

Categories Publishes Children's Fantasy and Science Fiction novels.

Insider Info Firebird is a paperback only imprint company that reprints and reissues between 12–18 books annually for an audience of teenagers and adults. The one exception is the hardcover anthology *Firebirds*, which contains original stories by authors connected with the imprint.

Submission Guidelines Firebird does not publish original fiction in paperback. They will edit original hardcover fantasy and science fiction for the Viking list (imprint for Penguin), however almost all of these works are solicited.

Recent Title(s) *Ratha's Creature,* Clare Bell (Reissue); *Journey Between Worlds*, Sylvia Engdahl (Paperback); *I'm Afraid You've Got Dragons*, Peter Beagle (Original Novella)

Tips Readers can sign up online to the Firebird newsletter, for periodic updates. Teenagers may ask to be part of the website's active teen advisory board.

Fitzhenry & Whiteside
195 Allstate Parkway, Markham, Ontario L3R 4T8, Canada
- 001 800 387 9776
- 001 800 260 9777
- submissions@fitzhenry.ca
- www.fitzhenry.ca

Contact President, Sharon Fitzhenry; Children's Publisher, Gail Winskill
Established 1966
Categories Publishes Children's Fiction and Non-Fiction, Picture books, Education books (Social Studies, Visual Arts, Biography, Environment) and Adult Fiction.
Imprint(s) Red Deer Press Inc
Fifth House
Trifolium Books
Insider Info Fitzhenry & Whiteside is a private limited corporation owned by the Fitzhenry family, with over 1,500 titles in print. They publish or reprint about 200 titles per annum.
Submission Guidelines No unsolicited manuscripts.
Recent Title(s) *A Company of Fools* (Paperback), Deborah Ellis; *A Bumblebee Sweater,* Betty Waterton (Author), Kim LaFave (Illustrator) (Picture Book); *Omar On Board*, Maryann Kovalski (Young Fiction)
Tips The company prefers Canadian authors.

Flammarion Group
87, quai Panhard et Levassor, 75647 Paris Cedex 13, France
- 0033 1 40 51 31 00
- 0033 1 43 29 21 48
- Online form
- www.flammarion.com

Imprint(s) Pere Castor
Castor Poche
Editions Flammarion

Caterman Jeunesse
Established 1875
Insider Info A leading French publisher which, along with its imprints, publishes many high quality children's books covering all subjects.
Submission Guidelines See individual imprints for submission guidelines.

Flux
2143 Wooddale Drive, Woodbury, Minnesota, 55125 USA
- 001 800 843 6666
- 001 651 291 1908
- submissions@fluxnow.com
- www.fluxnow.com

Parent Company Llewellyn Worldwide Ltd
Contact Acquisitions Editor, Nancy J. Mostad (Llewellyn Worldwide)
Categories Publishes Fiction for teens in the following subjects: Teen Issues, Romance, Science-Fiction, Fantasy and Gender.
Insider Info An imprint company that publishes books of most genres for children aged 12 and upwards.
Submission Guidelines Accepts unsolicited manuscripts and proposals. Flux accepts manuscripts and queries by email. Aims to respond in 6 months.
Recent Title(s) *Back Talk,* Alex Richards (Young Adult fiction)
Tips Submissions to Flux should be no less than 35,000 words. Visit website for full submission guidelines.

Free Spirit Publishing
217 Fifth Avenue North, Suite 200, Minneapolis, MN 55401-1299, USA
- 001 612 338 2068
- 001 612 337 5050
- help4kids@freespirit.com
- www.freespirit.com

Contact President, Judy Galbraith
Established 1983
Categories Publishes Learning Materials and Educational Resources for children, teachers, parents and the medical profession. Produces Audio and Posters, and Self-Help titles for teenagers, tackling subjects from bullying to grief.
Insider Info Free Spirit is the leading publisher of learning tools that support young people's social and emotional health. Publishes approximately 18–22 new books per year, with a backlist of over 100 books.

Submission Guidelines They advise authors to read their author guidelines before submitting any work as the books published are highly specialised and many authors are expert educators or health professionals. Visit the website for author guidelines. Aims to respond to proposals in two to six months.

Recent Title(s) *Accept and Value Each Person*, Cheri J. Meiners M.Ed; *The ADD & ADHD Answer Book*, Susan Ashley Ph.D

Front Street Books

815 Church Street, Honesdale, PA 18431

✆ 001 800 490 5111

✆ 001 501 372 5579

✉ contactus@frontstreetbooks.com

🌐 www.frontstreetbooks.com

Parent Boyds Mill Press

Contact President, Stephen Roxburgh

Established 1994

Categories Publishes Children's Fiction, Young Adult Novels and Picture books.

Insider Info Publishes high quality fiction for children and young adults and sophisticated picture books from here and abroad. They strive to expose young readers to the best literature available in other countries, cultures, and languages.

Submission Guidelines Accepts unsolicited manuscripts or queries. They are interested in imaginative picture books send entire manuscript. For fiction submit 3 chapter sample. For non-fiction send a detailed synopsis outlining what the books is about.

Recent Title(s) *Black-Eyed Suzie*, Susan Shaw (Dramatic Novel); *Seventeen*, Per Nilsson (Author) Tara Chace (Translator); *My Daddy*, Susan M. Paradis (Author) Susan M. Paradis (Illustrator)

Tips Front Street books address important and sensitive issues that face some young adults such as child abuse and depression and offers hope and encouragement to them through their words.

Giunti Editore S.p.A

Via Bolognese 165, 50139, Florence, Italy

✆ 0039 55 50621

✆ 0039 55 5062298

✉ segreteriaeditoriale@giunti.it

🌐 www.giunti.it

Parent Company Giunti Gruppo Editoriale

Contact Chairman, Sergio Giunti; Managing Director/Chief Executive Officer, Martino Montanarini; Editorial Manager, Bruno Mari

Imprint(s) Dami

Giunti

Giunti Demetra

Giunti Junior

Giunti Kids

Categories Publishes Non-Fiction and Children's titles on the following subjects: Art, Crafts, Education, Essays, Grandi Opere, Guidebooks, History, Multimedia, Practical, Science, School Journals, Teaching Resources, Tourism.

Insider Info Publishes 481 titles per year. Catalogue available online.

Recent Title(s) *Le Parole del Cuore*, Sabrina Carollo

Tips Giunti primarily publishes books and educational materials for children and students, including electronic resources.

Golden Books

1745 Broadway, New York, NY 10019, USA

✆ 001 212 782 9000

✆ 001 212 302 7985

🌐 www.randomhouse.com

Parent Random House Inc

Contact Editor, Melissa Lagonegro, Editor, Shana Corey, Editor, Diane Muldrow

Established 1942

Categories Publishes Children's Fiction and Non-Fiction, Picture books, Board books, Film, Television and Toy Tie-Ins, Educational Workbooks and Products.

Insider Info Many of the original Golden Book titles are still wildly popular. *Poky the Little Puppy*, *Tootle*, *The Saggy Baggy Elephant*, and *Scruffy the Tugboat* are among the top ten bestselling children's books of all time. Golden Books reissues the best of their backlist in hardcover as well as in the traditional Little Golden Book format.

Submission Guidelines No unsolicited manuscripts. Agent material only.

Recent Title(s) *Little Golden Book Collection: Farm Tales*, (Children's Fiction – Animals) (Little Golden Books Boxset); *Barbie the Island Princess: A Storybook*, Mary Man-Kong (Film Tie-In)

G.P. Putnam's Sons

345 Hudson Street, New York, NY, 10014

✆ 001 212 414 3610

🌐 www.penguin.com

Parent Company Penguin Group (USA)

Contact President and Publisher, Nancy Paulsen; Executive Editor, Kathy Dawson; Art Director, Cecilia Young

Established 1838

Categories Publishes Children's Fiction and Non-Fiction, Picture books.

Insider Info Publishes 50 hardcover and paperback titles per year for children. The imprint specialises in picture books, which annually climb to the top of the best sellers list.

Submission Guidelines For fiction and non-fiction books send a synopsis with sample chapters including a contents table for non-fiction. Include any publishing credits. Aims to respond to manuscripts in two months. For picture books send the entire manuscript. There are length guidelines for their books: young children's picture books 200–1,000 words; middle age range, 10,000–30,000 words; and young adult's fiction 40,000–50,000 words. Make contact for illustrator guidelines.

Recent Title(s) *Fat Kids Rule The World*, K.L Going

Graphia

222 Berkeley Street, Boston, Massachusetts, 02116, USA

☎ 001 617 351 5000

✆ www.hmco.com

Contact Editorial Director, Judy O'Mailey; Executive Editor, Margaret Raymo; Paperback Director, Julia Richardson; Senior Editor, Ann Rider; Submissions Coordinator, Hannah Rodgers; Editor Amy Flynn; Assistant Editor, Kate O'Sullivan

Parent Houghton Mifflin Inc

Insider Info Graphia imprint publishes both paperback originals and reprints in fiction and non-fiction, poetry and graphic novels. Graphia is recognised for its quality and unique books.

Submission Guidelines No unsolicited queries, manuscripts only via literary agents.

Recent Title(s) *What Your Mama Never Told You*, edited by Tara Roberts; *The Candy Darlings*, by Christine Walde

Grasset et Fasquelle

61, rue des Saints-Pères, 75006 Paris, France

☎ 0033 1 44 39 22 00

✆ 0033 1 42 22 64 18

✉ dfanelli@grasset.fr

✆ www.edition-grasset.fr

Contact Children's Editor, Marielle Gens

Categories Publishes Children's Fiction on the following subjects Animals and Family, Educational books, Fictional Series, Young Novels and CD-ROMS

Insider Info Grasset is one of France's leading publishers of quality fiction for adults and children. A backlist of over 3,000 titles and publishes 180 new titles a tear including adult.

Recent Titles *La Balade de Petit Poisson*, Dominique Beccaria; *Le petit monde merveilleux*, (A Small Marvellous World) ages 7+ by Gustave Akakpo (Author) Dominique Mwankumi (Illustrtor)

Greenwillow Books

10 East 53rd Street, New York, NY 10022, USA

☎ 001 212 261 6500

✆ 001 212 207 6927

✆ www.harpercollins.com

Parent Company HarperCollins Children's Books

Contact Senior Editor, Rebecca Davis; Editor, Steve Geck

Insider Info Greenwillow is an imprint of HarperCollins that publishes high quality books, which possess integrity and depth for children of every age.

Submission Guidelines Only accepts agented submissions.

Recent Title(s) *Behold the Bold Umbrellaphant*, Jack Prelutsky (Author), Carin Berger (Illustrator)

Grosset & Dunlap

345 Hudson Street, New York, NY 10014

☎ 001 212 366 2000

✆ 001 212 366 3393

✆ www.penguin.com

Parent Company Penguin Group (USA)

Contact President and Publishing, Debra Dorfman; Editorial Director, Bonnie Bader

Established 1898

Imprint(s) Platt & Munk
Somerville House USA
Planet Dexter

Categories Publishes Children's Fiction and Non-Fiction, Film tie-in titles, Picture books, Activity books and Board books.

Insider Info Grosset & Dunlap publishes about 175 books a year. They focus on licensing properties, original paperback series and capitalising on successful in-house brands.

Submission Guidelines Only accepts submissions via literary agents.

Recent Title(s) *Strawberry Shortcake*, *Sonic X* (License); Shapes, Jelly Belly (Board Book)

Groundwood Books

110 Spadina Avenue, Suite 801, Toronto, ON, M5V 2K4, Canada

☎ 001 416 363 4343

✆ 001 416 363 1017

✆ www.groundwoodbooks.com

Established 1978
Imprint Libros Tigrillo
Categories Publishes Picture books, Children's Fiction and Non-Fiction, Latino books.
Insider Info Groundwood books publishes a wide range of high quality books for children from Canadian authors. They also buy successful books from other countries. Since 1998 they have been publishing works by people of Latin American origin living in the Americas, both in English and in Spanish under their Libros Tigrillo imprint.
Submission Guidelines No picture book submissions. Send in a synopsis and sample chapters with a SAE. All work must be typed and double spaced. Aims to respond in four to six months. They accept multiple submissions as long as this is indicated in the manuscript. Address all correspondence to 'Submissions'. Visit website for illustration guidelines.
Recent Title(s) *Alfredito Flies Home*, Jorge Argueta (Author), Luis Garay (Illustrator) (Picture Book); *The Corps of the Bare-Boned Plane*, Polly Horvath (Dramatic Novel)
Tips Groundwood does not publish children's characters with anthropomorphic qualities.

Groupe Fleurus
15–27, rue Moussorgski, 75895 Paris Cedex 18, France
- 0033 1 53 26 33 35
- 0033 1 53 26 33 36
- editionsfleurus@fleurus-mame.fr
- www.editionsfleurus.com
Contact Director, M. Pierre-Marie Dumont; Children's Editor, Mme. Janine Boudineau
Categories Publishes Hobby, and Arts and Crafts books, Encyclopedias and Teenage Fiction
Insider Info A market leader in arts and crafts books for children.
Recent Titles *Je crée mes bijoux* (I Create my Jewels), Valérie Revol (Author), Dorothée Jost (Illustrator); How-to book for girls (Hobby)
10 histoires de princesses (Ten Princess Stories), Bénédicte Bortoli and Gaëlle Guilmard (Editors), Olivier Huissier (Illustrator); A well illustrated, funny story book with craft activities (Arts and Crafts)

Gulf Stream Editeur
31, quai des Antilles, 44200 Nantes, France
- 0033 2 40 48 62 63
- 0033 2 40 48 74 69
- contact@gulfstream.fr
- www.gulfstream.fr

Contact Assistant Editor, Bérénice Brossier
Categories Publishes Picture books, Illustrated stories, Teenage novels and Non-fiction on History, Nature and Animals
Recent Titles *Ce qui compte dans le premier baiser*, Thierry Lefevre (Author), Yves Besnier (Illustrator) (Teenage Novel)
Chats, pitres et compagnie (Cats, Clowns and Company), Nadia Gypteau (Author), Serge Cecarrelli (Illustrator) (Picture Book)

Gyldendal
Klareboderne 3, DK-1001, Copenhagen, K, Denmark
- 0045 33 755555
- 0045 33 755556
- gyldendal@gyldendal.dk
- www.gyldendal.dk
Imprint(s) Forlaget Forum
Forlaget Fremad
Hans Reitzels Forlag
Høst & Søns Forlag
Rosinante
Samlerens Forlag
Categories Publishes Non-fiction, Fiction and Children's titles on the following subjects: Art, Biography, Children's Fiction, Directories, Education, General Interest, How-To, Literary Fiction, Local Interest, Mainstream Fiction, Politics, Reference, Young Adult
Recent Title(s) *De ti Herskere*, Christian Mørk
Tips Gyldendal publishes various types of fiction and non-fiction through its many imprints. Check the individual imprint's website for submission guidelines.

Hachette Livre Publishing Group
43 quai de Grenelle, F-75905, Paris, Cedex 15, France
- 0033 1 43 92 30 00
- 0033 1 43 92 30 30
- info@hachette-livre.fr
- www.hachette.com
Contact Editor, Catherine Rouyer
Imprint(s) Hachette Education/Istra
Hachette Littératures
Hachette Pratique
Hachette Tourisme
Larousse
Hachette Livre UK
Categories Publishes Children's and Young Adult's General and Educational Non-Fiction, Novelty books, Picture books and some Poetry.

Insider Info Publishes 5,000 titles (adult and children's) per year. Authors paid by royalty, with advance offered.

Submission Guidelines Accepts unsolicited manuscripts and proposals.

Recent Title(s) *Astérix – la serpe d'or – Grande collection*, René Goscinny and Albert Uderzo (Children's Picture Book Collection)

Tips Hachette-Livre is a major French publisher with many varied imprints, also publishing adult titles. See website for editorial details and submission guidelines for each imprint.

Hachette Livre Australia
Level 17, 207 Kent Street, Sydney, New South Wales, 2000, Australia

- 0061 2 8248 0800
- 0061 2 8248 0810
- auspub@hachette.com.au
- www.hha.com.au

Parent Company Hachette Livre UK

Contact Managing Director, Malcolm Edwards; Publishing Director, Fiona Hazard; Publisher, Bernadette Foley; Publisher, Vanessa Radnidge; Non-Fiction Publisher, Matthew Kelly

Imprint(s) Hachette Children's Books

Categories Publishes Non-Fiction, Fiction and Children's titles on the following subjects: Australiana, Autobiography, Biography, Children's, Cookbooks, Current Affairs, General Interest, Health, History, Humour, Lifestyle, Literary Fiction, Mainstream Fiction, Self-Help, Sport, Travel.

Insider Info Authors paid by royalty, with advance offered. Aims to respond to proposals within three to six months.

Submission Guidelines Does not accept unsolicited proposals.

Recent Title(s) *Good Night Me*, Andrew Daddo (Author), Emma Quay (Illustrator) (Animal Picture Book)

Tips Hachette Livre Australia specialises in publishing Australian writers, but does not accept unagented submissions or proposals.

Handprint Books
413 Sixth Avenue, Brooklyn, New York, NY 11215-3310 USA

- 001 718 768 3696
- 001 718 369 0844
- submissions@handprintbooks.com
- www.handprintbooks.com

Contact Publisher, Christopher Franceschelli

Imprint(s) Blue Apple

Ragged Bears

Established 1982

Categories Publishes Children's Fiction and Non-Fiction, Picture books, Story books and Young novels.

Insider Info Handprint is an independent publishing company whose mandate is simply to publish good books for children and young adults.

Submission Guidelines Only accepts email submissions. For novels submit a query and a 7,500 word sample first. Aims to respond to manuscripts in three months. Accepts simultaneous. Illustrators are also asked to submit samples via email in jpeg files if possible.

Recent Title(s) *Green Butterfly*, Raphael Thierry (Author) (Picture Book)

Tips Submissions of the following are discouraged: series fiction, licensed characters, 'I can read' type books, and titles intended primarily for mass merchandise outlets.

Hanser Kinderbuch
10 Vilshofener Straße, 81679 München, Germany

- 0049 89 9983 0517
- 0049 89 9983 0462
- info@hanser.de
- www.hanser.de

Parent Carl Hanser Verlag

Categories An imprint that publishes high quality Hardcover Fiction and Non-Fiction books for children of all ages, Picture books, Board books, Film/Television Tie-Ins and Educational books.

Submission Guidelines Accepts unsolicited manuscripts with SAE. For illustrations, send three sample copies.

Recent Title(s) *Monster Blood Tattoo*, D.M Cornish (Horror)

Harcourt Children's Book
525 B Street, Suite 1900, San Diego, California, 92101, USA

- 001 619 699 6560
- 001 619 699 5555
- www.harcourtbooks.com

Parent Company Harcourt Trade Publishers

Imprint(s) Gulliver Books
Silver Whistle
Red Wagon Books
Harcourt Young Classics
Green Light Readers
Voyager Books/Libros Viajeros
Harcourt Paperbacks

Odyssey Classics
Magic Carpet Books.

Contact Editor in Chief, Allyn Johnston; Editors, Michael Sterns & Karen Grove; Executive Editor, Jeanette Larson; Editorial Director, Elizabeth Van Doren; Associate Editorial Director, Kathy Dawson

Categories Publishes picture books, board and novelty books, gift items, contemporary and historical fiction for teenage readers, and non-fiction for children of all ages.

Insider Info Pays 6–15 per cent royalty on retail price, with advance offered.

Submission Guidelines Does not accept unagented submissions.

Recent Title(s) *My Last Best Friend*, Julie Bowe

Tips Harcourt is a major educational and children's publisher, and will not accept unagented submissions or proposals.

Harcourt Education

6277 Sea Harbor Drive, Orlando, FL 32887, USA
- 001 407 345 2000
- 001 619 699 5555
- www.harcourt.com

Parent Company Reed Elsevier Group Plc

Imprint(s) Harcourt School Publishers
Holt, Rinehart and Winston
Harcourt Assessment
Saxon, Rigby
Steck-Vaughn
Greenwood
Heinemann
Harcourt Trade Publishers
DataDirector
Classroom Connect
eSchool Online.

Categories Publishes Children's and Adults Education titles and produces CD-ROMs on the following subjects: Curriculum, including Maths, Science, English and Languages and Assessment materials.

Insider Info A global education publisher, producing textbooks, reference and digital products. Pays 6–15 per cent royalty on retail price, with advance offered.

Submission Guidelines Does not accept unsolicited manuscripts or proposals.

Recent Title(s) *Think Math!*, Developed by the Educational Development Center Inc.

Tips Advertises jobs via their website.

Harcourt Trade Publishers

525 B Street, Suite 1900, San Diego, California, 92101, USA
- 001 619 699 6560
- 001 619 699 5555
- www.harcourtbooks.com

Parent Company Reed Elsevier Group Plc

Contact Editor in Chief, Rebecca Saletan; Managing Editor, David Hough

Imprint(s) Harcourt Children's Books

Categories Publishes Fiction and Literature, Non-Fiction, Poetry and Children's titles.

Insider Info Pays 6–15 per cent royalty on retail price, with advance offered.

Submission Guidelines Does not accept unsolicited manuscripts or proposals.

Recent Title(s) *The Aurora County All-Stars,* Deborah Wiles (Children's Fiction)

Tips See individual imprint for children's books. Harcourt is also a major international education publishing company.

HarperCollins Children's Books

10 East 53rd Street, New York, New York, 10022, USA
- 001 212 261 6500
- 001 212 207 6927
- www.harpercollins.com

Parent Company News Corporation

Contact Editorial Director, Alix Reid; Senior Editor, Ruth Katcher; Editors, Clarissa Hutton, Barbara Lalicki, Antonia Markiet, Maria Modugno, Robin Benjamin, Susan Rich; Editorial Director, Phoebe Yeh; Executive Editor, Abby McAden

Imprint(s) Amistad
Eos
Greenwillow Books
HarperCollins Children's Audio
HarperCollins Children's Books
HarperFestival
HarperEntertainment
HarperTeen
HarperTrophy
Joanna Cotler Books
Julie Andrews Collection
Katherine Tegen Books
Laura Geringer Books
Rayo

Categories Publishes Children's Fiction and Non-Fiction, Picture books, General Interest, series books, Teenage Fiction, Middle Grade books, Beginner books, Film/Television Tie-Ins and Seasonal books.

Insider Info Authors paid by royalty, with advance offered. HarperCollins is home to many children's classics, including *Charlotte's Web*, *The Chronicles of Narnia*, *Goodnight Moon*, *Where the Sidewalk Ends* and *Where the Wild Things Are* and the popular series, *A Series of Unfortunate Events* and *The Princess Diaries*.
Submission Guidelines HarperCollins generally only accepts agented submissions. Contact the company for individual imprint guidleines.
Recent Title(s) *The Growing Story*, Ruth Krauss (Author), Helen Oxenbury (Illustrator)

HarperCollins Children's Books (Canada)
2 Bloor Street East, 20th Floor, Toronto, Ontario, M4W 1A8, Canada
✆ 001 416 975 9334
✆ 001 416 975 5223
🖥 www.harpercollins.ca
Parent Company HarperCollins Canada Ltd
Contact President, David Kent
Categories Publishes Children's Fiction and Non-Fiction, Picture books, General Interest, series books, Teenage Fiction, Middle Grade books, Beginner books, Film/Television tie-ins and Seasonal books.
Insider Info HarperCollins is home to many of the classics of children's literature including; *Goodnight Moon*, *Where the Wild Things Are*, *The Giving Tree*, *Charlotte's Web*, *Ramona*, and *Lilly's Purple Plastic Purse*. Authors are paid by royalty, with an advance offered.
Submission Guidelines Does not accept unsolicited manuscripts or proposals.
Recent Title(s) *The Hungry City Chronicles*, Philip Reeve (Young Fiction Trilogy), *Ana's Story, A Journey of Hope*, Jenna Bushwith, Photographs by Mia Baxter (Biography)

HarperCollinsPublishers Australia
PO Box 321, 25 Ryde Road, Pymble, New South Wales, 2073, Australia
✆ 0061 2 9952 5000
✆ 0061 2 9952 5555
🖥 www.harpercollins.com.au
Parent Company News Corporation
Contact Chief Executive Officer (Australia and New Zealand), Robert Gorman; Publishing Director, Shona Martyn; Managing Editor, Belinda Yuille; Children's Publisher, Lisa Berryman
Imprint(s) Angus & Robertson
Fourth Estate
HarperCollins/Collins
HarperSports
HarperPerennial
Voyager
Categories Publishes Non-Fiction, Fiction and Children's titles on the following subjects: Academic, Business, Children's, Educational, General Interest, Genre Fiction, Mainstream Fiction, Multimedia, Professional, Religious, Spiritual.
Insider Info Authors are paid by royalty, with an advance offered.
Submission Guidelines Does not accept unsolicited manuscripts or proposals.
Recent Title(s) *A Little Bush Maid* (Non Standard Paperback), Mary Grant Bruce

HarperCollinsPublishers New Zealand
PO Box 1, 31 View Road, Glenfield, Auckland, New Zealand
✆ 0064 9 443 9400
✆ 0064 9 443 9403
✉ editors@harpercollins.co.nz
🖥 www.harpercollins.co.nz
Parent Company News Corporation
Contact Chief Executive Officer (Australia and New Zealand), Robert Gorman; Managing Director, Tony Fisk; Publishing Director, Lorain Day; Commissioning Editor (Non-Fiction), Tracey Wogan
Imprint(s) Flamingo
HarperCollins
HarperSports
Perennial
Voyager
Categories Publishes Non-Fiction, Fiction and Children's titles, Film/Television Tie-Ins, and Licensed products on the following subjects: Autobiography, Biography, History, Fantasy, Adventure/Action, Animals, Family and more.
Insider Info Authors are paid by royalty, with an advance offered. Aims to respond to proposals within six weeks.
Submission Guidelines Accepts unsolicited manuscripts or proposals.
Recent Title(s) *Archie's Adventures*, Leonie Thorpe (Fiction)
Tips HarperCollins New Zealand does accept unsolicited submissions of non-fiction or fiction, but only from New Zealand writers.

HarperFestival
10 East 53rd Street, New York, New York, 10022, USA
✆ 001 212 261 6500
✆ 001 212 207 6927

@ www.harpercollins.com

Parent Company Harper Collins Children's Books

Insider Info HarperFestival is an imprint of HarperCollins, they publish books, novelties and merchandise for ages 0–6. Festival boasts a wide range of novelty and holiday titles, as well as character based programs such as *Biscuit*, *Little Critter* and *The Berenstain Bears*.

Submission Guidelines Only accepts agented submissions.

Recent Title(s) *From Head to Toe Big Book*, Eric Carle, (Picture Book)

HarperTeen

10 East 53rd Street, New York, NY 10022, USA

O 001 212 261 6500

O 001 212 207 6927

@ www.harpercollins.com

Parent Company HarperCollins Children's Books

Insider Info HarperTeen is an imprint of HarperCollins, that publishes books that reflect teenage life, their everyday realities and their aspirations, struggles and triumphs. Produces contemporary novels through to lighthearted series books.

Submission Guidelines Only accepts agented submissions.

Recent Title(s) *In the Deep End*, Kate Cann; *Girl at Sea*, Maureen Johnson

Harry N. Abrams Inc

115 West 18th Street, New York, New York, 10011, USA

O 001 212 206 7715

O 001 212 519 1210

O submissions@abramsbooks.com

@ www.abramsbooks.com

Parent Company La Martiniere Groupe

Contact Chief Executive Officer, Michael Jacobs; Editor, Susan Van Metre

Imprint(s) Abrams Books
 Abrams Books for Young Readers (including Amulet Books for Middle Grade and Young Adult)
 Abrams Image
 Stewart, Tabori & Chang

Categories Publishes a wide range of Fiction and Non-Fiction for Children and Adults. Children's titles include: Picture books, Board books, Young Adult Novels, Graphic books, Comic Art, Poetry and General Interest.

Insider Info Publishes 250 titles per year. Does not accept simultaneous submissions. Aims to respond to proposals within six months, if interested.

Submission Guidelines Accepts unsolicited manuscripts and proposals. For Picture books, send entire manuscripts and for longer works send a synopsis with sample chapters.

Recent Title(s) *006 and a Half: A Daisy Book*, Kes Gray, Nick Sharratt (Fiction Series); *123 NYC: A Counting Book of New York City*, Joanne Dugan (Non-Fiction); *The Aspiring Writer's Journal*, Susie Morgenstern (Author), Theresa Bronn (Illustrator) (Non-Fiction); *ttyl*, Lauren Myracle (Epistolary Novel)

Hatier

8, rue d'Assas, 75278 Paris Cedex 06, France

O 0033 1 49 54 49 54

O 0033 1 40 49 00 45

O informationspedagogiques@editions-hatier.fr

@ www.editions-hatier.fr

Contact Director, Marie-Noëlle Audigier

Categories Publishes Board books, Picture books and Concept books. Also produces School and Multimedia products in all major school subjects for children.

Insider Info One of the most successful educational publishers in France and a leader in extra curricular books.

Recent Titles *Ça chauffe pour la Terre,* Bruno Goldman, Bruno Liance (Nature and Planet)
 100% Exos Maths TS
 Pépin and the black wardrobe, Marie-Hélène Place (Author), Caroline Fontaine-Riquier (Illustrator)

Hemma Editions

Rue de Chevron, 106, 4987 Chevron, Belgium

O 0032 86 43 01 01

O 0032 86 43 40 86

O hemma@hemma.be

@ www.hemma.be

Contact Director, Philippe Tonnon

Categories Publishes Activity and Game books, Arts and Crafts, Movie/TV Tie Ins, Young Fantasy, Girl Fiction, Music books and Novelty books

Recent Titles *Camille va à l'hôpital*, (Camille Visits The Hospital) by Aline de Pétigny (Author) Nancy Delvaux (Illustrator)

Tips Offices are situated in France, Canada and Switzerland.

Henry Holt and Company Inc

175 Fifth Avenue, New York, NY 10010, USA

O 001 646 307 5095

O 001 212 633 0748

@ www.henryholt.com

Contact Vice President, Laura Godwin; Editors, Kate Farrell and Christy Ottaviano
Established 1866
Categories Publishes Picture books, Children's Fiction and Non-Fiction on a wide variety of topics for Children of all ages and Adult titles.
Insider Info Publishes high quality books covering a wide variety of genres. Their books feature imaginative authors and illustrators who inspire young readers. Their list includes the classic picture books *Tikki Tikki Tembo* and *Brown Bear, Brown Bear, What Do You See?*
Submission Guidelines Accepts unsolicited manuscripts and illustrations. They will respond if interested in pursuing the project. Aims to respond in four to six months. Approximately 15 per cent of books are by first-time authors.
Recent Title(s) *Emmy and the Incredible Shrinking Rat* (Fiction)
Tips They do not publish textbooks, original board or novelty books, activity books, or instructional books.

High Interest Publishing
407 Wellesley Street East, Ontario, M4X 1H5, Canada
- 001 416 323710
- 001 416 323 0141
- info@hip-books.com
- www.hip-books.com

Parent Company Chestnut Publishing Group
Contact President, Terry Durkin; Editorial Director, Paul Kropp
Established 2001
Categories Publishes Young Adult Fiction and Non-Fiction.
Insider Info High Interest publishes novels that are specifically written, edited and designed for reluctant readers from ages eight to eighteen. In the past they reissued titles, but now develop entirely new titles for publishing. Also publishes professional books for teachers.
Submission Guidelines Contact the company directly for submission guidelines.
Recent Title(s) *Against All Odds*, Paul Kropp (Fiction)

Holiday House
425 Madison Avenue, New York, NY 10017, USA
- 001 212 421 6134
- 001 212 421 6134
- info@holidayhouse.com
- www.holidayhouse.com

Contact Editor In Chief, Regina Griffin; Editor, Mary Cash
Categories Publishes Children's Fiction and Non-Fiction, Picture books, Story books and Young Adult books.
Insider Info Holiday House is an independent publisher of children's books. They specialise in quality hardcovers from the picture book level to young adult, both fiction and non-fiction.
Submission Guidelines For initial proceedings send a query letter describing what the manuscript is about. They will respond if interested in pursuing the manuscript. They do not accept multiple submissions.
Recent Title(s) *The Animals Watched: An Alphabet Book*, John Warren Stewig (Author), Rosanne Litzinger (Illustrator) (Picture Book); *Albert Einstein: A Biography*, Milton Meltzer
Tips They are especially interested in acquiring literary middle-grade novels. They do not publish mass-market books, including, but not limited to, board books, pop-ups, activity books, sticker books, colouring books, series books, licensed books or paperback originals.

Houghton Mifflin Children's Books
222 Berkeley Street, Boston, Massachusetts, 02116, USA
- 001 617 351 5000
- www.hmco.com

Contact Editorial Director, Judy O'Mailey; Executive Editor, Magaret Raymo; Paperback Director, Julia Richardson; Submissions Coordinator, Hannah Rodgers
Parent Houghton Mifflin Inc
Insider Info Houghton Mifflin Children's Books publishes more than one hundred titles each year, and they are frequently lauded for the depth and breadth of their backlist. They are also recognised for encouraging and cultivating new talent.
Submission Guidelines Visit website for detailed submission guidelines.
Recent Title(s) *Out of the Egg*, Tina Matthews

Houghton Mifflin Trade and Reference Division
222 Berkeley Street, Boston, Massachusetts, 02116, USA
- 001 617 351 5000
- www.hmco.com

Contact Editorial Director, Judy O'Mailey; Executive Editor, Magaret Raymo; Paperback Director, Julia

Richardson; Submissions Coordinator, Hannah Rodgers

Imprint(s) Clarion Books
 Houghton Mifflin Books for Children
 Graphia
 Kingfisher
 Walter Lorraine Books

Categories Publishes Children's Fiction and Non-Fiction, Poetry and Reference.

Insider Info Publishes approximately 400 books annually. Authors are paid by royalty, with an advance offered. Accepts simultaneous submissions.

Submission Guidelines See individual imprints for submission guidelines.

Human & Rousseau

12th Floor, Naspers, 40 Heerengracht, Roggebaai, South Africa

✆ 0027 21 406 3033
🖷 0027 21 406 3812
✉ nb@nb.co.za
🌐 www.nb.co.za

Contact Managing Director, Eloise Woods; Publisher (Non-Fiction), Danita van Romburgh

Parent Company NB Publishers

Imprint(s) Human & Rousseau
 Kwela
 Pharos
 Tafelberg
 Best Books (Education)

Categories Publishes general African and English titles including: Young Adult titles, Mass market Children's books, Picture books and Educational books.

Insider Info Human & Rousseau is one of South Africa's leading general publishers, which primarily publishes quality African literature. They are currently expanding to publish more English titles.

Submission Guidelines A full manuscript is preferable but they will accept a proposal with two written chapters. All submissions must be typed. Include a covering letter naming any publishing credits to date. Aims to respond in three months.

Recent Title(s) *Vin the Virus Hunter*, Jeanine Henning (Science Fiction)

Tips Accepts submissions either by post or email, providing they are sent to the correct imprint.

Hyperion Books For Children

413 Sixth Avenue, Brooklyn, New York, NY 11215-3310, USA

✆ 001 718 768 3696
🖷 001 718 369 0844

✉ submissions@handprintbooks.com
🌐 www.handprintbooks.com

Contact Publisher, Christopher Franceschelli

Imprint(s) Jump at the Sun
 Volo
 Michael di Capua Books

Established 1991

Categories Publishes Children's Fiction and Non-Fiction, Picture books, Novelty books, Popular series and Teenage novels.

Insider Info Authors are paid by royalty with an advance offered. Publishes high quality children's books from renowned authors such as Julie Andrews, Rosemary Wells and William Wegman to name a few. A unique collaboration between Miramax Books and Hyperion Books for Children has also proven extremely successful, with the publication of *Artemis Fowl* by Eoin Colfer in May 2001.

Submission Guidelines Only accepts submissions via literary agents.

Recent Title(s) *Today I will Fly* (Picture Book)

Ideals Publications

535 Metroplex Drive, Nashville TN 37211, USA

✆ 001 615 333 0478
🖷 001 615 781 1447
✉ AtYourService@guideposts.org
🌐 www.idealspublications.com

Contact Managing Editor, Peggy Schaefer

Established 1944

Imprint(s) Candy Cane Press
 Ideals Children's Books
 GP Kids

Categories Publishes Non-Fiction titles on the following subjects: Science, Maths, Arts & Crafts, Games, Activities, How-To books, Religious books, Children's Fiction Picture books and Board books.

Insider Info Publishes 70 new titles annually for the children's and adult markets.

Submission Guidelines Accepts unsolicited manuscripts. Board book manuscripts should be kept to approximately 200 words. Picture book manuscripts should be close to 1,000 words. Please include a listing of previously published books if applicable. Multiple submissions are discouraged.

Recent Title(s) *If Jesus Lived Inside My Heart*; Jill Roman Lord (Author), Amy Wummer (Illustrator) (Religious Board Book)

Tips Seeking biblical characters, holidays, and patriotic and biographical themes.

Illumination Arts Publishing

PO Box 1865, Bellevue, NY, 10014, USA

- 001 212 366 2792
- 001 212 243 6002
- liteinfo@illumin.com
- www.illumin.com

Contact President John M. Thompson; Editorial Director, Ruth Thompson; Creative Consultant, Trey Bornmann

Established 1987

Categories Publishes Children's Picture books.

Insider Info Illumination is a wonderful children's book publisher focusing on books of unique new age topics, and exceptional illustrations.

Submission Guidelines All submissions must be typed and double spaced. Aim to respond to submissions in one month. Include an author biography and SAE. Illustration samples are accepted with submissions.

Recent Title(s) *Mrs. Murphy's Marvellous Mansion*, Emma Perry Roberts (Author), Robert Rogalski (Illustrator); *Just Imagine*, John M. Thompson and George M.Schultz (Authors), Wodin (Illustrator)

Tips Illumination is seeking children's fiction and non-fiction between 500–2,000 words. They do not accept chapter or full-length books.

Impact Publishing

PO Box 6016, Atascadero, CA 93423-6016, 10014, USA

- 001 805 644 7185
- info@impactpublishers.com
- www.impactpublishers.com

Established 1970

Categories Publishes Self-Help books, Psychology publications and Audio books on a wide range of sensitive issues, such as: Relationships, Divorce, Parenting, Stress, Personal growth and Mental health.

Insider Info Impact is an independent family run company. All its books are authored by qualified professionals in the human services.

Submission Guidelines They rarely accept submissions from authors outside of the USA. Aims to respond to proposal in four to twelve weeks.

Recent Title(s) *Divorce Help Book For Kids,* Cynthia MacGregor; *Teen Esteem: A self direction manual for Young Adults*, Pat Palmer

Tips Impact will publish books that serve human development. Visit their website for their criteria guidelines.

Innovative Kids

18 Ann Street, Norwalk, CT 06854, USA

- 001 203 838 6400
- 001 203 855 5582
- info@innovativekids.com
- www.innovativekids.com

Contact President and Publishing, Shari Kaufman

Categories Publishes Children's Fiction and Non-fiction, Gift ideas, Baby books, Phonic Comics series, Educational books and Game board books.

Insider Info A publisher of high quality educational children's books and manufacturer and designer of children's toys. Innovative combines toys and books in one to enhance the enjoyment of reading for young children.

Submission Guidelines They will only respond to submissions if interested in pursuing the script.

Recent Title(s) *Rose, The Fairy of Love*, Helen Parker (Author and Illustrator)

Tips Submissions for traditional picture books are not accepted. They seek educational and interactive manuscripts for children. Innovative Kids consider authors and illustrators on a work for hire basis, if you are interested then submit writing or art samples for future opportunities.

John Wiley & Sons Inc

111 River Street, Hoboken, New Jersey, 07030, USA

- 001 201 748 6000
- 001 201 748 6088
- info@wiley.com
- www.wiley.com

Contact President/Chief Executive Officer, William J. Pesce; Chairman, Peter B. Wiley

Established 1807

Imprint(s) Jossey-Bass

Categories Publishes educational titles for grades K-12 on all subjects for children and teachers. Also publishes health books.

Insider Info One of the oldest and most well established publishers in America. Offers an advance. Accepts simultaneous submissions.

Submission Guidelines Accepts unsolicited unsolicited proposals and manuscripts. A detailed set of submission guidelines for each division are published on the website.

Recent Title(s) *American Medical Association Boy's Guide to Becoming a Teen*; *Great Graphs and Sensational Statistics: Games and Activities That Make Math Easy and Fun*

Just Us Books

356 Glenwood Avenue, East Orange NJ 07017,
USA

- 001 973 672 7701
- 001 973 676 4345
- justusbook@aol.com; justusbooks@
mindspring.com
- www.justusbooks.com

Contact Associate Editor, Katura Hudson
Established 1987
Categories Publishes Black interest books for
Children, including: Educational books, Picture
books, Biographies, Chapter books, Young Adult
Fiction and History. Publishes four to six new titles
per year, and has an extensive backlist.
Insider Info Just Us Books is a recognised leader in
children's multicultural publishing.
Submission Guidelines No unsolicited
manuscripts. Accepts query letters containing an
author biography, a one to two page synopsis of the
script, and SAE. Aims to respond to queries
in 12 weeks.
Recent Title(s) *1 2 3 Book*, Wade and Cheryl Hudson
(Concept Book for Pre-schoolers)
Tips Visit their website for useful hints and tips for
creating black interest books for children. A new
imprint company, Marimba Books, will begin
publishing in 2008. It will be dedicated to children's
books, with spiritual and moral themes geared to
the African American market.

Juta & Company Ltd

PO Box 14373, Lansdowne, Cape Town, 7779,
South Africa

- 0027 21 763 3500
- 0027 21 761 5861
- cserv@juta.co.za
- www.juta.co.za

Contact Chief Executive Officer, Lynne du Toit;
Publisher (Juta Law), Chipo Chipidza; Publisher (Juta
Academic), Glenda Younge
Imprint(s) Double Storey
 Juta Academic
 Juta Law
 Juta Learning
Categories Publishes Educational books for Primary
through to Degree level on the following subjects:
Academic, Art, Biography, Business, Education,
Health, Law, Legal Interest, Local Interest, Memoirs,
Multimedia, Music, Psychology, Science, South
African Non-Fiction, Spirituality, Teacher Resources,
Tourism, International books.

Recent Title(s) *365 Ways to Change the World*,
Michael Norton
Tips Juta specialises mainly in law and legal matters
or education titles, but also publishes more
mainstream South African interest titles through the
Double Storey imprint.

Kane/Miller Book Publishers

PO Box 8515, La Jolla CA 92038, USA

- 001 858 456 0540
- 001 858 456 9641
- info@kanemiller.com
- www.kanemiller.com

Categories Publishes Children's Fiction and Non-
Fiction and Translated Children's books on a wide
variety of topics, including: Diversity, Friendship and
Family, Animals, Environment, Divorce, Baby books,
Gift ideas, Arts and Craft.
Insider Info Kane/Miller is an independent
publisher which specialises in foreign translated
books, they seek the world to find extraordinary
children's books to bring to a young
American audience.
Submission Guidelines Tends not to accept
unsolicited manuscripts, unless of the highest
quality. Send either the published book or sample
chapters of the script. Aims to respond in 60 working
days. No submissions via email or fax. Include a SAE.
Recent Title(s) *Breasts,* Yagyu Genichiro (Author and
Illustrator) (Japanese humour book for children)
Tips Currently seeking original, middle grade fiction
for children aged seven to eleven, written by authors
living outside the United States.

Key Porter Books Ltd

6 Adelaide Street East, 10th Floor, Toronto,
Ontario, M5C 1H6, Canada

- 001 416 862 7777
- 001 416 862 2304
- info@keyporter.com
- www.keyporter.com

Contact Publisher, Jordan Fenn; Editor-in-Chief,
Clare McKeon
Imprint(s) Key Porter Kids
Categories Publishes Non-fiction and Children's
titles on the following subjects: Art, Fantasy,
Biography, Business, Children's themes, Gift book,
Health, History, How-To, Humour, Illustrated books,
Science, Self-Help, Translation, Travel and
Young Adult.
Insider Info Publishes 100 titles per year. Authors
paid by royalty, with advance offered. Receives 1,000

queries per year and 500 manuscripts per year. Aims to respond to proposals within six months.

Submission Guidelines Does not accept unsolicited manuscripts, but will usually respond to proposals or queries.

Recent Title(s) *Lawrence High Yearbook Wild Thing*, David A. Poulsen (Young Fiction); *The Feathered Cloak*, Sean Dixon (Fantasy)

Tips Visit the Key Porter Wire Blog spot on their website for the latest news and information on Key Porter's children's and young reader's books.

Kids Can Press
29 Birch Avenue, Toronto, Ontario, M4V 1E2, Canada
- 001 800 265 0884
- 001 416 960 5437
- webmaster@kidscan.com
- www.kidscan.com

Contact Publisher, Valerie Hussey, Karen Boersma

Categories Publishes Children's Fiction and Non-Fiction, Poetry, Picture books, Novelty books, Craft books, Activity books, Hands-on science experiment books, How-To books for children, Nature books and General Non-Fiction.

Insider Info Publishes approximately 50 children's books a year. Famous children's book characters are *Franklin the Turtle* and *Eloise Moose*.

Submission Guidelines For fiction send in plot synopsis and three chapter samples. For picture books send the entire manuscript. Include SAE. All manuscripts must be typed and doubled spaced. Aims to respond within six months. Address the envelope to 'Acquisitions Editor'. Send illustration samples and CV to the 'Art Director'.

Recent Title(s) *For Now*, Gayle Friesen (Young Novel); *Bugs Up Close,* Diane Swanson (Author), Paul Davidson (Illustrator) (Nature Book)

Tips The company does not accept unsolicited submissions from authors outside of Canada, or from teenagers or children.

Kingfisher
222 Berkeley Street, Boston, Massachusetts, 02116, USA
- 001 617 351 5000
- www.hmco.com

Contact Editor, Eden Edwards

Parent Houghton Mifflin Inc

Insider Info Kingfisher is an imprint company that specialises in non-fiction for children of all ages. Known around the world for its informative and engaging reference books, activity books, and early learning books, classic anthologies and original picture books.

Submission Guidelines No unagented submissions.

Recent Title(s) *Kingfisher Knowledge Series*

La Compagnie Creative
42, rue Albert Thomas, 33000 Bordeaux, France
- 0033 5 56 90 16 97
- 0033 5 56 93 83 85
- contact@la-compagnie-creative.com
- www.la-compagnie-creative.com

Contact Editor, Mme. Claude Dagail

Categories Publishes Children's Picture books, Illustrated books, Poems, Cultural Fiction, Early Readers and Short novels.

Recent Titles *Paroles de lait* (Words of Milk), Roncaglia Silvia (Author), Cerretti Cristina (Illustrator) (Illustrated Poems)

Le buveur de pluiem, (African Culture), Boubacar Diallo (Author), Véronique Vernette (Illustrator) (Illustrated Fiction)

Laura Geringer Books
10 East 53rd Street, New York, New York, 10022, USA
- 001 212 261 6500
- 001 212 207 6927
- www.harpercollins.com

Parent Company HarperCollins Children's Books

Contact Publisher, Laura Geringer

Insider Info Laura Geringer Books is an imprint of HarperCollins, it publishes high quality and innovative books for children of all ages. It aims to push the boundaries and discover new, talented authors.

Submission Guidelines Only accepts agented submissions.

Recent Title(s) *Luck*, Jean Craighead George (Author), Wendell Minor (Illustrator)

Learning Media Ltd
PO Box 3293, Wellington, 6001, New Zealand
- 0064 4 472 5522
- 0064 4 472 6444
- info@learningmedia.co.nz
- www.learningmedia.co.nz

Contact Chief Executive Officer, Gillian Candler; Manager (Sales Publishing), Michelle Kelly; Manager (Curriculum Publishing), Kirsty Farquharson; Manager (Mori Publishing), Huhana Rokx

Categories Publishes Non-fiction, Fiction and Children's titles on the following subjects: Academic, Education, Language, Literacy, Multimedia, Pasifika Language, Student Resources, Teacher Resources, Translation, Young Adult.

Insider Info Aims to respond to proposals within 12 weeks. Manuscript guidelines are available online.

Submission Guidelines Accepts unsolicited manuscripts or proposals.

Recent Title(s) *The Legend of Pheidippides*, David Hill

Tips Learning Media publishes educational material for a specific region, and prints in many different Pasifika languages. Learning Media recommends that submissions be written for a particular series, and are currently seeking submissions for the Tupu series in particular.

L'école Des Loisirs

11, rue de Sèvres, F-75006 Paris, France
- 0033 1 42 22 94 10
- 0033 1 45 48 04 99
- edl@ecoledesloisirs.com
- www.ecoledesloisirs.fr

Contact Director, Jean Delas; Foreign Rights Manager, Isabelle Darthy

Categories Publishes School books, Children's General Fiction, Early Readers, Series and Picture books

Insider Info L'école des Loisirs is the second largest independent family owned children's book publishing company. They specialise in foreign translations and school books, with a backlist of over 2,500 titles and 250 new titles a year.

Recent Titles *Aboiements,* Elisabeth Duval (Author), Pascal Vilcollet (Illustrator) (Picture Book)

Tips The company has offices in Spain, Italy and Germany and an imprint in Belgium.

Lerner Publishing Group

241 1st Avenue N, Minneapolis, MN 55401, USA
- 001 800 328 4929
- 001 800 332 1132
- info@lernerbooks.com
- www.lernerbooks.com

Contact Executive Editor, Ellen Stein; Non-Fiction Editor, Jennifer Zimian

Imprint(s) Lerner Publications
 Millbrook Press
 Carolrhoda Books
 Graphic Universe
 Twenty-First Century Books
 Ediciones Lerner
 Lerner Classroom

Kar-Ben Publishing

Established 1959

Categories Publishes Children's Fiction and Non-Fiction, Young Adult novels and Photographic books on topics such as: Science, Social Studies and Language/Arts Curriculum. Also produces titles on high interest topics such as Sports and Vehicles & Crafts, as well as engaging Picture books and Chapter books.

Insider Info The children's book publisher publishes mainly for the school and library markets. They have about 3,500 titles in print.

Submission Guidelines No unsolicited manuscripts. Visit website for further submission guidelines.

Recent Title(s) *101 Questions about Muscles*, (Educational Series)

Tips Their website contains listings of targeted submission topics they wish to pursue.

Little, Brown Children's Books

1271 Avenue of the Americas, 11th Floor, New York, NY 10020, USA
- 001 212 243 6002
- 001 212 243 6002
- amy.hsu@twbg.com
- www.hachettebookgroupusa.com/children

Parent Company Hachette Book Group USA

Contact Editor-In-Chief, Megan Tingley; Executive Editor, Andrea Spooner; Senior Editor, Cindy Eagan; Editor, Amy Hsu

Imprint(s) LB Kids
 Poppy

Established 1926

Categories Publishes Children's Fiction and Non-Fiction titles on topics including: Romance, Science-Fiction, Fantasy, Religion, Health and Self-Help. Also produces Picture books for Middle Grade Children and Young Adult books. LB Kids publishes Novelty and Licensed Tie-Ins whilst Poppy publishes the Paperback Original series for Teenage girls.

Insider Info Publishes approximately 135 books annually, including many bestselling children's series such as *The Adventures of Tin Tin.*

Submission Guidelines No unagented submissions.

Recent Title(s) *Fred Stays With Me!*, Nancy Coffelt (Picture Book)*; Vampirates: Tide of Terror*, Justin Somper (Sequel Fantasy/Horror)

Lobster Press

1620 Sherbrooke St. West, Suites C & D, Montreal, QC H3H 1C9, Canada

001 514 904 1100
001 514 904 1101
www.lobsterpress.com
Contact President and Publisher, Alison Fripp;
Editor, Meghan Nolan
Established 1998
Categories Publishes Children's Fiction and Non-Fiction, Picture books, Board books and books written in French.
Insider Info Lobster press has published over 100 titles for young readers since its inception.
Submission Guidelines No unsolicited manuscripts. They are currently seeking original literary fiction for young adults, and mystery and horror fiction for ages 9–12 or 13+. They are also looking for non-fiction books, or children's reference books for readers in all age ranges.
Recent Title(s) *Dear Jo: The story of losing Leah...and searching for hope,* Christina Kilbourne (Dramatic Novel/Teenage & Child Safety Awareness); *Don't Squash that Bug! The Curious Kid's Guide to Insects,* Natalie Rompella (Nature Book)
Tips Prefers Canadian authors.

Lumen Infantil
Travessera de Gràcia 47–49, 08021 Barcelona, Spain
0034 93 366 0300
0034 93 366 0449
www.randomhousemondadori.es
Parent Random House Mandadori
Categories Publishes Children's Classics, Illustrated books and Contemporary Stories.
Insider Info The imprint seeks to enrich a child's mind with its books, stressing the importance of learning and reading books. *A favor de las ninas* (In Favour of the Girls), is a contemporary classic in the Lumen Infantil catalogue, which teaches equality between the sexes.
Tips The imprint seeks to publish unconventional and groundbreaking illustrated books by new artists. All its books are distributed in the Random House territories.

Macmillan Education Australia
Level 115–19 Claremont Street, South Yarra 3141, Melbourne Victoria, Australia
0061 3 9825 1025
0061 3 9825 1010
mea@macmillan.com.au
www.macmillan.com.au
Imprint(s) Palgrave MacMillan (Academic trade, Professional and Reference)

Categories Publishes Children's Educational Books on a wide range of school subjects, including: English, Humanities, Science, Health/PE, Reference, Technology, Arts, Sports, Dictionaries, How-To books, and Encyclopedias.
Insider Info Macmillan Education Australia is one of the leading educational publishers in Australia, with a vigorous publishing programme, catering to the needs of Primary and Secondary Schools.
Recent Title(s) *Spelling Rules!*
Tips Also publishes sets of novels that all young students will choose to read - *Out of this World, Kids Inc., Boyz Rule!* and *Girlz Rock!*

Macmillan South Africa
PO Box 32484, Braamfontein, 2017, South Africa
0027 11 731 3300
0027 11 731 3500
info@macmillan.co.za
www.macmillansa.co.za
Parent Company Boleswa
Imprint(s) Clever Books
 Guidelines
Categories Publishes Non-fiction, Fiction and Children's titles on the following subjects: African Literature, Education, General Interest, How-To, Literacy, Mainstream Fiction, Reference, Science, Scholarly, Self-Help, Teaching Guides.
Insider Info Authors paid by royalty, with advance offered.
Tips Macmillan South Africa is interested in educational non-fiction about literacy, numeracy and similar subjects. Macmillan South Africa is currently developing their website, so check back frequently for possible submission guidelines.

Madison Press
1000 Yonge Street, Suite 200, Toronto, Ontario, M4W 2K2, Canada
001 416 923 5027
001 416 923 9708
info@madisonpressbooks.com
www.madisonpressbooks.com
Contact Publisher, Oliver Salzmann; Editorial Director, Wanda Nowakowska
Established 1979
Categories Publishes Children's Illustrated books, Young Adult Fiction and Non-Fiction.
Insider Info Madison Press Books is one of the world's leading independent book producers, with companies in many different countries, including the UK and Europe.

Submission Guidelines Contact the company directly for submission guidelines.

Recent Title(s) *Being a Girl: Navigating the Ups and Downs of Teen Life*, Kim Cattrall (Self Help/Biography)

Mallinson Rendel Publishers Ltd

PO Box 9409, Level 5, 15 Courtenay Place, Wellington, New Zealand

- 0064 4 802 5012
- 0064 4 802 5013
- publisher@mallinsonrendel.co.nz
- www.mallinsonrendel.co.nz

Contact Publishing Director, Ann Mallinson

Categories Publishes Children's titles on the following subjects: Children's Fiction, Education, Mainstream Fiction and Picture books.

Recent Title(s) *Hairy Maclary's Hat Tricks*, Lynley Dodd (Picture book); *Duet*, David Hill (Young Fiction)

Tips Mallinson Rendel specialise in illustrated children's books.

Margaret K. McElderry Books

1230 Avenue of the Americas, New York, NY, 10020, USA

- 001 212 698 2808
- 001 212 698 4350
- www.simonsayskids.com

Parent Simon and Schuster Inc

Contact Vice President and Associate Publisher, Emma Dryden; Executive Editor, Karen Wojtyla

Established 1972

Categories Publishes Children's Fiction and Non-Fiction, Picture books, Fantasy, Easy to Read books, Poetry and Teenage novels.

Insider Info Recent lists include the first ever authorised sequel to J. M. Barrie's *Peter Pan*, Geraldine McCaughrean's *Peter Pan in Scarlet* and *Ironside* by Holly Black. Aims to respond to manuscripts in three months.

Submission Guidelines No unsolicited manuscripts. Accepts queries, proposals or manuscripts with SAE for the attention of the Submissions Editor. Approximately ten per cent of books are by first-time authors.

Recent Title(s) *Smile, Principessa!*, Judith Ross Enderle and Stephanie Jacob Gordon (Authors), Serena Curmi (Illustrator) (Young Picture Book); *The Mortal Instruments - City of Bones*, Cassandra Clare (Fantasy)

Marshall Cavendish Benchmark

99 White Plains Road, Tarrytown, NY 10591, USA

- 001 914 332 8888
- 001 914 332 1082
- customerservice@marshallcavendish.com
- www.marshallcavendish.us

Parent Company Marshall Cavendish Corporation

Categories Publishes Non-Fiction on the following subjects: American Studies, Animals, Bilingual Readers, Spanish books, Art, Science, Maths, Literature, Religion, Social Studies, Poetry, Cooking and Kaleidoscope.

Insider Info Marshall Cavendish is a leading North American publisher of children's books, illustrated encyclopedias and non-fiction series for adults.

Submission Guidelines Send complete manuscript or a synopsis.

Recent Title(s) *American Heroes*, Sneed B. Collard (American History for Young Adults)

Marshall Cavendish Children's Books

99 White Plains Road, Tarrytown, NY 10591, USA

- 001 914 332 8888
- 001 914 332 1082
- customerservice@marshallcavendish.com
- www.marshallcavendish.us

Parent Company Marshall Cavendish Corporation

Categories Publishes Children's Board books, Chapter books, Cooking, Information Picture books, Middle Grade Fiction, Spanish books, Paperback Fiction and Picture books, Picture books, Teenage Fiction and Poetry.

Insider Info Marshall Cavendish is a leading North American publisher of children's books, illustrated encyclopedias and non-fiction series for adults.

Submission Guidelines Accepts unsolicited manuscripts. For novels send three sample chapters, or 30 pages and for picture books send the entire manuscript.

Recent Title(s) *Avielle of Rhia*, Dia Calhoun (Fantasy); *The Best Hanukkah Ever*, Barbara Diamond Goldin (Author), Avi Katz (Illustrator) (Picture Book)

Tips Marshall Cavendish Children's Books is starting a new line of books called Marshall Cavendish Classics that will be composed of out of print books worthy of being brought back into print. They welcome authors to submit any pre-published work for licencing on a royalty basis. Out of print books can be submitted to Margery Cuyler.

Maskew Miller Longman (Pty) Ltd

Cnr Logan Way and Forest Drive, Pinelands 7405, South Africa

- ☎ 0027 21 531 8103
- 🖷 0027 21 531 4877
- ✉ tembela@mml.co.za
- 🌐 www.mml.co.za

Contact Publishing Director, Jaipa Pienaar
Parent Pearson Education
  Caxton Publishers and Printers Ltd.
Categories Publishes Educational books, Dictionaries, Reference materials for students and teachers and African Literature covering a wide range of genres including: Creative Writing, Novels, Poetry and Short stories.
Insider Info Maskew Miller Longman are the leading educational publishers in Sub-Saharan Africa. As partners to the government in the educational arena they develop local products for local conditions.
Submission Guidelines Visit website for full submission details for their different subject areas.
Tips Maskew publishes the *Young Africa* youth literature series, which comprises refreshingly original novels dealing with themes relevant to a young reader. It has enjoyed considerable international success. The *Young Africa* series was launched in 1986, to encourage new talent in local writing, in English.

McGraw-Hill Australia and New Zealand

Level 2, The Everglade Building, 82 Waterloo Road, North Ryde, NSW 1670, Australia

- ☎ 0061 2 9900 1800
- ✉ cservice_sydney@mcgraw-hill.com
- 🌐 www.mcgraw-hill.com.au

Contact Publishing Director; Michael Tully; Schools Acquisitions Editor, Eiko Bron
Imprint Mimosa Shortland Publications
Categories Publishes Educational books and Multimedia products covering all school subjects including: Maths, English and Science
Insider Info McGraw-Hill Australia is a leading and dynamic educational publisher, with interests in many emerging educational trends, such as online learning. McGraw-Hill Australia publishes and distributes products in three main market focus areas: Higher Education; Primary and Secondary Education (grades K to 12); and Professional (including Medical, General and Reference).

Submission Guidelines Visit their website to download an Author guide for publishing and submission details.
Tips McGraw-Hill has a rapidly expanding publishing programme and is always looking for new and potential authors, their dedicated editorial department will work closely to develop manuscripts to their best potential.

Michel Lafon

7–13, Boulevard Paul-Emile Victor, 92521, Neuilly on Seine, Cedex, France

- ☎ 0033 1 41 43 85 85
- 🖷 0033 1 46 24 00 95
- ✉ service-litteraire@michel-lafon.fr
- 🌐 www.michel-lafon.fr

Categories Publishes Young Adult titles on the following subjects: Romance, Thrillers, English translations, Biographies, Historical Fiction and Humour
Insider Info Publishes 150 books per year, including children's and adult titles.
Submission Guidelines The company is not accepting submissions at the present time
Recent Titles *Once Upon a Time in Gorée,* Joseph N'Diaye (Teenage Historical Fiction)

Michelle Anderson Publishing

PO Box 6032, Chapel Street North, South Yarra 3141, Australia

- ☎ 0061 3 9826 9028
- 🖷 0061 3 9826 8552
- ✉ mapubl@bigpond.net.au
- 🌐 www.michelleandersonpublishing.com

Contact Director, Michelle Anderson
Categories Publishes Picture books for Children aged 3–8, Fiction and Non-Fiction and Adult titles.
Insider Info Michelle Anderson Publishing specialise in the areas of general health, mind/body and spirituality titles. Publish two children's titles per year and has six in print.
Submission Guidelines Accepts unsolicited synopsis; allow a month for a response.
Recent Title(s) *What About Me?,* George Vlamakis (Author) Elise Hurst (Illustrator) (Fiction for siblings of sick children)
Tips Michelle Anderson Publishing tends to focus on non-fiction for children addressing important issues such as family life, health issues and life and death.

Milet Publishing

333 North Michigan Avenue, Suite 530, Chicago, IL 60601, USA
- ☎ 001 312 337 0747
- 🖷 001 312 337 5985
- ✉ info@milet.com
- 🌐 www.milet.com

Categories Publishes Children's books, World books, Dictionaries, Translated books, Picture books, Flashcards and Language learning books.

Insider Info Milet is a leading independent publisher of books for children, young adults and adults. They specialise in multicultural and bilingual books, featuring bold, artistic style with engaging storylines. Milet has sister companies in the UK and Australia, and distribution facilities across the whole world.

Submission Guidelines At the present time Milet is not accepting submissions, but check the website for up to date information.

Recent Title(s) *Minutka: The Bilingual Dog*, Anna Mycek-Wodecki (English–Polish); *Jump, Jog, Leapfrog: Fun with Action Words*, Tracy Traynor and Laura Hambleton

Milkweed Editions

Open Box Building, 1011 Washington Avenue South, Suite 300, Minneapolis, Minnesota, 55415, USA
- ☎ 001 612 332 3192
- 🖷 001 612 215 2550
- 🌐 www.milkweed.org

Contact Editor in Chief, Daniel Slager

Imprint(s) Milkweeds for Young Readers

Categories Publishes Non-Fiction, Fiction, Poetry and Children's titles on the following subjects: Children's Fiction, Culture, General Interest, Literary Fiction, Nature, Poetry, Social Studies and Young Adult.

Insider Info Publishes 20 titles per year. Pays six per cent royalty on retail price, with advance offered. 70 per cent of books come from unagented writers and 30 per cent from first-time authors. Accepts simultaneous submissions. Average lead time of 18 months.

Submission Guidelines Accepts unsolicited manuscripts and proposals. Aims to respond to manuscripts within six months.

Recent Title(s) *The Linden Tree*, Ellie Mathews (Young Novel); *No Place,* Kay Haugaard (Young Novel)

Tips Milkweed publishes *Stories From Where We Live*, an educational series for children about the environment.

Milly Molly Publishing

PO Box 539, Gisborne, New Zealand
- ☎ 0064 6 868 7769
- ✉ info@millymolly.com
- 🌐 www.millymolly.com

Contact Publishing Directors, John and Gill Pitar

Categories Publishes Picture books, Gifts such as Dolls, and Interactive CD Roms.

Insider Info Milly Molly publishes only the *Milly Molly* book series at the present time, with part of the earnings going to the The Friends of Milly Molly Inc, a charity which helps needy children and aims to increase children's awareness of literature in poor countries.

Mitchell Lane Publishers Inc.

PO Box 196, Hockessin, DE 19707, USA
- ☎ 001 302 234 9426
- ☎ 001 866 834 4164
- ✉ customerservice@mitchelllane.com
- 🌐 www.mitchelllane.com

Categories Publishes Children's Non-Fiction and Series on the following subjects: Art, History, Biographies, Sports, Environment, Geography, Music and many more.

Insider Info Publishes 85 new educational books a year, with an extensive backlist.

Submission Guidelines No unsolicited manuscripts. Only accepts non-fiction.

Recent Title(s) *Art Profiles For Kids* (Art series on all the famous artists of the last couple of centuries)

Tips Mitchell Lane Publishers contracts with established authors on a work for hire basis. For first-time writers send a resume including any previously published work, a covering letter expressing your interest, and an unedited writing sample that does not need to be returned.

Montena

Travessera de Gràcia 47–49, 08021 Barcelona, Spain
- ☎ 0034 93 366 0300
- 🖷 0034 93 366 0449
- 🌐 www.randomhousemondadori.es

Parent Random House Mandadori

Categories Publishes Young Adult Fiction, Non-Fiction and Fantasy novels.

Insider Info The imprint publishes books that are unconventional and go against social norms, the result being stories that show real life, complete with all the problems and conflicts experienced by young people today. Its long running series *Chicas* reflects this ideology and has published well over 70 titles in its ten years.

Tips The imprint publishes a series for beginner readers; *Hadas Arco Iris* (Rainbow Magic) and and *La escuela de Cazadragones* (The School of Dragon Hunters). All its books are distributed in the Random House territories.

Napoleon Publishing/RendezVous Press
178 Willowdale Avenue, Suite 201, Toronto, Ontario, M2N 4Y8, Canada
- 001 416 730 9052
- 001 416 730 8096
- editorial@transmedia95.com
- www.rendezvouspress.com

Contact Publisher, Sylvia McConnell; Editor, Allister Thompson
Imprint(s) Dark Star Fiction
Napoleon Publishing
RendezVous Crime
RendezVous Press
Categories Publishes Fiction and Children's titles on the following subjects: Canadian Literature, Children's Fiction, Contemporary Fiction, Crime Fiction, Literary Fiction, Mainstream Fiction and Mystery Fiction.
Insider Info Publishes 20 titles per year. Receives 200 queries and 100 manuscripts per year. 80 per cent of books come from unagented writers, and 50 per cent from first-time authors. Aims to respond to manuscripts within six months. Accepts simultaneous submissions. Average lead time is 18 months.
Submission Guidelines Accepts unsolicited manuscripts and proposals.
Recent Title(s) *Pioneer Poltergeist*, Mel Malton (Young Fiction/Mystery)
Tips Napoleon/RendezVous Press usually only accept work from Canadian writers. See the website to check which imprints are accepting submissions at any given time.

NB Publisher (Pty) Ltd
PO Box 879, Cape Town, 8000, South Africa
- 0027 21 406 3033
- 0027 21 406 3812
- nb@nb.co.za

- www.nb.co.za

Contact Publisher (Non-Fiction), Danita van Romburgh
Imprint(s) Human & Rousseau
Kwela
Pharos
Tafelberg
Categories Publishes Non-fiction, Fiction and Children's titles on the following subjects: Afrikaans Novels, Children's Fiction, Children's Non-fiction, Cookery, Craft, Dictionaries, General Interest, Health, Literary Fiction, Local Interest, Mainstream Fiction, Picture books, Spirituality, Young Adult.
Insider Info Aims to respond to manuscripts within three months.
Submission Guidelines Accepts unsolicited manuscripts and proposals.
Recent Title(s) *Verkeerdespruit*, Michiel Heynes
Tips Accepts submissions either by post or email, providing they are sent to the correct imprint.

New Africa Books (Pty) Ltd
99 Garfield Road, Claremont 7700, PO Box 46962, Glosderry 7702, South Africa
- 0027 21 674 4136
- 0027 21 674 3358
- info@newafricabooks.co.za
- www.newafricabooks.co.za

Contact Managing Director, Brian Wafawarowa
Imprint(s) David Philip Publishers (African Literature)
Spearhead Press (General trade/Consumer/International Market)
New Africa Education Publishing
Categories Publishes Children's Fiction and Non-Fiction, African literature and Educational and Reference books.
Insider Info New Africa Books strives to be a leading publisher in South Africa. To achieve this New Africa Education, David Philip and Spearhead will operate as separate imprints, serving their specific markets while exploiting synergies among themselves.
Recent Title(s) *A Mozambican Summer,* Nokuthula Mazibuko; (Young Novel/Girls); *Building an essay: A practical guide for students*, JD Lewis-Williams

New Frontier Publishing
Forest Central, Building 7, Unit 4/49 Frenchs Forest Road, Frenchs Forest NSW 2086, Australia
- 0061 2 9453 1525
- 0061 2 9975 2531
- info@newfrontier.com.au
- www.newfrontier.com.au

Contact Director, Peter Whitfield

Categories Publishes Children's Fiction and Non-Fiction, Picture books, Activity books, Dictionaries and Textbooks for five to ten year olds.

Insider Info Advance offered, with authors paid by royalty.

Submission Guidelines Accepts unsolicited manuscripts. Does not favour multiple submissions.

Recent Title(s) *Dragon Mode*, Sally Odgers (Author) Chantal Stewart (Illustrator) (Fantasy Picture Book)

Tips New Frontier offers all writers a submissions pack, which includes three hardback picture books and two junior novels. The pack explains why these books were selected for publication. Visit their website for the order form.

New Zealand Council for Educational Research

10 th Floor, West Block, Education House, 178–182 Willis Street, Wellington 6011, New Zealand

- 0064 4 384 7939
- 0061 4 384 7933
- robyn.baker@nzcer.org.nz
- www.nzcer.org.nz

Contact Director, Robyn Baker

Categories Publishes Books, Assessment instruments, Kits and Periodicals on the following subjects: Education (covering most school subjects), Human Resources, Psychology, Parent Education, Mental Health, Speech Pathology and Autism Spectrum Disorders.

Insider Info NZCER is a non-governmental educational research organisation which researches and develops educational products across New Zealand. Its publishing arm, NZCER Press, publishes and distributes books, tests and resources.

Submission Guidelines All submitted proposals or manuscripts should be evidence or research based. Visit their website for full details.

Recent Title(s)
Spell Right! Endings (Interactive CD ROM)

Tips Visit their website to download their book and product catalogues.

Northword Books For Young Readers

11571 K-Tel Drive, Minnetonka, MN 55343, USA

- 001 952 933 7537
- 001 952 933 3630
- michellekackman@tnkidsbooks.com
- www.tnkidsbooks.com

Parent Company T & N Children's Publishing

Categories Publishes Fiction Picture books, Series books, Non-Fiction Nature books and Wildlife books on the following subjects; Environment, Arts & Crafts, Cooking, Outdoor Sports and Building Projects for children aged up to 12.

Insider Info A specialist imprint company that publishes educational books for children in fun and interactive formats to help install the love of the natural world.

Submission Guidelines For non-fiction submit an outline plus sample chapters. Northword is currently seeking picture book submissions with natural history, animal, nature, and environmental themes for children, from infant to eight years old. Accepts illustration submissions.

Recent Title(s) *The Arctic,* Wayne Lynch (Author and Photographer) (Series)

Tips Northword is seeking submissions ideas for children's non-fiction series. Northword is not seeking submissions with a heavy religious theme.

Oliver Press Inc

Charlotte Square, 5707 West 36th Street, Minneapolis, MN 55416-2510, USA

- 001 952 926 8981
- 001 952 926 8965
- orders@oliverpress.com
- www.oliverpress.com

Contact Editor, Denise Sterling

Categories Publishes History Series, Biographies and Science books for Young Adults.

Insider Info A small scale publishing company dedicated to introducing history in a fun and engaging medium. They publish seven curriculum based series.

Submission Guidelines Accepts unsolicited manuscripts. Writers are invited to submit a proposal, include a biography including any published work.

Recent Title(s) *How It Happens at the Motorcycle Plant*, Shawndra Shofner (Author) Bob and Diane Wolfe (Photographs) (How It Happens Series)

Tips Oliver Press prefers proposals to fit into one of their seven established series.

Orca Book Publishers

Box 5626, Station B, Victoria, BC, V8R 6S4, Canada

- 001 800 210 5277
- 001 877 408 1551
- orca@orcabook.com
- www.orcabook.com

Contact Bob Tyrrell Publisher

Categories Publishes Picture books, Early Chapter books (Orca Echoes and Orca Young Readers),

Novels (Orca Currents, Orca Sports & Orca Soundings series for reluctant readers), Teenage Novels, Hiking guidebooks.

Insider Info Orca Book Publishers is Western Canada's premier children's publisher. With over 350 titles in print and more than 60 new titles a year, Orca publishes award winning, bestselling books in a number of genres.

Submission Guidelines Orca only publishes books from Canadian authors. Visit their website for submission details.

Recent Title(s) *Hello, Groin,* Beth Goobie (Teenage Fiction); *Bang*, Norah McClintock (Orca Soundings)

Orchard Books
95 Madison Avenue, New York NY, 10016, USA
- 001 212 951 2600
- 001 212 213 435
- www.orchardbooks.co.uk

Parent The Watts Publishing Group

Contact Editor, Ana Cerro; Assistant Editors, Lisa Hammon and Tamson Weston

Categories Publishes Picture books, Board books, Novelty books, Juvenile, Middle reader, Audio books, Gift books, Poetry, Series books featuring the successful *Rainbow Magic* fairytale stories, and Young Adult.

Insider Info Publishes innovative children's fiction for children of all ages. All the picture books feature beautiful and colourful illustrations.

Submission Guidelines No unsolicited manuscripts.

Recent Title(s) *Rainbow Magic: Megan the Monday Fairy* (Fantasy Series)

Otava Publishing Company Ltd
Uudenmaankatu 10, SF-00120, Helsinki, Finland
- 00358 9 19961
- 00358 9 199 6560
- name.surname@otava.fi
- www.otava.fi

Parent Company Otava Books and Magazines Group Ltd

Contact Managing Director, Antti Reenpää; Publishing Director (Otava General Literature), Leena Majander; Publishing Director (Otava Education), Jukka Vahtola

Imprint(s) Otava Education
Otava General Literature

Categories Publishes Illustrated and Educational Children's Fiction and Non-fiction books

Insider Info Publishes 600 titles per year, including adult titles.

Recent Title(s) *Santa Claus*, Mauri Kunnas; *Mr Boo*, Hannu Mäkelä

Tips Otava supports new writers and has an 'open minded, yet resolute' approach to publishing.

Oxford University Press Southern Africa
Vasco Boulevard, N1 City, Goodwood, Cape Town 7460, South Africa
- 0027 21 596 2300
- 0027 21 596 1234
- oxford.za@oup.com
- www.oxford.co.za

Contact Publishing Director, M.R. Griffin

Categories Publishes Educational books, Dictionaries, Reference materials for Students and Teachers based on the demands of South Africa. Also publishes general interest including Children's Fiction and Non-Fiction, Classics and Adult titles.

Insider Info Oxford University Press is committed to the development of South Africa with over 700 published African authors.

Submission Guidelines Accepts proposals with three sample chapters via post. Include a covering letter detailing the target audience, competition and any publishing credits. Visit their website to download a manuscript information form, for higher education books and novels and dictionaries.

Recent Titles *Blitz Maths Grade 3*, M. Facer

Oxford University Press (US)
198 Madison Avenue, New York, New York, 10016, USA
- 001 212 726 6000
- www.oup.com/us

Contact Vice President/Editorial Director, Joan Bossert; President, Laura Brown

Categories Publishes Biography, Letters and Memoirs, Early Readers, History, Literature, Music and Art, Myths, Legends and Fairy tales, Picture books, Poetry, Reference and Science.

Insider Info Pays 0–15 per cent royalty on retail price, with an advance offered. 80 per cent of books come from unagented writers, and 40 per cent from first-time authors. Average lead time of ten months. Catalogue available free on request.

Submission Guidelines Accepts unsolicited manuscripts and proposals. Aims to respond to proposals within three months. Accepts simultaneous submissions.

Recent Title(s) *The Egyptians;* Neil Grant

Tips Oxford University Press is a major publisher of academic books for children.

Pacific View Press

PO Box 2897, Berkeley CA 94702, USA

☎ 001 415 285 8538

☎ 001 510 843 5835

✉ Bobness4_@excite.com

🌐 www.pacificviewpress.com

Contact Bob Schildgen, Nancy Ippolito

Established 1992

Categories Publishes multicultural Non-Fiction and literature for children with a focus on the culture and history of China, Japan, the Philippines, Mexico, and other countries of the Pacific Rim. Also publishes adult titles on acupuncture and contemporary Asian and Asian American affairs books.

Insider Info A small scale corporately owned Chinese and Asian publishing company. They emphasise good writing, engaging tales, beautiful illustrations by culturally knowledgeable artists and factual accuracy. Every effort is made to publish works by unknown artists and writers.

Submission Guidelines Contact the company directly for submission details.

Recent Title(s) *Monkey King,* Teresa Chin Jones (Fiction); *Cloud Weavers: Ancient Chinese Legends*, Rena Krasno and Yeng-Fong Chiang

Pan Macmillan Australia

Level 25, 1 Market Street, Sydney, NSW 2000, Australia

☎ 0061 3 9825 1000

☎ 0061 3 9825 1010

✉ ross.gibb@macmillan.com.au

🌐 www.macmillan.com.au

Contact Directors, Ross Gibb, James Fraser and Roxarne Burns

Imprint(s) Macmillan

Pan

Picador

Macquarie Library

Pancake

St. Martins Press

Tor

Forge

Griffin and Sidgwick

Jackson

Categories Publishes Children's Fiction and Non-Fiction, Picture books, Sticker books, Teenage novels, Fantasy, Children's Reference, Novelty/Other licenced, and Colouring & Activity books.

Insider Info Pan Macmillan Australia is a major Australian publisher and distributor, which publishes a wide range of children's and adult titles under its imprints.

Submission Guidelines Accepts unsolicited manuscripts. Send a covering letter with a detailed synopsis and preferably three sample chapters. Photocopies of selected illustrations or photos (if applicable). All submissions must be typed and double spaced.

Recent Title(s) *The Cat on the Mat is Flat*, Andy Griffiths and Terry Denton; *Wildwood Dancing*, Juliet Marillier

Tips Only the works of the highest quality will be accepted as they are cutting back on their publishing programme. They do not accept submissions for short story collections or poetry.

Paragon Publishing

440 Park Avenue South, 13th Floor, NY, 10006

☎ 001 212 629 9733

✉ usinfo@parragon.com

🌐 www.parragon.com

Categories Publishes Children's Picture books, Activity books, Illustrated Board and Story books and Adult titles on Cooking, Gardening, History and much more.

Insider Info Parragon is the largest promotional value publisher in the world.

Submission Guidelines Contact Parragon for submission details.

Peachtree Publishers

1700 Chattahoochee Avenue, Atlanta, Georgia, 30318, USA

☎ 001 404 876 8761

☎ 001 404 875 2578

✉ hello@peachtree-online.com

🌐 www.peachtree-online.com

Contact Submissions Editor, Helen Harriss

Imprint(s) Peachtree Children's Books

Categories Publishes Non-fiction, Fiction and Children's titles on the following subjects: American South Guidebooks, Education, Health, Outdoor Pursuits, Parenting, Picture books, Psychology, Self help, Young Adult.

Insider Info Publishes 30 titles per year. Authors paid by royalty, with an advance offered. 75 per cent of books come from unagented writers, and 25 per cent from first-time authors. Peachtree receives approximately 20,000 submissions per year. Accepts simultaneous submissions. Average lead time is one year. Catalogue available free on request – send a SAE.

Submission Guidelines Send in full manuscript for children's submissions with a SAE including details of any published work to date. Aims to respond to manuscripts within six months. No email or faxed submissions. Address all manuscripts to Helen Harriss.

Recent Title(s) *About Amphibians,* Cathryn Sill (Author), John Sill (Illustrator) (Educational Wildlife Series); *Can You Cuddle Like A Koala?* John Butler (Author and Illustrator) (Board Book)

Pearson Education Australia
PO Box 1024, South Melbourne 3205, Victoria, Australia
- 0061 3 9811 2800
- 0061 3 9811 2999
- firstname.surname@pearsoned.com.au
- www.pearsoned.com.au

Parent Company Pearson Plc

Contact Editor in Chief (Higher Education), Paul Petrulis; Senior Acquisitions Editor and Development Manager (Higher Education), Alison Green; Publisher (Professional and Vocational Education), Diane Gee-Clough; Senior Acquisitions Editor (Professional and Vocational Education), Natalie Muir

Imprint(s) Addison Wesley
 Allyn & Bacon
 Benjamin Cummings
 Longman
 Prentice Hall

Categories Publishes Non-fiction and Children's titles on the following subjects: Academic, Children's Education, Education, Multimedia, Online, Reference, Science, Sociology, Teacher Resources, Technology, Textbook.

Insider Info Authors paid by royalty with an advance offered.

Submission Guidelines Accepts unsolicited manuscripts and proposals.

Recent Title(s) *Gaining Word Power*, Dorothy Rubin

Tips Pearson Education Australia accepts submissions of educational non-fiction or reference material. See website for a full list of acquisitions editors and their interests.

Pearson Education Canada
26 Prince Andrew Place, Toronto, Ontario, M3C 2T8, Canada
- 001 416 447 5101
- 001 416 443 0948
- firstname.lastname@pearsoncanada.ca
- www.pearsoncanada.ca

Parent Company Pearson Plc

Contact Executive Acquisitions Editor (Accounting, Decision Science, Finance), Samantha Scully; Executive Acquisitions Editor (Anthropology, History,

Linguistics, Modern Languages, Political Science), Laura Forbes; Executive Acquisitions Editor (Engineering, Science, Math, Geography, Health, Nursing), Michelle Sartor

Imprint(s) Addison-Wesley
 Allyn & Bacon
 Copp Clark
 Longman
 Prentice Hall

Categories Publishes Non-Fiction, eBooks, Series, CD-ROMs on the following subjects: Maths, Science, Social Studies, Arts, Languages, English and Business and Technology.

Insider Info Authors paid by royalty, with an advance offered.

Submission Guidelines Accepts unsolicited manuscripts and proposals.

Recent Title(s) *Literacy In Action*

Tips Pearson Education Canada accepts submissions of educational non-fiction or reference material. See website for a full list of acquisitions editors and their interests.

Pearson Education New Zealand
PO Box 102902, North Shore, North Shore City, Auckland, 0745, New Zealand
- 0064 9 442 7400
- 0064 9 442 7401
- firstname.surname@pearsoned.co.nz
- www.pearsoned.co.nz

Parent Company Pearson Plc

Contact Publisher (Higher Education), Bronwen Nicholson; Publisher (Higher Education), Norman Mailer; Publisher (Schools), Ken Harrop

Imprint(s) Addison-Wesley
 Allyn & Bacon
 Benjamin Cummings
 Longman
 Prentice Hall

Categories Publishes Non-fiction and Children's books and Textbooks on the following subjects: Academic, Children's Education, Education, Multimedia, Online, Reference, Science, Sociology, Teacher Resources and Technology.

Insider Info Authors paid by royalty with an advance offered.

Submission Guidelines Accepts unsolicited manuscripts and proposals.

Recent Title(s) *Sigma Mathematics: NCEA Level 3 Statistics and Modelling*

Tips Pearson Education New Zealand accepts submissions of educational non-fiction or reference material. See website for a full list of acquisitions editors and their interests.

Pearson Scott Foresman

345 Hudson Street, New York, NY, 10014, USA

☎ 001 800 552 2259

🌐 www.scottforesman.com

Parent Company Pearson Education Inc

Contact President and Publishing, Stephan Lurie; Editorial Director, Donna Brooks; Art Director, Sara Reynolds

Established 1896

Categories Publishes Educational Resources, School Curriculum Material for all subjects, Assessment Materials and Interactive Products.

Insider Info A leading elementary publisher committed to improving reading in young children. This is best exemplified by *The Levelled Readers Collection*, a collection with many subject areas, from Animals to Space.

Recent Title(s) *Reading Street grades pre K-6*

Pelican Publishing

1000 Burmaster Street, Gretna, Louisiana, 70053-2246, USA

☎ 001 504 368 1175

☎ 001 504 368 1195

✉ editorial@pelicanpub.com

🌐 www.pelicanpub.com

Contact Editor, Nina Kooij

Categories Publishes Children's Ficton, Picture books and Seasonal books. Also publishes Travel Guides, and Art and Architecture books.

Insider Info Pelican has a backlist of over 1,500 titles and 50–60 new titles were produced in 2007.

Submission Guidelines No unsolicited manuscripts. Young children's books cannot exceed 1,100 words. Books for middle readers should be at least 25,000 words.

Recent Title(s) *Toby Belfer and the High Holy Days*, Gloria Teles Pushker (Picture Book/Jewish)

Penguin Group (Australia)

250 Camberwell Road, Camberwell, Victoria, 3124, Australia

☎ 0061 3 9811 2400

☎ 0061 3 9811 2620

✉ childrens.publishing@au.penguingroup.com

🌐 www.penguin.com.au

Parent Company Pearson Plc

Imprint Puffin

Contact Managing Director, Gabrielle Coyne; Publishing Director, Robert Sessions; Children's Publishers, Julie Watts and Laura Harris; Commissioning Editor, Lisa Riley

Categories Publishes Non-fiction, Fiction, Licensed books, Baby books and Teenage novels on subjects such as Fantasy, Action/Adventure, Magic, Family, Animals, Romance and more.

Insider Info Authors paid by royalty with an advance offered.

Submission Guidelines No unsolicited manuscripts or proposals. Does not accept simultaneous submissions.

Recent Title(s) *The Misadventures of Batholomew Piff*, Jason Lethcoe (Fiction/Magic)

Tips Penguin Australia publishes an email newsletter, *The Squawk*, for children aged 8–13.

Penguin Group (Canada)

90 Eglinton Avenue East, Suite 700, Toronto, Ontario, M4P 2Y3, Canada

☎ 001 416 925 2249

☎ 001 416 925 0068

✉ info@penguin.ca

🌐 www.penguin.ca

Parent Company Pearson Plc

Established 1974

Contact President, Ed Carson

Imprint(s) Penguin Canada
Puffin Canada
Viking Canada

Categories Publishes Non-fiction, Fiction and Children's titles on the following subjects: Canadian Interest, Children's Fiction, Contemporary Fiction, Education, General Interest, How-To, Mainstream Fiction, Reference, Self-Help.

Insider Info Authors paid by royalty with an advance offered.

Submission Guidelines Does not accept unsolicited manuscripts or proposals.

Recent Title(s) *Camp X Fool's Gold*, Eric Walker (Historical Fiction); *Mythology*, Dugald Steer (Editor) (Educational Series)

Tips Penguin Canada specialises in writing about Canada, and the work of Canadian writers. Penguin Canada does not except unagented submissions or proposals.

Penguin Group (New Zealand)

67 Apollo Drive, Albany, Auckland, 10, New Zealand

☎ 0064 9 442 7400

☎ 0064 9 442 7401

✉ info@penguin.co.nz

🌐 www.penguin.co.nz

Parent Company Pearson Plc

Categories Publishes Non-fiction, Fiction and Children's titles on the following subjects: Children's Fiction, Contemporary Fiction, Education, General Interest, How-To, Local Interest, Mainstream Fiction, Reference, Self-Help and Licensed books.

Insider Info Authors paid by royalty, with an advance offered. Aims to respond to queries within two months.

Submission Guidelines Accepts unsolicited manuscripts and proposals.

Recent Title(s) *Mister Pip*, Lloyd Jones (Historical Fiction)

Tips Penguin New Zealand recommends submissions be directed through a literary agent, but they will also accept unsolicited proposals, although the odds of them being accepted are very low.

Penguin Group (USA) Inc

375 Hudson Street, New York, New York, 10014, USA

- 001 212 366 2000
- www.penguin.com

Parent Company Pearson Plc

Contact Chief Executive Officer, David Shanks; President, Susan Petersen Kennedy; President (Books for Young Readers), Doug Whiteman

Imprint(s) Dial Books
 Duttons Children's Books
 Firebird
 Frederick Warne
 G.P.Putnum's Sons
 Grosset & Dunlap
 Philomel
 Price Stern Sloan
 Puffin
 Razorbill
 Speak
 Viking

Categories Publishes Non-fiction, Fiction and Children's titles on the following subjects:
 General Interest, Mainstream, Contemporary, How-To, Self-Help, Reference, Education.

Insider Info Authors paid by royalty, with an advance offered.

Submission Guidelines Does not accept unsolicited manuscripts or proposals.

Recent Title(s) *Hairspray: The Novel*, Tracey West (Media Tie-In)

Tips Penguin does not generally except unagented submissions, except for on rare occasions where one or another imprint may be seeking new titles. Penguin's website has current details of which imprints are open for submission.

Père Castor

87, quai Panhard et Levassor, 75013, Paris, France

- 0033 1 40 51 31
- 0033 1 46 33 45
- Online form
- www.flammarion.com

Contact Children's Publisher, Hélène Wadowski

Parent Flammarion Group

Categories Publishes Picture books, Board and Novelty books, How-To books, Pop-Up books, Fantasy and Fairytales.

Submission Guidelines Aims to respond to manuscripts in two months. All manuscripts must be typed and double spaced.

Recent Titles *Les Chiffres*, Marion Ticket (Picture Book)

Tips Works of fiction are preferred.

Philomel Books

345 Hudson Street, New York, NY, 10014, USA

- 001 212 366 2000
- 001 212 366 3393
- www.penguin.com

Parent Company Penguin Group (USA)

Contact Vice President and Publisher, Michael Green; Editor, Patricia Lee Gauch

Established 1980

Categories Publishes Children's Fiction and Non-fiction, Picture books, Fantasy, Historical Fiction, Board books.

Insider Info Publishes 25 titles per year for children of all ages. Philomel has a distinguished list of published books, such as Barbara Berger's *Grandfather Twilight*, Virginia Hamilton's Newbery Honor-winning *Sweet Whispers, Brother Rush* and Caldecott winner *Owl Moon* by Jane Yolen and John Schoenherr.

Submission Guidelines No unsolicited manuscripts. There are length guidelines for their books, ranging from 1,000 words for Picture books, to 20,000 words for young adults. Send illustration samples with a CV and tearsheets. All communication via post should include SAE. Aims to respond in a month. Approximately five per cent of published books are by first-time authors.

Recent Title(s) *The Great Tree of Avalon: The Eternal Flame*, T. A. Barron (Fantasy); *Ranger's Apprentice*, John Flanagan (Fantasy); *G Is for Goat*, Patricia Polacco (Author and Illustrator) (Board Book)

Pippin Publishing Corporation

PO Box 242, Don Mills, Ontario, M3C 2S2, Canada

- ☎ 001 416 510 2918
- ☎ 001 416 510 3359
- ◉ cynthia@pippinpub.com
- ◍ www.pippinpub.com

Categories Publishes Non-fiction titles on the following subjects: Art, Autobiography, Biography, Canadian Interest, Education (all school subjects), Teaching Methods.

Recent Title(s) *Writing In The Middle Years*, Marion Crowhurst (English Educational)

Tips Pippin Publishing is an educational publisher, and prints books written by teachers or similarly qualified academics.

Planeta & Oxford

Avenida Diagonal, 662-66408034, Barcelona, Spain

- ☎ 0034 93 492 8155
- ☎ 0034 93 496 7041
- ◉ mgallardo@planeta.es
- ◍ www.planetainfantil.com

Parent Grupo Planeta

Categories Publishes Educational books and Textbooks.

Insider Info A relatively recent imprint which is a fusion of Oxford University Press and Planeta. Publishes books for the Spanish education system.

Planeta Junior

Avenida Diagonal, 662-66408034 Barcelona, Spain

- ☎ 0034 93 492 8155
- ☎ 0034 93 496 7041
- ◉ editorialplanetajunior@planeta.es
- ◍ www.editorialplanetajunior.com

Parent Grupo Planeta

Categories Publishes Activity books, Sticker books, Film/Television Tie-Ins and Picture books.

Insider Info The imprint's publishing line is aimed at entertaining children. The main sectors are: BBC Worldwide Ltd, The Walt Disney Company, Guinness World Record, Sesame Workshop, The Jim Henson Company and Warner Bros.

Recent Titles *Princesas Stickermanía; WITCH 14. La negaci Ón de la reina*

Pleasant St. Press

PO Box 520, Raynham Center, MA 02768, USA

- ☎ 001 508 822 3075
- ☎ 001 508 977 2498
- ◉ acochran@pleasantpress.com
- ◍ www.pleasantstpress.com

Contact President, Alan Cochran

Established 2006

Categories Publishes Children's Fiction and Non-fiction, Young Adult novels, Photographic books

Insider Info Pleasant St. Press is a newly established independent children's illustrated book publisher. They publish high quality, illustrated picture books. Pleasant St.'s first list is due Spring 2008.

Submission Guidelines At the present time Pleasant St. Press is only accepting picture book manuscripts. Include a short biography including contact details and any published work. For picture books larger than 800 words please contact them before any submission. Simultaneous submissions are accepted.

Recent Title(s) *Farmer Brown and His Little Red Truck*, Jean M. Cochran (Author), Daryl Enos (Illustrator) (Farm Animals); *If A Monkey Jumps Onto Your School Bus*, Jean M. Cochran (Author), Jennifer E. Morris (Illustrator)

Tips Pleasant St. Press anticipates including new genres in the future. Check the website for updates to their submission guidelines.

Pocket Jeunesse

12, avenue d'Italie, 75013 Paris, France

- ☎ 0033 1 44 16 05 00
- ☎ 0033 1 44 16 05 20
- ◉ editeur@pocket.fr
- ◍ www.pocket.fr

Contact Publisher, Jean-Claude Dubost

Parent Univers Poche

Categories Publishes Children's Fiction for ages three to six, six to nine, nine to twelve and thirteen plus; Picture books, Film and Television Tie-Ins and Board books.

Insider Info Since its inception, Pocket Jeunesse has published 841 titles to date, and 138 titles per year.

Submission Guidelines Will consider unsolicited manuscripts, allow a month for a response.

Recent Titles *Transformers*, (Film Tie-In); *Nina et son double*, Anne-Marie POL (Girls' Fiction)

Tips Manuscripts must be for an age range of 0–6 year olds.

Price Stern Sloan

345 Hudson Street, New York, NY, 10014, USA

☎ 001 212 366 2792

🖷 001 416 2122 436002

🌐 www.penguin.com

Parent Company Penguin Group (USA)

Contact President and Publisher, Debra Dorfman

Established 1964

Categories Publishes Children's Fiction and Non-fiction, Proprietary brands, Movie Tie-In titles, Novelty/Lift-flap books, Graphic readers.

Insider Info Publishes 70 titles per year for pre-school children to young adults. Original titles include the popular proprietary brands, such as *Mad Libs, Wee Sing, Mr. Men & Little Miss* and *Serendipity*. Film tie-ins include *Charlie and the Chocolate Factory, Wallace & Gromit, Everyone's Hero* and *Happy Feet*.

Submission Guidelines Send query letter with SAE. Aims to respond within three weeks.

Recent Title(s) *Mr. Bean's Holiday Mad Libs*, Roger Price and Leonard Stern; *Inside the Little Old Woman's Shoes*, Chuck Reasoner

Tips PSS also produces a successful annual list of desk calendars, and occasional humour titles for the adult market.

Puffin Books

345 Hudson Street, New York, NY, 10014, USA

☎ 001 212 366 2792

🖷 001 212 366 3393

🌐 www.penguin.com

Parent Company Penguin Group (USA)

Contact President and Publisher, Eileen Bishop Kreit; Editor, Rebecca McNally; Editor, Shannon Dean Smith

Established 1941

Categories Publishes Children's Fiction and Non-fiction, Classics, Series Fiction, Film/Television Tie-Ins, Picture books, Lift-flap books, Board books.

Insider Info One of the most prestigious children's paperback publishers in the United States. Publishes approximately 225–275 titles a year.

Submission Guidelines Accepts a maximum of 30 pages for longer works. No picture book submissions. Must include an SAE.

Recent Title(s) *Our Secret,* Siri Aang, Christina Kessler (Fiction); *The Hero's Trail*, T. A. Barron (Non-Fiction); *Tiny Goes Camping*, Cari Meister (Author), Rich Davis (Illustrator) (Picture Books Easy to Read Series); *Hoofbeats*, Kathleen Duey (Fiction Series for Girls)

Raincoast Books

9050 Shaughnessy Street, Vancouver, BC, V6P 6E5, Canada

☎ 001 604 323 7100

🖷 001 604 323 2600

✉ info@raincoast.com

🌐 www.raincoast.com

Established 1981

Imprint(s) Polestar

Press Gang

Categories Publishes Children's Picture books, Middle-Grade and Young Adult Fiction, Non-Fiction and Adult books.

Insider Info Raincoast is one of Canada's most successful independent publishing houses, with great success in the last five years, and since the arrival of Harry Potter.

Submission Guidelines No unsolicited manuscripts. Send a query letter with a sample chapter. Aims to respond in eight to sixteen weeks.

Recent Title(s) *Harry Potter and The Deathly Hallows*, J.K. Rowling (Children's Fiction/Fantasy); *Canadian Flyer Adventures; Crazy for Gold*, Frieda Wishinsky (Author), Dean Griffit (Illustrator) (Children's Fiction Series)

Tips Only accepts submissions from Canadian residents.

Random House Australia Pty Ltd

20 Alfred Street, Milsons Point, New South Wales, 2061, Australia

☎ 0061 2 9954 9966

🖷 0061 2 9954 4562

✉ random@randomhouse.com.au

🌐 www.randomhouse.com.au

Parent Company Bertelsmann Book Group

Contact Managing Director, Margaret Seale; Head of Publishing, Jane Palfreyman; Children's Publisher, Lindsay Knight

Categories Publishes Non-fiction, Fiction and Children's titles on the following subjects: Biography, Children's Fiction and Series, Licensed products, Contemporary Fiction, Education, General Interest, How-To, Literary Fiction, Local Interest, Mainstream Fiction, Reference, Self-Help, Travel.

Insider Info Authors are paid by royalty, with an advance offered. Aims to respond to manuscripts within nine months.

Submission Guidelines Accepts unsolicited manuscripts and proposals for non-fiction only. Fiction submissions are only accepted by a previously published writer, or by a new writer represented by an agent.

Recent Title(s) *The Astrosaurs 10: Star Pirates*, Steve Cole (Fiction Series)

Random House Inc

1745 Broadway, New York, NY 10019, USA
- 001 212 782 9000
- 001 212 302 7985
- www.randomhouse.com

Parent Bertelsmann AG
Established 1925
Contact Chief Executive Officer, Peter Olson; President, Erik Engstrom
Imprint(s) Alfred A. Knopf Books for Young Readers
 Bantam Books
 David Fickling Books
 Delacorte Press Books for Young Readers
 Delacorte Press Trade Paperbacks
 Dragonfly
 Yearling Books
 Disney Books for Young Readers
 Golden Books
 Wendy Lamb Books
Categories Publishes Adult Non-fiction, Fiction, Children's titles, Audio, and Reference. See individual imprints for Children's titles.
Insider Info A leading global publisher, Random House together with its imprints publishes fiction and non-fiction, both original and reprints, by some of the foremost and most popular writers of our time. Authors are paid by royalty, with an advance offered.
Submission Guidelines No unsolicited manuscripts or proposals. Only accepts submissions from agents.
Recent Title(s) *Harry Potter and the Deathly Hallows*, J.K. Rowling (Fiction/Fantasy); *Eldest*, Christopher Paolini (Science Fiction/Fantasy)

Random House Mondadori

Travessera de Gràcia 47–49, 08021 Barcelona, Spain
- 0034 93 366 0300
- 0034 93 366 0449
- www.randomhousemondadori.es

Parent Bertelsmann AG
Imprints Beasco
 Lumen
 Montena
Categories Publishes a wide variety of Children's and Adult books.
Insider Info Random House Mondadori is organised into three geographical divisions: Spain; Argentina, Chile and Uruguay; and Mexico, Colombia and Venezuela. It is dedicated to promoting the richness

and vitality of the Spanish Language. Random House is also a packager and printer.
Tips See children's imprints for submission details.

Random House of Canada Ltd

1 Toronto Street, Unit 300, Toronto, Ontario, M5C 2V6, Canada
- 001 416 364 4449
- 001 416 364 6863
- www.randomhouse.ca

Parent Company Bertelsmann Book Group
Contact Chairman, John Neale
Imprint(s) Anchor Canada
 Doubleday Canada Group
 Knopf Canada
 Random House Canada
 Seal Books
 Vintage
Categories Publishes Non-fiction, Fiction and Children's titles on the following subjects: Biography, Children's Fiction, Contemporary Fiction, Education, General Interest, How-To, Literary Fiction, Local Interest, Mainstream Fiction, Reference, Self-Help, Travel.
Insider Info Authors are paid by royalty, with an advance offered.
Submission Guidelines Does not accept unsolicited manuscripts or proposals.
Recent Title(s) *Cutie Pie!* Matthew Kempler (Novelty Book); *Honk if You Hate Me*, Deborah Halverson (Teen Fiction)

Ravensburger Buchverlag

Postbox 1860, 88188 Ravensburg, Germany
- 0049 751 860
- 0049 751 861311
- internet@ravensburger.com
- www.ravensburger.de/buchverlag

Parent Company Ravensburger AG
Contact Managing Directors, Renate Herres and Johannes Hauenstein; Publisher, Alexander Eisele; Editor In Chief, Nicole Splechna
Categories Publishes Baby books, Children's Non-Fiction and Fiction, Easy Reads, Activity books, Picture books, Novelty/Board books, Series, Puzzles and Educational games.
Insider Info Publishes approximately 450 titles each year with 1500 in print. Successful authors with Ravensburger include Morton Rhue, Thomas Brezina and Anthony Horowitz.
Submission Guidelines Accepts unsolicited manuscripts or sample chapters, however due to the sheer volume of scripts they receive, they are unable

to give feedback unless interested in pursuing the book. Aims to respond within six months.

Recent Titles *Die Knickerbocker Bande:13 blaue Katzen*, Thomas Brezina (Children's Series)

Tips Ravensburger has subsidiaries all over the world, including the UK. It is a market leader in puzzles, crafts and games. Ravensburger Germany deals exclusively with publishing children's books.

Razorbill
345 Hudson Street, New York, NY, 10014, USA
- 001 212 366 2792
- 001 212 266 3393
- eloise.flood@us.penguin.com
- www.penguin.com

Parent Company Penguin Group (USA)

Contact President and Publisher, Ben Schrank; Editor, Eloise Flood; Editor, Kristen Pettit

Categories Publishes Children's Fiction and Non-Fiction, Young Adult novels, Fantasy.

Insider Info Razorbill publishes between 30 and 40 titles per year. Razorbill's backlist includes *New York Times* bestselling author Scott Westerfeld's *So Yesterday* and *Peeps*.

Submission Guidelines Accepts a maximum of 30 pages for longer works, with a covering letter describing the genre, age group and any publishing credits. No picture book submissions. All novel submissions must include a SAE.

Recent Title(s) *Vampire Academy*, Richelle Mead (Fantasy/Horror); *Hex Education*, Emily Gould & Zareen Jaffery (Fiction/Fantasy)

Tips The majority of published books are contemporary commercial fiction.

Red Deer Press Inc
1512, 1800 4th Street, SW Calgary, AB, T2S 2S5, Canada
- 001 403 509 0800
- 001 403 228 6503
- rdp@reddeerpress.com
- www.reddeerpress.com

Contact Publisher, Dennis Johnson; Children's Editor, Peter Carver

Parent Fitzhenry & Whiteside

Established 1973

Categories Publishes Children's books, Science-Fiction, and Adult Fiction and Non-Fiction

Insider Info The imprint company publishes between 14 to 16 books and eight reprints a year. Red Deer Press' mandate is to publish books by, about, or of interest to Canadians - with special emphasis upon the Prairie West. The company

publishes approximately one third children's illustrated and young fiction; one-third literary fiction, poetry, drama, creative non-fiction and belle lettres; and one-third literary and trade non-fiction.

Submission Guidelines Due to a high volume of manuscripts they are only accepting unsolicited manuscripts with excellent potential.

Recent Title(s) *Orphans in the Sky*, Jeanne Bushey (Author), Vladyana Krykorka (Illustrator); *Wild Orchid*, Beverley Brenna (Teen Fiction); *Carmen*, Carole Frechette, Translated by Susan Ouriou (Teen Fiction)

Tips The company prefers Canadian authors.

Reed Publishing (New Zealand) Ltd
PO Box 34901, 39 Rawene Road, Birkenhead, Auckland 10, New Zealand
- 0064 9 441 2960
- 0064 9 480 4999
- info@reed.co.nz
- www.reed.co.nz

Parent Company Reed Elsevier Group Plc

Contact Managing Director, Alan Smith; Publishing Manager, Peter Janssen

Imprint(s) Heinemann Education
Reed Books
Reed Children's Books

Categories Publishes Non-fiction and Children's titles on the following subjects: Biography, Children's Fiction, Cooking, Education, General interest, History, Humour, Language, Mainstream Fiction, Maori Culture, New Zealand interest, Outdoor, Picture books, Tourism.

Submission Guidelines Accepts unsolicited manuscripts and proposals.

Recent Title(s) *Adventures of Hutu and Kawa*, Avis Acres

Tips Mostly publish non-fiction of New Zealand interest, and mass market children's books. They publish very little adult fiction.

Richard C.Owen Publishers Inc
PO Box 585, Katonah, NY 10536, USA
- 001 914 232 3903
- 001 914 232 3977
- chrisarendt@rcowen.com
- www.rcowen.com

Contact Publisher, Richard C. Owen; Customer Service, Chris Arendt

Established 1982

Categories Publishes Educational materials for K-8, and books for teachers.

Insider Info A publishing company committed to improving reading and writing for children.

Submission Guidelines Accepts unsolicited manuscripts.
Recent Title(s) *Reader's Theater*

Roaring Brook Press
175 Fifth Avenue, New York, NY 10010, USA
- 001 646 307 5151
- 001 212 243 6002
- www.holltzbrinckus.com

Parent Company Holltzbrinck Publishers
Contact Senior Editor, Deirdre Langeland; Editor, Neal Porter
Established 1852
Categories Publishes Picture books, Fiction, Graphic novels, Non-fiction, Young Adult.
Insider Info Publishes about 40 titles a year.
Submission Guidelines No unsolicited manuscripts.
Recent Title(s) *Kid Blink Beats the World*, Don Brown (Author and Illustrator)
Tips Roaring Press advertise jobs on their website.

RSVP Publishing Company Ltd
PO Box 47–166, Ponsonby, Auckland, New Zealand
- 0064 9 372 8480
- 0064 9 372 8480
- rsvppub@iconz.co.nz
- www.rsvp-publishing.co.nz

Contact Publisher, Stephen Picard; Editorial Manager, Rosie Parkes
Categories Publishes Non-fiction, Fiction, Children's titles and Picture books on the following subjects: Contemporary Fiction, General interest, Local interest, New Zealand Metaphysical books.
Insider Info Publishes six titles per year.
Submission Guidelines Accepts unsolicited manuscripts and proposals.
Recent Title(s) *Ride a White Horse,* Dawn McMillan and Julia Crouth (Picture Books for Children aged 5–9)
Tips RSVP primarily publish New Zealand metaphysical books, but are also willing to accept other forms of innovative non-fiction or fiction.

Running Press Kids
125 South 22nd Street, Philadelphia, PA 19103-4399, USA
- 001 215 567 5080
- 001 215 568 2919
- perseus.promos@perseusbooks.com
- www.perseusbooksgroup.com/runningpress

Parent Company Running Press
Contact Editors, Andra Serlin and Elizabeth Shiflett
Established 1972
Categories Publishes Children's Fiction and Non-fiction, Picture books, Action books, Lift-flap books, Seasonal books, Educational books, Explore books, Series, Toy books, Television Tie-Ins, Basic concept books for young readers, and books plus products.
Insider Info Publishes 200 new titles a year, including adult titles. Children's feature titles include *Lithgow Boredom Blasters; Magic Windows: Touch & Feel* and *Bruce Blitz*.
Submission Guidelines Seeking interactive non-fiction, basic concepts books (such as letters, numbers, opposites, or shapes), or beginning reading projects and excellent picture books. No submissions via email. For picture books send the entire manuscript. Accepts illustration submissions, but do not send originals. Aims to respond between six to eight weeks.
Recent Title(s) *My Pop-Pop is a Pirate*, Pat Croce (Lift the flap book)
Tips At the present time Running Press is not accepting submissions for children's novels, or any fiction longer than picture book length.

Sanoma WSOY Education and Books
PO Box 222, SF-00121, Helsinki, Finland
- 00358 9 61681
- 00358 9 6168 3560
- firstname.lastname@wsoy.fi
- www.wsoy.fi

Parent Company Werner Söderström Corporation
Contact President/Chairman, Hannu Syrjänen; Literary Director (General Literature), Touko Siltala
Imprint(s) Bertmark Media AB
General Literature
WSOYpro
WSOY Educational Corporation
Categories Publishes Non-Fiction, Fiction and Children's titles on the following subjects: Children's Fiction, Contemporary Fiction, Dictionaries, Directories, Education, Finnish Fiction, General Interest, Language/Literature, Literary Fiction, Local Interest, Mainstream Fiction, Practical, Reference, Teaching Resources, Textbooks, Translated Foreign Fiction, Young Adult.
Insider Info Publishes 800 titles per year.
Recent Title(s) *Huolimattomat*, Kari Hotakainen
Tips WSOY is one of Finland's largest book publishers, mostly specialising in educational resources for all age ranges and abilities.

Scholastic Australia Pty Ltd

76–80 Railway Crescent, Lisarow, New South Wales, 2250, Australia

- ☎ 0061 2 4328 3555
- ✆ 0061 2 4323 3827
- ✉ customer_service@scholastic.com.au
- 🌐 www.scholastic.com.au

Parent Company Scholastic Inc

Contact General Manager (Publishing), Andrew Berkhut

Imprint(s) Omnibus Books
Scholastic Australia
Scholastic Press

Categories Publishes Children's Non-fiction and Fiction, Licensed products and Picture books.

Insider Info Authors are paid by royalty, with an advance offered. Receives 1,000 plus manuscripts per year.

Submission Guidelines Accepts submissions of full manuscripts for children's non-fiction, fiction and picture books from Australian writers. Aims to respond to manuscripts within three months.

Tips Scholastic Australia is always seeking illustrators for picture books.

Scholastic Canada Ltd

175 Hillmount Road, Markham, Ontario, L6C 1Z7, Canada

- ☎ 001 416 915 3500
- ✆ 001 416 849 7912
- 🌐 www.scholastic.ca

Parent Company Scholastic Inc

Imprint(s) Les Editions Scholastic
North Winds Press

Categories Publishes Non-fiction, Fiction and Young Children's titles, Picture books, Educational titles and Young Adult, and Film Tie-In titles.

Insider Info Publishes 40 titles per year. Pays five to ten per cent royalty on retail price, with advance offered. 50 per cent of books come from unagented writers, and three per cent of books from first-time authors. Does not accept simultaneous submissions. Average lead time of one year. Catalogue available free with a SAE.

Submission Guidelines No unsolicited manuscripts. Aims to respond to proposals within six months.

Recent Title(s) *Ballerina Wishes*, Carol Barton (Fiction Series); *The Extraordinary Adventures of Ordinary Basil*, Wiley Miller (Children's Fiction)

Tips Scholastic Canada publishes books for children and young adults, generally from Canadian authors only. To check if Scholastic Canada is open to submissions, phone their publishing status line on: 001 905 887 7323, extension 4308, or check their website.

Scholastic Education

557 Broadway, New York, NY 10012, USA

- ☎ 001 212 343 6100
- ✆ 001 212 343 4713
- ✉ info@scholastic.com
- 🌐 www.scholastic.com

Contact CEO, Richard Robinson; Executive Vice President and President, Margery W. Mayer; Education Consultant, Ramon C. Cortines

Parent Scholastic Inc.

Categories Publishes Educational Textbooks, Magazines, and Products on a wide variety of subjects.

Insider Info Scholastic's Education division - a leader in the education marketplace - provides research based technology programmes, supplemental educational materials and high quality literature. These support student achievement in grades pre-K, through to high school, and include magazines and an online companion for teachers and schools. Scholastic has also helped develop technologies to assess children's reading capabilities in schools.

Submission Guidelines Accepts unagented proposals for professional education books only. Most works are submitted by literary agents, or are created under a contract.

Recent Title(s) *Do The Math Grades 2–5,* Marilyn Burns; *Zip Zoom English Grades K-3*, Dr Maria S. Carlom, Dr Elfrieda H. Hiebert and Mr. Chauncey Veatch

Scholastic New Zealand Ltd

21 Lady Ruby Drive, East Tamaki, Auckland, New Zealand

- ☎ 0064 9 274 8112
- ✆ 0064 9 274 8114
- ✉ publishing@scholastic.co.nz
- 🌐 www.scholastic.co.nz

Parent Company Scholastic Inc

Contact Publishing Manager, Christine Dale

Categories Publishes Children's Fiction and Non-fiction, Picture books and Young Adult titles, Licensed products and books and Film/Television Tie-Ins.

Insider Info Authors are paid by royalty, with advance offered. Aims to respond to manuscripts within three months.

Submission Guidelines Accepts unsolicited manuscripts and proposals.

Tips Scholastic New Zealand accepts submissions for their *Survive!* and *My Story* series from New Zealand writers. See the website for guidelines.

Scholastic Trade Division
557 Broadway, New York, NY 10012, USA
- ☎ 001 212 343 6100
- 🖷 001 212 343 4713
- ✉ info@scholastic.com
- 🌐 www.scholastic.com

Contact President and CEO, Richard Robinson; Editorial Director, Elizabeth Szabla

Established 1920

Imprint(s) Arthur A. Levine Books
 Cartwheel Books
 The Chicken House
 Graphix
 Little Scholastic
 Little Shepherd
 Michael di Capua Books
 Orchard Books
 Point
 PUSH
 Scholastic Licensed Publishing (Scholastic Non-Fiction; Scholastic Paperbacks; Scholastic Press; Scholastic Reference)
 The Blue Sky Press
 Klutz

Categories Publishes Children's Fiction and Non-Fiction, Picture books, Movie/Television Tie-Ins, Series, Easy Reads on a wide variety of Children's themes.

Insider Info Scholastic Trade is the largest publisher and distributor of children's books and related products to home and school. Scholastic's children's book publishing and distribution business is comprised of trade, school-based Book Clubs, school-based Book Fairs and Scholastic At Home continuity programs. Scholastic publishes more than 500 new hardcover, paperback, and novelty books each year. The list includes the phenomenally successful publishing properties; *Harry Potter*; *Captain Underpants*; *Clifford The Big Red Dog*; and *I Spy*. They also distribute approximately 400 million children's books per year.

Submission Guidelines Does not generally accept unsolicited manuscripts or proposals. Most works are submitted by literary agents, or are created under a contract.

Recent Title(s) *Harry Potter and the Deathly Hallows*, J.K. Rowling (Children's Fiction)

Tips Scholastic is major publisher of children's education and fiction books. They accept unagented proposals for professional education books only.

Shuter & Shooter Publishers (Pty) Ltd
21c Cascades Crescent, Pietermaritzburg, KwaZulu-Natal, 3201, South Africa
- ☎ 0027 33 347 6100
- 🖷 0027 33 347 6120
- ✉ dryder@shuter.co.za
- 🌐 www.shuter.co.za

Contact Managing Director, Dave Ryder

Imprint(s) Ziptales

Categories Publishes Non-Fiction, Fiction and Children's titles on the following subjects: Afrikaans Literature, Art, Craft, Education, General Interest, History, How-To, Literacy, Local Interest, Mainstream Fiction, Poetry, Reference, Science, Scholarly, Teaching Guides, Textbooks.

Recent Title(s) *Ngingu Sosobala Mbatha*, DBZ Ntuli

Tips Shuter & Shooter primarily publishes Zulu fiction and poetry, as well as educational material for the whole South African region.

Simon & Schuster Books for Young Readers
1230 Avenue of the Americas, New York, NY 10020, USA
- ☎ 001 212 698 2808
- 🖷 001 212 698 4350
- 🌐 www.simonsayskids.com

Parent Simon and Schuster Inc

Contact Vice President and Associate Publisher, Elizabeth Law; Senior Editor, Emily Thomas; Editorial Director, David Gale; Editor, Alexander Cooper

Categories Publishes Children's Fiction and Non-fiction for all ages.

Insider Info Some of the most notable Simon & Schuster Books for Young Readers titles are *Sylvester and the Magic Pebble* by William Steig and *Strega Nona* by Tomie DePaola.

Submission Guidelines No unsolicited manuscripts. Accepts queries only. Aims to respond to queries in two months.

Recent Title(s) *Pendragon - The Pilgrims of Rayne*, D.J. MacHale (Fiction Series); *Insiders - Egypt*, Joyce Tyldesley (Non-Fiction Series); *The Busy Little Squirrel*, Nancy Tafuri (Author and Illustrator)

Simon & Schuster Inc
1230 Avenue of the Americas, New York, NY, 10020, USA

☎ 001 212 698 2808
☎ 001 212 698 4350
🌐 www.simonsays.com
Contact President Jack Romanos
Established 1924
Imprints Aladdin Paperbacks
Atheneum Books for Young Readers
Little Simon
Margaret K
McElderry Books
Simon & Schuster Books for Young Readers
Simon Pulse
Simon Spotlight
Categories Publishes Children's and Adult Fiction and Non-fiction, Children's books for all ages including Picture books, Board books, Humour, Children's Series, Young Adult Novels, Media Tie-Ins.
Insider Info Simon & Schuster publish approximately 1,800 titles annually.
Submission Guidelines No unsolicited manuscripts. Only accepts submissions from literary agents.
Recent Title(s) *Franny K. Stein, Mad Scientist*, Jim Benton (Author and Illustrator) (Monster Maker Series); *Greed – Seven Deadly Sins*, Robin Wasserman (Young Novel); *Scared Silly! SpongeBob's Book of Spooky Jokes*, David Lewman (SpongeBob SquarePants)
Tips Simon & Schuster Inc is the major publisher of the *Star Trek* series. There are detailed guidelines on their website for writer's wishing to submit *Star Trek* manuscripts.

Simon Pulse Paperback Books
1230 Avenue of the Americas, New York, NY, 10020, USA
☎ 001 212 698 2808
☎ 001 212 698 4350
🌐 www.simonsayskids.com
Parent Simon and Schuster Inc
Contact Associate Publisher, Bethany Buck; Executive Editor, Jennifer Klonsky; Associate Editor, Sangeeta Mehta
Categories Publishes Children's Fiction and Non-fiction, Young Novels, Media
Insider Info Simon Pulse is an imprint that publishes paperback books for teenagers in various categories and formats, including reprints, original paperbacks and original series.
Submission Guidelines Accepts queries, proposals or manuscripts for the attention of the submissions editor.
Recent Title(s) *Confessions*, Kate Brian (Young Novel); *Warriors Don't Cry*, Melba Pattillo Beals

(Biography); *Freaks Alive, on the Inside!*, Annette Curtis Klause (Young Novel)
Tips Runs a monthly Teen Literature magazine.

Sylvan Dell Publishing
976 Houston Northcutt Boulevard, Suite 3, Mount Pleasant, SC 29464, USA
☎ 001 877 958 2600
☎ 001 843 216 3804
✉ info@sylvandellpublishing.com
🌐 www.sylvandellpublishing.com
Contact Editor, Donna German
Categories Publishes Picture books.
Insider Info A new company that aims to educate in maths, science and nature, using picture book stories. They add a 'Creative Minds' section to their books, which include fun facts, crafts, vocabulary and games to reinforce the educational value and to support national science and math standards.
Submission Guidelines Visit the website for detailed submission guidelines. Emailed submissions are preferred.
Recent Title(s) *Burro's Tortillas*, Terri Fields (Author), Sherry Rogers (Illustrator); *In Arctic Waters*, Laura Crawford (Author), Ben Hodson (Illustrator)

Thomas Nelson
1120, Birchmount Road, Scarborough, ON, M1K 5G4, Canada
☎ 001 416 752 9448
☎ 001 416 752 8101
✉ inquire@nelson.com
🌐 www.nelson.com
Parent Company Thomas Canada Ltd
Contact President, Greg Pilon
Established 1914
Categories Publishes Educational Books and Products, and Reference books.
Insider Info Publishes all the core subjects for school (K-12) and higher education.
Submission Guidelines There are detailed manuscript guidelines for textbooks, available to download from their website.
Recent Title(s) *Math Focus K-9* (Educational Textbook)

Thomson Learning Australia and New Zealand
Level 7, 80 Dorcas Street, South Melbourne, Victoria 3205, Australia
☎ 0061 3 9685 4111
✉ customer_service@thomson.com.au

⊛ www.thomsonlearning.com.au
Parent Company Thomson
Contact Acting General Manager - School Division, John Mehan
Imprint(s) Nelson
 New House
Categories Publishes Children's Educational books, and products for all school subjects for Primary and Secondary years.
Insider Info Thomson Learning Australia is a leading provider of learning solutions in the school and higher education markets of Australia and New Zealand.
Recent Titles *Nelson Essential History Skills*, First Edition
Tips For Thomas Learning New Zealand, phone: 0064 9 415 6850.

Timun Mas
Avenida Diagonal, 662-66408034, Barcelona, Spain
☎ 0034 93 492 8155
🖷 0034 93 496 7041
✉ info@timunmas.com
⊛ http://infantil.timunmas.com
Parent Grupo Planeta
Categories The imprint company publishes Picture books, Board books, Activity books, Young Fiction, Learning books and Television Tie-Ins for children aged up to seven years old.
Recent Titles *Carla*, José Luis Ágreda; *Teo va de vacaciones*, Violeta Denou (Illustrator)

Tor Books
175 Fifth Avenue, New York, 10010, USA
☎ 001 212 388 0100
🖷 001 212 388 0191
⊛ www.tor-forge.com
Parent Company Tom Doherty Associates Llc
Imprint(s) Forge Books
 Orb Books
 Starscape Books
 Tor Books
 Tor Teen Books
Categories Publishes Non-fiction, Fiction and Children's titles on the following subjects: Autobiography, Biography, Children's Fiction, Contemporary Fantasy, Crime Fiction, Dark Fantasy, Epic Fantasy, General Interest, Genre Fiction, Graphic Novels, Historical Fiction, History, Horror, Humour, Memoir, Science, Science Fiction, Short Stories, Space Opera, Westerns, Young Adult.

Insider Info Authors are paid by royalty, with advance offered. Aims to respond to manuscripts within six months.
Submission Guidelines Accepts unsolicited manuscripts and proposals.
Recent Title(s) *New Spring*, Robert Jordan
Tips Tor publishes all types of genre fiction and maintains an open submissions policy, meaning that they will accept proposal packages from absolutely anyone. See the website for further details.

Tor Teen
175 Fifth Avenue, New York, NY 10010, USA
☎ 001 212 388 0100
🖷 001 212 388 1091
⊛ www.tor.com
Parent Company Tom Doherty Associates LLC
Contact Editors, Jonathan Schmidt and Kathleen Doherty
Categories Publishes Children's Science-Fiction and Fantasy.
Insider Info A specialist science fiction publishing company, for children aged eight and upwards.
Submission Guidelines Visit website for detailed submission guidelines.
Recent Title(s) *Winter of the Dead: A Novel of the Founding of Jamestown*, Elizabeth Massie

Tricycle Press
PO Box 7123, Berkeley CA 94707, USA
☎ 001 510 559 1600
🖷 001 510 559 1629
⊛ www.tenspeed.com
Parent Company Ten Speed Press
Contact Publisher, Nicole Geiger; Assistant Editor, Abigail Samoun
Categories Publishes Children's Fiction and Non-Fiction on: Activities, Animals Board books, Food, Language Arts, Life Lessons and Social Skills, Math, Science, Nature, Multicultural and Folktales and Picture books and Board books.
Insider Info An imprint company that publishes quality children's books, that they hope inspire and encourage children to learn and grow.
Submission Guidelines For picture books and board books send the entire manuscript. For novels send three sample chapters, and for real life books submit a table of contents and an outline, plus three sample chapters. Aims to respond in 24 weeks. Accepts submissions from illustrators, photographers and designers. Email a CV to: portfolio@tenspeed.com.

Recent Title(s) *Rough Tough Charley*, Adam Gustavson and Verla Kay (Biographical Picture Book); *Don't Laugh at Me,* Steve Seskin and Glin Dibley

Tundra Books
75 Sherbourne Street, 5th Floor, Toronto, Ontario, M5A 2P9, Canada
- tundra@mcclelland.com
- www.tundrabooks.com

Parent Company McClelland & Stewart Ltd
Contact Publisher, Kathy Lowinger
Categories Publishes Fiction and Children's titles on the following subjects: Art, Children's Literature, Contemporary Fiction, Picture books.
Submission Guidelines Accepts unsolicited manuscripts and proposals.
Recent Title(s) *1, 2, 3*, Tom Slaughter
Tips Tundra Books does not accept many unsolicited manuscripts and will not accept art submissions at all, unless of gallery standard.

Two Can Books for Young Readers
11571 K-Tel Drive, Minnetonka, MN 55543, USA
- 001 952 933 7537
- 001 952 933 3630
- michellekackman@tnkidsbooks.com
- www.tnkidsbooks.com

Parent Company T & N Children's Publishing
Categories Publishes Educational books on the following subjects: Maths, Science, History, Arts and Crafts, Spanish books, Fact books and Easy Reads.
Insider Info An imprint that publishes a wide variety of engaging educational books for young children.
Submission Guidelines For non-fiction submit an outline, plus sample chapters. Currently seeking picture book submissions with natural history, animal, nature, and environmental themes for children aged up to 12.
Recent Title(s) *Battles and Weapons*, Caroline Chapman ('Picture That' series)

Uitgeverij Hillen
Prinses Marielaan 8, 3743 JA Baarn, Netherlands
- 0031 35 548 6311
- 0031 35 542 3855
- info@defonteinbaarn.nl
- www.hillenboeken.nl

Parent De Fontein
Contact Publishers, Jacqueline Wilson, Clara Hillen
Categories Publishes Picture books, Gift books, Fiction and Very Young books.

Insider Info Publishes approximately 12–18 new titles a year.
Submission Guidelines Accepts unsolicited manuscripts with SAE. For illustrations, send three sample copies.
Recent Title(s) *Mijn feén-mobile boek*, Rosalind Beardshaw; *Magnetenspeelboek*, Lara Jones (Author), Poekie Poes (Illustrator) (Picture Book)
Tips Buys and sells foreign rights.

Uitgeverij Sjaloom
Postbox 1895, 1000 BW Amsterdam, Netherlands
- 0031 20 620 6263
- 0031 20 428 8540
- post@sjaloom.nl
- www.sjaloom.nl

Contact Willem Wildeboer
Categories Publishes Children's Fiction and Non-Fiction, Picture books and Board books.
Submission Guidelines Accepts unsolicited manuscripts with SAE. For illustrations, send three sample copies.
Recent Title(s) *Operatie Kasteelkat*, Verena Koppel; *De koning met de kikker op zijn hoofd*, Stefan Wolters (Picture Book)

University Of Queensland Press
PO Box 6042, Staff House Road, St. Lucia, Queensland, 4067, Australia
- 0061 7 3365 2127
- 0061 7 3365 7579
- uqp@uqp.uq.edu.au
- www.uqp.uq.edu.au

Categories Publishes Non-fiction, Fiction, Poetry and Children's titles on the following subjects: Australian History, Biography, Children's Fiction, Current Affairs, Indigenous Issues, Literary Fiction, Poetry, Politics, Social Studies, Young Adult.
Insider Info Aims to respond to proposals within six months.
Submission Guidelines Accepts unsolicited manuscripts and proposals.
Recent Title(s) *A Boat for Bridget*, James Roy (Fiction/Adventure)
Tips University of Queensland Press accepts unsolicited non-fiction submissions, but will only accept fiction submissions through a literary agent.

Viking Children's Books
345 Hudson Street, New York, NY, 10014, USA
- 001 212 366 2792

☎ 001 212 366 3393
🌐 www.penguin.com
Parent Company Penguin Group (USA)
Contact Publisher, Regina Hayes; Acquisitions Editor, Catherine Frank; Editor, Tracy Gates
Established 1933
Categories Publishes Children's Fiction and Non-fiction, Picture books, Board/Lift-flap books.
Insider Info Viking publishes approximately 60 titles per year for a wide age range, from pre-school to young adults. Receives 7,500 queries per year. The current Viking list is known for such classic characters as Madeline, Corduroy, Pippi Longstocking, Roald Dahl's Matilda and many more.
Submission Guidelines No unsolicited manuscripts. Send query letter with SAE. Will respond to queries or submissions only if interested. Approximately 25 per cent of of books are by first-time authors.
Recent Title(s) *Campy*, David A. Adler, Gordon James (Non-Fiction); *Catch a Tiger by the Toe*, Ellen Levine (Fiction)

Walker & Company
104 Fifth Avenue, 7th Floor, New York, NY, 10011, USA
☎ 001 212 727 8300
📠 001 212 727 0984
🌐 www.walkerbooks.com
Parent Company Bloomsbury Publishing Plc (see entry under UK & Irish Book Publishers)
Contact Managing Editor, Karen Rinaldi; Publisher, George Gibson
Categories Publishes Non-fiction, Fiction and Children's titles on the following subjects: Biography, Business/Economics, Children's books, Health/Medicine, History, Literary Fiction, Mystery Fiction, Nature, Picture books, Science, Sports, Technology, Young Adult.
Insider Info Does not accept simultaneous submissions.
Submission Guidelines Accepts unsolicited manuscripts and proposals.
Recent Title(s) *Curse of the Narrows*, Laura M. MacDonald
Tips Walker will consider material from new or unagented writers, but is currently only accepting submissions for children's and young adult books, particularly young adult novels and high quality picture books.

Warner Books
Time & Life Building, 1271 Avenue of the Americas, New York, NY, 10020, USA
☎ 001 212 522 7200
📠 001 212 522 7993
📧 info@warnerbooks.com
🌐 www.twbookmark.com
Parent Company Hachette Book Group USA
Contact Publisher, Maureen Egen; Senior Vice President/Publisher, Jamie Raab; Associate Publisher, Les Pockell; Vice President/Editorial Director (Trade Paperback), Amy Einhorn; Editorial Director (Mass Market Paperback), Beth de Guzman
Imprint(s) Aspect
Mysterious Press
Walk Worthy Press
Warner Business
Warner Faith
Warner Vision
Categories Publishes Non-fiction, Fiction and Children's titles on the following subjects: Biography, Business, Children's, Cooking, Economics, Education, Fantasy, General Interest, Historical, Horror, Mainstream/Contemporary Fiction, Reference, Romance, Science Fiction, Self-Help, Sports.
Insider Info Publishes 250 titles per year. Authors are paid by royalty, with advance offered. Average lead time of two years.
Submission Guidelines Does not accept unsolicited manuscripts and proposals.
Recent Title(s) *Failing America's Faithful: How Today's Churches Are Mixing God with Politics and Losing Their Way*, Kathleen Kennedy Townsend
Tips Warner Books publishes a diverse range of material, but does not accept unagented submissions or proposals.

Weldon Owen Education
Level 1, 39 Market Place, Auckland, New Zealand
☎ 0064 9 358 0190
📠 0061 9 358 0793
📧 info@weldonowen.co.nz
🌐 www.nzcer.org.nz
Contact Director, Robyn Baker
Categories Publishes Education and Literary books, and Resources for Home schooling for Children, aged three to twelve years of age
Insider Info Weldon Owen is an educational publishing company with offices in Australia and the US.
Submission Guidelines All submitted proposals or manuscripts should be evidence or research based. Visit their website for full details.

Recent Title(s)
Spell Right! Endings (Interactive CD-ROM)
Tips Visit their website to download their book and product catalogues.

Wendy Lamb Books
1745 Broadway, New York, NY 10019, USA
- 001 212 782 9000
- 001 212 302 7985
- www.randomhouse.com

Parent Random House Inc
Contact President and Publisher, Wendy Lamb
Established 2002
Categories Publishes Young Adult Fiction
Insider Info Publishes approximately 12 books per year. The imprint seeks to discover new talent and publishes many first novels.
Submission Guidelines Accepts international submissions. Send a query letter with SAE outlining the plot, the intended age group and any publishing credits to date. You may include ten pages of manuscript. Aims to respond to queries within six weeks. No emailed or faxed submissions. Send SAE with illustration samples.
Recent Title(s) *Fresh Girl,* Jaira Placide (Young Fiction); *How I Live Now,* Meg Rosoff (Young Fiction); *White Magic Spells to Hold You, A Novel,* Kelly Easton (Young Fiction)
Tips Wendy Lamb does not publish picture books.

Whitecap Books Ltd
351 Lynn Avenue, North Vancouver, British Columbia, V7J 2C4, Canada
- 001 416 469 1555
- 001416 537 0588
- www.whitecap.ca

Contact President, Michael E.Burch; Publisher, Robert McCullough
Established 1977
Categories Publishes Children's Fiction and Non-Fiction, Picture books, Young Nature series, Young novels and Adult titles.
Insider Info Whitecap is one of the top ten Canadian owned publishers and distributors. Picture books like *Gilbert de la Frogponde* and *Dog Tales* have become standards for library reading programs across Canada and the United States. Authors are paid by royalty, with an advance offered.
Submission Guidelines For picture books send the whole manuscript. For other submissions send a synopsis and three chapter samples, plus any publishing credits to date. Send illustration and

photograph samples with SAE. If you are submitting from outside of Canada, please include an international postal voucher.
Recent Title(s) *Buffalo Sunrise, The Story of a North American Giant,* Diane Swanson (Nature Book); *Canadian Boys Who Rocked the World,* Tanya Lloyd Kyi (Fiction); *Dot to Dot in the Sky* (Astronomy Series)

Women's Press
180 Bloor Street West, Suite 801, Toronto, Ontario, M5S 2V6, Canada
- 001 416 929 2774
- 001 416 929 1926
- info@womenspress.ca
- www.womenspress.ca

Parent Company Canadian Scholars' Press Inc
Contact Publishing Manager, Rebecca Conolly; Editorial Director, Megan Mueller
Categories Publishes Non-fiction, Fiction and Children's titles on the following subjects: Autobiography, Biography, Children's Literature, Contemporary Fiction, Creative Non-fiction, Literary Fiction, Memoirs, Plays, Poetry, Women's Writing.
Submission Guidelines Accepts unsolicited manuscripts and proposals.
Tips Women's Press now only accepts a select few manuscripts per year, and no longer accepts any children's material. Most Women's Press titles are aimed at students of women's studies, gender studies and social studies.

Workman Publishing Co.
225 Varick Street, New York, NY 10014, USA
- 001 212 254 5900
- 001 212 254 8098
- info@workman.com
- www.workman.com

Contact Editor in Chief, Susan Bolotin; Executive Editor, Suzanne Rafer; Senior Editor, Ruth Sullivan; Senior Editor, Margot Herrera; Senior Editor, Richard Rosen; Senior Editor (Children's), Raquel Jaramillo
Imprint(s) Algonquin
Artisan
Greenwich Workshop Press
Storey
Timber
Categories Publishes Non-fiction, Children's and Calendars on the following subjects: Business, Cookbooks, Economics, General Interest, Guidance, Health, How-To, Humour, Self-Help.
Insider Info Publishes 40 titles per year. Authors are paid by royalty, with advance offered. Receives

thousands of queries per year. Accepts simultaneous submissions. Average lead time of one year.

Submission Guidelines Accepts unsolicited manuscripts and proposals.

Recent Title(s) *Food to Live By*, Myra Goodman

Tips Workman welcomes unsolicited manuscript submissions by post only, no email submissions.

Zirkoon Uitgevers
Passeerdersgracht 34–38 Sous, 1016 XH Amsterdam, Netherlands
- 0031 20 623 3426
- 0031 20 623 4031
- post@zirkoon.nl
- www.sjaloom.nl

Contact Willem Wildeboer

Categories Publishes Children's Picture books, Poetry, Series, Fiction and Non-Fiction.

Submission Guidelines Accepts unsolicited manuscripts with SAE. For illustrations, send three sample copies.

Recent Title(s) *Lola en de leasekat; Ben ik het die ik zie?*, Bas Rompa (Picture Book)

Tips Zirkoon is branching out into poetry for children, with the aim of publishing new work by up and coming poets.

MAGAZINES

MAGAZINES FOR WRITERS FOR CHILDREN

Armadillo
Coleridge & White, 20 Powis Mews, London, W11 1JN
- maryhoffman@armadillomagazine.com
- www.armadillomagazine.com

Editor Mary Hoffman

Contact Web Editor, Rhiannon Lassiter

Established 1994

Insider Info A literary e-zine, issued quarterly (March, June, September, December), covering children's book reviews, interviews and articles. Publishes contributor's reviews, but does not accept unsolicited submissions. No payment offered. Review guidelines are available online.

Non-fiction Publishes articles on the children's book trade and marketing, interviews with authors and publishers, and book reviews, subjects covered include: Picture books, Children's Non-fiction and Poetry, and Young Adult Non-Fiction and Poetry

Submission Guidelines Does not accept unsolicited manuscripts. Accepts queries from potential reviewers by email.

Tips *Armadillo* ceased print publication in 2004 but is still available online as an e-zine for subscribers. Old material is archived and made available to non-subscribers. Armadillo covers every aspect of the children's book trade, and is always looking for new reviewers. Contact by email if interested.

The Bookseller
5th Floor, Endeavour House, 189 Shaftesbury Avenue, London, WC2H 8TJ
- 020 7420 6006
- 020 7420 6103
- joel.rickett@bookseller.co.uk
- www.thebookseller.com

Parent Company VNU Entertainment Media

Contact Editor in Chief, Neil Denny; Deputy Editor, Joel Rickett; Children's Books Staff Writer, Caroline Horn

Established 1858

Insider Info A trade magazine, issued weekly, covering the book trade.

Non-fiction Publishes News, Features, Interviews, Bestseller Charts and Information on the book publishing trade.

Tips *The Bookseller* covers the whole of the book publishing industry, but also publishes a regular *Children's Bookseller* supplement that focuses exclusively on the children's book trade. It also publishes the *Children's Buyer's Guide* which previews the upcoming children's books of the next six months. Specific children's book trade news and articles are also available on the website, which is updated daily.

Books for Keeps
1 Effingham Road, London, SE12 8NZ
- 020 8852 4953
- 020 8318 7580
- enquiries@booksforkeeps.co.uk
- www.booksforkeeps.co.uk

Parent Company School Bookshop Association Ltd
Editor Rosemary Stones
Established 1980
Insider Info A literary magazine, issued bi-monthly, covering the children's book industry. Present circulation of 8,500. Accepts queries by mail or email. Sample copy is available online.
Non-fiction Publishes articles on Children's Fiction, Non-Fiction and Poetry, Features, Interviews/Profiles, Reviews, General Interest Articles and Opinions (excluding letters to the editor).
Fiction Publishes some Children's Fiction.
Tips Aimed at adults, mostly teachers, librarians and parents. It contains articles about the latest developments in children's books, interviews and reviews, excerpts and critical essays. Articles tend to lean towards an academic and critically informative style. The website also has a community forum.

Carousel

The Guide to Children's Books
The Saturn Centre, 54–76 Bissell Street, Birmingham, B5 7HX
- 0121 622 7458
- 0121 666 7526
- carousel.guide@virgin.net
- www.carouselguide.co.uk
Editor Jenny Blanch
Established 1995
Insider Info A literary magazine, with three issues per year (March, June, October), covering the children's book trade. Present circulation is 10,000. Accepts queries by mail or email. Sample articles are available online.
Non-fiction Publishes Features, Interviews/Profiles, Reviews, and Opinion (excluding letters to the Editor).
Tips *Carousel* is a critical guide to the latest children's books and stories. It has a good reputation in the literary market as a publication that offers serious and non-condescending criticism of children's books. It also covers children's illustrators to a limited degree.

Child Education

Villiers House, Clarendon Avenue, Leamington Spa, CV32 5PR
- 0845 850 4411
- childed@scholastic.co.uk
- www.scholastic.co.uk
Parent Company Scholastic UK Ltd
Editor Michael Ward
Contact Deputy Editor, Charlotte Ronalds

Established 1923
Insider Info A trade journal, issued monthly, covering practical education and lesson plans. Present circulation is 16,665.
Non-fiction Publishes Features, Practical Activities, Lesson Plans and Resources.
Submission Guidelines Accepts articles from specialists of between 600–1,200 words. Payment by arrangement.
Tips *Child Education* is a teaching magazine from the book publisher Scholastic. It is primarily concerned with practical articles and resources from specialist writers covering Key Stage 1. The magazine is fully illustrated and comes with an A1 size picture poster.

Child Education Topics

Villiers House, Clarendon Avenue, Leamington Spa, CV32 5PR
- 0845 850 4411
- childed@scholastic.co.uk
- www.scholastic.co.uk
Parent Company Scholastic UK Ltd
Editor Michael Ward
Established 1978
Insider Info A trade journal, issued bi-monthly, covering project activities.
Non-fiction Publishes Features and Ideas for Classroom project activities.
Submission Guidelines Accepts articles from specialists of between 500–1,000 words. Payment by arrangement. Most material is specially commissioned.
Tips *Child Education Topics* is the sister magazine to *Child Education*. It contains suggestions and plans for classroom based teaching activities.

Early Years Activity Bank

Villiers House, Clarendon Avenue, Leamington Spa, CV32 5PR
- 01926 887799
- 01926 883331
- earlyyears@scholastic.co.uk
- www.scholastic.co.uk
Parent Company Scholastic UK Ltd
Editor Sarah Sodhi
Established 2000
Insider Info A trade journal, issued bi-monthly, covering support material for early years practitioners.
Non-fiction Publishes Teaching Resources, Ideas, Play-based Activities and Classroom support material.

Tips *Early Years Activity Bank* aims to provide early years professionals with a 'bank' of activities and resources to cover a range of teaching needs. Will accept occasional short articles of up to 500 words.

Inis

1st Floor, 17 North Great Georges Street, Dublin 1, Ireland
- 00353 1 872 7475
- 00353 1 872 7476
- inis@childrensbooksireland.com
- www.childrensbooksireland.com/inis

Parent Company Children's Books Ireland
Editor Paddy O'Doherty
Established 1989
Insider Info A literary magazine, issued quarterly, covering the children's book trade in Ireland and abroad. Issued free to members of Children's Books Ireland. Sample articles are available online.
About Publishes reviews of Picture books, Children's Fiction, Non-fiction and Poetry, and Young Adult Fiction, Non-fiction and Poetry, as well as reviews of books for Children's writers and General articles.
Tips *Inis* covers the latest news and reviews from the children's book trade. It has an international scope, but focuses mainly on Irish books and authors. *Inis* is always looking for contributors; query by email for further details.

Junior

2 Balcombe Street, London, NW1 6NW
- 020 7042 4000
- editorial@juniormagazine.co.uk
- www.juniormagazine.co.uk

Parent Company Future Publishing Ltd
Editor Catherine O'Dolan
Contact Commissioning Editor, Suzanne Milne
Established 1998
Insider Info A consumer magazine, issued monthly, covering child care and parenting. Present circulation is 52,500. Pays £150 per 1,000 words and £300 per photo feature.
About Publishes Children's Health and Development, Food and Nutrition, Education, Lifestyle and Travel articles.
Tips *Junior* is aimed at parents of children up to eight years old, who already have established careers and homes. The magazine covers all aspects of parenting and childcare. Most articles are specially commissioned.

Junior Education

Villiers House, Clarendon Avenue, Leamington Spa, CV32 5PR
- 01926 887799
- 01926 883331
- juniored@scholastic.co.uk
- www.scholastic.co.uk

Parent Company Scholastic UK Ltd
Editor Michelle Guy
Contact Deputy Editor, Victoria Paley
Established 1977
Insider Info A trade journal, issued monthly, covering primary education news and practical teaching. Present circulation is 11,220.
About Publishes News, Practical Teaching articles, Product reviews, Study packs and resources.
Submission Guidelines Accepts practical teaching articles of between 800–1,000 words. Payment by arrangement.
Tips *Junior Education* is aimed at teachers of 7–11 year olds and covers primary education news, and also publishes practical teaching articles and resources. All articles are photocopiable for use in the classroom.

Junior Education Topics

Villiers House, Clarendon Avenue, Leamington Spa, CV32 5PR
- 01926 887799
- 01926 883331
- jet@scholastic.co.uk
- www.scholastic.co.uk

Parent Company Scholastic UK Ltd
Editor Michelle Guy
Established 1982
Insider Info A trade journal, issued monthly, covering teaching resources.
Non-fiction Publishes Themed teaching Supplements, Articles and Resources.
Tips *Junior Education Topics* is the sister publication of *Junior Education*. Each issue is based on a theme that ties in with the National Curriculum. The majority of the journal consists of photocopiable teaching resources, with A1 and A3 full-colour posters.

Literacy

UKLA, 4th Floor, Attenborough Building, University of Leicester, Leicester, LE1 7RH
- 0116 229 7450
- 0116 229 7451
- admin@ukla.org

www.ukla.org
Parent Company The United Kingdom Literary Association
Editor Henrietta Dombey
Established 1966
Insider Info A literary journal, with three issues per year, covering literacy and education. Accepts queries by email.
Non-fiction Publishes Research reports, Policy critiques and Theory and Practice articles.
Submission Guidelines Accepts articles between 2,000 to 6,000 words.
Tips *Literacy* is issued free to all members of the UKLA and covers a wide range of practical, theoretical and legal issues relating to literacy and education. *Literacy* is always interested in general interest, or special literacy related articles.

Literacy Time
Villiers House, Clarendon Avenue, Leamington Spa, CV32 5PR
01926 887799
01926 883331
juniored@scholastic.co.uk
www.scholastic.co.uk/literacytime
Parent Company Scholastic UK Ltd
Editor Helen Watts
Insider Info A literary magazine/ resource pack covering literacy and education.
Non-fiction Publishes teaching Resources, Articles and Group activities.
Tips *Literacy Time* is a selection of posters, group booklets and magazines that covers the National Literacy Framework. Three levels are available for 5–7 year olds, 7–9 year olds, and 9–11 year olds. *Literacy Time* has been relaunched with added online resources and downloadable content, available from their website.

Mary Glasgow Magazines
Euston House, 24 Eversholt Street, London, NW1 1DB
0800 085 8080
020 7756 7797
email@maryglasgowmags.co.uk
www.maryglasgowmagazines.com
Parent Company Scholastic UK Ltd
Established 1957
Insider Info A publisher of 17 magazines for young learners of foreign languages.
Tips *Mary Glasgow Magazines* is a wholly owned subsidiary of Scholastic. It publishes a range of magazines for children and students, covering

languages including English, French, German and Spanish. It also publishes resource books for teachers of English as a foreign language.

NATE Classroom
50 Broadfield Road, Sheffield, S8 0XJ
0114 255 5419
0114 255 5296
info@nate.org.uk
www.nate.org.uk
Parent Company National Association for the Teaching of English
Established 2007
Insider Info A trade magazine, with three issues per year, covering primary and secondary school English education and activities. Accepts queries by post or email. Submission guidelines available online.
Non-fiction Publishes Reviews and Articles on practical teaching strategies and resources.
Submission Guidelines Accepts articles of between 500 to 1,500 words by email or post. Payment is £120 per 1,500 words.
Tips *NATE Classroom* aims to help get children and teenagers interested in reading by encouraging submissions from education professionals about their practices and experiences of teaching English (at primary or secondary level). *NATE Classroom* also accepts reviews of up to 450 words of teaching resources, textbooks and young people's fiction books. All submissions must be received no later than six months before the publication date.

NATE News
50 Broadfield Road, Sheffield, S8 0XJ
0114 255 5419
0114 255 5296
info@nate.org.uk
www.nate.org.uk
Parent Company National Association for the Teaching of English
Editor Ian McNeilly
Insider Info A trade newsletter, with five issues per year, covering news, activities and education articles.
Non-fiction Publishes News, Activities, Topical articles, Current issues and Education articles.
Tips *NATE News* is the official newspaper of the National Association for the Teaching of English. It mostly covers news and affairs concerning NATE, but also prints articles and current affairs information about primary and secondary school English teaching. NATE also publishes the 'English in Education' research journal and the 'English Dram Media' journal three times a year.

Nursery Education

Villiers House, Clarendon Avenue, Leamington Spa, CV32 5PR

☎ 01926 887799

🖷 01926 883331

✉ juniored@scholastic.co.uk

🌐 www.scholastic.co.uk/literacytime

Parent Company Scholastic UK Ltd

Editor Helen Dead

Contact Deputy Editor, Lesley Sudlow

Established 1997

Insider Info A trade journal, issued monthly, covering early years childcare. Present circulation is 17,226.

Non-fiction Publishes Theme based activities, Features and Articles about caring for under fives.

Tips Nursery Education is aimed at teachers, managers and childcare workers caring for under fives. Includes many theme based activities, linked to the QCA Curriculum Guidance for the Foundation stage. Most material is commissioned.

Nursery World

174 Hammersmith Road, London, W6 7JP

☎ 020 8267 8409

✉ liz.roberts@haymarket.com

🌐 www.nurseryworld.co.uk

Parent Company Haymarket Business Publications Ltd

Editor Liz Roberts

Insider Info A trade magazine, issued weekly, covering nursery level education and childcare. Present circulation of 23,784. Accepts queries by mail or email.

Non-fiction Publishes Policy news, Career advice, 'How-to' features and Childcare articles.

Submission Guidelines Send complete manuscript for articles of between 800 and 1,300 words.

Images Send photos with submission.

Tips Nursery World is the leading magazine for early years and childcare practitioners. Its guides for managers and practitioners, all written by early years experts, cover every aspect of childcare and education, from babies up to eight years old. These guides include subjects such as behaviour, additional learning needs, planning, working with under threes and nursery food. Articles should be as practical and informal as possible. Include any relevant photographs.

Practical Parenting

Blue Fin Building, 110 Southwark Street, London, SE1 0SU

☎ 020 3148 5000

🖷 020 7261 6542

✉ susie_boon@ipcmedia.com

🌐 www.practicalparenting.co.uk

Parent Company IPC Media Ltd

Editor Susie Boon

Contact Features Assistant, Cassandra Roberts

Established 1987

Insider Info A consumer magazine, issued monthly, covering childcare and parenthood. Present circulation of 43,465. Accepts queries via mail and email. Media packs available online.

Non-fiction Publishes How-to, Features and Parenting/Childcare articles.

Submission Guidelines Accepts query with complete manuscript. Articles must be between 750 and 3,000 words.

Tips Aimed at pregnant women and mothers with children aged up to five years old. They are interested in long feature articles, or shorter viewpoint pieces, written in the existing style of the magazine.

Publishing News

7 John Street, London, WC1N 2ES

☎ 020 7405 2500

🖷 020 7404 7698

✉ lizthomson@publishingnews.co.uk

🌐 www.publishingnews.co.uk

Parent Company Publishing News Ltd

Editor Liz Thomson

Contact Children's Page Editor, Graham Marks; Deputy Editor, Roger Tagholm

Established 1979

Insider Info A trade journal, issued weekly, covering the book trade. Present circulation is 10,000.

Non-fiction Publishes News, Interviews, Comment, Features and Articles.

Tips Publishing News is a weekly trade journal that covers every aspect of the book trade. It has a dedicated children's page, which prints news and articles about the latest developments in children's books. Contact the Children's Page Editor at: grahammarks@publishingnews.co.uk with proposals for articles.

Report

7 Northumberland Street, London, WC2N 5RD

☎ 020 7930 6441

📞 020 7930 1359
✉ report@atl.org.uk
🌐 www.atl.org.uk
Parent Company Association of Teachers and Lecturers
Editors Guy Goodwin; Victoria Poskitt
Established 1978
Insider Info A trade journal, issued monthly, covering education issues. Present circulation is 160,000.
Non-fiction Publishes News, Features, Articles and Comment about all levels of Education.
Tips *Report* is the official journal of the ATL and covers the latest news and issues facing teachers, lecturers and education support staff.

Right Start
9 Savoy Street, London, WC2E 7HR
📞 020 7878 2338
📞 020 7379 6261
✉ lynette@rightstartmagazine.com
🌐 www.rightstartmagazine.co.uk
Parent Company Ten Alps Publishing
Editor Lynette Lowthian
Contact Deputy Editor, Liz Granirer; Art Editor, Ruby Gordon
Established 1989
Insider Info A consumer magazine, issued bi-monthly, covering children's health and education. Present circulation is 56,000.
Non-fiction Publishes Features and Articles on; Children's Eating, Health, Education, Behaviour and Family life.
Submission Guidelines Does not accept unsolicited manuscripts.
Tips *Right Start* is aimed at parents of children between six months to seven years old.

The School Librarian
Unit 2, Lotmead Business Village, Wanborough, Swindon, SN4 0UY
📞 0870 777 0979
📞 0870 777 0987
✉ info@sla.org.uk
🌐 www.sla.org.uk
Parent Company School Library Association
Editor Steve Hird
Established 1937
Insider Info A trade journal, issued quarterly, covering school library services and the children's book trade. Present circulation is 4,000. Accepts queries by email.

Non-fiction Publishes News, Articles, Features and Reviews of Children's Fiction, Non-fiction, Multimedia and Websites.
Submission Guidelines Accepts queries by email to: sleditor@sla.org.uk
Tips *The School Librarian* is the official journal of the School Library Association. It covers both school library services and every aspect of the children's book trade. *The School Librarian* is always keen to receive contributors articles or reviews. Contact the Editor for further information.

The Times Educational Supplement
Admiral House, 66–68 East Smithfield, London, E1W 1BX
📞 020 7782 3067
📞 020 7782 3200
✉ editor@tes.co.uk
🌐 www.tes.co.uk
Parent Company TSL Education Ltd
Editor Wendy Berliner (Acting Editor)
Established 1910
Insider Info A consumer magazine, issued weekly, covering Education. Present circulation is 76,645. Accepts queries by mail.
Non-fiction Interested in News, Features, Reviews and Specialist articles on Education.
Submission Guidelines Accepts queries (including published clips and CV) for articles of between 1,000 to 2,000 words.
Tips *The Times Educational Supplement* is Britain's leading publication covering the world of primary, secondary and further education – as well as the market leader for teaching job vacancies. Specialist knowledge in the teaching industry is required for all submissions, but a sense of humour is also important. Includes the *TES Teacher*, a weekly supplement containing practical ideas and resources for lesson plans.

The Times Educational Cymru
Sophia House, 28 Cathedral Road, Cardiff, CF11 9LJ
📞 029 2066 0201
📞 029 2066 0207
✉ cymru@tes.co.uk
🌐 www.tes.co.uk/cymru
Parent Company TSL Education Ltd
Editor Nicola Porter
Established 2004
Insider Info A consumer magazine, issued weekly, covering education. Present circulation is 3,500. Accepts queries by mail.

Non-fiction Interested in News, Features, Reviews and specialist articles on Education.
Submission Guidelines Accepts queries (including published clips and CV) for articles of between 1,000 to 2,000 words.
Tips *TES Cymru* covers the education industry in Wales. All articles must contain specialist content and be from a practising education professional.

The Times Educational Supplement Scotland

Scott House, 10 South St. Andrew Street, Edinburgh, EH2 2AZ
- 0131 557 1133
- 0131 558 1155
- scoted@tes.co.uk
- www.tes.co.uk/scotland

Parent Company TSL Education Ltd
Editor Neil Munro
Established 1965
Insider Info A consumer magazine, issued weekly, covering Scottish education. Present circulation is 6,528 Accepts queries by mail.
Non-fiction Interested in News, Features, Interviews/Profiles and Technical or Specialist articles on Scottish Education.
Submission Guidelines Accepts queries (including published clips and CV) for articles of between 1,000 to 2,000 words.
Tips *The Times Educational Supplement Scotland* is the sister magazine to *The Times Educational Supplement*. It covers the world of primary, secondary and further education in Scotland, and is the market leader for Scottish teaching job vacancies.

Under 5

The Fitzpatrick Building, 188 York Way, London, N7 9AD
- 020 7697 2500
- 020 7700 0319
- editor.u5@pre-school.org.uk
- www.pre-school.org.uk

Parent Company Pre-School Learning Alliance
Editor Anna Roberts
Established 1963
Insider Info A consumer magazine, issued monthly, covering education and childcare. Present circulation is 17,000.
Non-fiction Publishes Practical Articles and Features.
Tips *Under 5* is aimed pre-school childcare workers, parents, and teachers caring for the under 5s.

Articles cover the care and education of babies and young children, and contain practical information and advice.

Young People Now

174 Hammersmith Road, London, W6 7JP
- 020 8267 4706
- 020 8267 4728
- ypn.editorial@haynet.com
- www.ypnmagazine.com

Parent Company Haymarket Publishing
Editor Ravi Chandiramani
Contact Features Editor, Andy Hillier
Established 1989
Insider Info A trade journal, issued weekly, covering social services and welfare for young people. Present circulation is 14,688.
Non-fiction Publishes News and Features.
Tips *Young People Now* is the only weekly title for those who work with young people between the ages of 11 to 25. It is an industry publication, so a specialist knowledge in the field of child care/youth guidance is essential for contributors.

MAGAZINES FOR CHILDREN

Adventure Box

1st Floor, 2 King Street, Peterborough, PE1 1LT
- 01733 565858
- contact@bayard-magazines.co.uk
- www.bayard-magazines.co.uk

Parent Company Bayard Presse
Contact Editor in Chief, Simona Sideri; Managing Publisher, Christine Auberger; Art Director, Pat Carter
Insider Info An educational magazine for six to nine year olds, issued monthly, covering the natural world, stories, puzzles and quizzes.
Non-fiction Publishes Natural World articles.
Fiction Publishes Illustrated Chapter stories and Comic strips.
Tips *Adventure Box* contains a variety of stories, educational articles, interactive puzzles and quizzes to encourage young children to read.

Alternative Kidz

47 Woodplace Lane, Coulsdon, Surrey, CR5 1NE
- 01737 554664
- info@alternativekidz.com
- www.alternativekidz.com

Parent Company Alphabet Books Ltd
Editor Lucy Baker
Established 2001
Insider Info An educational magazine, issued quarterly, covering lifestyle articles, news, world affairs and activities. Present circulation is 1,200.
Non-fiction Publishes articles on Alternative Lifestyle, Arts, Cookery, Craft, News, Puzzles and World Affairs.
Tips *Alternative Kidz* is an independent magazine aimed at younger children that encourages 'green' living and healthy lifestyles. It discourages computers, television and shopping. It is aimed at both boys and girls, and also at parents.

Amy
Room A1136, Woodlands, 80 Wood Lane, London, W12 0TT
- 020 8433 2000
- bea.appleby@bbc.co.uk
- www.bbcmagazines.com/amy
Parent Company BBC Worldwide Publishing
Editor Bea Appleby
Established 2006
Insider Info A children's magazine for five to eight year old girls, issued every three weeks, covering lifestyle, television, film and toys.
Non-fiction Publishes CBBC tie-in articles and Activity articles.
Fiction Publishes Short Stories.
Tips *Amy* is a young girls' lifestyle magazine that mostly covers CBBC content, including *Tracey Beaker*, *Blue Peter*, *Smart* and *Really Wild Show*. Each issue also has a cover-mounted free gift.

Animal Action
Wilberforce Way, Southwater, Horsham, RH13 9RS
- 0870 010 1181
- 0870 753 0048
- publications@rspca.org.uk
- www.rspca.org.uk
Parent Company RSPCA
Editor Sarah Evans
Contact Sub Editor, Debra Austin
Established 1994
Insider Info An educational magazine for 8–13 year olds, issued bi-monthly, covering animals, pets and wildlife issues. Present circulation is 32,907.
Non-fiction Publishes Ecology, Wildlife and Pet care articles, as well as True Life stories, Celebrity Interviews and Animal-themed Activities.

Tips *Animal Action* is a bimonthly magazine that covers the latest RSPCA initiatives, as well as general articles about animals and pets. It is mostly educational in tone.

Animals & You
2 Albert Square, Dundee, DD1 9QJ
- 01382 575733
- 01382 322214
- mmonaghan@dcthomson.co.uk
- www.dcthomson.co.uk
Parent Company D.C. Thomson & Co. Ltd
Editor Margaret Monaghan
Contact Chief Sub Editor, Jacquie Turriff; Features and Competitions Editor, Jackie Guild; Picture Editor, Jeanette Taylor
Established 1998
Insider Info An educational magazine for sven to ten year old girls, issued monthly, covering animals and pets. Present circulation is 70,000. Average lead time is five weeks.
Non-fiction Publishes Animal and Pet care articles, as well as True Life stories, Puzzles, Products and animal themed Activities.
Tips *Animals & You* is a monthly magazine that covers animals and pets. It is aimed primarily at young girls and also contains children's lifestyle articles, product reviews and activities.

AQUILA
Studio 2, Willowfield Studios, 67a Willowfield Road, Eastbourne, East Sussex, BN22 8AP
- 01323 431313
- 01323 731136
- office@aquila.co.uk
- www.aquila.co.uk
Parent Company New Leaf Publishing Limited
Editor Jackie Berry and Karen Lutener
Contact Publisher, Ron Bryant-Funnell
Established 1993
Insider Info A monthly consumer magazine for children, covering primary learning and education. Present circulation of 8,000. Sample copy is available for a cost.
Non-fiction Publishes Photo Features, Features and General Interest articles.
Submission Guidelines Accepts queries for articles of between 600 and 800 words.
Fiction Publishes Short Fiction.
  * Pays between £80 and £90 for fiction articles.
Submission Guidelines Accepts queries for articles of between 1,000 and 1,500 words.

Tips The magazine takes a non-denominational approach, and is not restricted in any way, or limited by school curriculum requirements. It aims to provide quality ideals, and to encourage children to develop caring and thoughtful attitudes towards others and their environment.

Art Attack

Panini House, Coach & Horses Passage, The Pantiles, Tunbridge Wells, TN2 5UJ
- 01892 500100
- 01892 545666
- ahaincole@panini.co.uk
- www.paninicomics.co.uk

Parent Company Panini UK Ltd
Editor Alex Hain-Cole
Contact Senior Editor, Karen Brown
Established 1996
Insider Info An educational magazine for 7–12 year olds, issued every three weeks, covering art and craft. Present circulation is 102,000.
Non-fiction Publishes Drawing, Painting, Sculpting and Craft 'How-to' Articles.
Tips *Art Attack* magazine is based on the popular children's television show. It contains fully illustrated how-to articles and tutorials, and each issue comes with a free gift.

Balamory

Woodlands, 80 Wood Lane, London, W12 0TT
- 020 8433 2356
- www.bbcmagazines.com/balamory

Parent Company BBC Worldwide Publishing
Insider Info A magazine for pre-school children, issued monthly, covering activities and puzzles.
Tips *Balamory* magazine is based on the popular children's television show. It contains puzzles, activities, colouring, and games based around Balamory characters.

Barbie

4th Floor, 184–192 Drummond Street, London, NW1 3HP
- 020 7380 6430
- Online form
- www.egmontmagazines.co.uk

Parent Company Egmont Magazines
Insider Info A magazine for three to eight year old girls, issued fortnightly, covering Barbie products and characters. Present circulation is 68,765
Non-fiction Publishes Product reviews, Lifestyle articles, Activities, and Barbie-related information.

Tips *Barbie* magazine, based on the popular toy, covers aspects of fashion, friends and fun activities. Each issue comes with a free gift.

Big Cook Little Cook

Woodlands, 80 Wood Lane, London, W12 0TT
- 020 8433 2000
- www.bbcmagazines.com/bigcooklittlecook

Parent Company BBC Worldwide Publishing
Insider Info An educational magazine for pre-school age children, issued monthly, covering food and cookery.
Non-fiction Publishes practical Children's Cookery articles and Health information.
Tips *Big Cook Little Cook*, based on the popular television series, is the only pre-school publication in the market dedicated to food and cooking.

Blast Off!

PO Box 173, Peterborough, PE2 6WS
- 01733 375000
- 01733 375001
- editorial@rnib.org.uk
- www.rnib.org.uk

Parent Company RNIB
Insider Info A magazine for 7–11 year olds, issued monthly, covering stories, features and puzzles.
Non-fiction Publishes Features, Activities and Puzzles.
Fiction Publishes Stories.
Tips *Blast Off!* is a children's magazine published by the Royal National Institute of Blind People. It is printed in braille and double spaced for easy reading, and contains stories, features and activities of popular children's magazines.

Bliss

Panini House, Coach and Horses Passage, The Pantiles, Tunbridge Wells, TN2 5UJ
- 01892 500100
- 01892 546666
- bliss@panini.co.uk
- firstinitiallastname@panini.co.uk
- www.mybliss.co.uk

Parent Company Panini UK Ltd
Editor Leslie Sinoway
Contact Features Editor, Angeli Milburn; Features Writer, Rebecca Davies
Established 1995
Insider Info A monthly consumer magazine covering teenage girls' lifestyle topics. Present

Circulation of 151,729. A media pack is available online.

Non-fiction Publishes General Interest Features, Interviews and Photo Features on Television, Real Life, Fashion, Beauty, Celebrities, Health and Entertainment.

Tips *Bliss*' target audience is girls aged 12 to 18. The website gives a good idea of the magazine's style, and has its own editorial content.

Bob the Builder
Woodlands, 80 Wood Lane, London, W12 0TT
- 020 8433 2356
- www.bbcmagazines.com/bobthebuilder

Parent Company BBC Worldwide Publishing

Insider Info A magazine for pre-school age children, issued every three weeks, covering stories and activities.

Non-fiction Publishes Features, Activities and Articles on Recycling and Environmental issues.

Fiction Publishes 'Bob the Builder' stories.

Tips *Bob the Builder* magazine is based on the popular television series and contains related stories, activities and features. The magazine has an environmental theme and aims to teach children about recycling and other environmental issues.

Braille at Bedtime
PO Box 173, Peterborough, PE2 6WS
- 01733 375000
- 01733 375001
- editorial@rnib.org.uk
- www.rnib.org.uk

Parent Company RNIB

Insider Info A magazine for 7–11 year olds, issued bi-monthly, covering fiction.

Fiction Publishes Short stories.

Tips *Braille at Bedtime* is a children's magazine published by the Royal National Institute of Blind People. It is printed in single sided braille and contains a variety of short stories for children to read on their own, or for adults to read out loud.

Bratz
2 Albert Square, Dundee, DD1 9QJ
- 01382 575684
- 01382 322214
- ghenney@dcthomson.co.uk
- www.dcthomson.co.uk

Parent Company D.C. Thomson & Co. Ltd

Editor Gillian Henney

Established 2004

Insider Info A magazine for 7–12 year old girls, issued monthly, covering children's lifestyle and Bratz fashion dolls. Present circulation is 43,226.

Non-fiction Publishes Fashion tips, Make-up tips, Celebrity interviews, Gossip columns, Competitions and Lifestyle articles.

Tips *Bratz* magazine covers a wide range of gossip, celebrity and fashion topics, as well as the Bratz fashion doll toys.

Breakout
20 Marcham Road, Abingdon, OX14 1AA
- 01235 553444
- 01235 547819
- news@couriergroup.com
- www.oxfordjournal.co.uk

Parent Company Courier Newspapers (Oxford) Ltd

Editor Amanda Williams

Insider Info A magazine for 7–11 year olds, with three issues per year, covering competitions and general interest. Present circulation is 10,000 a year.

Non-fiction Publishes Competitions, News, Features, Film reviews, Toy and Game reviews and Articles.

Tips *Breakout* is a local magazine, focused on the Abingdon area. It contains competitions for the latest toys and games, as well as film and product reviews and youth orientated news.

Cbeebies Weekly
Room A1130, Woodlands, 80 Wood Lane, London, W12 0TT
- 020 8433 2356
- cbeebiesweekly@bbc.co.uk
- www.cbeebiesmagazine.com

Parent Company BBC Worldwide Publishing

Insider Info A Cbeebies magazine for pre-school children, issued weekly, including fun activities.

Non-fiction Publishes Cbeebies Features, Puzzles, Colouring, Songs and Craft articles.

Tips *Cbeebies Weekly* runs alongside the Cbeebies television program and aims to encourage early learning in pre-school children.

Charlie and Lola
Woodlands, 80 Wood Lane, London, W12 0TT
- 020 8433 2356
- charlienadlolamagazine@bbc.co.uk
- www.charliesandlola.com

Parent Company BBC Worldwide Publishing

Insider Info A magazine for pre-school age children, issued monthly, covering arts and craft.

Non-fiction Publishes Arts and Craft Activities and Articles.
Tips *Charlie and Lola* is based on the popular television series, and uses the characters to teach pre-school age children about arts and craft. Each issue comes with a free craft kit and stickers.

Daisy

4th Floor, 184–192 Drummond Street, London, NW1 3HP
- 020 7380 6430
- 020 7380 6444
- jtubbs@euk.egmont.com
- www.egmontmagazines.co.uk

Parent Company Egmont Magazines
Editor Joanna Tubbs
Established 2005
Insider Info A magazine for 4–7 year old girls, issued monthly, covering characters and lifestyle. Present circulation is 40,053.
Non-fiction Publishes Puzzles, Activities and Children's Lifestyle articles.
Fiction Publishes Character stories and Comic strips.
Tips *Daisy* is the sister publication to *GO Girl* magazine and aims to provide a bridge between single character magazines and pre-teenage lifestyle magazines.

Discovery Box

1st Floor, 2 King Street, Peterborough, PE1 1LT
- 01733 565858
- contact@bayard-magazines.co.uk
- www.bayard-magazines.co.uk

Parent Company Bayard Presse
Contact Editor in Chief, Simona Sideri; Managing Publisher, Christine Auberger; Art Director, Pat Carter
Insider Info An educational magazine for 9–12 year olds, issued monthly, covering non-fiction, stories and activities.
Non-fiction Publishes History, Natural World and Science articles.
Fiction Publishes Short stories.
Tips *Discovery Box* contains stories, recipes, activities, puzzles and quizzes, on three main sections covering animals, history and science.

Disney and Me

4th Floor, 184–192 Drummond Street, London, NW1 3HP
- 020 7380 6430
- Online submission form
- www.egmontmagazines.co.uk

Parent Company Egmont Magazines
Established 1991
Insider Info A magazine for 4–7 year olds, issued fortnightly, covering Disney. Present circulation is 49,022.
Non-fiction Publishes Features, Games and Puzzles.
Fiction Publishes Stories and Comic strips.
Tips *Disney and Me* is rated among the top ten children's magazines. It contains stories, articles and puzzles related to the latest Disney characters.

Disney Fairies

4th Floor, 184–192 Drummond Street, London, NW1 3HP
- 020 7380 6430
- 020 7380 6444
- jryall@euk.egmont.com
- www.egmontmagazines.co.uk

Parent Company Egmont Magazines
Editor Jeanette Ryall
Established 2006
Insider Info A magazine for 5–7 year old girls, issued monthly, covering the Disney Fairies brand.
Non-fiction Publishes Features, Puzzles and Activities.
Fiction Publishes Stories and Comic strips.
Tips *Disney Fairies* is part of a new global brand from Disney, which contains stories, features and activities relating to Tinkerbell and her friends.

Disney Girl

30 Monmouth Street, Bath, BA1 2BW
- 01225 442244
- 01225 446019
- kate.evans@@futurenet.co.uk
- www.futurelicensing.com

Parent Company Future Publishing Ltd
Editor Kate Evans
Established 2002
Insider Info A magazine for 7–10 year old girls, issued monthly, covering Disney. Present circulation is 42,847.
Non-fiction Publishes Lifestyle Hints and Tips, Craft articles, Cooking recipes, Songs, Dances and Puzzles.
Fiction Publishes Stories and Comic Strips.
Tips *Disney Girl* is a lifestyle magazine for young girls who are interested in Disney films and animation. The licence was awarded to Future in 2006; it was previously licenced to BBC Worldwide.

Disney's Big Time

30 Monmouth Street, Bath, BA1 2BW

- 01225 442244
- 01225 446019
- www.futurelicensing.com

Parent Company Future Publishing Ltd

Insider Info A magazine for 7–12 year old boys, issued monthly, covering Disney. Present circulation is 29,000.

Non-fiction Publishes Features, Toy, Game, Film, and Music reviews, Celebrity gossip, Competitions, Posters and Puzzles.

Fiction Publishes Stories and Comic Strips.

Tips *Disney's Big Time* is one of Disney's longest established titles. It is designed to appeal mostly to boys. The licence was awarded to Future in 2006, it was previously licenced to BBC Worldwide.

Disney's Princess

4th Floor, 184–192 Drummond Street, London, NW1 3HP

- 020 7380 6430
- Online form
- www.egmontmagazines.co.uk

Parent Company Egmont Magazines

Insider Info A magazine for 3–7 year old girls, issued fortnightly, covering Disney's Princess brand. Present circulation is 75,016.

Non-fiction Publishes Features, Puzzles and Activities.

Fiction Publishes Stories and Comic strips.

Tips *Disney's Princess* magazine is aimed at young girls interested in Disney Princesses. All content is related to the global Disney Princess Brand.

DK FindOut!

Titan House, 144 Southwark Street, London, SE1 0UP

- 0870 428 8219
- 020 7620 0032
- dk.editor@titanemail.com
- www.titanmagazines.co.uk

Parent Company Titan Magazines

Editor Kate Lloyd

Contact Assistant Editor, Zoe Hedges

Established 2002

Insider Info An educational magazine, issued monthly, covering general interest and facts. Present circulation is 30,000.

Non-fiction Publishes Geography, History, Natural World and Science articles.

Tips *DK FindOut!* aims to provide interesting facts and knowledge to children in an interesting manner, often printing educational articles based on the latest films.

Doctor Who Adventures

Woodlands, 80 Wood Lane, London, W12 0TT

- 020 8433 3825
- dwa@bbc.co.uk
- www.bbcmagazines.com/doctorwhoadventures

Parent Company BBC Worldwide Publishing

Insider Info A children's magazine, issued fortnightly, covering Doctor Who.

Non-fiction Publishes Features, Episode reviews and Puzzles.

Fiction Publishes Stories and Comic strips.

Tips *Doctor Who Adventures* is based on the current BBC series and contains stories, fact files and other features related to Doctor Who.

Doctor Who Magazine

Panini House, Coach and Horses Passage, The Pantiles, Tunbridge Wells, TN2 5UJ

- 01892 500100
- 01892 545666
- paninicomics@panini.co.uk
- www.paninicomics.co.uk

Parent Company Panini UK Ltd

Editor Tom Spilsbury

Insider Info A children's magazine, issued fortnightly, covering Doctor Who.

Non-fiction Publishes Features, Episode reviews and Celebrity interviews.

Fiction Publishes Stories and Comic strips.

Tips *Doctor Who Magazine* is based on the popular television series. It features comic strip stories and episode reviews, alongside more serious articles about filming and producing the show.

Dora the Explorer

136–142 Bramley Road, London, W10 6SR

- 020 7565 3000
- 020 7565 3050
- harriet.murphy@johnbrowngroup.co.uk

Parent Company John Brown Group

Editor Harriet Murphy

Established 2005

Insider Info A magazine for 3–5 year olds, issued monthly, covering the Dora the Explorer brand. Present circulation is 46,014.

Non-fiction Publishes Features, Puzzles, Educational articles and simple Spanish tuition.

Fiction Publishes Stories and Comic strips.

Tips *Dora the Explorer* magazine focuses on educational articles about the natural world and culture for children. It also uses the Dora the Explorer characters to teach simple Spanish.

Fifi and the Flowertots
Woodlands, 80 Wood Lane, London, W12 0TT
- 020 8433 2356
- www.bbcmagazines.com/fifiandtheflowertots

Parent Company BBC Worldwide Publishing
Insider Info A magazine for 3–5 year olds, issued monthly, covering Fifi and the Flowertots characters.
Non-fiction Publishes Colouring pages, Cookery recipes and Activity pages.
Fiction Publishes Picture stories.
Tips *Fifi and the Flowertots* magazine is based on the popular children's television show and aims to teach children about healthy living. The magazine also contains parents notes to encourage joint participation.

Fimbles
Room A1130, Woodlands, 80 Wood Lane, London, W12 0TT
- 020 8433 2000
- 020 8433 2941
- divinia.fleary@bbc.co.uk
- www.bbcmagazines.com/fimbles

Parent Company BBC Worldwide Publishing
Editor Paddy Kempshall
Contact Editorial Assistant, Divinia Fleary
Insider Info A magazine for 2–4 year olds, issued monthly, covering Fimbles characters. Present circulation is 45,009.
Non-fiction Publishes Colouring pages, Craft pages, Puzzles and Activity pages.
Fiction Publishes Picture stories.
Tips *Fimbles* magazine is based on the popular children's television show. It often comes with Fimble related free gifts.

Fireman Sam
4th Floor, 184–192 Drummond Street, London, NW1 3HP
- 020 7380 6430
- 020 7380 6444
- jtarrant@euk.egmont.com
- www.egmontmagazines.co.uk

Parent Company Egmont Magazines
Editor Jane Tarrant
Established 2006

Insider Info A magazine for 3–6 year old boys, issued monthly, covering Fireman Sam characters.
Non-fiction Publishes Puzzles, Colouring and Activity pages.
Fiction Publishes Picture stories.
Tips *Fireman Sam* magazine is based on the classic television show, which is broadcast in over 40 countries.

Full On!
The Busworks, United House, North Road, London, N7 9DP
- 020 7609 4254
- 020 7609 4424
- jude@fullonmag.co.uk
- www.fullonmag.co.uk

Parent Company Full On Publications Ltd
Editor Jude Schofield
Established 2002

Insider Info A magazine for 13–16 year olds, issued bi-monthly, covering teenage lifestyle, gossip, reviews and careers. Present circulation is 80,000.
Non-fiction Publishes General Teenage interest articles, Celebrity gossip, Music, Film and Game reviews, Study guides, Career information and Educational articles.
Tips *Full On!* is distributed to secondary school students across the UK, and aims to provide useful career and education information, as well as teenage lifestyle articles.

Fun to Learn Bag-o-Fun
Canon Court East, Abbey Lawn, Shrewsbury, SY2 5DE
- 01743 364433
- 01743 271528
- info@redan.com
- www.redan.co.uk

Parent Company Redan Publishing Ltd
Insider Info An educational magazine for 3–7 year olds, with ten issues per year, covering activities and licenced characters. Present circulation is 80,000. Media pack is available online.
Non-fiction Publishes Activity pages, Colouring pages and Puzzles.
Fiction Publishes Picture stories with licenced characters.
Tips *Bag-o-Fun* is an educational magazine. Licenced characters include Barney, Miffy and Pingu. Each issue comes with an activity pack featuring a Magic Painting booklet, paintbrush, crayons or pencils, stickers and a free gift.

Fun to Learn Barney

Canon Court East, Abbey Lawn, Shrewsbury, SY2 5DE

☎ 01743 364433
✆ 01743 271528
✉ info@redan.com
🌐 www.redan.co.uk

Parent Company Redan Publishing Ltd
Contact Senior Editor, Becca Bland
Established 1996
Insider Info An educational magazine for 3–7 year olds, issued monthly, covering activities and Barney the Dinosaur. Present circulation is 50,000. Media pack is available online.
Non-fiction Publishes Activities and Puzzles.
Fiction Publishes Picture stories.
Tips *Barney* is an educational magazine that uses the licenced character; Barney the Dinosaur, to teach children about 'sharing, caring, imagining, dancing and learning'. It also supports the National Curriculum's Early Learning Goals. Each issue comes with a sticker sheet and free gift.

Fun to Learn Best of Barney

Canon Court East, Abbey Lawn, Shrewsbury, SY2 5DE

☎ 01743 364433
✆ 01743 271528
✉ info@redan.com
🌐 www.redan.co.uk

Parent Company Redan Publishing Ltd
Insider Info An educational magazine for 3–7 year olds, issued bi-monthly, covering activities and Barney the Dinosaur. Present circulation is 30,000. Media pack is available online.
Non-fiction Publishes Activities and Puzzles.
Fiction Publishes Picture stories.
Tips *Best of Barney* is the sister publication to *Barney* and primarily contains reprinted activities and stories, as well as lots of extra material. Each issue comes with a colouring book, crayons, and several free gifts.

Fun to Learn Discovery

Canon Court East, Abbey Lawn, Shrewsbury, SY2 5DE

☎ 01743 364433
✆ 01743 271528
✉ info@redan.com
🌐 www.redan.co.uk

Parent Company Redan Publishing Ltd
Contact Editorial Director, Diana Turner

Insider Info An educational magazine for 3–7 year olds, issued quarterly, covering activities and stories. Present circulation is 35,000. Media pack is available online.
Non-fiction Publishes themed Activities and Puzzles.
Fiction Publishes themed Stories.
Tips *Discovery* has a different theme each issue, such as 'Easter', 'Christmas' or 'Witches'. It covers the National Curriculum's Early Learning Goals and each issue comes with a free gift.

Fun to Learn Favourites

Canon Court East, Abbey Lawn, Shrewsbury, SY2 5DE

☎ 01743 364433
✆ 01743 271528
✉ info@redan.com
🌐 www.redan.co.uk

Parent Company Redan Publishing Ltd
Editor Jen Barker
Established 1998
Insider Info An educational magazine for 3–7 year olds, issued every three weeks, covering activities and popular licenced characters. Present circulation is 70,113. Media pack is available online.
Non-fiction Publishes Activities and Puzzles.
Fiction Publishes Picture stories with licenced characters.
Tips *Favourites* is a compilation magazine that contains activities and stories using popular licenced characters, such as 'Curious George', 'Dora the Explorer' and 'Spongebob SquarePants'. Each issue also includes a pull out workbook and sticker sheet to allow for parent child interactivity.

Fun to Learn Friends

Canon Court East, Abbey Lawn, Shrewsbury, SY2 5DE

☎ 01743 364433
✆ 01743 271528
✉ info@redan.com
🌐 www.redan.co.uk

Parent Company Redan Publishing Ltd
Insider Info An educational magazine for 3–7 year olds, issued fortnightly, covering activities and popular licenced characters. Present circulation is 72,270. Media pack is available online.
Non-fiction Publishes Activities and Puzzles.
Fiction Publishes Picture stories with licenced characters.
Tips *Friends* is identical in format to the Fun to Learn *Favourites* magazine, including the free workbook.

Licenced characters include 'LazyTown', 'Peppa Pig', 'Backyardigans' and 'Thomas & Friends'.

Fun to Learn Letterland
Canon Court East, Abbey Lawn, Shrewsbury, SY2 5DE
- 01743 364433
- 01743 271528
- info@redan.com
- www.redan.co.uk

Parent Company Redan Publishing Ltd
Contact Senior Editor, Fiona Christmas
Insider Info An educational magazine for 3–7 year olds, issued monthly, covering the 'Letterland Learning' system. Present circulation is 45,000. Media pack is available online.
Non-fiction Publishes Activities, Puzzles and Early Reading exercises.
Fiction Publishes Phonics-based stories.
Tips *Letterland* aims to teach children early reading skills, using the Letterland story-based phonics system.

Fun to Learn Peppa Pig
Canon Court East, Abbey Lawn, Shrewsbury, SY2 5DE
- 01743 364433
- 01743 271528
- info@redan.com
- www.redan.co.uk

Parent Company Redan Publishing Ltd
Established 2007
Insider Info An educational magazine for 3–7 year olds, issued monthly, covering activities and the 'Peppa Pig' character. Present circulation is 80,000. Media pack is available online.
Non-fiction Publishes Activities and Puzzles.
Fiction Publishes Picture stories.
Tips *Peppa Pig* magazine contains educational stories, puzzles and activities based on the popular children's television show, which supports the National Curriculum's Early Learning Goals.

Girl Guiding Magazine
17–19 Buckingham Palace Road, London, SW1W 0PT
- 020 7834 6242
- 020 7828 5791
- guiding@girlguiding.org.uk
- www.girlguiding.org.uk

Parent Company Girl Guiding UK
Editor Wendy Kewley

Insider Info A magazine, issued monthly, covering girl guides. Present circulation is 80,000.
Non-fiction Publishes News, Event listings, Features and Activity ideas.
Tips *Girl Guiding Magazine* is the official magazine of the Girl Guides organisation.

Girl Talk
Room A1130, Woodlands, 80 Wood Lane, London, W12 0TT
- 020 8433 1010
- 020 8433 2941
- girltalk.magazine@bbc.co.uk
- www.bbcgirltalk.com

Parent Company BBC Worldwide Publishing
Editor Samantha Robinson
Contact Publishing Director, Toni Round; Acting Deputy Editor, Emily Baxter; Art Director, Carol Gook
Established 1995
Insider Info A bi-weekly consumer magazine covering pre-teenage interest. Present circulation is 87,915.
Non-fiction Publishes Features, Interviews, Profiles, Reviews, Puzzles and Craft articles.
Tips *Girl Talk* is aimed at girls between the ages of 7 and 12, covering interest topics such as pop bands and movies, crafts and activities, puzzles, games and real-life stories from girl readers.

GO Girl
4th Floor, 184–192 Drummond Street, London, NW1 3HP
- 020 7380 6485
- 020 7380 6444
- eprosser@euk.egmont.com
- www.egmontmagazines.co.uk

Parent Company Egmont Magazines
Contact Deputy Editor, Emma Prosser; Picture Editor, Paul Ashman
Established 2000
Insider Info A magazine for 7–11 year old girls, issued every three weeks; covering girl's lifestyle. Present circulation is 44,058. Media pack is available online.
Non-fiction Publishes articles on Beauty, Celebs, Fashion, Gossip, Pets, as well as Readers' stories, Music, Film and Book reviews, Puzzles and Quizzes.
Tips *GO Girl* is a young girl's lifestyle magazine. Each magazine comes with at least one free gift. Accepts stories, letters and pictures only from readers.

Goodie Bag

2 Albert Square, Dundee, DD1 9QJ

- 01382 575885
- 01382 575750
- igolden@dcthomson.co.uk
- www.dcthomson.co.uk

Parent Company D.C. Thomson & Co. Ltd
Editor Irene Golden
Contact Chief Sub Editor, Gillian Henney; Fashion Editor, Lesley Manuel
Established 2003
Insider Info A magazine for 7–11 year old girls, issued monthly, covering girl's lifestyle. Present circulation is 25,000. Average lead time is five weeks. Media pack is available online.
Non-fiction Publishes articles on Beauty, Celebrity Interviews, Fashion, Gossip, Posters, Reader stories, Puzzles and Quizzes.
Tips *Goodie Bag* is a young girl's lifestyle magazine. Each magazine comes with a selection of free gifts.

Hot Wheels

4th Floor, 184–192 Drummond Street, London, NW1 3HP

- 020 7380 6430
- Online form
- www.egmontmagazines.co.uk

Parent Company Egmont Magazines
Established 2004
Insider Info A magazine for 6–9 year old boys, issued monthly, covering cars and racing. Present circulation is 31,263. Media pack is available online.
Non-fiction Publishes articles on Cars, Bikes, Skateboards, Formula One Racing and Hot Wheels Toys.
Tips *Hot Wheels* magazine is based around the popular Hot Wheels toy brand, and covers a wide range of racing and vehicle subjects.

iaw!

Swyddfa'r Urdd, Llanbadarn Road, Aberystwyth, SY23 1EY

- 01970 613118
- 01970 626120
- iaw@urdd.org
- www.urdd.org

Parent Company Urdd Gobaith Cymru
Editor Sian Eleri Davies
Established 1995
Insider Info An educational magazine for 11–18 year olds, issued monthly, covering Welsh culture. Present circulation is 3,000.

Non-fiction Publishes articles on Welsh language tuition and Welsh culture, as well as lifestyle articles.
Tips *iaw!* is a Welsh language magazine including teaching supplements for Key Stage 3 and 4 of the Welsh Second Language National Curriculum. It is distributed throughout Welsh schools.

In the Night Garden

Woodlands, 80 Wood Lane, London, W12 0TT

- 020 8433 2000
- sarah.o'neill@bbc.co.uk
- www.bbcworldwide.com/magazines.htm

Parent Company BBC Worldwide Publishing
Editor Sarah O'Neill
Established 2007
Insider Info A magazine for children aged 18 months to 3 years old, issued monthly, covering 'In the Night Garden' television show characters.
Fiction Publishes Picture stories, 'Quiet Time' stories and Sticker stories.
Tips *In the Night Garden* magazine contains a pull-out poster in each issue.

Junior Puzzles

Stonecraft, 69 Station Road, Redhill, Surrey, RH1 1EY

- 01737 378700
- 01737 781800
- catherine.filby@puzzlermedia.com
- www.puzzler.com

Parent Company Puzzler Media Ltd
Insider Info A magazine for 7–12 year olds, with seven issues per year, covering puzzles and quizzes.
Non-fiction Publishes Spot the difference, Word searches, Crosswords, Mazes and Competitions.
Tips *Junior Puzzles* is a puzzle magazine for children, mostly containing word searches and crosswords, that aims to be educational and entertaining. Each magazine comes with a free gift.

Kick

Unit 1.08 Clerkenwell Workshops, 27–31 Clerkenwell Close, London, EC1R 0AT

- 020 7014 3762
- monique@atticmedianetwork.com

Parent Company Attic Media Network
Editor Ian Pollard
Contact Consultant Editor, Monique Webber
Established 2006
Insider Info A magazine for 6–13 year old boys, issued monthly, covering football.

Non-fiction Publishes articles on Football, Lifestyle, Celebrity interviews, Match reports, Statistics, Gossip and Competitions.

Tips *Kick* is a football magazine for boys, which covers every aspect of professional football lifestyle.

Kraze Club
Unit 1.08 Clerkenwell Workshops, 27–31 Clerkenwell Close, London, EC1R 0AT
- 020 7014 3767
- 020 7426 3295
- monique@atticmedianetwork.com
- www.krazeclub.com

Parent Company Attic Media Network
Editor Monique Webber
Established 2004
Insider Info A monthly consumer magazine covering children's lifestyle and interests. Present circulation is 54,686.
Non-fiction Publishes Features, Reviews, Profiles and Competitions.
Tips *Kraze Club* is aimed at children aged between 7–12. It covers toys, sweets, computer games, sports, celebrities and a general 'tomboy' lifestyle.

Lazer
4th Floor, 184–192 Drummond Street, London, NW1 3HP
- 020 7380 6430
- mcrossick@euk.egmont.com
- www.egmontmagazines.co.uk

Parent Company Egmont Magazines
Editor Matt Crossick
Established 2007
Insider Info A magazine for 5–8 year old boys, issued monthly, covering features and activities based on television characters. Present circulation is 100,000.
Non-fiction Publishes articles on Sports, Computer games and Films, as well as Character based features.
Fiction Publishes Stories and Comic strips.
Tips *Lazer* is a new magazine from Egmont, aimed at younger boys. It covers a wide range of children's lifestyle subjects and character based features.

Lazy Town
Titan House, 144 Southwark Street, London, SE1 0UP
- 020 7620 0200
- 020 7620 0032
- jennifer.anstruther@titanemail.com
- www.titanmagazines.co.uk

Parent Company Titan Magazines
Editor Jennifer Anstruther
Established 2007
Insider Info A magazine for 4–7 year olds, issued monthly, covering Lazy Town characters. Present circulation is 160,000.
Non-fiction Publishes Activities, Games and Puzzles.
Fiction Publishes Picture stories.
Tips *Lazy Town* magazine is based on the popular children's television show, and includes puzzles, activities and stories based around the Lazy Town characters.

Learning is Fun!
Room A1130, Woodlands, 80 Wood Lane, London, W12 0TT
- 020 8433 2000
- 020 8433 2941
- stephanie.cooper@bbc.co.uk
- www.bbcmagazines.com/learningisfun

Parent Company BBC Worldwide Publishing
Editor Stephanie Cooper
Contact Deputy Editor, Emma Goldhawk; Picture Editor, Shaila Bux
Established 1996
Insider Info An educational magazine for 5–7 year olds, issued monthly, covering education, maths and numeracy. Present circulation is 34,364.
Non-fiction Publishes Reading, Writing and Mathematics activities, as well as Parenting articles.
Fiction Publishes Picture stories and Illustrations.
Tips *Learning is Fun!* magazine aims to help children work their way through Key Stage 1 of the National Curriculum, including the National Literacy and Numeracy Strategy. It also contains a section for parents, with parenting articles and tips to improve learning.

Learn with Bob the Builder
Woodlands, 80 Wood Lane, London, W12 0TT
- 020 8433 2356
- www.bbcmagazines.com/learnwithbobthebuilder

Parent Company BBC Worldwide Publishing
Insider Info An educational magazine for 3–5 year olds, issued monthly, covering early learning.
Non-fiction Publishes Reading, Writing and Mathematics activities.
Tips *Learn with Bob the Builder* uses characters from the popular Bob the Builder series to help teach young children basic literary and numeracy skills. Each issue also includes a 16-page workbook, parental notes and a free gift.

The Magic Key Adventures

Woodlands, 80 Wood Lane, London, W12 0TT

- 020 8433 2883
- emma.goldhawk@bbc.co.uk
- www.bbcmagazines.com/teletubbies

Parent Company BBC Worldwide Publishing

Contact Deputy Editor, Emma Goldhawk; Picture Editor, Shaila Bux

Insider Info A magazine for 5–7 year olds, issued every four weeks, covering the Oxford Reading Tree scheme. Present circulation is 32,096.

Non-fiction Publishes Puzzles and Activities.

Fiction Publishes Stories, Plays and Poems.

Tips *The Magic Key Adventures* supports the Oxford Reading Tree scheme and Key Stage 1 of the National Curriculum. It aims to encourage an interest in literacy and reading in young children.

The Max

PO Box 173, Peterborough, PE2 6WS

- 01733 375000
- 01733 375001
- editorial@rnib.org.uk
- www.rnib.org.uk

Parent Company RNIB

Insider Info A magazine for 16–19 year old boys, issued monthly, covering lifestyle. Available in braille, on disk or by email.

Non-fiction Publishes features on the Music scene, Sport, Interviews with personalities and a Problem page.

Tips *The Max* is a lifestyle magazine for teenagers and young men, published by the Royal National Institute of Blind People. It is available in a number of different formats.

Me Too!

Room A1130, Woodlands, 80 Wood Lane, London, W12 0TT

- 020 8433 2000
- 020 8433 2941
- www.bbcmagazines.com/metoo

Parent Company BBC Worldwide Publishing

Editor Paddy Kempshall

Established 2006

Insider Info A magazine for 3–6 year olds, issued monthly, covering activities and games. Present circulation is 49,156.

Non-fiction Publishes Games, Puzzles, Activities and Competitions.

Fiction Publishes Picture stories.

Tips *Me Too!* is based on the children's television show, and focuses on interactive puzzles and games that children and parents can do together.

Missy

PO Box 173, Peterborough, PE2 6WS

- 01733 375000
- 01733 375001
- editorial@rnib.org.uk
- www.rnib.org.uk

Parent Company RNIB

Insider Info A magazine for 12–15 year old girls, issued monthly, covering lifestyle. Available in braille, on disk, or by email.

Non-fiction Publishes Pop gossip, Interviews, Horoscopes, Real-life stories, Problem pages, Reviews and General lifestyle articles.

Fiction Publishes Stories.

Tips *Missy* is a teenage girls' lifestyle magazine, published by the Royal National Institute of the Blind. It is available in a number of different formats.

Mizz

Panini House, Coach & Horses Passage, The Pantiles, Tunbridge Wells, TN2 5UJ

- 01892 500100
- 01892 545666
- info@mizz.com
- www.mizz.com

Parent Company Panini UK Ltd

Editor Karen Brown

Contact Deputy Editor, Julie Scott; Features Writer, Lucy Saxton

Established 1985

Insider Info A bi-weekly consumer magazine covering pre-teenage/teenage female interests. Present circulation is 59,934.

Non-fiction Publishes Fashion, Advice, Features, Problem pages, Career section and Gossip articles.

Tips *Mizz* is aimed at girls aged between 10 and 14.

myBOOKSmag

4 Froxfield Close, Winchester, SO22 6JW

- 01962 620320
- guy@newbooksmag.com
- www.newbooksmag.com

Parent Company New Books

Editor Guy Pringle

Established 2002

Insider Info Quarterly consumer magazine covering children's literary interests. Present circulation is 5,000.

Non-fiction Publishes Photo features, Features, Interviews/Profiles and Reviews.
Submission Guidelines Accepts queries.
Fiction Publishes Fiction and Children's book excerpts.
Submission Guidelines Accepts queries.
Tips *myBOOKSmag* is a literary magazine aimed at 5–7 year olds. It contains extracts from children's books, as well as activities, author and illustrator information, reviews and directories. Often requires reviews of current children's books, especially with a seasonal theme.

My Little Pony
Canon Court East, Abbey Lawn, Shrewsbury, SY2 5DE
- 01743 364433
- 01743 271528
- info@redan.com
- www.redan.co.uk

Parent Company Redan Publishing Ltd
Editor Jen Barker
Insider Info A magazine for 4–9 year old girls, issued monthly, covering My Little Pony. Present circulation is 50,000.
Non-fiction Publishes Activities, Games and Puzzles.
Fiction Publishes Stories.
Tips *My Little Pony* magazine is based on the popular toy brand and aims to encourage learning through fun. Each issue comes with a free gift.

National Geographic Kids
Unit 1.08 Clerkenwell Workshops, 27–31 Clerkenwell Close, London, EC1R 0AT
- 020 7014 3777
- 020 7014 3776
- lauren@atticmedianetwork.com
- www.ngkids.co.uk

Parent Company Attic Media Network
Editor Lauren Jarvis
Established 2006
Insider Info An educational magazine for 6–14 year olds, issued monthly, covering nature, science and technology, the environment and world affairs. Present circulation is 130,000.
Non-fiction Publishes Scientific articles, Environmental articles, Fact files, World affairs, Games, Puzzles, Sports and Media reviews.
Tips *National Geographic Kids* is primarily an educational magazine focusing on science and nature. It also prints teenage lifestyle articles, and reviews the latest films, music and games.

Noddy
4th Floor, 184–192 Drummond Street, London, NW1 3HP
- 020 7380 6430
- 020 7380 6444
- Online form
- www.egmontmagazines.co.uk

Parent Company Egmont Magazines
Insider Info A magazine for 3–6 year olds, issued monthly, covering early learning. Present circulation is 39,229.
Non-fiction Publishes Early learning activities, Puzzles and Games.
Fiction Publishes Picture stories.
Tips *Noddy* magazine uses characters from Chorion's Noddy brand to encourage early learning in pre-school age children.

Play & Learn Thomas & Friends
4th Floor, 184–192 Drummond Street, London, NW1 3HP
- 020 7380 6430
- 020 7380 6444
- Online form
- www.egmontmagazines.co.uk

Parent Company Egmont Magazines
Established 2000
Insider Info A magazine for 3–6 year olds, issued fortnightly, covering early learning. Present circulation is 48,095.
Non-fiction Publishes Early learning activities, Puzzles and Games.
Fiction Publishes Picture stories.
Tips *Play & Learn Thomas & Friends* uses the *Thomas the Tank Engine* characters to teach children basic literacy and numeracy, in preparation for Key Stage 1.

Pokemon World
Richmond House, 33 Richmond Hill, Bournemouth, BH2 6EZ
- 01202 586219
- nick.roberts@imagine-publishing.co.uk
- www.pokemon-world.co.uk

Parent Company Imagine Publishing
Contact Publisher, Nick Roberts
Established 2000
Insider Info A magazine for 6–14 year olds, issued monthly, covering the Pokemon brand. Present circulation is 25,000.
Non-fiction Publishes Game, Toy and Book reviews, News, Tips and Pokemon related features.

Fiction Publishes Comic strips and stories.

Tips *Pokemon World* covers every aspect of the Pokemon brand, as well as reviews of other multi-format products.

Pony Magazine

Headley House, Headley Road, Grayshott, Hindhead, GU26 6TU

📞 01428 601020

📠 01428 601027

✉ pony@djmurphy.co.uk

🌐 www.ponymag.co.uk

Parent Company D.J. Murphy (Publishers) Ltd

Editor Janet Rising

Contact Assistant Editor, Lousie Bland

Established 1949

Insider Info A magazine, issued monthly, covering horse care and riding. Present circulation is 42,742.

Non-fiction Publishes Pony Healthcare and Grooming articles, Riding Tips and Tricks, Interviews, Kit reviews, Classifieds and News.

Tips *Pony Magazine* covers a wide range of pony related subjects, from healthcare to lifestyle. It is aimed at children and teenagers interested in riding.

Pretty Pony Club

Office Block 1, Southlink Business Park, Hamilton Street, Oldham, OL4 1DE

📞 0161 624 0414

📠 0161 628 4655

✉ nicola.littlejohn@toontasticpublishing.com

Parent Company Toontastic Publishing

Editor Nicola Littlejohn

Contact Editor in Chief, James Hill

Established 1998

Insider Info A magazine for 3–12 year old girls, issued every three weeks, covering pony care and riding. Present circulation is 25,000.

Non-fiction Publishes Features, Tips, True life stories, Competitions and Games.

Fiction Publishes Stories.

Tips *Pretty Pony Club* covers every aspect of pony riding and owning for young girls. It contains a mix of tips and technical articles, pony related stories and competitions.

Pure

PO Box 173, Peterborough, PE2 6WS

📞 01733 375000

📠 01733 375001

✉ editorial@rnib.org.uk

🌐 www.rnib.org.uk

Parent Company RNIB

Insider Info A magazine for 16–19 year old girls, issued monthly, covering lifestyle. Available in braille, on disk or by email.

Non-fiction Publishes articles on: Love and Relationships, Fashion, Health and Beauty, Celebrity news, Real life stories, Horoscopes and a Problem page.

Tips *Pure* is a lifestyle magazine for teenagers and young women published by the Royal National Institute of Blind People. It is available in a number of different formats.

Quiz Kids

Stonecroft, 69 Station Road, Redhill, Surrey, RH1 1EY

📞 01737 378700

📠 01737 781800

✉ reception@puzzlermedia.com

🌐 www.puzzler.com

Parent Company Puzzler Media Ltd

Insider Info A magazine for 7–11 year olds, issued bi-monthly, covering puzzles.

Non-fiction Publishes Games, Puzzles, Quizzes and Competitions.

Fiction Publishes Comic strips.

Tips Rather than just being a straightforward puzzle magazine, *Quiz Kids* prints comic strips about the Quiz Kids Gang, that incorporate a range of quizzes and puzzles.

Scooby Doo! Mystery Solvers!

Follingsby Road, Gateshead, NE10 8BR

📞 0870 043 6400

✉ enquiries@deagostini.co.uk

🌐 www.deagostini.co.uk/ scoobydoo_mystery_solvers

Parent Company DeAgostini

Insider Info An educational magazine, issued weekly, covering science and nature.

Non-fiction Publishes Science and Nature articles, Puzzles and Games.

Fiction Publishes Comic strips and stories.

Tips *Scooby Doo! Mystery Solvers!* is an educational magazine that uses the *Scooby Doo* characters to teach children about science and nature.

Shoot Monthly

King's Reach Tower, Stamford Street, London, SE1 9LS

📞 020 7261 6287

📠 020 7261 6019

shoot@ipcmedia.com
www.shoot.co.uk
Parent Company IPC Media Ltd
Editor Colin Mitchell
Established 1969
Insider Info A consumer magazine publication, issued monthly, covering football for young people. Present circulation of 28,505. Accepts queries by mail and email.
Non-fiction Interested in Photo features and Football articles.
Submission Guidelines Send query before sending submissions. Articles must be 500–2,000 words.
Images Send photos with submission.
Tips Publishes football related articles aimed at a fairly young/teenage market. Features must be topical, hard hitting and off beat. Aim for something relevant, but that is not usually covered in the magazine.

Shout

2 Albert Square, Dundee, DD1 9QJ
01382 223131
01382 200880
mwelch@shoutmag.co.uk
www.shoutmag.co.uk
Parent Company D.C. Thomson & Co. Ltd
Editor Maria Welch
Contact Assistant Editor, Michael Stirling; Problem Page Editor, Laura Brown
Established 1993
Insider Info A bi-weekly consumer magazine covering teenage girls' interests. Present circulation is 80,910.
Non-fiction Publishes Features, Interviews, Profiles, Reviews and True-life stories.
* Pays £50 for true-life stories.
Submission Guidelines For true-life stories fill in the online form.
Tips *Shout* is aimed at younger teenage girls, covering health, beauty, fashion, celebrity gossip, boys and relationship advice. *Shout* is always looking for embarrassing or shocking true-life stories from readers.

Showtime Weekly

Panini House, Coach and Horses Passage, The Pantiles, Tunbridge Wells, TN2 5UJ
01892 500100
01892 545666
showtime@panini.co.uk
www.paninicomics.co.uk
Parent Company Panini UK Ltd

Editor Tom O'Malley
Insider Info A comic for 2–5 year olds, issued weekly, covering pre-school television characters.
Non-fiction Publishes Activities, Games and Puzzles.
Fiction Publishes Comic strips and Picture stories.
Tips *Showtime Weekly* brings together characters from every pre-school television channel in stories and activities for young children.

Sky Kids

The New Boathouse, 136–142 Bramley Road, London, W10 6SR
020 7565 3000
020 7565 3094
helen.ward@jbjunior.com
www.sky.com/skykids
Parent Company John Brown Group
Contact Group Editor, Helen Ward; Associate Editor, Paul Virr
Established 2004
Insider Info A magazine for 6–12 year olds, issued monthly, covering children's television. Present circulation is 800,000.
Non-fiction Publishes Features and Reviews.
Tips *Sky Kids* is issued free to any household that has Sky television. It covers all the children's television programming available on Sky.

Smallville

Titan House, 144 Southwark Street, London, SE1 0UP
020 7620 0200
020 7620 0032
smallville@titanemail.com
www.titanmagazines.co.uk
Parent Company Titan Magazines
Insider Info A magazine, issued bi-monthly, covering Smallville.
Non-fiction Publishes News, Features, Reviews, Interviews, Profiles and Competitions.
Tips *Smallville* magazine covers the *Smallville* television series, and is aimed at fans of the show, including young adults and teenagers.

Sparkle World

Canon Court East, Abbey Lawn, Shrewsbury, SY2 5DE
01743 364433
01743 271528
info@redan.com
www.redan.co.uk
Parent Company Redan Publishing Ltd

Contact Senior Editor, Beccy Bland
Insider Info A magazine for 4–9 year old girls, issued monthly, covering popular children's characters. Present circulation is 95,000.
Non-fiction Publishes Activities and Puzzles.
Fiction Publishes Picture stories.
Tips *Sparkle World* uses a range of popular children's characters, including Polly Pocket, Care Bears and Rainbow Magic. Each issue comes with a free gift.

Stargate SG-1
Titan House, 144 Southwark Street, London, SE1 0UP
- 020 7620 0200
- 020 7620 0032
- stargatesg-1@titanemail.com
- www.titanmagazines.co.uk
Parent Company Titan Magazines
Editor Acting Editor, Emma Matthews
Insider Info A magazine, issued bi-monthly, covering Stargate SG-1 and Stargate Atlantis.
Non-fiction Publishes News, Interviews, Reviews, Features and Articles about Stargate.
Tips *Stargate SG-1* covers news and features on the *Stargate SG-1* television show and its sister show, *Stargate: Atlantis*. It is aimed at enthusiasts of all ages, including young adults and teenagers.

Star Trek
Titan House, 144 Southwark Street, London, SE1 0UP
- 020 7620 0200
- 020 7620 0032
- startrek@titanemail.com
- www.titanmagazines.co.uk
Parent Company Titan Magazines
Editor Paul Simpson
Established 1995
Insider Info A magazine, issued bi-monthly, covering *Star Trek*. Present circulation is 27,000.
Non-fiction Publishes News, Reviews, Features and Articles about *Star Trek*.
Fiction Publishes Stories.
Tips *Star Trek* magazine, based on the popular television show, is aimed at all science fiction fans, including young adults and teenagers.

Star Wars Insider
Titan House, 144 Southwark Street, London, SE1 0UP
- 020 7620 0200
- 020 7620 0032
- starwars@titanemail.com
- www.titanmagazines.co.uk
Parent Company Titan Magazines
Editor Brian Robb
Insider Info A magazine, issued bi-monthly, covering *Star Wars*. Present circulation is 50,000.
Non-fiction Publishes News, Reviews, Features and Articles about *Star Wars*.
Tips *Star Wars Insider* covers everything related to *Star Wars* and is aimed at *Star Wars* enthusiasts, including young adults and teenagers.

Story Box
1st Floor, 2 King Street, Peterborough, PE1 1LT
- 01733 565858
- contact@bayard-magazines.co.uk
- www.bayard-magazines.co.uk
Parent Company Bayard Presse
Contact Editor in Chief, Simona Sideri; Managing Publisher, Christine Auberger; Art Director, Pat Carter
Insider Info An educational magazine for 3–6 year olds, issued monthly, covering the natural world, numeracy, stories and poetry.
Non-fiction Publishes Animal and Science articles, and Numeracy activities.
Fiction Publishes Picture stories and Read aloud stories.
Poetry Publishes Poetry.
Tips *Story Box* is aimed at very young children, and the stories within are designed to be read aloud by parents or carers. Numeracy and science activities are included to encourage early learning.

Sugar
64 North Row, London, W1K 7LL
- 020 7150 7087
- 020 7150 7678
- sugarreaders@sugarmagazine.co.uk
- www.sugarmagazine.co.uk
Parent Company Hacette Filipacchi
Editor Annabel Brog
Contact Features Editor, Diane Leeming
Established 1994
Insider Info A monthly consumer magazine for teenage girls. Present circulation of 200,187. Queries accepted by mail.
Tips The magazine's content concentrates mainly on the opposite sex, fashion, celebrities, and real stories about teenagers. *Sugar* helps solve 'female' issues by publishing articles that offer helpful advice. *Sugar* seeks real life stories, but also practical articles of help dealing with teenage issues. Experience as

either a guidance counsellor, or a previously troubled teenager, would add to any article idea.

tBkmag

4 Froxfield Close, Winchester, SO22 6JW
- 01962 620320
- www.newbooksmag.com

Parent Company New Books
Editor Guy Pringle
Insider Info A quarterly book magazine for pre-teenage readers (the sister publication of *myBOOKSmag*). Present circulation of 10,000.
Non-fiction Publishes Features, Interviews/Profiles, Reviews, General Interest articles and Event news.
Submission Guidelines Send query before submitting.
Fiction Publishes Book excerpts.
Submission Guidelines Send query before submitting.
Tips Publishes book reviews, information on children's and young adult books, book excerpts, interviews, and reports on events for young readers. *tBkmag* often requires reviews and book excerpts from the latest children's and young people's books.

Teletubbies

Woodlands, 80 Wood Lane, London, W12 0TT
- 020 8433 2356
- www.bbcmagazines.com/teletubbies

Parent Company BBC Worldwide Publishing
Insider Info A magazine for pre-school children, issued monthly, covering the Teletubbies.
Non-fiction Publishes Activities, Puzzles and Craft articles.
Fiction Publishes Picture stories.
Tips *Teletubbies* focuses on creative activities for pre-school children, in order to help build their confidence and imagination.

Thomas & Friends

4th Floor, 184–192 Drummond Street, London, NW1 3HP
- 020 7380 6430
- 020 7380 6444
- Online form
- www.egmontmagazines.co.uk

Parent Company Egmont Magazines
Established 1999
Insider Info A magazine for 3–6 year old boys, issued fortnightly, covering *Thomas & Friends* characters. Present circulation is 50,002.
Non-fiction Publishes Puzzles and Activities.

Fiction Publishes Comic strips and Picture stories.
Tips *Thomas & Friends* focuses mainly on stories that can be read aloud by parents, but does also contain limited activities and puzzles.

Thomas & Friends Classic Story Collection

4th Floor, 184–192 Drummond Street, London, NW1 3HP
- 020 7380 6430
- 020 7380 6444
- Online form
- www.egmontmagazines.co.uk

Parent Company Egmont Magazines
Insider Info A magazine for 3–6 year old boys, issued monthly, covering *Thomas & Friends* characters. Present circulation is 31,397.
Fiction Publishes reprinted stories.
Tips *Thomas & Friends Classic Story Collection* reprints longer versions of classic *Thomas & Friends* stories. Each issue also comes with pull-out posters.

Thunderbirds

Canon Court East, Abbey Lawn, Shrewsbury, SY2 5DE
- 01743 364433
- 01743 271528
- info@redan.com
- www.redan.co.uk

Parent Company Redan Publishing Ltd
Editor Anita Cash
Insider Info A magazine for boys aged five and over, issued monthly, covering Thunderbirds characters. Present circulation is 45,000.
Non-fiction Publishes Activities and Puzzles.
Fiction Publishes Picture stories.
Tips *Thunderbirds* is based on the popular children's television series. It has a pull out puzzle section, and comes with a free gift.

Top of the Pops

Room A1136, Woodlands, 80 Wood Lane, London, W12 0TT
- 020 8433 3910
- 020 8433 2763
- peter.hart@bbc.co.uk
- www.totpmag.com

Parent Company BBC Worldwide Publishing
Editor Peter Hart
Contact Publisher, Duncan Gray; Art Director, Terry Hewitt; Assistant Editor, Lara Hutcheson

Insider Info A monthly consumer magazine covering Popular Music. Present circulation is 105,025.

Non-fiction Publishes Features, Interviews, Profiles, Reviews and Event listings.

Tips *Top of the Pops* magazine is aimed at teenagers.

Toxic
4th Floor, 184–192 Drummond Street, London, NW1 3HP

- 020 7380 6430
- 020 7380 6444
- myeo@euk.egmont.com
- www.egmontmagazines.co.uk

Parent Company Egmont Magazines

Contact Senior Editor, Matt Yeo; Sub Editor, Andy Davidson

Insider Info A magazine for 7–12 year old boys, issued fortnightly, covering lifestyle and fun. Present circulation is 50,006.

Non-fiction Publishes Movie, Music and Game reviews, Competitions, Puzzles, Games and Activities.

Fiction Publishes Comic strips.

Tips *Toxic* is a popular magazine for younger boys, offering a variety of lifestyle orientated articles and fun comic stories. Each issue comes with a free gift.

Toybox
Room A1130, Woodlands, 80 Wood Lane, London, W12 0TT

- 020 8433 2000
- 020 8433 2941
- divinia.fleary@bbc.co.uk
- www.bbcmagazines.com/toybox

Parent Company BBC Worldwide Publishing

Editor Paddy Kempshall

Contact Editorial Assistant, Divinia Fleary

Insider Info A magazine for 3–5 year olds, issued every three weeks, covering a variety of CBeebies characters. Present circulation is 90,997.

Non-fiction Publishes Colouring pages, Craft pages, Puzzles and Activity pages.

Fiction Publishes Picture stories.

Tips *Toybox* magazine contains stories and activities based on a wide range of Cbeebies characters. Each magazine also comes with a free gift.

TV Hits! Magazine
The Tower, Phoenix Square, Wyncolls Road, Severalls Industrial Park, Colchester, Essex, CO4 9HU

- 01206 851117
- 01206 849078
- hello@tvhitsmagazine.co.uk
- www.tvhits.co.uk

Parent Company Essential Publishing Ltd

Editor Charlotte Acock

Contact Assistant Editor, Viki Waters; Editorial Assistant, Jo Higgins

Established 1989

Insider Info A magazine for 9–16 year olds, issued monthly, covering lifestyle and media culture. Present circulation is 47,321.

Non-fiction Publishes Music, Film and Game reviews, Interviews, Celebrity gossip, Features, News and True life stories.

Tips *TV Hits! Magazine* is lifestyle and culture magazine aimed at pre-teenagers and teenagers. It mainly focuses on television and other media, as well as celebrity gossip and lifestyle.

Tweenies
Woodlands, 80 Wood Lane, London, W12 0TT

- 020 8433 2356
- www.bbcmagazines.com/tweenies

Parent Company BBC Worldwide Publishing

Insider Info A magazine for pre-school age children, issued fortnightly, covering early learning activites.

Non-fiction Publishes Songs, Games and Craft Articles.

Fiction Publishes Stories and Role plays.

Tips *Tweenies* magazine is aimed at pre-school age children, and mixes educational craft and learning articles with Tweenies related stories and games.

Underground Ernie
Woodlands, 80 Wood Lane, London, W12 0TT

- 020 8433 2356
- www.bbcmagazines.com

Parent Company BBC Worldwide Publishing

Editor Paddy Kempshall

Established 2007

Insider Info A magazine for 3–5 year olds, issued every four weeks, covering Underground Ernie characters.

Non-fiction Publishes Puzzles, Activities, Colouring sheets and Competitions.

Fiction Publishes Picture stories.

Tips *Underground Ernie* is based on the popular television show of the same name, and aims to be both fun and educational. Each issue comes with a free gift.

Vibe

PO Box 173, Peterborough, PE2 6WS
☎ 01733 375000
📠 01733 375001
✉ editorial@rnib.org.uk
🌐 www.rnib.org.uk
Parent Company RNIB
Insider Info A magazine for 12–15 year old boys, issued monthly, covering lifestyle. Available in braille, on disk or by email.
Non-fiction Publishes Sports news, True life stories, General interest features and Pop news.
Fiction Publishes Stories.
Tips *Vibe* is a teenage boys lifestyle magazine published by the Royal National Institute of Blind People. It is available in a number of different formats – see the website for further information.

Winnie the Pooh & Friends

4th Floor, 184–192 Drummond Street, London, NW1 3HP
☎ 020 7380 6430
📠 020 7380 6444
✉ Online form
🌐 www.egmontmagazines.co.uk
Parent Company Egmont Magazines
Insider Info A magazine for 2–5 year olds, issued monthly, covering *Winnie the Pooh* characters. Present circulation is 23,297.
Non-fiction Publishes Games, Puzzles and Activities.
Fiction Publishes Picture stories.
Tips *Winnie the Pooh & Friends* contains stories and activities based on the popular Disney characters. It is designed for children to read along with their parents.

W.I.T.C.H.

Woodlands, 80 Wood Lane, London, W12 0TT
☎ 020 8433 3825
✉ witch@bbc.co.uk
🌐 www.bbcmagazines.com/content/magazines/witch/
Parent Company BBC Worldwide Publishing
Editor Bea Appleby
Contact Art Editor, Steve Clarke; Fashion & Beauty Editor, Emma Arnold; Editorial Assistant, Olivia McLearon
Established 2005
Insider Info A magazine for 8–11 year old girls, issued monthly, covering W.I.T.C.H. characters and lifestyle.

Non-fiction Publishes Fashion and Beauty features, Gossip, Relationship articles, Horoscopes, Puzzles and Competitions.
Fiction Publishes Comic strips.
Tips *W.I.T.C.H.* magazine is based on the popular television show of the same name, and is the fastest growing girls magazine in the world. As well as comic strips, it also covers teenage lifestyle articles, including fashion, celebrity gossip and boys.

Young Scot

Roseberry House, 9 Haymarket Terrace, Edinburgh, EH12 5EZ
☎ 0131 313 2488
📠 0131 313 6800
✉ info@youngscot.org
🌐 www.youngscot.org
Parent Company Young Scot Organisation
Established 2001
Insider Info A magazine for 12–26 year olds, issued quarterly, covering youth information and lifestyle.
Non-fiction Publishes News, Information, Features and Competitions.
Tips *Young Scot* magazine is published by Young Scot, the national youth information and discount charity. It is aimed at young people in Scotland and contains informative advice on a range of subjects.

Young Writer

Glebe House, Church Road, Weobley, Herefordshire, HR4 8SD
☎ 01544 318901
📠 01544 318901
✉ kate@youngwriter.org
🌐 www.youngwriter.org
Editor Kate Jones
Established 1995
Insider Info A magazine, with three issues per year, covering young people's writing.
Non-fiction Publishes technical Articles, Tips, Ideas and Prizes.
Fiction Publishes Short stories and Non-fiction by Children.
Poetry Publishes Poems by Children.
Submission Guidelines Submit writing via online form.
Tips *Young Writer* is an international platform for young people's writing up to the age of 18. It publishes short stories, non-fiction and poetry from young writers. It does not accept submissions from adults, but may be interested in technical writing craft articles aimed at young writers.

2000 AD

The Studio, Brewer Street, Oxford, OX1 1QN
- 01865 200603
- 01865 792254
- publicrelations@2000adonline.com
- www.2000adonline.com

Parent Company Rebellion
Editor Matt Smith
Established 1977

Insider Info A weekly comic covering Science Fiction and Fantasy. Manuscript guidelines are available online.

Fiction Interested in Science-Fiction comic scripts for the 'Future Shock' series, which is a five-page sci-fi story with a twist ending.

Submission Guidelines Accepts a one page 'Future Shock' script by post along with details of previously published work or a full script that demonstrates an understanding of comic book formats. Include a SAE for return. Established writers can send in a proposal for a new series but new writers begin by submitting Future Shocks.

Illustration Interested in Pencilling, Inking, Lettering and Colouring submissions.

Submission Guidelines Accepts copies (for pencilers and inkers), or files on CD or ZIP disk (for colourists) by post, with SAE for return.

Tips *2000 AD* is a long established science fiction comic. It is considered a proven ground for young art and writing talent and submissions are very hotly contested. Does not accept unsolicited submissions by email or proposals by telephone. Be aware that although *2000 AD* appeals to young adult readers, it is often considered an adult publication.

Action Man A.T.O.M.

Panini House, Coach and Horses Passage, The Pantiles, Tunbridge Wells, Kent, TN2 5UJ
- 01892 500100
- 01892 500146
- paninicomics@panini.co.uk
- www.paninicomics.co.uk

Parent Company Panini UK Ltd
Editor Ed Caruana
Contact Managing Editor, Alan O'Keefe
Established 2006

Insider Info A consumer magazine published every three weeks. The magazine is aimed at children and fans of *Action Man*. Present circulation is 53,000. 50

per cent of the publication is written by freelance writers. A media pack is available online.

Non-fiction Publishes Reviews and Information on *Action Man* products.

Fiction Publishes Comic strip stories based around *Action Man*.

Illustration Publishes Cartoon Illustrations of the *Action Man* stories.

Tips The magazine is specifically aimed at 6–12 year old readers and contains collectible features and fact files on the heroes, villains and hi-tech gadgets of the A.T.O.M. world, with lots of puzzles and competitions. The ethos is that a mixture of imaginative editorial, modern, urban design, and cool, aspirational heroes will attract a broad range of readers.

Astonishing Spider-Man

Panini House, Coach and Horses Passage, The Pantiles, Tunbridge Wells, TN2 5UJ
- 01892 500100
- 01892 545666
- astonspid@panini.co.uk
- www.paninicomics.co.uk

Parent Company Panini UK Ltd
Insider Info A comic, issued fortnightly, covering *Spider-Man* and *DareDevil* characters.

Fiction Publishes American *Spider-Man* and *DareDevil* reprints.

Tips *Astonishing Spider-Man* reprints the American comic strips, complete with the original illustrations from Stan Lee and other artists.

The Avengers United

Panini House, Coach and Horses Passage, The Pantiles, Tunbridge Wells, TN2 5UJ
- 01892 500100
- 01892 545666
- collectorsed@panini.co.uk
- www.paninicomics.co.uk

Parent Company Panini UK Ltd
Editor Scott Gray
Insider Info A monthly comic covering *The Avengers* and other *Marvel* characters.

Fiction Publishes new *Avengers* comic strips, as well as classic reprints.

Tips *The Avengers United* publishes new *Avenger* comic strips with original art from Stan Lee, Jack Kirby and others.

Batman Legends

Titan House, 144 Southwark Street, London,
SE1 0UP

- 020 7620 0200
- 020 7620 0032
- batmanlegends@titanemail.com
- www.titanmagazines.co.uk

Parent Company Titan Magazines
Editor Ned Hartley
Established 2006
Insider Info A comic for 8–12 year old boys, issued monthly, covering the Batman character. Present circulation is 30,000.
Fiction Publishes reprints of *Batman* comic strips.
Tips *Batman Legends* primarily publishes reprints of classic DC *Batman* strips. It prints letters from readers and runs various competitions.

The Beano

2 Albert Square, Dundee, DD1 9QJ

- 01382 575185
- 01382 454599
- beano@dcthomson.co.uk
- www.dcthomson.co.uk

Parent Company D.C. Thomson & Co. Ltd
Insider Info A comic for 7–12 year old boys, issued weekly, covering *Beano* characters.
Fiction Publishes Comic strips and stories.
Tips *The Beano* is an established comic for young and teenage boys. Regular characters include 'Dennis the Menace' and 'Gnasher'.

The BeanoMAX

2 Albert Square, Dundee, DD1 9QJ

- 01382 223131
- 01382 322214
- jekerr@dcthomson.co.uk
- www.dcthomson.co.uk

Parent Company D.C. Thomson & Co. Ltd
Editor Euan Kerr
Contact Features Editor, Michelle O'Donnell
Established 2007
Insider Info A comic for 8–13 year old boys, with ten issues per year, covering teenage lifestyle and *Beano* characters. Present circulation is 120,000.
Non-fiction Publishes Teenage Lifestyle articles, Puzzles, Game reviews, Competitions and Celebrity interviews.
Fiction Publishes short and long *Beano* character comic strips.

Tips *The BeanoMAX* is an extension of the classic Beano comic. It has longer strips than the *Beano*, and also has lifestyle focused articles and reader's letters.

The Best of the Simpsons

Titan House, 144 Southwark Street, London,
SE1 0UP

- 020 7620 0200
- 020 7620 0032
- simpsonspresents@titanemail.com
- www.titanmagazines.co.uk

Parent Company Titan Magazines
Insider Info A comic, with eight issues per year, covering *The Simpsons* characters.
Fiction Publishes Comic strips.
Tips *The Best of the Simpsons* publishes reprints of classic and rare *Simpsons* comic strips.

Beyblade

Office Block 1, Southlink Business Park,
Hamilton Street, Oldham, OL4 1DE

- 0161 624 0414
- 0161 628 4655
- nicola.littlejohn@toontasticpublishing.com

Parent Company Toontastic Publishing
Editor Nicola Littlejohn
Insider Info A comic for 8–14 year old boys, issued monthly, covering *Beyblade* characters. Present circulation is 42,542.
Fiction Publishes Features and *Beyblade* comic strips.

Tips *Beyblade* magazine is based on the popular animated television show. It contains comics, puzzles, competitions and *Beyblade* related features.

Cartoon Network

Panini House, Coach and Horses Passage, The
Pantiles, Tunbridge Wells, TN2 5UJ

- 01892 500100
- 01892 545666
- www.paninicomics.co.uk

Parent Company Panini UK Ltd
Editor Simon Frith
Insider Info A comic for 7–12 year olds, issued six-weekly, covering Cartoon Network characters. Present circulation is 110,000.
Non-fiction Publishes Film Reviews and Competitions.
Fiction Publishes Cartoon Network comic strips.
Tips *Cartoon Network* is a comic that features strips with all the major Cartoon Network characters,

including *Scooby Doo* and the *Powerpuff Girls*. Each issue also features a free gift.

The Dandy
2 Albert Square, Dundee, DD1 9QJ
- 01382 575185
- 01382 454599
- dandy@dcthomson.co.uk
- www.dcthomson.co.uk
Parent Company D.C. Thomson & Co. Ltd
Insider Info A weekly comic for 7–12 year old boys covering Dandy characters.
Fiction Publishes Comic strips and stories.
Tips *The Dandy* is an established comic for young and teenage boys. Regular characters include 'Desperate Dan'.

DreamWorks Tales
Titan House, 144 Southwark Street, London, SE1 0UP
- 020 7620 0200
- 020 7620 0032
- dreamworks@titanemail.com
- www.titanmagazines.co.uk
Parent Company Titan Magazines
Editor Steve White
Established 2007
Insider Info A comic for 8–14 year olds, issued monthly, covering DreamWorks characters.
Non-fiction Publishes News, Features and Reviews.
Fiction Publishes Comic Strips and stories.
Tips *DreamWorks Tales* is a new magazine covering characters from DreamWorks Productions' animated films.

Essential X-Men
Panini House, Coach and Horses Passage, The Pantiles, Tunbridge Wells, TN2 5UJ
- 01892 500100
- 01892 545666
- collectorsed@panini.co.uk
- www.paninicomics.co.uk
Parent Company Panini UK Ltd
Insider Info A comic, issued monthly, covering *X-Men* characters.
Fiction Publishes new and reprinted *X-Men* comic strips.
Tips *Essential X-Men* is a comic that prints new and classic strips featuring the *Marvel X-Men* characters.

Fantastic Four Adventures
Panini House, Coach and Horses Passage, The Pantiles, Tunbridge Wells, TN2 5UJ
- 01892 500100
- 01892 545666
- collectorsed@panini.co.uk
- www.paninicomics.co.uk
Parent Company Panini UK Ltd
Insider Info A comic, issued monthly, covering the Fantastic Four characters.
Fiction Publishes new and reprinted Fantastic Four comic strips.
Tips *Fantastic Four Adventures* primarily reprints classic comic strips from older *Fantastic Four* titles, including story and artwork by Stan Lee, Jack Kirby and other original artists.

Futurama
Titan House, 144 Southwark Street, London, SE1 0UP
- 020 7620 0200
- 020 7620 0032
- planetexpressmail@titanemail.com
- www.titanmagazines.co.uk
Parent Company Titan Magazines
Insider Info A comic, issued monthly, covering *Futurama* television characters.
Fiction Publishes *Futurama* comic strips.
Tips *Futurama* magazine will print letters and artwork from their readers.

Jetix
Building 12, Chiswick Park, Chiswick High Road, London, W4 5AN
- webmaster_uk@jetixeurope.net
- www.jetix.co.uk
Parent Company Jetix Europe Ltd
Insider Info A comic for 7–11 year old boys, issued monthly, covering Jetix characters.
Non-fiction Publishes Features, Reviews, Puzzles and Quizzes.
Fiction Publishes Comic strips.
Tips *Jetix* magazine is an off-shoot of the Jetix television channel, and focuses on action packed comic strips featuring Jetix characters.

Justice League Legends
Titan House, 144 Southwark Street, London, SE1 0UP
- 020 7620 0200
- 020 7620 0032

justicelegends@titanemail.com
www.titanmagazines.co.uk
Parent Company Titan Magazines
Editor Andrew James
Established 2007
Insider Info A comic for anyone over 12 years old, issued monthly, covering DC Comics Justice League characters.
Fiction Publishes Comic strips.
Tips Publishes reprints of classic *Justice League of America* comic strips from DC Comics.

Kids Alive!
101 Newington Causeway, London, SE1 6BN
020 7367 4911
020 7367 4710
kidsalive@salvationarmy.org.uk
www.salvationarmy.org.uk/kidsalive
Parent Company Salvation Army
Editor Justin Reeves
Established 1996
Insider Info A weekly comic for 7–12 year olds dealing with Salvation Army themes. Present circulation is 21,000.
Non-fiction Publishes Educational and Evangelical articles and features.
Fiction Publishes Educational Comic strips
Tips *Kids Alive!* is a comic from the Salvation Army that aims to teach children about its beliefs. Most articles are illustrated in a similar fashion to comic books.

Lucky Bag Comic
Office Block 1, Southlink Business Park, Hamilton Street, Oldham, OL4 1DE
0161 624 0414
0161 628 4655
james.hill@toontasticpublishing.com
Parent Company Toontastic Publishing
Contact Editor in Chief, James Hill
Established 2002
Insider Info A magazine for 6–12 year olds, issued monthly, covering lifestyle and comic strips. Present circulation is 34,000.
Non-fiction Publishes Movie and Music reviews, Lifestyle articles, Puzzles and Games.
Fiction Publishes Comic strips and stories.
Tips *Lucky Bag Comic* publishes a variety of children's lifestyle features and comic strip stories. It also runs competitions and often includes free gifts.

Lunar Jim
Titan House, 144 Southwark Street, London, SE1 0UP
020 7620 0200
020 7620 0032
jennifer.anstruther@titanemail.com
www.titanmagazines.co.uk
Parent Company Titan Magazines
Editor Jennifer Anstruther
Established 2007
Insider Info A comic for 3–6 year olds, issued monthly, covering Lunar Jim characters.
Non-fiction Publishes Puzzles and Activities.
Fiction Publishes Comic strips and stories.
Tips *Lunar Jim* Comic is based on the popular children's television show.

Marvel Legends
Panini House, Coach and Horses Passage, The Pantiles, Tunbridge Wells, TN2 5UJ
01892 500100
01892 545666
marvellegends@panini.co.uk
www.paninicomics.co.uk
Parent Company Panini UK Ltd
Insider Info A comic, issued monthly, covering Marvel characters.
Fiction Publishes Comic strips.
Submission Guidelines Visit their website for writer and illustrator submission guidelines. Any work must be relevant to licensed characters. Do not send in any original work, copies will not be returned.
Tips *Marvel Legends* is a comic anthology that reprints material from *Captain America*, *Iron Man* and *The Mighty Thor* comic books. Marvel advertises jobs via their website, send CV and letter to: paninicomics@panini.co.uk

Mighty World of Marvel
Panini House, Coach and Horses Passage, The Pantiles, Tunbridge Wells, TN2 5UJ
01892 500100
01892 545666
collectorsed@panini.co.uk
www.paninicomics.co.uk
Parent Company Panini UK Ltd
Insider Info A comic, issued monthly, covering Marvel characters.
Fiction Publishes Comic strips
Submission Guidelines Visit their website for writer and illustrator submission guidelines. Any work must be relevant to licensed characters. Do not send in any original work, copies will not be returned.

Tips *Mighty World of Marvel* reprints classic Marvel comic strips.

Plus & Eagles Wings
The Barn, Flaxlands Manor Farm, Wootton Bassett, Wiltshire, SN4 8DY
- 01666 510153
- info@hayespress.org
- www.hayespress.org

Parent Company Hayes Press
Insider Info A comic for 6–10 year olds, issued monthly, covering Christianity.
Fiction Publishes Bible-based Comic stories.
Tips *Plus & Eagles Wings* is a Christian comic for young readers. It focuses mainly on bible-based stories.

Postman Pat
Panini House, Coach and Horses Passage, The Pantiles, Tunbridge Wells, TN2 5UJ
- 01892 500100
- 01892 545666
- collectorsed@panini.co.uk
- www.paninicomics.co.uk

Parent Company Panini UK Ltd
Insider Info A comic for 3–6 year olds, issued every three weeks, covering Postman Pat characters.
Non-fiction Publishes Activities, Games and Puzzles.
Fiction Publishes Comic strips and Picture stories.
Submission Guidelines Visit their website for writer and illustrator submission guidelines. Any work must be relevant to licensed Postman Pat characters. Do not send in any original work, copies will not be returned.
Tips *Postman Pat* comic is based on the popular television series and contains Postman Pat related stories and activities.

Rugrats
Office Block 1, Southlink Business Park, Hamilton Street, Oldham, OL4 1DE
- 0161 624 0414
- 0161 628 4655
- james.hill@toontasticpublishing.com

Parent Company Toontastic Publishing
Contact Managing Director, A. Young; Editor in Chief, James Hill
Insider Info A comic for 5–10 year olds, issued monthly, covering *Rugrats*, *Wild Thornberries* and *All Grown Up* characters. Present circulation is 30,000.
Non-fiction Publishes Puzzles and Competitions.
Fiction Publishes Comic strips.

Tips *Rugrats* comic prints comic strips based on the *Rugrats*, *Wild Thornberries* and *All Grown Up* television shows.

Scooby Doo
Panini House, Coach and Horses Passage, The Pantiles, Tunbridge Wells, TN2 5UJ
- 01892 500100
- 01892 545666
- collectorsed@panini.co.uk
- www.paninicomics.co.uk

Parent Company Panini UK Ltd
Editor Kate Rhead
Established 2003
Insider Info A comic for 6–9 year olds, issued every three weeks, covering *Scooby Doo* characters. Present circulation is 52,804.
Non-fiction Publishes Activities, Games and Puzzles.
Fiction Publishes Comic strips and Picture stories.
Submission Guidelines Visit their website for writer and illustrator submission guidelines. Any work must be relevant to licensed *Scooby Doo* characters. Do not send in any original work copies will not be returned.
Tips *Scooby Doo* comic is based on the popular animated television series, and contains stories and activities using the *Scooby Doo* characters.

Shaun the Sheep
Titan House, 144 Southwark Street, London, SE1 0UP
- 020 7620 0200
- 020 7620 0032
- shaun@titanemail.com
- www.titanmagazines.co.uk

Parent Company Titan Magazines
Editor Natalie Clubb
Established 2007
Insider Info A comic for 5–8 year olds, issued monthly, covering *Shaun the Sheep*.
Non-fiction Publishes Puzzles, Games and Activities.
Fiction Publishes Comic strips.
Tips *Shaun the Sheep* comic publishes comic strips and activities based on the *Shaun the Sheep* children's television show.

Spectacular Spider-Man
Panini House, Coach and Horses Passage, The Pantiles, Tunbridge Wells, TN2 5UJ
- 01892 500100
- 01892 545666
- specspidey@panini.co.uk

● www.paninicomics.co.uk
Parent Company Panini UK Ltd
Editor Ed Hammond
Insider Info A comic for 5–10 year old boys, issued every three weeks, covering *Spider-Man* characters. Present circulation is 70,000.
Non-fiction Publishes Activities, Games and Puzzles.
Fiction Publishes Comic strips.
Tips *Spectacular Spider-Man* publishes new *Spider-Man* comic strips based on the popular television show.

Spider-Man & Friends
Panini House, Coach and Horses Passage, The Pantiles, Tunbridge Wells, TN2 5UJ
● 01892 500100
● 01892 545666
● sfrith@panini.co.uk
● www.paninicomics.co.uk
Parent Company Panini UK Ltd
Editor Simon Frith
Established 2006
Insider Info A comic for 3–5 year olds, with ten issues per year, covering pre-school activities.
Non-fiction Publishes Activities, Games and Puzzles.
Fiction Publishes Comic strips
Submission Guidelines Visit their website for writer and illustrator submission guidelines. Any work must be relevant to licensed *Spider-Man* characters. Do not send in any original work, copies will not be returned.
Tips *Spider-Man & Friends* uses popular *Spider-Man* comic book characters to tell pre-school friendly stories and activities. Each issue come with a free activity drawing book.

SpongeBob Squarepants
Titan House, 144 Southwark Street, London, SE1 0UP
● 020 7620 0200
● 020 7620 0032
● spongebob@titanemail.com
● www.titanmagazines.co.uk
Parent Company Titan Magazines
Editor Ned Hartley
Established 2004
Insider Info A comic for 4–11 year olds, issued monthly, covering *SpongeBob Squarepants*. Present circulation is 39,287.
Non-fiction Publishes Puzzles, Games, Activities, Cartoon news and Educational articles.
Fiction Publishes Comic strips and stories.

Tips *SpongeBob Squarepants* comic is mostly based on the popular children's television show, but does also contain news from the Cartoon Network and educational articles about the ocean and sea life.

Superman Legends
Titan House, 144 Southwark Street, London, SE1 0UP
● 020 7620 0200
● 020 7620 0032
● ned.hartley@titanemail.com
● www.titanmagazines.co.uk
Parent Company Titan Magazines
Editor Ned Hartley
Established 2007
Insider Info A comic for 8–12 year olds, issued monthly, covering DC Comics *Superman* characters. Present circulation is 30,000.
Fiction Publishes Comic strips.
Submission Guidelines Visit their website for writer and illustrator submission guidelines. Any work must be relevant to licensed *Superman* characters. Do not send in any original work, copies will not be returned.
Tips Publishes reprints of classic *Superman* comic strips.

TMNT
Titan House, 144 Southwark Street, London, SE1 0UP
● 020 7620 0200
● 020 7620 0032
● tmnt@titanemail.com
● www.titanmagazines.co.uk
Parent Company Titan Magazines
Insider Info A comic for 8–12 year olds, issued monthly, covering TMNT characters.
Non-fiction Publishes Reviews, Features, Puzzles and Competitions.
Fiction Publishes Comic strips.
Tips *TMNT* comic publishes comic strips featuring the *Teenage Mutant Ninja Turtles* characters, based largely on the recent film and television series. Also contains a variety of merchandise-related reviews and articles.

Tom & Jerry
Panini House, Coach and Horses Passage, The Pantiles, Tunbridge Wells, TN2 5UJ
● 01892 500100
● 01892 545666
● collectorsed@panini.co.uk
● www.paninicomics.co.uk

Parent Company Panini UK Ltd
Editor Jason Quinn
Insider Info A comic for 5–9 year olds, issued monthly, covering *Tom & Jerry* characters. Present circulation is 30,000.
Non-fiction Publishes Activities, Games and Puzzles.
Fiction Publishes Comic strips.
Submission Guidelines Visit their website for writer and illustrator submission guidelines. Any work must be relevant to licensed *Tom & Jerry* characters. Do not send in any original work, copies will not be returned.
Tips *Tom & Jerry* comic is based on the popular animated characters, and features a variety of comic strips, competitions and free gifts.

Tractor Tom
Panini House, Coach and Horses Passage, The Pantiles, Tunbridge Wells, TN2 5UJ
- 01892 500100
- 01892 545666
- collectorsed@panini.co.uk
- www.paninicomics.co.uk
Parent Company Panini UK Ltd
Editor Jason Quinn
Insider Info A comic for 3–5 year olds, issued monthly, covering *Tractor Tom* characters. Present circulation is 60,000.
Non-fiction Publishes Competitions, Games and Puzzles.
Fiction Publishes Comic strips.
Submission Guidelines Visit their website for writer and illustrator submission guidelines. Any work must be relevant to licensed *Tractor Tom* characters. Do not send in any original work, copies will not be returned.
Tips *Tractor Tom* comic is based on the popular television show of the same name. Each issue comes with a free gift.

Transformers
Titan House, 144 Southwark Street, London, SE1 0UP
- 020 7620 0200
- 020 7620 0032
- transformers@titanemail.com
- www.titanmagazines.co.uk
Parent Company Titan Magazines
Established 2007
Insider Info A comic, issued monthly, covering *Transformers* characters.
Non-fiction Publishes Reviews, Interviews, Features, Puzzles and Competitions.
Fiction Publishes Comic strips.

Tips *Transformers* comic contains original comic strips based on the recent *Transformers* movie, rather than the original comics. It also includes features, reviews, interviews and other information about the movie.

Ultimate Spider-Man & X-Men
Panini House, Coach and Horses Passage, The Pantiles, Tunbridge Wells, TN2 5UJ
- 01892 500100
- 01892 545666
- collectorsed@panini.co.uk
- www.paninicomics.co.uk
Parent Company Panini UK Ltd
Insider Info A comic, issued monthly, covering *Spider-Man* and *X-Men* characters.
Fiction Publishes Comic strips.
Tips *Ultimate Spider-Man & X-Men* contains re-imaginings of the original comic strips, using digital art in preference to hand illustration.

Wallace and Gromit Comic
Titan House, 144 Southwark Street, London, SE1 0UP
- 020 7620 0200
- 020 7620 0032
- crackingpost@titanemail.com
- www.titanmagazines.co.uk
Parent Company Titan Magazines
Insider Info A comic, issued monthly, covering *Wallace & Gromit* characters.
Non-fiction Publishes Games, Puzzles features and Competitions.
Fiction Publishes Comic strips and Picture stories.
Tips *Wallace & Gromit* comic is based on the animated films from Aardman Animations. Each issue comes with a free gift.

Wolverine & Deadpool
Panini House, Coach and Horses Passage, The Pantiles, Tunbridge Wells, TN2 5UJ
- 01892 500100
- 01892 545666
- collectorsed@panini.co.uk
- www.paninicomics.co.uk
Parent Company Panini UK Ltd
Editor Scott Gray
Insider Info A comic for teenagers, issued monthly, covering the *Wolverine* and *Deadpool* characters.
Fiction Publishes Comic strips.
Tips *Wolverine & Deadpool* reprints classic Marvel comic strips, aimed at the over 12s.

Chill Out

Premier Newspapers, Napier House, 2 Auckland Park Bond Avenue, Bletchley, Milton Keynes, MK1 1BU

- 01908 651270
- 01908 632214
- karen.jeffery@mkcitizen.co.uk
- www.miltonkeynes.co.uk

Editor Karen Jeffery
Established 1992
Insider Info A newspaper for 8–12 year olds, with three issues per year, covering local event and activity listings and entertainment. Present circulation is 25,000.
Tips *Chill Out* is distributed to all children living in the Milton Keynes area during the March, July and October school holidays. It aims to provide local event listings and suggestions of what to do during the holidays.

Clonc

Ty Cerrig, Cwmann, Llanybydder, SA48 9SX

- 01570 480590

Editor Eifion Davies
Insider Info A local newspaper, issued monthly (excepting January and August), covering regional news and events. Has a children's corner. Present circulation is 900.
Tips *Clonc* is a Welsh language paper serving the Lampeter district. It has a children's corner that prints features, articles and event listings for younger readers.

First News

Newsbridge Ltd, First News House
95 The Street, Horsley, Surrey, KT24 6DD

- 01483 281005
- nicky.cox@firstnews.co.uk
- www.firstnews.co.uk

Editor Nicky Cox
Contact Editorial Director, Piers Morgan; Deputy Editor, Gabrielle Utton; Editorial Assistant, Kirsty MacDonald
Established 2006
Insider Info A newspaper for 7–14 year olds, issued weekly, covering news, reviews, features, problem pages, media reviews, travel, sports reports, competitions, current affairs and celebrity gossip. Present circulation is 200,000. Free sample is available free by download. Media pack is available on request.
Tips *First News* is a high profile, hard hitting newspaper aimed at children and teenagers. It is available from UK schools and news stands, and aims to encourage children to take an interest in world affairs.

Headliners

Exmouth House, 3–11 Pine Street, London, EC1R 0JH

- 020 7833 2577
- 020 7278 7722
- enquiries@headliners.org
- www.headliners.org

Contact Editorial Director, Oliver Benson
Established 1994
Insider Info A news charity for 8–18 year olds, covering News, Interviews, Journalism, Current affairs and Social comment.
Tips *Headliners*, formerly known as *Children's Express*, is a news charity for children that enables young people to produce journalism and social comment for publication in print and broadcast media. *Headliners* was relaunched at the beginning of 2007 as a website, but also has offices in London, Belfast and Foyle.

Newsademic

Newsademic.com, Hill House
210 Upper Richmond Road, London, SW15 6NP

- 020 8816 8781
- 020 8789 5326
- admin@newsademic.com
- www.newsademic.com

Insider Info A global newspaper, issued fortnightly, covering; International news and Current affairs.
Submission Guidelines Submit topical/international news stories via their online form. No payment is offered, but a byline is given.
Tips *Newsademic* is an international newspaper for young readers, or people learning the English language. It is delivered by email as a PDF file, or available to subscribers online. It is available in either UK English or American English. They will accept topical articles as long as they have an international appeal, and are written in a similar style to the rest of the newspaper.

The Newspaper
Young Media Holdings Ltd, Peregrine House Peel Road, Douglas, Isle of Man, IM1 5EH
- ☎ 0845 094 0646
- ☏ 0845 286 2684
- ✉ tracey@young-media.co.uk
- 🌐 www.thenewspaper.org.uk

Editor Buffy Whiting
Contact Managing Editor, Tracey Comber
Established 2000
Insider Info A newspaper for 8–14 year olds, issued bi-monthly, covering News, Interviews, Reviews and Current Affairs. Present circulation is 150,000.
Submission Guidelines Accepts features and short news stories of 800–1,000 words. No payment offered.
Tips *The Newspaper* is a bi-monthly newspaper for young children, designed to be used as a teaching aid in the classroom. It supports Key Stage 2 and 3 in English, Literacy and Citizenship.

OINK!
Oink News Corporation Ltd, PO Box 47368 London, NW3 6YW
- ☎ 0870 755 0810
- ✉ mail@oinknewscorp.com
- 🌐 www.piggybank.co.uk

Editor Ernest Henry
Established 2002
Insider Info A business newspaper for 7–12 year olds, issued monthly, covering; Business, Finance, Money matters, Features, Reviews and Interviews. Present circulation is 100,000.
Tips *OINK!* is a business magazine aimed at children. As such it contains articles about personal finance, taxes and other money matters. It also prints opinion articles and satire, with the aim of educating children about politics.

Papur y Cwm
Brynteg, Heol Maes-y-Bont, Castell-y-Rhingyll, Llanelli, SA14 7NA
- ☎ 01269 842151
- ☏ 01269 832170
- ✉ dafyddthomas@btopenworld.com

Editor Dafydd Thomas
Contact Deputy Editor, Sian Thomas
Established 1982
Insider Info A local newspaper, issued monthly (excepting August and September), covering; Local news, Regional news, Sports, Arts and Events. Has a Children's corner. Present circulation is 1,000.

Tips *Papur y Cwm* is aimed at Welsh language speakers living in the Llanelli district. It has a children's corner that prints features and articles for younger readers, including schooling information.

Plu'r Gweunydd
Eirianfa, New Road, Llanfair Caereinion, Welshpool, SY21 0SB
- ☎ 01938 810048
- ☏ 01938 810785
- ✉ clicied@computerserve.com

Editor Mary Steele
Insider Info A local newspaper, issued monthly (except August), covering local news and Welsh language learning. Has a Children's corner. Present circulation is 750.
Tips *Plu'r Gweunydd* is a Welsh language paper serving the Llanfyllin and Welshpool districts. It has a children's corner that prints features and articles for younger readers.

Young Voices
Gleaner Voice Group UK Ltd, 6th Floor Northern & Shell Tower, 4 Selsdon Way, London, E14 9GL
- ☎ 020 7510 0340
- ☏ 020 7510 0341
- ✉ newsdesk@gvmedia.co.uk
- 🌐 www.young-voices.co.uk

Editor Dionne Grant
Contact Assistant Editor, Rodney Hinds
Established 2003
Insider Info A newspaper for 11–19 year olds, issued monthly, covering; Lifestyle, Celebrity gossip, News, Interviews, Reviews and Current affairs. Present circulation is 150,000.
Tips *Young Voices* is a national newspaper for black Britons, which covers teenage lifestyle, with a particular focus on urban music and fashion.

Y Rhwyd
Ty Daffydd, Valley, Holyhead, LL65 3EY
- ☎ 01407 742040

Editor Arthur Roberts
Insider Info A local newspaper, issued monthly (excepting January and September), covering; Local News, Nature and Sports. Also publishes Children's columns. Present circulation is 1,350.
Tips *Y Rhwyd* is aimed at Welsh language speakers living in North West Anglesey. It prints children's columns on sports, nature and local events.

Y Tincer

Tincer Committee, Rhos Helyg
23 Maes Yr Efail, Penrhyn-coch, Aberystwyth, SY23 3HE
☎ 01970 828017
✉ rhoshelyg@btinternet.com
Editor Ceris Gruffudd

Established 1977
Insider Info A local newspaper, issued monthly (except July and August), covering; Local News and Events. Has a Children's corner. Present circulation is 1,200.
Tips *Y Tincer* is a Welsh language paper serving the Aberystwyth districts. It has a children's corner that prints features and articles for younger readers.

PACKAGERS

Aladdin Books

2–3 Fitzroy Mews, London, W1T 6DF
☎ 020 7383 2084
☏ 020 7388 6391
✉ alexandra.mew@aladdinbooks.co.uk
🌐 www.aladdinbooks.co.uk
Contact Managing Director, Charles Nicholas
Established 1979
Insider Info Aladdin Books Ltd creates highly illustrated non-fiction books for children aged from 1 to 16. The company focuses on reading schemes, and social, environmental and world issues.
Non-Fiction Subjects covered include: Maths, Science and Technology, Natural History, Arts, Crafts and Hobbies, Geography and Environment, General and Novelty.

The Albion Press Ltd

Spring Hill, Idbury, Oxfordshire, OX7 6RU
☎ 01993 831094
☏ 01993 831982
Contact Managing Director, Emma Bradford
Established 1984
Insider Info Specialises in children's books.
Submission Guidelines No unsolicited manuscripts or synopses.

Amber Books Ltd

Bradley's Close, 74–77 White Lion Street, London, N1 9PF
☎ 020 7520 7600
☏ 020 7520 7606/ 7607
✉ editorial@amberbooks.co.uk
🌐 www.amberbooks.co.uk
Contact Managing Director, Stasz Gynch
Insider Info Amber Books presents a broad range of illustrated non-fiction for children and adults.

Non-Fiction Children's books on History, Fantasy, Transport, Activity, Science and Nature and Technology.
Submission Guidelines Send a synopsis, contents list, a sample chapter or two, and a single page CV or resume to the Publishing Manager. Illustrators should send photocopies or photos to the Design Manager. Never send originals, no work will be returned, even with an SAE. All paper is recycled.
Tips Amber Books welcome good ideas on any non-fiction subject suitable for an illustrated book. No fiction, biography or poetry.

Bender Richardson White

PO Box 266, Uxbridge, UB9 5BD
☎ 01895 832444
☏ 01895 835213
✉ firstname@brw.co.uk
🌐 www.brw.co.uk
Contact Partner, Lionel Bender (Editorial); Partner, Ben White (Design)
Insider Info BRW produces around 70 titles per year (including adult books) for publishers around the world, and develops its own projects for the international co-edition market. It specialises in illustrated non-fiction for children and adults.
Non-Fiction Subjects covered include Educational resources, Home Learning materials, Dictionaries, Encyclopaedias, Computers, Science, History, Maths, English, Religion, Reference titles, Natural History, Activities.
Submission Guidelines Accepts query with a SAE.

Bookwork Ltd

Unit 7, Piccadilly Mill, Lower Street, Stroud, Gloucestershire, GL5 2HT
☎ 020 8771 5115
☏ 020 8771 9994
✉ bookwork@compuserve.com

Contact Director, Louise Pritchard (Editorial); Director, Alan Plank (Production); Editor, Annabel Blackledge; Art Editor, Kate Mullins
Insider Info Produces activity, board, novelty and reference books for children. Also packages under the Pangolin imprint.

Brainwaves Ltd
31 Chart Lane, Reigate, Surrey, RH2 7DY
- 01737 224444
- 01737 225777

Contact Keith Faulkner
Insider Info Packages children's activity, board, novelty, picture and gift books.

Breslich and Foss Ltd
Unit 2a Union Court, 20–22 Union Road, Clapham, London, SW4 6JP
- 020 7819 3990
- 020 7819 3998

Contact Directors, Paula Breslich, K.B. Dunning
Established 1978
Insider Info Breslich and Foss package in children's and adult's non-fiction.
Non-Fiction Children's subjects include General Non-fiction topics and picture books.
Submission Guidelines Ideas welcome, send synopses and a SAE.

Brown Reference Group (BRG)
8 Chapel Place, Rivington Street, London, EC2A 3DQ
- 020 7920 7500
- 020 7920 7501
- info@brownreference.com
- www.brownreference.com

Contact Managing Director, Sharon Hutton; Children's Publisher, Anne O'Daly; Editorial Director, Lindsay Lowe; Design Manager, Sarah Williams
Established 1995
Insider Info The Brown Reference Group (BRG) is a leading packager of high quality reference books and encyclopedias for all age groups, including titles for children.
Non-Fiction Children's subjects include Crafts, Encyclopedias, Science, Atlases, Music, Nature and Science.

Brown Wells & Jacobs Ltd
Foresters Hall, 25–27 Westow Street, London, SE19 3RY

- 020 8771 5115
- 020 8771 9994
- www.bwj.org

Contact Managing Director, Graham Brown
Established 1978
Insider Info Produces high quality non-fiction children's books. Package around 40 titles per year. Also packages under the Book Street imprint.
Non-Fiction Specialists in Children's Novelty and pop-up books.
Fiction Packages some Children's books with licenced characters.

Cambridge Publishing Management Ltd
Unit 2, Burr Elm Court, Main Street, Caldecote, Cambridgeshire, CB3 7NU
- 01954 214000
- 01954 214001
- firstinitial.lastname@cambridgepm.co.uk
- www.cambridgepm.co.uk

Contact Managing Editor, Jackie Dobbyne; Managing Editor, Karen Beaulah
Insider Info A creative book production company, offering a comprehensive service to publishers. Specialises in the complete project management of trade, travel, educational (including for children) and ELT titles.

Cowley Robinson Publishing Ltd
8 Belmont, Bath, BA1 5DZ
- 01225 339999
- 01225 339995
- stewart.cowley@cowleyhunter.com
- www.cowleyrobinson.com

Established 1998
Insider Info Produces children's novelty titles for the co-edition market, specialising in paper engineering and licensed character publishing.

Creations for Children/Inky Press
- info@inkypress.com
- www.inkypress.com

Insider Info Produces children's paper engineered non-fiction and illustration-led picture book titles for readers aged 0–9.
Submission Guidelines Accepts unsolicited submissions; send texts, illustrations or design concepts. Send hard copies (not originals) with a brief covering letter and a SAE. Aims to reply to submissions within three months.

David West Children's Books

7 Princeton Court, 55 Felsham Road, London, SW15 1AZ

- ☎ 020 8780 3836
- ☎ 020 8780 9313
- ⊙ dww@btinternet.com
- ⊛ www.davidwestchildrensbooks.com

Insider Info Produces highly illustrated children's information books produced specifically for the international market and designed for translation.

Non-Fiction Children's subjects covered include Mysteries and Ancient Civilisations, the Animal Kingdom, Cinema, History, Science, Aviation, Sports, Machines and Fashion.

Design Eye Ltd

226 City Road, London, EC1V 2TT

- ☎ 020 7812 8601
- ☎ 020 7253 4370
- ⊙ info@designeye.co.uk
- ⊛ www.quarto.com

Contact Publisher, Sue Grabham

Insider Info Design Eye publishes innovative interactive kit books for children and adults, often incorporating extras such as craft materials, moulded figures or working models.

Elm Grove Books Ltd

Elm Grove, Henstridge, Somerset, BA8 0TQ

- ☎ 01963 362498
- ⊙ hugh@elmgrovebooks.com

Contact Directors, Hugh Elwes, Susie Elwes

Established 1993

Insider Info Specialist children's book packager.

Emma Treehouse Ltd

Little Orchard House, Mill Lane, Beckington, Somerset, BA11 6SN

- ☎ 01373 831215
- ☎ 01373 831216
- ⊙ info@emmatreehouse.com
- ⊛ www.emmatreehouse.com

Contact Director, David Bailey; Creative and Editorial Director, Richard Powell

Established 1992

Imprints Treehouse Children's Books

Insider Info As well as publishing its own books under the Treehouse Children's Books imprint (see entry under Book Publishers), Emma Treehouse also packages children's novelty, pop-up and board books for international publishers.

Non-Fiction Publishes Children's Activity and Gift titles.

Fiction Publishes Children's Board books and Activity titles.

Graham Cameron Publishing & Illustration

The Studio, 23 Holt Road, Sheringham, Norfolk, NR26 8NB

- ☎ 01263 821333
- ☎ 01263 821334
- ⊙ enquiry@graham-cameron-illustration.com
- ⊛ www.graham-cameron-illustration.com

Contact Partners, Mike Graham-Cameron, Helen Graham-Cameron, Duncan Graham-Cameron

Established 1985

Insider Info As well as being an illustration agency, Graham Cameron also packages illustrated books, both fiction and non-fiction, for children.

Non-Fiction Deals with Educational, Reference, Activity and Picture books.

Fiction Deals with Picture books and Activity books.

Hart McLeod Ltd

14 Greenside, Waterbeach, Cambridge, CB5 9HP

- ☎ 01223 861495
- ☎ 01223 862902
- ⊙ inhouse@hartmcleod.co.uk
- ⊛ www.hartmcleod.co.uk

Contact Partners, Graham Hart, Chris McLeod, Joanne Barker

Insider Info A leading supplier of editorial, design and production services in the UK. The company is at the forefront of developments in interactive publishing for UK schools. It produces around 200 titles a year, largely revision books and school texts.

Hawcock Books

Grafton House, High Street, Norton St. Philip, Nr. Bath, BA2 7LG

- ☎ 01373 834055
- ☎ 01373 834622
- ⊙ online form
- ⊛ www.hawcockbooks.co.uk

Insider Info Packager specialising solely in pop-up, novelty and paper engineering designs for the publishing industry.

HL Studios Ltd

17 Fenlock Court, Blenheim Office Park, Long Hanborough, Oxfordshire, OX29 8LN

☎ 01993 881010
🖷 01993 882713
✉ info@hlstudios.eu.com
🌐 www.hlstudios.eu.com
Contact Managing Director, Robin Hickey
Established 1985
Insider Info HL Studios Ltd specialise in educational titles, general non-fiction co-editions and multimedia.
Non-Fiction Subjects include: Primary, Secondary and Academic Education.

Interpretation
84a Hough Green, Chester, CH4 8JW
☎ 01244 676741
✉ tony@heritageinterpretation.co.uk
🌐 www.heritageinterpretation.co.uk
Contact Tony Bowerman
Insider Info Among other things, Interpretation conceive, write and develop children's non-fiction publications for organisations and publishers.
Non-fiction Specialisms include Historical, Natural and Environmental subjects.

John Brown
The New Boathouse, 136–142 Bramley Road, London, W10 6SR
☎ 020 7565 3000
🖷 020 7565 3060
🌐 www.jbcp.co.uk
Contact Director, Andrew Jarvis
Insider Info As well as being a well-known magazine publisher and PR firm, John Brown also packages children's part works and educational titles.

Marshall Editions Ltd
The Old Brewery, 6 Blundell Street, London, N7 9BH
☎ 020 7700 6764
🖷 020 7700 4191
✉ info@marshalleditions.com
🌐 www.quarto.com
Contact Publisher, Richard Green
Insider Info Marshall Editions publishes highly illustrated non-fiction books in co-edition for both adults and children.
Non-Fiction Subjects include titles on History, Natural History and Popular Science.

Mathew Price Ltd
The Old Glove Factory, Bristol Road, Sherborne, Dorset, DT9 4HP
☎ 01935 816010
🖷 01935 816310
✉ mathewp@mathewprice.com
🌐 www.mathewprice.com
Contact Managing Director, Mathew Price
Insider Info Produces novelty and picture books, educational titles and fiction for children up to eleven years old.

Miles Kelly Packaging Ltd
The Bardfield Centre, Great Bardfield, Essex, CM7 4SL
☎ 01371 811309
🖷 01371 811393
✉ info@mileskelly.net
🌐 www.mileskelly.net
Contact Publisher, Jim Miles; Publisher, Gerard Kelly
Established 1996
Imprint(s) Miles Kelly
 Bardfield Press
Insider Info As well as publishing its own titles (see entry under Book Publishers), Miles Kelly also packages illustrated children's books for other publishing companies.
Non-Fiction Publishes Children's Gift book and Reference titles.
Fiction Publishes Children's Illustrated titles.
Poetry Publishes Children's Illustrated Poetry.

Monkey Puzzle Media Ltd
Gissing's Farm, Fressingfield, Eye, Suffolk, IP21 5SH
☎ 01379 588044
🖷 01379 588055
✉ info@monkeypuzzlemedia.com
Contact Director, Roger Goddard-Coote
Established 1998
Insider Info Packager of non-fiction for trade, school, library and mass markets. Creates about 80 titles a year.

Nicola Baxter
PO Box 215, Framingham Earl, Yelverton, Norwich, NR14 7UR
☎ 01508 491111
Contact Proprietor and Commissioning Editor, Nicola Baxter; Submissions, Sally Delaney

Insider Info Deals with the packaging of children's books, from concept to production.

Orpheus Books Ltd
6 Church Green, Witney, Oxfordshire, OX28 4AW
- 01993 774949
- 01993 700330
- info@orpheusbooks.com
- www.orpheusbooks.com

Contact Executive Director, Nicholas Harris
Established 1992
Insider Info Orpheus Books are known for their unique concepts and use of die cuts, flaps and foldouts. The company list has a wide ranging subject matter, for children from 3 to 12 years. Orpheus also produces high quality encyclopedias and atlases.
Submission Guidelines Freelance writers should send their CVs. Illustrators should send sample copies.

Pinwheel Limited
Winchester House, 259–269 Old Marylebone Road, London, NW1 5XJ
- 020 7616 7200
- 020 7616 7201
- www.pinwheel.co.uk

Parent Company Alligator Books
Contact Managing Director, Andrew Flatt
Imprint(s) Pinwheel Children's Books
 Andromeda Children's Books
 Gullane Children's Books
Insider Info As well as publishing its own children's books under the Gullane and Andromeda imprints (see entry under Book Publishers), Pinwheel also packages novelty, illustrated children's books for international publishers.
Non-Fiction Packages Children's, Cloth, Novelty, Gift, Illustrated, Reference, Dictionary and General Non-Fiction titles on the following subjects:
 Baby and Child's Early Learning, Religion, Natural History.
Fiction Packages Children's Picture book and Illustrated Fiction titles.

Playne Books Ltd
Park Court Barn, Trefin, Haverfordwest, Pembrokeshire, SA62 5AU
- 01348 837073
- 01348 837063
- playne.books@virgin.net
- www.playnebooks.co.uk

Contact Design and Production Director, David Playne; Editor, Gill Davies
Established 1987
Insider Info Produces early learning titles and novelty books for young children, but also highly illustrated adult non-fiction, on a range of subjects.

Quarto Children's Books
The Old Brewery, 6 Blundell Street, London, N7 9BH
- 020 7700 6700
- 020 7700 4191
- quartokids@quarto.com
- www.quartobooks.com

Contact Publisher, Katharine Milburn
Insider Info A co-edition publisher of innovative children's titles. Quarto produce highly illustrated paper engineered, novelty and component based titles for all ages from pre-school to 8+ years.
Non-Fiction Subjects include Educational and Reference topics that are generally curriculum-based for international markets.

Salariya Book Company Ltd
Book House, 25 Marlborough Place, Brighton, East Sussex, BN1 1UB
- 01273 603306
- 01273 693857
- salariya@salariya.com
- www.salariya.com

Contact Managing Director, David Salariya
Insider Info The Salariya Book Company is an award-winning publisher specialising in illustrated information books for children. In the UK it publishes under its own imprint, Book House, which was founded in 2002.
Non-Fiction Topics include Technology, Science, History, Earth and the Environment, and Animals.

Small World Design
72a Pope Lane, Penwortham, Lancashire, PR1 3DA
- 01772 750885
- 01772 750885
- Online form
- www.smallworlddesign.co.uk

Contact Partners, David Peet and Sue Chadwick
Established 1985
Insider Info A freelance design company who write, illustrate, design and package pre-school material, novelty books, big books, games, jigsaw puzzles, activity packs, licenced products, creative and

educational products. Also produces resource books for teachers.

Stonecastle Graphics Ltd
Highlands Lodge, Chartway Street, Sutton Valence, ME17 3HZ
- 01622 844414
- 01622 844414
- info@stonecastle-graphics.co.uk
- www.stonecastle-graphics.com

Contact Partners, Paul Turner and Sue Pressley
Insider Info Complete book design, photography, editorial, illustration and packaging service. Illustrated general non-fiction is commissioned for children and adults across a range of subjects.
Non-Fiction Children's subjects include Games, Activities, History, Nature, Science and Crafts.

Tangerine Designs Ltd
2 High Street, Freshford, Bath, BA2 7WE
- 01225 720001
- tangerinedesign@btinternet.com

Contact Managing Director, Christine Swift
Established 2000
Insider Info Packagers and co-edition publishers of children's books.
Submission Guidelines Accepts submissions with a SAE.

Tango Books Ltd
PO Box 32595, London, W4 5YD
- 020 8996 9970
- 020 8996 9977
- sales@tangobooks.co.uk
- www.tangobooks.co.uk

Contact Director, Sheri Safran (Children's Fiction, Non-Fiction)
Established 1982
Insider Info As well as publishing its own books (see entry under Book Publishers), Tango also package novelty children's books for international publishers.
Non-Fiction Packages Children's titles on a wide variety of subjects.
Fiction Packages Novelty titles.

Tony Potter Publishing Ltd
1 Stairbridge Court, Bolney Grange Business Park, Stairbridge Lane, Bolney, West Sussex, RH17 5PA
- 01444 232889
- 01444 232142
- info@tonypotter.com
- www.tonypotter.com

Contact Director, Tony Potter
Insider Info Tony Potter Publishing creates innovative paper based products and high quality books for the international co-edition market. Specialising in interactive books for children (from 1 to 12 years old), the company also publishes custom and own brand books for adults and children.
Recent Title(s) *Land Ahoy!* (Interactive information book), Duncan Crosbie (Author), Kay Dixie (Illustrator)
Submission Guidelines Tony Potter Publishing is happy to consider unsolicited ideas (although most of their work is generated in-house). Send ideas in hard copy form only and enclose a SAE.

Toucan Books Ltd
3rd Floor, 89 Charterhouse Street, London, EC1M 6HR
- 020 7250 3388
- 020 7250 3123
- info@toucanbooks.co.uk
- www.toucanbooks.co.uk

Contact Director, Robert Sackville West; Managing Director, Ellen Dupont
Established 1985
Insider Info Toucan Books has a leading reputation as a packager of illustrated reference titles. Specialising in international co-editions, Toucan commissions illustrated non-fiction for both children and adults. The company client list includes Reader's Digest and the BBC.
Recent Titles *The Periodic Table: Elements with style* (Children's Non-fiction)

Tucker Slingsby Ltd
5th Floor, Regal House, 70 London Road, Twickenham, TW1 3QS
- 020 8744 1007
- 020 8744 0041
- www.tuckerslingsby.co.uk

Insider Info A packager specialising in children's non-fiction, anthologies, religious and activity books. They also produce health and beauty titles for adults.

Working Partners Ltd
1 Albion Place, London, W6 0QT
- 020 8748 7450
- 020 8748 7450
- enquiries@workingpartnersltd.co.uk
- www.workingpartnersltd.co.uk

Contact Managing Directors, Chris Snowdon and Charles Nettleton

Established 1995

Insider Info A creative team dedicated to the development of quality commercial fiction, contracted to supply fully edited texts. Working Partners has created some of the most recognised series in children's fiction, for example the classic *Animal Ark* series. Working Partners Two was founded in 2006 to create novels across most adult genres, hopefully to recreate the successes of the children's list in the adult market.

Submission Guidelines No unsolicited manuscripts, although they will accept emailed CVs from freelance writers.

Zoe Books Ltd

15 Worthy Lane, Winchester, Hampshire, SO23 7AB

☎ 01962 851318

✉ enquiries@zoebooks.co.uk

🌐 www.zoebooks.co.uk

Contact Managing Director, Imogen Dawson

Insider Info Zoe Books creates and publishes quality full colour reference books, for children and young adults, and for trade and educational markets worldwide. The company specialises in series co-editions for the school and library markets.

Non-Fiction Children's subjects covered include: Food, Clothes, Crafts, Sports, Science, Geography, History, Travel and World Habitats

Recent Titles *The Science of Weather Series*; Titles include, *Drought and the Earth*, *Drought and People*, *Snow and the Earth*, *Snow and People*.

TELEVISION

The BBC
BBC Television Centre, Wood Lane, London, W12 7RJ

☎ 020 8743 8000

📧 firstname.lastname@bbc.co.uk

🌐 www.bbc.co.uk

Contact Director General, Mark Thompson; Deputy Director General, Mark Byford; Director, BBC Vision, Jana Bennett; Director of Sport, Roger Mosey; Director of BBC Future Media and Technology, Ashley Highfield; Creative Director, Alan Yentob

About The BBC as a whole is split into five areas: Radio and Music; Drama, Entertainment and Children's; Factual and Learning; Sport; and News. All information on commissioning in each of these areas can be found at: www.bbc.co.uk/commissioning.

Proposals from members of the public to BBC national programming may only be submitted in these three areas: Drama and comedy scripts, should be sent via the Writers Room (see listing); Entertainment formats, including quiz and game shows should be sent to: Format Entertainment Development Team, Room 4010, BBC Television Centre; and Factual entertainment treatments sent to: Factual Entertainment Development, Room 4010, BBC Television Centre. All other areas of programming, including most for children, are commissioned through independent production companies.

BBC Drama, Entertainment and Children's
BBC Television Centre, Wood Lane, London, W12 7RJ

☎ 020 8743 8000

📧 firstname.lastname@bbc.co.uk

Contact Controller, BBC Children's, Richard Deverell; Director, Drama Production, Nicolas Brown; Creative Director, Drama, Sally Woodward Gentle; Controller, In House Drama, John Yorke; Controller, BBC Fiction, BBC Vision, Jane Tranter; Controller, Entertainment Group, BBC Vision Studios, Jon Beazley; Creative Director, Entertainment Production, BBC Vision Studios, Karen Smit

CBBC
BBC Television Centre, Wood Lane, London, W12 7RJ

☎ 020 8743 8000

📧 firstname.lastname@bbc.co.uk

📧 cbbcanimation.submissions@bbc.co.uk

🌐 www.bbc.co.uk/cbbc

Contact CBBC Creative Director, Anne Gilchrist; Head of CBBC Drama and Animation, Jon East; Head of CBBC Co-productions and Acquisitions, Jesse Cleverly

About Aimed at children and young people, CBBC runs two commissioning rounds a year. Details of closing dates are posted on www.bbc.co.uk/commissioning. It is a self-commissioning, self-scheduling department, with programmes such as *Blue Peter* and *Grange Hill*. Independent producers may submit proposals to Anne Gilchrist, or Jon East for drama. Acquisitions and animation enquiries should be directed to Jesse Cleverly. A final decision will be given no longer than 20 weeks after receipt of the proposal. Children's drama is one of a few departments that accept unsolicited proposals from writers. See www.bbc.co.uk/writersroom/writing/submissions_other_childrens for submission guidelines.

CBeebies
BBC Television Centre, Wood Lane, London, W12 7RJ

☎ 020 8743 8000

📧 firstname.lastname@bbc.co.uk

🌐 www.bbc.co.uk/cbeebies

Contact Cbeebies Creative Director, Michael Carrington; Head of Cbeebies Acquisitions and Animation, Kay Benbow

About Aimed at a very young audience, content includes entertainment, drama, comedy and factual programming. Recent programmes include *Teletubbies* and *The Tweenies*. Cbeebies run two commissioning rounds a year, details of which appear on www.bbc.co.uk/commissioning. Independent producers may send proposals to Michael Carrington, and direct animation, or acquisition enquiries to Kay Benbow. Replies to proposals should be within five weeks. The department is one of few that still accept unsolicited proposals from writers themselves. For submission guidelines see: www.bbc.co.uk/writersroom/writing/submissions_other_cbeebies

Channel 4
124 Horseferry Road, London, SW1P 2TX
- 020 7396 4444
- 020 7306 8356
- www.channel4.com

Contact Director of Television, Kevin Lygo; Broadcasting Controller, Rosemary Newell; Head of Programmes, Julian Bellamy; Commissioning Editor, T4 and Music, Neil McCallum; Deputy Commissioning Editor, T4 and Music, Sangeeta Bhaskar; Editor, T4 and Music, Cath Lovesey

About Channel 4 first broadcast in 1981. It now broadcasts across the UK, except to parts of Wales covered by S4C. It is a free to air, public service channel, funded entirely by advertising revenue and sponsorship. In terms of its younger viewers, slots very early in the morning tend to cater for a very young audience with programmes such as *The Hoobs* and *The Treacle People*. Teenagers are catered for with the weekday soap *Hollyoaks*, produced by Lime Pictures, and the T4 branded programming, broadcast throughout weekend mornings and early afternoons. One of its digital channels, E4, also caters for teenage/young adult audiences.

All content is commissioned through independent production companies or producers. For up to date names and contact details of the entire Channel 4 commissioning structure, visit www.channel4.com/corporate/4producers where there are downloadable documents. For opportunities to showcase your talent to the channel, visit the website www.channel4.com/corporate/4talent, where you will find details of schemes, competitions and opportunities for members of the public.

E4
124 Horseferry Road, London, SW1P 2TX
- 020 7396 4444
- www.channel4.com/e4

Contact Head of E4, Danny Cohen; Editor, Ruby Kuraishe

About A digital station from Channel 4, which screens repeats from terrestrial television, as well as the original programming and first broadcasts of US programmes. For all commissioning details for independent producers, visit: www.channel4.com/corporate/4producers.

CITV
200 Gray's Inn Road, London, W1X 8HF
- 020 7843 8000
- 020 7843 8158
- www.citv.co.uk

Contact Chief Executive, Iona Jones; Director of Commissioning, Rhian Gibson

About CITV includes ITV's programming for children both on the main terrestrial channel and its own digital channel. At least 25 per cent of all ITV output is commissioned through independent producers and production companies. For details on the procedures, visit the 'producer's page' on the ITV website, www.itv.com.

Five
22 Long Acre, London, WC2E 9LY
- 020 7550 5555/0845 705 0505
- 020 7550 5554
- customerservices@five.tv, firstname.lastname@five.tv
- www.five.tv

Contact Chief Executive, Jane Lighting; Managing Director of Content, Lisa Opie; Director of Children's Programmes, Nick Wilson; Assistant, Children's Programming, Jessica Symons

About Five is the final terrestrial free to view channel, which launched in 1997. It is a major broadcaster of British children's animation and broadcasts 22 hours of children's programmes every week on the terrestrial channel, with a further 42 hours a week on the Five Life digital channel. These programmes come under the Milkshake brand, whose target audience is children between two and seven years old. Milkshake airs from 6am to 9am every weekday, 6am to 10am on Sunday, and 7am to 10am on Saturday on Five, and from 6am to 12pm daily on Five Life. Five commission, co-produce and acquire pre-school programming with co-productions being increasingly popular. Programmes include *Roary the Racing Car* and *Fifi and The Flowertots*. For details of submitting programme ideas (mainly for independent producers/companies), visit www.five.tv/aboutfive/producersnotes.

Of particular interest are strong storytelling pre-school animation – preferably 3D (model/claymation/cgi), although sometimes cell/2D will be considered. The director states that he likes 'programmes with a real tangibility about them – a sense that you can reach in and touch the characters.' Five are also interested in drama for four to seven year olds as well as pre-school docusoaps of around 25 episodes at five to seven minutes long. The director states that 'drama ideas should be big, bright and bold – with a hint of pantomime about them and probably quarter hours rather than half hours. I am not looking for a pre-school *Eastenders*!'. Presenter-led shows are not sought. Producers should send showreels of around one to two minutes on DVD or VHS by post, along with a CV.

Five Life
22 Long Acre, London, WC2E 9LY
- 020 7550 5555/0845 705 0505
- 020 7550 5554
- customerservices@five.tv
- www.five.tv/life

Contact Controller, Nick Thorogood
About Broadcasts children's programs under the Milkshake brand. See the main Five entry for more details.

GMTV
London Television Centre, Upper Ground, London, SE1 9TT
- 020 7827 7000
- 020 7827 7249
- firstname.sirname@gmtv.co.uk
- www.gm.tv

Contact Managing Director, Paul Corley; Director of Programmes, Peter McHugh; Managing Editor, John Scammell; Editor, Martin Frizell
About GMTV owns ITV1's breakfast franchise and has been broadcasting since 1993. It is owned by ITV Plc and Disney. GMTV2 is broadcast on ITV2, the network's digital channel. Children's programming is branded *Toonatik*, and is broadcast on weekday mornings on GMTV2 and weekend mornings on GMTV.

Radio Telef's Éireann (RTÉ)
Donnybrook, Dublin 4, Republic of Ireland
- 00353 1 208 3111
- 00353 1 208 3080
- info@rte.ie, youngpeoples@rte.ie
- www.rte.ie

Contact Director General, Cathal Goan; Managing Director, Television, Noel Curran; Commissioning Editor, Young People's Programming, Sheila de Courcy; Assistant Commissioning Editor, Factual/Young Peoples, Tonyia Dowling

About Ireland's public service broadcaster, which outputs content on television, radio and the internet. Children's output includes *Den Tots*, pre-school entertainment for young children shown on RTÉ Two on weekdays from 9am and *The Den*, aimed at slightly older children. *The Den* airs on RTÉ Two on weekdays from 6.00am. TTV is a brand of programming aimed at older children and teens, aiming to keep up to date on all the latest in sports, careers, showbiz gossip, movies, music, web trends, gadgets fads and entertainment. It airs on RTÉ Two on weekdays, from 5.30pm. Overall, programmes are designed to appeal to specific audience groups, namely the under fives; under eights; under twelves; teens and young adults. Programmes can be both live action and animation. Particular attention is paid to programming during school holidays and the interactive elements of all programming. The website states: 'When considering programme ideas for this schedule, key words include original; humour; unpredictable; safe; relevant; viewer ownership; smart.' For full details on commissioning for independent producers, including commissioning rounds and procedures, visit the website: www.rte.ie/commissioning.

S4C
Parc Ty Glas, Llanishen, Cardiff, CF14 5DU
- 029 2074 7444
- 029 2075 4444
- s4c@s4c.co.uk
- www.s4c.co.uk

Contact Chief Executive, Iona Jones; Director of Commissioning, Rhian Gibson
About Currently a channel broadcast in Wales, in place of Channel 4. As such, rescheduled Channel 4 content makes up some of the programming, as do outputs from ITV Wales and the BBC. The majority of programmes are commissioned from independent producers, including some for children. In 2009, at the time of the digital switchover, S4C will cease showing Channel 4 programmes, as Channel 4 will then be available in Wales. To contact Rhian Gibson, Director of Commissioning, approach Gwerfyl Griffiths at rhaglennide@s4c.co.uk, or on 029 2074 1422. For details on the commissioning procedures for independent producers, visit www.s4c.co.uk/production.

BabyTV
Baby Network Limited, PO Box 51770, London, NW1 6US
- info@babytvchannel.com

www.babytvchannel.com
About A channel aimed at providing 24 hour programming for the under threes.

Boomerang
Turner House, 16 Great Marlborough Street, London, W1W 8HF
- 020 7693 1000
- 020 7693 1001
- www.boomerangtv.co.uk

About A 24 hour cartoon channel, it broadcasts mainly from Warner Brothers and Hanna-Barbera archives.

Cartoon Network
Turner House, 16 Great Marlborough Street, London, W1W 8HF
- 020 7693 1000
- 020 7693 1001
- www.cartoon-network.co.uk

About A cartoon channel owned by Turner Entertainment, a division of Time Warner. Cartoon Network + 1 broadcasts the same programming with a one hour delay.

Cartoon Network Too
Turner House, 16 Great Marlborough Street, London, W1W 8HF
- 020 7693 1000
- 020 7693 1001
- www.cartoon-network.co.uk

About A spin off channel from Cartoon Network, broadcasting a mixture of archived cartoons and identical programming to its sister channel.

Discovery Kids
Discovery House, Chiswick Park Building 3, 566 Chiswick High Road, London, W4 5YB
- 020 8811 3000
- 020 8811 3100
- firstname_lastname@discovery-europe.com
- www.discoverykids.co.uk

Contact News Editor and Press Officer, Caroline Watt
About Television, which encourages children to 'find out' and 'discover', whilst having fun. It is a broadly educational channel. Programme ideas should be registered at http://producers.discovery.com or sent to The Commissioning Editor, Commissioning Department.

Disney Channel
Building 12, 2nd Floor, 566 Chiswick High Road, London, W4 5AN
- 0870 880 7080
- studio@disneychannel.co.uk
- www.disneychannel.co.uk

Contact Managing Director (Disney TV Europe), John Hardie; Executive Producer, Steve Wynne
About Live action shows, animations and original films make up the content for this children's channel. Also broadcasts Disney Channel + 1, which shows the same programmes one hour later.

Disney Cinemagic
Building 12, 2rd Floor, 566 Chiswick High Road, London, W4 5AN
- 0870 880 7080
- studio@disneychannel.co.uk
- www.disney.co.uk/DisneyChannel/cinemagic

Contact Managing Director (Disney TV Europe), John Hardie
About Broadcasts live action and animated Disney films.

Five
22 Long Acre, London, WC2E 9LY
- 020 7550 5555/0845 705 0505
- 020 7550 5554
- customerservices@five.tv
- www.five.tv

Contact Chief Executive, Jane Lighting; Managing Director of Content, Lisa Opie
About Five is the final terrestrial free to view channel, which launched in 1997. For details of submitting programme ideas (mainly for independent producers/companies) visit www.five.tv/aboutfive/producersnotes.
 The site contains controller level contacts and development priorities in all areas of programming. Each controller specifies how to submit ideas in their area. Response time is around four weeks.

Jetix
Building 12, 2nd Floor, 566 Chiswick High Road, London, W4 5AN
- webmaster_uk@jetixeurope.net
- www.jetix.co.uk

Contact UK Managing Director, Boel Ferguson
About Digital channel dedicated to children's programming. Also broadcasts Jetix + 1, a channel showing identical programmes to Jetix, but running

one hour later. The Walt Disney Company owns a 75 per cent share in the channel.

MTV
180 Oxford Street, London, W1D 1DS
- 020 7478 6000
- 020 7478 6007
- contact@mtvne.com
- www.mtv.co.uk

Contact Managing Director, MTV UK and Ireland, Michiel Bakker; VP MTV Channels, Michael Barry; Executive Producer and News Editor, Lisa Stokoe

About A music television channel aimed at teenagers and young adults, broadcasting music videos, documentaries, comedy and celebrity related programming. Also broadcasts live studio programmes.

MTV2
180 Oxford Street, London, W1D 1DS
- 020 7478 6000
- 020 7478 6007
- contact@mtvne.com
- www.mtv.co.uk/channel/mtv2

Contact Managing Director, MTV UK and Ireland, Michiel Bakker; VP MTV Channels, Michael Barry; Executive Producer, Jamie Rae; News Editor, Joleen Moore

About A music television channel focused around new and alternative music. Aimed at teenagers and young adults.

MTV Base
180 Oxford Street, London, W1D 1DS
- 020 7478 6000
- 020 7478 6007
- contact@mtvne.com
- www.mtv.co.uk/mtvbase

Contact Managing Director, MTV UK and Ireland, Michiel Bakker; VP MTV Channels, Michael Barry

About A music television channel focused on urban music, aimed at teenagers and young adults.

MTV Dance
180 Oxford Street, London, W1D 1DS
- 020 7478 6000
- 020 7478 6007
- contact@mtvne.com
- lastname.firstname@mtvne.com
- www.mtv.co.uk/channel/mtvdance

Contact Managing Director, MTV UK and Ireland, Michiel Bakker; VP MTV Channels, Michael Barry; News Editor and Press Officer, Zoe Stafford

About A music television channel focused on dance music, aimed at teenagers and young adults.

MTV Flux
180 Oxford Street, London, W1D 1DS
- 020 7478 6000
- 020 7478 6007
- contact@mtvne.com
- www.mtv.co.uk/channel/flux

Contact Managing Director, MTV UK and Ireland, Michiel Bakker; VP MTV Channels, Michael Barry; Controller of Programmes, Steve Shannon

About A music video channel that allows viewers to publish messages and video content, via mobile phone or the internet. These then play alongside music videos of the viewers' choice. The channel is aimed at teenagers and young adults.

MTV Hits
180 Oxford Street, London, W1D 1DS
- 020 7478 6000
- 020 7478 6007
- contact@mtvne.com
- www.mtv.co.uk/hits

Contact Managing Director, MTV UK and Ireland, Michiel Bakker; VP MTV Channels, Michael Barry

About A chart music channel. Features requests, competitions, features, a forum and charts. Aimed at teenagers and young adults.

Nick Jr.
15–18 Rathbone Place, London, W1T 1HU
- 020 7462 1000
- 020 7462 1030
- howard.litton@nickelodeon.co.uk
- www.nickjr.co.uk/primary/nickjr.aspx

Contact Director of Channels, Howard Litton; News Editor, Louise Condon

About A digital channel for pre-school children, which aims to combine entertainment with learning and development. Much of the programming is produced in collaboration with child development experts.

Nickleodeon
15–18 Rathbone Place, London, W1T 1HU
- 020 7462 1000
- 020 7462 1030

howard.litton@nickelodeon.co.uk
www.nicktv.co.uk

Contact Director of Channels, Howard Litton; News Editor, Louise Condon

About A digital channel for children, broadcasting a mixture of live studio programmes, comedy dramas and animations.

Nicktoons

15–18 Rathbone Place, London, W1T 1HU
020 7462 1000
020 7462 1030
howard.litton@nickelodeon.co.uk
www.nick.co.uk/nicktoons

Contact Director of Channels, Howard Litton

About A digital channel for children broadcasting entirely animated shows.

Playhouse Disney

Building 12, 2nd Floor, 566 Chiswick High Road, London, W4 5AN
0870 880 7080
studio@disneychannel.co.uk
www.disney.co.uk/disneychannel/playhouse

Contact Managing Director, Disney TV Europe, John Hardie; Channel Manager, Jonathan Boseley

About Disney programmes for younger children.

Pop

37 Harwood Road, London, SW6 4QP
020 7371 5999
020 7736 6462
rorry@popclub.tv
www.popclub.tv

Contact Music Contact, Matt Howes; Press Officer, Francesca Newington

About A mixture of cartoons and pop music for children.

Sky One

Grant Way, Isleworth, TW7 5QD
0870 240 3000
0870 240 3060
www.skyone.co.uk

Contact Head of Sky 1, 2 and 3, Richard Woolfe; Commissioning Editor, Specialist Factual and Factual Entertainment, Emma Read; Commissioning Editor, Entertainment, Andrea Hamilton; Commissioning Editor, Drama, Elaine Pyke; Commissioning Editor, Features, Sky 1, 2 and 3, Donna Taberer; Commissioning Editor, Factual, Andrew O'Connell;

Commissioning Editor, Entertainment and Factual Entertainment, Steve Jones

About The UK's leading non-terrestrial channel, broadcasting a mixture of drama, factual and entertainment programming, including shows for children and teens. For independent production companies, all details of commissioning routes can be found at www.skyone.co.uk/commissioning, where the specific needs of individual commissioning editors are displayed.

Smash Hits

Mappin House, 4 Winsley Street, London, W1W 8HF
020 7436 1515
020 7376 1313
firstname.lastname@emap.com
www.smashhits-tv.co.uk

Contact Brand and Communications Director, Vikki Timmons; Commercial Manager, Katie Teesdale; Head of TV Radio Sponsorship and Promotions, Darren Kahn; Head of Press and PR Emap Radio, Maureen Corish; Director of Music, Simon Sadler; Programme Controller, Phil Poole; Programme Director, David Young

About A pop music video channel based around the same brand as the former teenage magazine, *Smash Hits*.

TG4

Baile na hAbhann, Co. na Gaillimhe, Republic of Ireland
00353 91 505050
00353 91 505021
eolas@tg4.ie
firstname.lastname@tg4.ie
www.tg4.ie

Contact Director of Television, Alan Esslemont; Commissioning Editor, Proinsias Ni Ghrainne; Commissioning Editor, Maire Ni Chonlain

About An Irish digital channel celebrating Irish storytelling, sport, music, drama and culture. Programmes are often in the Irish language. Programmes for children tend to be broadcast during the early morning slots. For submission information, visit www.tg4.ie/Bearla/Fais/fais. Submissions from independent companies are invited for documentaries, music, comedy, drama, soaps, lifestyle and travel. All submissions must be via the downloadable form on the website.

Tiny Pop

37 Harwood Road, London, SW6 4QP

- 020 7371 5999
- 020 7736 6462
- firstname@popclub.tv
- www.popclub.tv

Contact Music Contact, Matt Howes; Press Officer, Francesca Newington

About A mixture of cartoons and pop music for very young children. Formerly Pop Plus.

TMF

17–29 Hawley Crescent, London, NW1 8TT

- 020 7284 7777
- 020 7284 6466
- lastname.firstname@mtvne.com
- www.mtv.co.uk/tmf

Contact Controller of Programmes, Michael Barry; Programme Director, Jed Mahoney

About A digital music channel broadcasting music videos, entertainment and features on popular music. Aimed at teenagers and young adults.

Trouble

160 Great Portland Street, London, W1W 5QA

- 020 7299 5000
- 020 7299 5516
- firstname_lastname@flextech.co.uk
- www.trouble.co.uk

Contact Director of Programmes, Jonathan Webb; Channel Editor, Celia Taylor; News Editor and PR Manager, Jakki Lewis

About A children's digital channel broadcasting mainly US children's and teenage drama and comedies.

RADIO

BBC Radio and Music

BBC Broadcasting House, Portland Place, London, W1A 1AA

- 020 7580 4468
- firstname.lastname@bbc.co.uk

Contact Director of BBC Radio and Music, Jenny Abramsky CBE; Head of Compliance, Susan Binney; Finance Director, Jo Brindley; (Acting) Head of Rights and Business, Radio and Music, and Head of Talent Rights Group, Simon Hayward-Tapp; Head of Press and Publicity, Sue Lynas; Head of Radio Drama, Alison Hindell; Head of Radio Entertainment, Paul Schlesinger; Head of BBC Radio News, Stephen Mitchell; Head of Radio Current Affairs, Gwyneth Williams; Head of BBC Radio Sport, Gordon Turnball; Controller, BBC Popular Music, Lesley Douglas

BBC 1 Xtra

1 Xtra, PO Box 1X, London, W1A 1AA

- 020 7580 4468
- 1xtra@bbc.co.uk
- www.bbc.co.uk/1xtra

Contact Controller, 1 Xtra, Andy Parfitt; Managing Editor, Tarrant Steele; Commissioning Editor, Documentaries, Russell Crewe; News Editor, Angela Clark

About A digital station whose target audience is 16–24 year old fans of black music. Recent programmes include *Friday Night Mixtape* and *Uptown Anthems*.

Development priorities can be viewed at www.bbc.co.uk/commissioning. Most content is made in-house, although documentaries are made by a combination of freelancers, in-house producers and independent production companies. Documentaries are preferred in the first person narrative, and must be of direct relevance to the target audience. Commissioning rounds take place through the year, but a short synopsis may be submitted to Russell Crewe on 020 7765 5551 or by email, as an initial query before submitting through the RAP system.

BBC 7

Room 4015, BBC Broadcasting House, Portland Place, London, W1A 1AA

- 020 7580 4468
- firstname.lastname@bbc.co.uk
- www.bbc.co.uk/bbc7

Contact Controller, BBC 7, Mark Damazer; Head of Programmes and News Editor, Mary Kalemkerian; CBeebies Creative Director, Michael Carrington

About A digital radio station for comedy and drama, also incorporating CBeebies radio for young children from 2–5pm and the Big Toe Books programme from 7–8am on weekdays. All CBeebies branded programmes are aimed at children aged 0–6 years. For all commissioning needs, visit www.bbc.co.uk/commissioning and read the CBeebies page. This section includes needs for all platforms, including radio.

Fun Radio
One Passage Street, Bristol, BS2 0JF
- ☎ 0800 731 9721
- ✉ funradio@funradiolive.com
- 🌐 www.funradiolive.com

Contact Susan Stranks
About A radio station entirely for children, available on DAB digital radio in the following parts of the country: London, Essex, Berkshire, Wiltshire, Bristol, Cardiff, Kent, Sussex, Bournemouth, and on Sky Digital 0162 and Virgin Media (selected areas). Recent programmes include *Breakfast With Toby* and *Animal Hour*.

ANIMATION COMPANIES

Aardman Animations
Gas Ferry Road, Bristol, BS1 6UN
- ☎ 0117 984 8485
- ☎ 0117 984 8486

Contact Creative Director of Features, Sarah Smith
Established 1972
Insider Info Produces material for film and television. Specialists in animation, traditionally using models but more recently using CGI. Well-known characters include *Wallace and Gromit* and *Angry Kid*. Will not accept previously published material. Submissions will not be returned.
Submission Guidelines No unsolicited manuscripts.

Blue-zoo Productions
18 Rupert Street, London, W1D 6DE
- ☎ 020 7434 4111
- ✉ info@blue-zoo.co.uk
- 🌐 www.blue-zoo.co.uk

Contact Executive Producer, Daniel Isman
Established 2000
Insider Info Blue Zoo produces computer animations for television. Clients include the BBC and Nickelodeon. Also produces original material. Credits include *Blue Cow* and *Those Scurvy Rascals*, which received a BAFTA nomination for Best Children's Animation, and also received British Animation Awards for Best Children's Series, and the Children's Choice Award.

Calon Ltd
See entry under Production Companies

Collingwood O'Hare Entertainment
10–14 Crown Street, London, W3 8SB
- ☎ 020 8993 3666
- ☎ 020 8993 9595
- ✉ info@crownstreet.co.uk
- 🌐 www.collingwoodohare.com

Contact Managing Director & Producer, Christopher O'Hare; Writer & Director, Tony Collingwood; Head of Development, Helen Stroud
Established 1988
Insider Info A leading animation studio for children's television. Productions include *The Magic Key* for BBC and *Pond Life* for Channel 4.
Submission Guidelines No unsolicited submissions.
Tips Interested in new writing, although it is normally sourced through industry contacts or agents.

Cosgrove Hall Films
8 Albany Road, Chorlton cum Hardy, Manchester, M21 0AW
- ☎ 0161 882 2500
- ☎ 0161 882 2555
- ✉ animation@cosgrovehall.com
- 🌐 www.cosgrovehall.com

Parent Company Granada Media
Contact Managing Director, Anthony Utley
Established 1976
Insider Info Specialists in animation of all kinds, for film and television. Develops mainly children's programmes, although animation for adults is also produced.
Tips Cosgrove Hall has produced both series, such as *Andy Pandy* for CBeebies, and feature films such as *Roald Dahl's BFG*. Co-productions are becoming increasingly popular, as are series that have an international audience without alienating British audiences.

Entertainment Rights
See entry under Production Companies

Farnham Film Company

See entry under Production Companies

The Foundation TV Productions Ltd
The Maidstone Studios, Maidstone, Kent, ME14 5NZ
- 01622 691111
- 01622 684421
- enquiries@foundationtv.co.uk
- www.foundationtv.co.uk

Insider Info Produces educational and animated television and website content. Clients include the BBC. Credits include *The Basil Brush Show, Brilliant Creatures* and *Eureka TV*.
Tips Focuses mainly on web-based content, including Flash animation.

HIT Entertainment

See entry under Production Companies

Kickback Media
Silverlocks, Cradducks Lane, Staplehurst, Kent, TN12 0DN
- 01580 890107
- john@kickbackmedia.com
- www.kickbackmedia.com

Contact Managing Director, John Bullivant
Established 2002
Insider Info Kickback Media produces character and design based animated intellectual property for the children's and teenage market. Clients include Granada Media and Lego. Characters include *Captain Mack* and *Big Zofty*.
Tips Specialises in both 2D and 3D animation.

Loonland UK Ltd
3rd Floor Royalty House, 72–74 Dean Street, London, W1D 3SG
- 020 7434 2377
- 020 7434 1578
- tv-sales@tv-loonland.com
- www.loonland.com

Contact President/CEO, Simon Flamank; Managing Director, Olivier Dumont; Head of Production of TV-Loonland & Managing Director of Telemagination, Beth Parker
Insider Info Loonland UK produces animated children's and youth programming for television. Credits include *Cramp Twins, Jem, My Little Pony* and *Transformers*.

Tips Loonland UK is owned by German company TV-Loonland, which has offices all over the world. Loonland UK also incorporates the Telemagination studio, its main production arm (see separate entry).

Lupus Films
Studio 212, Black Bull Yard, 24–28 Hatton Wall, London, EC1N 8JH
- 020 7419 0997
- 020 7404 9474
- info@lupusfilms.net
- www.lupusfilms.net

Contact Directors, Camilla Deakin and Ruth Fielding
Established 2002
Insider Info Lupus Films produce animated features, shorts, and series, mainly for television. They work with puppetry and 2D techniques. Credits include *Combat Club* for Channel Five and *Meerkats Luvvies* for UKTV Documentaries.
Tips The vast majority of programming is aimed at young children and families. New projects in development are published on the website and give an idea as to current priorities.

Pesky Ltd
11 Morecambe Street, London, SE17 1DX
- 020 7703 2080
- hodge@pesky.com
- www.pesky.com

Contact Creative Director, David Hodgson; Animation Director, Claire Underwood
Established 1997
Insider Info Pesky produces Flash animation and cross-platform media for television and the Internet. Clients include the BBC, Channel 4, Cartoon Network, Philips and Nestlé. Credits include T*he Amazing Adrenalini Brothers, MissyMiss* and *Stress Maniacs*.
Tips Pesky do not have any submission guidelines available, but are always interested in meeting new animators and scriptwriters.

Ragdoll Ltd

See entry under Producers & Production Companies

Rubber Duck Entertainment
120 New Cavendish Street, London, W1W 6XX
- 020 7909 3773
- 020 7907 3777
- jlofts@rde.co.uk
- www.rde.co.uk

Contact Director, Joan Lofts; Head of Development & Production, Laura Campbell; Creative Development Executive, Alexi Wheeler

Insider Info Rubber Duck Entertainment produces animated programs for children. Clients include CITV and Five. Credits include *Bzots*, *Peppa Pig* and *Tractor Tom*. Part of the Contender Entertainment Group.

Submission Guidelines Send ideas for children's animation series with a comedy or action slant to Alexi Wheeler. Do not send original artwork. Current needs are programmes for children aged six to nine, and eight to twelve.

Submission details to: awheeler@rde.co.uk

Tips Although currently working on established projects, Rubber Duck are always looking out for new ideas. Be aware that the need for pre-school programming is not great at present.

Spellbound Entertainment Ltd

6 Primrose Mews, Sharpleshall Street, Primrose Hill, London, NW1 8YL

- 020 7483 2172
- 020 7483 2059
- info@spellbound.uk.com
- www.spellbound.uk.com

Contact Managing Director/Creative Director, Peter Curtis

Established 2001

Insider Info Spellbound Entertainment produces animated programming for international clients. Clients include the BBC, Disney Channel and ABC. Credits include *The Koala Brothers*.

Tips Primarily a rights holding company specialising in the ownership, creative management, distribution and merchandising of high quality children's and family programming.

Telemagination

Royalty House, 72–74 Dean Street, London, W1D 3SG

- 020 7434 1551
- 020 7434 3344
- mail@tmation.co.uk
- www.telemagination.co.uk

Parent Company Loonland UK Ltd

Contact Managing Director, Beth Parker

Established 1983

Insider Info Telemagination is a 2D animation studio, mainly producing content for children's television and occasionally producing feature films. Credits include *Heidi* (feature film) and *The Cramp Twins II* (series).

Submission Guidelines Animators, designers, storyboarders and digital artists should send in their CVs, a covering letter and samples of work if interested in working with Telemagination.

Tips Programmes tend to be aimed specifically at young children. View the filmography on the website for examples.

Tiger Aspect Productions

See entry under Production Companies

Walt Disney Company Ltd

See entry under Production Companies

PRODUCTION COMPANIES

ACP Television & Crosshands Ltd

Crosshands, Ludlow, Shropshire, SY8 3AR

- 01584 890893
- 01584 890893
- webmaster@acptv.com
- www.acptv.com

Contact Richard Uridge

Insider Info A producer of television and radio documentaries. Work has previously been broadcast on satellite channels such as UKTV Style.

Tips Contact Richard Uridge for more information on the company. Does not produce drama or other fictional programming.

All3Media

87–91 Newman Street, London, W1T 3EY

- 020 7907 0177
- 020 7907 0199
- information@all3media.com
- www.all3media.com

Contact Creative Director, David Liddiment

Established 2003

Insider Info Produces material for film and television. All3Media group encompasses a range of production companies: ARG; Bentley Productions; Cactus TV; Company Pictures; IdtV Productions; Lion Television; Lime Pictures; North One Television and

Pacific Pictures. Among them they produce high-profile programming nationally and internationally.
Tips All3Media's output is varied, depending on the subsidiary company involved. Visit each company's section of the website for further details, but be aware that much of the programming is commercially very high-profile. Examples include *Midsomer Murders* and *Richard and Judy*. Youth programmes include *Mad For It*, nominated for three RTS awards, and *Off the Wall*.

Available Light Productions Ltd
The Victorian Parade, 3a Boyce's Avenue, Clifton, Bristol, BS8 4AA
- 0117 908 4433
- info@availablelight.tv
- www.availablelight.tv

Contact Managing Director/Producer, David Parker; Production Manager, Sue Bennett
Established 1994
Insider Info Available Light Productions produces documentary and factual programmes for network television, as well as interactive media including web, CD and DVD projects. Clients include the BBC, Channel 4, Grid Club, ITV and Teachers TV. Credits include *Brunel's Big Achievements* and *Skills For Life*, both for Teachers TV.
Tips Aside from factual documentaries Available Light also specialise in producing Flash based e-learning websites for major broadcasters, including Teachers TV. *Brunels Britain*, a Teachers TV/Grid Club project, was nominated for a Childrens BAFTA in the interactive category at the 2006 awards.

Big Heart Media
Flat 4, 6 Pear Tree Court, London, EC1R 0DW
- 020 7608 0352
- 020 7250 1138
- info@bigheartmedia.com
- www.bigheartmedia.com

Contact Director of Programmes, Colin Izod
Established 1998
Insider Info Producers of educational, factual and dramatic programming for television, radio and the web. Clients include the BBC, Pearson Education, Teacher's TV and Channel 4.
Submission Guidelines Accepts query with synopsis by email only. No unsolicited manuscripts.
Tips Although the full catalogue is not available on the website, there are samples and clips of work across all media platforms, which give a sense of the style and content of the company's productions.

Calon Ltd
3 Mount Stuart Square, Butetown, Cardiff, CF10 5EE
- 029 2048 8400
- 029 2048 5962
- enquiries@calon.tv
- www.calon.tv

Contact Head of Development, Andrew Offiler
Insider Info Produces material for television – live action and animated drama, and entertainment for children.
Submission Guidelines Accepts query with synopsis. No unsolicited manuscripts.
Tips Formerly Siriol Productions, the focus has traditionally been on animated series such as *SuperTed* and *Hilltop Hospital*. Calon is now moving into live action programming. View clips in the production section of their website for programmes in development.

Children's Film and Television Foundation
Ealing Studios, Ealing Green, London, W5 5EP
- 07887 573479
- info@cftf.org.uk
- www.cftf.org.uk

Contact Chief Executive, Anna Home
Established 1951
Insider Info Produces films and television content for children, such as *The Borrowers* and *The Queen's Nose*, both for the BBC. The production archive is administered by Granada International.
Tips The most recent source of funding has stopped, therefore the Foundation are no longer undertaking new projects.

Childsplay Productions
8 Lonsdale Road, London, NW6 6RD
- 0831 600400

Contact Producer, Peter Tabern
Insider Info Childsplay Productions produces children's and family drama programmes for television. Clients include the BBC. Credits include *Feather Boy* and *Johnny and the Bomb*.
Tips Childsplay Productions specialise in high-profile adaptations of popular children's books, such as *Stig of the Dump* and Terry Pratchett's *Johnny and the Bomb*. These are often produced for the BBC, sometimes under the name Childsplay Television.

The Comedy Unit

Glasgow Media Park, Craigmont Street, Glasgow, G20 9BT

- ☎ 0141 305 6666
- ☏ 0141 305 6600
- ✉ info@comedyunit.co.uk
- 🌐 www.comedyunit.co.uk

Contact Marketing and Talent Manager, Claire Hancock

Established 1996

Insider Info The Comedy Unit produce comedy programmes for network and satellite television, radio and websites. Credits include *Chewin' the Fat* and *Rab C. Nesbitt*. The company works with 20 to 50 writers and performers per year and will accept previously published material. Submissions accompanied by SAE will be returned, although they will not send a catalogue to writers on request. The company aims to respond to queries within two days and submissions within 25 days. Payment is in accordance with industry standards.

Submission Guidelines For children's and youth formats submit a completed script. Email or postal submissions are welcome (email: gavinsmith@comedyunit.co.uk). Scripts themselves should be emailed as an attachment.

Endemol UK

Shepherd's Building Central, Charecroft Way, London, W14 0EE

- ☎ 0870 333 1700
- ☏ 0870 333 1800
- ✉ info@endemoluk.com
- 🌐 www.endemoluk.com

Contact Creative Director, Richard Osman

Insider Info Produces material for television, the web and digital content. Endemol are a leading producer of factual and entertainment formats for television, including *Big Brother* for Channel 4 and *Totally Frank* for Channel 4's T4. Endemol UK companies include Brighter Pictures, Cheetah Television, Endemol Gaming, Endemol Mobile, Hawkshead, Initial, Showrunner, Victoria Real, Zeppotron.

Tips Endemol's productions are largely very high profile and they are unlikely to commission unsolicited manuscripts. They do not tend to produce straight drama, although the Endemol company Zeppotron does produce comedy programming.

Entertainment Rights

Colet Court, 100 Hammersmith Road, London, W6 7JP

- ☎ 020 8762 6200
- ☏ 020 8762 6299
- ✉ info@entertainmentrights.com
- 🌐 www.entertainmentrights.com

Contact CEO, Michael Heap; Head of Creative Services, Sarah Slatter; Producer, Annika Bluhm

Established 1999

Insider Info Entertainment Rights produces animated and live action children's and family television. Clients include the BBC, Cartoon Network, Hasbro, Mattel, Nickelodeon and Scholastic. Credits include *3-2-1 Penguins!*, *Clifford the Big Red Dog* and *The Tweenies*.

Tips Entertainment Rights is one of the UK's leading specialist media companies. They own the rights to approximately 2,000 hours of programming, including characters such as *He-Man, Postman Pat* and *Rupert the Bear*. The company mainly focuses on purchasing rights to existing characters or shows, and unsolicited material is not likely to be successful.

Farnham Film Company

34 Burnt Hill Road, Lower Bourne, Farnham, GU10 3LZ

- ☎ 01252 710313
- ☏ 01252 725855
- ✉ info@farnfilm.com
- 🌐 www.farnfilm.com

Contact Company Directors, Ian Lewis and Melloney Roffe

Established 1985

Insider Info Producers of television programmes and occasional low budget feature films. Credits include *Gumdrop*, an animated children's series, and *Cafes of Europe*, a factual series. Submissions accompanied by SAE will be returned.

Submission Guidelines For feature films, submit full scripts. For series, submit one or two episodes (not the first) and a further six or so outlines. No email submissions.

Tips Particular needs are for feature films and children's television scripts including drama, comedy, animation and factual (but not game shows). Any children's ideas should have series potential. No unpublished or self-published novels, handwritten scripts or short films.

Film & General Productions Ltd

4 Bradbrook House, Studio Place, London, SW1X 8EL

- 020 7235 4495
- 020 7245 9853
- cparsons@filmgen.co.uk

Contact Producer, Clive Parsons
Established 1971
Insider Info Produces film and television drama for general audiences and children. Credits include *The Queen's Nose* for the BBC and the feature film *Tea with Mussolini*. Works with three scripts and writers per year and purchases film and television rights on accepted material. Will accept previously published material and submissions accompanied by SAE will be accepted. Aims to respond to queries within three days and submissions within two weeks. Writers will be paid for their work in accordance with industry standards. Will not send a catalogue to a writer on request.
Submission Guidelines Accepts query with synopsis.
Tips Do not send full scripts without querying first.

Ginger Productions

1st Floor 3 Waterhouse Square, 138–142 Holborn, London, EC1N 2NY

- 020 7882 1020
- 020 7882 1040
- production@ginger.com
- www.ginger.tv

Contact Creative Directors, Ed Stobart and Stephen Joel
Insider Info Produces factual entertainment and light entertainment television formats. Credits include *Jack Osbourne: Adrenaline Junkie* and *Whatever*, a children's entertainment magazine show. Owned by SMG productions.
Tips Ginger's style tends to be light hearted, humorous and aimed at a fairly young teenage/adult audience.

Granada Kids

The London Television Centre, Upper Ground, London, SE1 9LT

- 020 7620 1620
- www.granadamedia.com

Insider Info Granada Kids produces documentary, factual, drama and game show programmes, as well as some animation. Clients include the BBC, Channel 4, Five and Sky. Credits include *The Illustrated Mum* and *My Parents are Aliens*.

Tips Granada Kids is one of the largest commercial producers of children's television in the UK. Cosgrove Hall Films (see separate entry) is the animation house that produces all animated programming for Granada Kids.

Hi8us Projects Ltd

Ground Floor West, Towpath House, Limehouse Court, 3–11 Dod Street, London, E14 7EQ

- 020 7538 8080
- 020 7987 4522
- julia@hi8us.co.uk
- www.hi8us.co.uk

Insider Info Hi8us produces television programmes, short films, websites and DVD media projects. Clients include Channel 4 and Carlton Television. Credits include *L8R* and *Projecting Stoke*. Hi8us is a network organisation and has offices in London, Cornwall, the Midlands, the North and the South. Contact information for each office is available on the website.
Tips Hi8us gives young people across the UK the opportunity to gain experience of innovative media production. Projects are often aimed at a teenage audience.

HIT Entertainment

5th Floor Maple House, 149 Tottenham Court Road, London, W1T 7NF

- 020 7554 2500
- Online form
- www.hitentertainment.com

Contact Chairman, Greg Dyke; CEO, Bruce Steinberg
Established 1989
Insider Info HIT Entertainment produces children's entertainment programmes and animated series for network television. Clients include BBC2, Cbeebies and Nick Jr. Credits include *Angelina Ballerina, Barney & Friends, Bob the Builder, Pingu* and *Thomas & Friends*.
Submission Guidelines HIT Entertainment will only accept submissions through an agent, publisher or other content provider.
Tips HIT Entertainment is the world's leading independent children's producer and rights owner. The company is open to a wide range of ideas but is primarily interested in material aimed at pre-school children with long running series potential and a global appeal. Submission guidelines are available on the website, but HIT will only accept submissions through an agent or other similar representative.

Jam Creative

18 Soho Square, London, W1D 3QL
- 020 7439 1600
- mail@jamcreative.com
- www.jamcreative.com

Contact Jon Harvey; Eddie Marshall

Insider Info Jam Creative produces branded entertainment, commercials, programme sponsorships, and television idents, as well as short films for website and DVD media. Clients include The Discovery Channel, Nick Jr, Penguin and Persil. Credits include *Little Green Fingers* and the *Be My Coach* campaign for Persil.

Tips Jam Creative's core business is on-air marketing for broadcasters and blue chip clients, but they also create material for clients that is suitable for different media.

Libra Television

4th Floor, 22 Lever Street, The Northern Quarter, Manchester, M1 1EA
- 0161 236 5599
- 0161 236 6877
- hq@libratelevision.com
- www.libratelevision.com

Contact Managing Directors, Louise Lynch and Madeline Wiltshire

Established 1999

Insider Info Producers of children's television and educational programming. Credits include *Sci-Busters* for Discovery Kids and *How To Be A Bully* for the BBC education department.

Tips Broadcast outlets include Teacher's TV, the BBC, Discovery Kids, 4Learning, Channel 4 and CITV. People wishing to work or gain experience with children's television production should research the company carefully before sending their CV to the Managing Directors.

Ragdoll Ltd

Timothy's Bridge Road, Stratford upon Avon, CV37 9NQ
- 01789 404100
- 01789 404136
- info@ragdoll.co.uk
- www.ragdoll.co.uk

Contact Creative Director, Anne Wood

Established 1984

Insider Info Ragdoll produces live action, animated and puppetry programmes for young children. Clients include the BBC, Channel 4 and ITV. Credits include *Brum*, *In The Night Garden*, *Rosie & Jim*, *The Teletubbies* and *Tots TV*.

Tips Ragdoll specialise in producing programmes for pre-school children, and aim to have an international appeal.

SMG Productions

Pacific Quay, Glasgow, G51 1PQ
- 0141 300 3000
- website@smgproductions.tv
- www.smgproductions.tv

Contact Managing Director, Elizabeth Partyka

Insider Info Produces adult and children's television programming, including drama, documentaries, factual, and entertainment formats. Credits include *Funhouse* and *Taggart* for ITV. SMG Productions also incorporates Ginger Productions.

Tips SMG's range of programming is varied in style, however most output is broadcast on major terrestrial and satellite channels, often in prime time slots. Unsolicited manuscripts from new writers are unlikely to be picked up, due to the high profile needed for the shows.

Sunset & Vine Productions

Elsinore House, 77 Fulham Palace Road, London, W6 8JA
- 020 7478 7400
- 020 7478 7412
- enquiries@sunsetvine.co.uk
- www.sunsetvine.co.uk

Established 1983

Insider Info Produces sports television programming, including both live coverage and features for major broadcasters and entertainment formats. Credits include *The Tour de France* for ITV and *RAD* for Five.

Submission Guidelines No unsolicited manuscripts will be considered. Accepts commissions only.

Tips Sunset & Vine focus mainly on sports productions and does not often work on projects for children.

Talent Television

Lion House, 72–75 Red Lion Street, London, WC1R 4NA
- 020 7421 7800
- 020 7421 7811
- entertainment@talenttv.com
- www.talenttv.com

Contact Creative Director, John Kaye-Cooper

Established 2002

Insider Info Produces entertainment and factual television programmes for UK and international broadcasters. Credits include *Skatoony* for the Cartoon Network and *Best of Friends*.

Tips No drama or fictional output will be accepted. A full back catalogue is published on the website.

Television Junction
Waterside House, 46 Gas Street, Birmingham, B1 2JT

☎ 0121 248 4466
☎ 0121 248 4477
✉ info@televisionjunction.co.uk
🌐 www.televisionjunction.co.uk

Contact Managing Directors, Yvonne Davies and Paul Davies
Established 1997
Insider Info Produces material for television, websites, DVD, CD-ROM and print, including educational programming for television. Credits include *What's So Good About Jacqueline Wilson?* for Channel 4.
Submission Guidelines Television Junction is happy to receive and review programme ideas.
Tips Programmes should be educational. Productions include documentaries, animation and drama. Two of the main broadcast routes are Teachers' TV and Channel 4 daytime.

Tiger Aspect Productions
7 Soho Street, London, W1D 3DQ

☎ 020 7434 6700
☎ 020 7434 1798
✉ general@tigeraspect.co.uk
🌐 www.tigeraspect.co.uk

Contact Managing Director, Andrew Zein
Insider Info Producers of comedy, drama, entertainment, factual, animation and wildlife programming for television, and feature films. Credits include *Charlie and Lola* for CBeebies and *Animated Mr Bean* for ITV.
Submission Guidelines Accepts agented submissions only.
Tips No unsolicited manuscripts, programme ideas, or showreels will be considered.

TwoFour Productions Ltd
TwoFour Studios, Estover, Plymouth, PL6 7RG

☎ 01752 727400
☎ 01752 727450
✉ enq@twofour.co.uk
🌐 www.twofour.co.uk

Contact Creative Director and Executive Producer, Stuart Murphy
Established 1987
Insider Info TwoFour produce factual entertainment for UK and international terrestrial and satellite television channels. Credits include *A Different Life* and *Watch Us Grow*, both for children.
Tips Although TwoFour is predominantly known for factual and light entertainment, it has recently opened a new drama department and plans to expand its studio space in Plymouth to accommodate the filming of new drama features and series. This department is headed by Jo Wright.

Two Hand Productions
Unit 7, The Old Power Station, 121 Mortlake High Street, London, SW14 8SN

☎ 020 8878 9777
☎ 020 8878 9801
✉ info@twohandproductions.com
🌐 www.twohandproductions.com

Contact Managing Directors, Jonathan Frisby and Luke Gallie
Established 1996
Insider Info Two Hand Productions produces documentary, educational and light entertainment programming for children and adults. Clients include The Discovery Channel and Five. Credits include *Animal Families* and *No Girls Allowed*.
Tips In 2006 Two Hand Productions was the sixth largest supplier of programmes to Channel Five.

United International Pictures (UIP)
Building 5, Chiswick Park, 566 Chiswick High Road, London, W4 5YF

☎ 020 3184 2500
✉ enquiries@uip.com
🌐 www.uip.com

Established 1981
Insider Info UIP is a leading film distributor. Clients include Paramount and Universal. Credits include *Blades of Glory*, *Hot Fuzz* and *Charlotte's Web*.
Submission Guidelines UIP does not accepted unsolicited manuscripts.
Tips UIP is one of the worlds leading film distribution companies and is jointly owned by Paramount and Universal. UIP has distribution offices in 19 countries, but does not accept any form of submission.

Walsh Bros Ltd

4 The Heights, London, SE7 8JH

☎ 020 8854 5557

✉ development@walshbros.co.uk

🌐 www.walshbros.co.uk

Contact John Walsh, David Walsh

Insider Info Produce high-end documentaries, television drama and feature films. Credits include *Trex* for Five and the feature film *The Sleeper*.

Submission Guidelines Accepts query via email.

Tips Particular needs for submissions are published on the website. Priorities for 2007/8 are contemporary teenage drama and contemporary British science fiction.

Walt Disney Company Ltd

3 Queen Caroline Street, London, W6 9PE

☎ 020 8222 1000

☎ 020 8222 2795

✉ customer.support.london@disney.co.uk

🌐 www.disney.co.uk

Insider Info The London offices of the Disney Corporation, producing live action and animated feature films and television, primarily for children and families.

Submission Guidelines No unsolicited manuscripts.

Tips All Disney's commissioning takes place in the US Office and is through script and film agents only.

Warner Bros.

Warner House, 98 Theobalds Road, London, WC1X 8WB

☎ 020 7984 5000

🌐 www.warnerbros.co.uk

Insider Info The UK office of the major US production company. Produce feature films and television series, including *The Polar Express* and *Friends*.

Submission Guidelines Accepts agented writers only.

LITERARY

The Agency (London) Ltd
24 Pottery Lane, Holland Park, London, W11 4LZ
- 020 7727 1346
- 020 7727 9037
- info@theagency.co.uk
- www.theagency.co.uk

Contact Director, Hilary Delamere (Children's Authors/Illustrators); Assistant, Harriet Barnes
Established 1995

Insider Info Currently handles authors and illustrators for children's books, as well as television, radio and stage writers, directors, producers and composers. Proposals will be returned if accompanied by SAE. Obtains new clients through queries and submissions. Commission rates of ten per cent for domestic sales, with foreign sale commission by arrangement. Does not charge a reading fee.
Member of the Association of Authors' Agents.
Fiction Will consider Children's Fiction and Illustrated titles.
Scripts Will consider Film, Television, Radio and Theatre scripts.
Submission Guidelines Send a query letter with SAE.
Recent Sale(s) *Chitty Chitty Bang Bang*, Jeremy Sams (Eon Productions)
Client(s) Neil Arksey, Malorie Blackman, Michael Bond, Tony Bradman, Terrance Dicks, Joyce Dunbar, Tom Macrae, Karen McCombie, Andrew Norriss, Jeremy Sams, Amanda Swift, David Henry Wilson
Tips Does not accept unsolicited manuscripts.

Aitken Alexander Associates
18–21 Cavaye Place, London, SW10 9PT
- 020 7373 8672
- 020 7373 6002
- reception@aitkenalexander.co.uk
- www.aitkenalexander.co.uk

Contact Gillon Aitken; Kate Shaw (Literary and Popular Fiction for Adult's and Children's Authors)
Established 1977

Insider Info Actively seeking clients. Currently handles non-fiction books, novels, children's books, television and film scripts. Aims to respond to queries and proposals within eight weeks. Unsuccessful submissions are returned with SAE. Commission rates are ten per cent for domestic sales, 20 per cent for foreign sales, and ten per cent for film sales. Do not charge a reading fee.
Member of the Association of Authors' Agents.
* The agents have mainly come from publishing and editorial backgrounds.
Fiction Considers mainstream Children's Fiction titles.
Submission Guidelines Send query letter with outline, biography and a 30 page sample of your writing. All pages should be single-sided and double-spaced.
Tips Unable to answer queries by email. Postal queries and submissions only. A list of writing credits (in any genre) would be useful to include with the submission.

A.M. Heath
6 Warwick Court, Holborn, London, WC1R 5DJ
- 020 7242 2811
- 020 7242 2711
- www.amheath.com

Contact Sarah Molloy (Children's writers)
Established 1919

Insider Info Actively seeking clients. Currently handles non-fiction books, children's books and novels. Aims to respond within four months. Proposals returned if accompanied by SAE. Commission rates of 15 per cent for domestic sales, 20 per cent for foreign sales, 15 per cent for film sales. No reading fee charged.
Member of the Association of Authors' Agents.
Non-Fiction Will consider Children's Education, General Interest and History titles.
Fiction Will consider Children's fiction.
Submission Guidelines Send query letter with SAE, synopsis and three sample chapters. Submission should be double-spaced on single-sided A4 paper.
Client(s) Lloyd Alexander, Helen Cresswell, Nick Gifford, Emma Young
Tips A.M. Heath does not accept manuscripts or queries by email.

The Ampersand Agency

Ryman's Cottages, Little Tew, Chipping Norton, Oxfordshire, OX7 4JJ

- 01608 683677/683898
- 01608 683449
- peter@theampersandagency.co.uk
- www.theampersandagency.co.uk

Contact Peter Buckman
Established 2003

Insider Info Seeking both new and established writers. Considers children's non-fiction and fiction books. Represents more than 35 clients, 85 per cent of whom are new or previously unpublished writers. Will consider simultaneous submissions. Aims to respond to queries within two weeks and manuscripts within four weeks. Unsuccessful proposals will be returned with SAE. New clients are obtained through queries and submissions and recommendations from others. The Ampersand Agency will sometimes approach writers with ideas. 14 book projects have been sold in the past year. Commission rates are 10–15 per cent for domestic sales, 20 per cent for foreign sales and 15 per cent for film sales. Offers a written contract that may be terminated at any time. Does not charge a reading fee or offer a criticism service.
Member of the Association of Authors' Agents.
* The agency specialises in good story-telling, whether in fiction or non-fiction, and is made distinct by its candour and rapid responses. Before becoming an agent, Peter Buckman was a publisher and then a full-time writer.

Non-Fiction Will consider Children's Education, History and Humour titles.

Fiction Will consider Children's and Young Adult Fiction.

Scripts Only handles scripts from existing book author clients.

Submission Guidelines Send query letter with outline, one or two sample chapters and author biography. Also accept queries via email. Are actively seeking good stories, commercial and literary fiction and non-fiction, for adults and young people. Does not want poetry, science fiction or fantasy.

Recent Sale(s) *Olaf the Viking*, Martin Smith; *Zelah Green, Queen of Clean*, Vanessa Curtis; *The Chronicles of West Rock*, Derek Keilty

Client(s) Vanessa Curtis, Cora Harrison, Derek Keilty, Martin Smith

Tips Does not accept illustrated children's books.

Andrew Mann Ltd

1 Old Compton Street, London, W1D 5JA

- 020 7734 4751
- 020 7287 9264
- info@manuscript.co.uk

Contact Anne Dewe; Tina Betts; Sacha Elliot
Established 1975

Insider Info Actively seeking clients. Considers non-fiction books, children's books, novels, television scripts, movie scripts and stage plays. Submissions accompanied by SAE will be returned. Clients are usually acquired through queries/submissions. Commission rates of 15 per cent for domestic sales, 20 per cent for foreign sales. No reading fees charged.
Member of the Association of Authors' Agents.

Non-Fiction Will consider General Interest and Children's titles.

Fiction Will consider Children's Fiction.

Scripts Will consider scripts for Film, Television and Radio plays.

Submission Guidelines Send submissions with SAE, synopsis and three sample chapters. Queries accepted by email. No poetry considered.

Tips Manuscripts sent by email will not be accepted, send a synopsis only. Unsolicited manuscripts will only be accepted with an accompanying letter.

Annette Green Authors' Agency

1 East Cliff Road, Tunbridge Wells, Kent, TN4 9AD

- 01892 514275
- 01892 518124
- annettegreen@aol.com
- www.annettegreenagency.co.uk

Contact Annette Green, David Smith
Established 1998

Insider Info Actively seeking clients. Considers non-fiction books, children's books and novels. Simultaneous submissions accepted. Aims to respond to queries/proposals within four weeks. Submissions accompanied by SAE will be returned. Clients usually acquired through queries/submissions. Commission rates of 15 per cent for domestic sales and 20 per cent for foreign sales. No reading fee charged.
Member of the Association of Authors' Agents.
* Annette Green established her own literary agency in 1998 after working at A.M. Heath & Co. Ltd. for several years. David Smith joined as a partner in 2001.

Non-Fiction Will consider Children's History and Science/Technology titles.

Fiction Will consider Children's and Young Adult Fiction.

Submission Guidelines Send query letter with SAE, synopsis and 5,000–10,000 words of the opening chapters by post or email: emailsubmissions@ aol.com. No dramatic scripts, poetry, science fiction or fantasy considered.

Recent Sale(s) *All American Girl*, Meg Cabot

Client(s) Meg Cabot, Arnult Handley, Mary Hogan, Gwyn Morgan

Tips Specialises in discovering new exciting talent. Annette Green does not consider poetry, dramatic scripts, science fiction or fantasy.

Antony Harwood Ltd
103 Walton Street, Oxford, OX2 6EB
- 01865 559615
- 01865 310660
- mail@antonyharwood.com
- www.antonyharwood.com

Contact Antony Harwood; James MacDonald Lockhart

Established 2000

Insider Info Actively seeking clients. Considers non-fiction books, novels and children's fiction. Submissions accompanied by SAE will be returned. Clients usually acquired through queries/ submissions. No reading fee charged.
 Member of the Association of Authors' Agents.
 * Before establishing the agency in 2000, Antony Harwood began in publishing at Chatto & Windus in 1978, then became an agent at Gillon Aitken. In 1990 he joined the Curtis Brown Group as a director, before returning for a period to Gillon Aitken. James MacDonald Lockhart was with Hodder Headline before going to Gillon Aitken in 1998. Two years later he joined Antony Harwood to set up their own independent agency.

Non-Fiction Will consider all genres except books for young children.

Fiction Will consider all genres except books for young children.

Submission Guidelines Send query letter with SAE, synopsis and three sample chapters. Queries accepted by email. No material for children under ten. Screenwriting or poetry considered.

Recent Sale(s) *Lady Friday*, Garth Nix (fantasy); *The Witchking*, Amanda Craig (fantasy)

Client(s) Amanda Craig, Carlo Gébler, Amanda Hemingway, Garth Nix

Tips Antony Harwood Ltd accept submissions in a wide range of genres, including teenage fiction and fantasy fiction.

A.P. Watt Ltd
20 John Street, London, WC1N 2DR
- 020 7405 6774
- 020 7831 2154
- apw@apwatt.co.uk
- www.apwatt.co.uk

Contact Caradoc King (Top Children's Authors); Sheila Crowley (Young Adult and General Children's Fiction)

Established 1875

Insider Info Actively seeking clients. Considers non-fiction books, children's books, novels, television scripts, movie scripts, stage plays. Unsuccessful submissions will be discarded. Commission rates of 15 per cent for domestic sales, 20 per cent for foreign sales. Does not charge a reading fee.
 Member of the Association of Authors' Agents.

Non-Fiction Will consider General Interest titles.

Fiction Will consider Children's and Young Adult Fiction.

Scripts Will consider Television/Film scripts and Stage Plays.

Submission Guidelines Send query letter. No poetry considered.

Recent Sale(s) *The Perils of the Pushy Parents: A Cautionary Tale*, Boris Johnson

Client(s) Quentin Blake, Melvin Burgess, Julia Cole, Rudyard Kipling, Philip Pullman, Kate Saunders

Tips A.P. Watt is the longest established literary agency in the world. No unsolicited manuscripts will be accepted.

Author Literary Agents
53 Talbot Road, Highgate, London, London, N6 4QX
- 020 8341 0442
- 020 8341 0442
- agile@authors.co.uk

Contact John Havergal

Established 1997

Insider Info Actively seeking clients. Considers non-fiction books, children's books, novels, television scripts, movie scripts and animation. Prefers to receive exclusive submissions. Aims to respond to queries within seven days. Submissions accompanied by SAE will be returned. Clients usually acquired through recommendation, or queries/ submissions. Does not charge reading fee.

Non-Fiction Will consider Children's Education and General Interest titles.

Fiction Will consider Picture books and Children's and Young Adult Fiction.

Scripts Will consider Action/Adventure, Cartoon/Animation and Contemporary scripts.

Submission Guidelines Send query letter with SAE, outline, synopsis, biography and first chapter. Queries accepted by fax, email and telephone.

The Bell Lomax Agency

James House, 1 Babmaes Street, London, SW1Y 6HF
- 020 7930 4447
- 020 7925 0118
- agency@bell-lomax.co.uk

Contact Executives, Eddie Bell, Pat Lomax, Paul Moreton, June Bell

Established 2000

Insider Info Actively seeking clients. Considers non-fiction books, children's books and novels. Unsuccessful proposals are returned with SAE. Obtains new clients through queries and submissions. Does not charge a reading fee.

Non-Fiction Considers Children's Non-Fiction titles.

Fiction Considers General and Children's Fiction.

Submission Guidelines Send query letter. Will not accept scripts.

Tips Do not send any manuscripts before approaching with a query letter.

Brie Burkeman

14 Neville Court, Abbey Road, London, NW8 9DD
- 0870 199 5002
- 0870 199 1029
- brie.burkeman@mail.com

Contact Isabel White

Established 2000

Insider Info Seeking both new and established writers. Considers young adult non-fiction books and novels, television scripts, film scripts, and stage plays. Prefers to receive exclusive submissions. Unsuccessful proposals will be returned with SAE. Obtains new clients through recommendations from others, queries and submissions. Does not charge a reading fee, or offer a criticism service. Member of the Association of Authors' Agents.

Non-Fiction Considers General Interest Young Adult titles.

Fiction Considers Young Adult Fiction.

Scripts Considers Action/Adventure, Comedy and Contemporary issues scripts.

Submission Guidelines Send query letter with an outline, sample chapters and author biography. Do not send any poetry, musicals, text books or academic titles.

Caroline Sheldon Literary Agency

Thorley Manor Farm, Thorley, Yarmouth, PO41 0SJ
- 01983 760205
- carolinesheldon@carolinesheldon.co.uk
- pennyholroyde@carolinesheldon.co.uk
- www.carolinesheldon.co.uk

Contact Caroline Sheldon, Penny Holroyde

Established 1985

Insider Info Actively seeking clients. Considers children's books, picture books, non-fiction and novels. Aims to respond to proposals within four weeks. Unsuccessful proposals will be returned with SAE. Obtains new clients through queries and submissions. Commission rates of 10–15 per cent for domestic sales and 20 per cent for foreign sales. Does not charge a reading fee. Member of the Association of Authors' Agents.

* Before establishing her agency, Caroline Sheldon was a publisher at Hutchinson/Arrow, specialising in women's and children's books. Penny Holroyde has worked at Walker Books and as a rights director for Candlewick Press in the USA. She joined Caroline Sheldon in 2004.

Non-Fiction Considers Humour and General Interest Children's Non-Fiction.

Fiction Considers Picture books, Children's and Young Adult novels.

Submission Guidelines Send query letter with a synopsis, three sample chapters and SAE. Pages should be double-spaced and single-sided A4. No staples or bound manuscripts. Do not send scripts.

Illustration Considers black and white and full colour illustrations for Picture books, Film and Television.

Illustration Guidelines Send cover letter with printed samples and/or JPEG or TIFF images on disc, with SAE for return. Always send copies, never originals. Also, send any ideas for texts or book dummies.

Tips All submissions to be sent to the Thorley Manor Farm address, and a letter giving ambitions and future aspirations should be included. Submissions will not be accepted by email. Both agents are looking for good voice and characterisation. Also seeking fresh approaches to children's illustration and illustrated novelty books. Illustrators may also submit cover letter by email if including a link to their online gallery.

Cecily Ware Literary Agents

19C John Spencer Square, London, N1 2LZ
- 020 7359 3787

☎ 020 7226 9828

✉ info@cecilyware.com

🌐 www.cecilyware.com

Contact Cecily Ware, Warren Sherman, Gilly Schuster

Established 1972

Insider Info Seeking both new and established writers. Considers television, film and radio scripts. Unsuccessful proposals are returned if accompanied by SAE. Obtains new clients through queries and submissions. Commission rates of ten per cent for domestic sales and 10–20 per cent for foreign sales. Does not charge a reading fee.

Scripts Considers Comedy, Family, Adaptations and Series scripts.

Submission Guidelines Send query letter with SAE.

Tips Never send entire manuscript unless requested.

Celia Catchpole

56 Gilpin Avenue, London, SW14 8QY

☎ 020 8255 7755

🌐 www.celiacatchpole.co.uk

Contact Celia Catchpole

Established 1996

Insider Info Seeking both new and established writers. Considers children's books and novels. Simultaneous submissions are accepted. Unsuccessful proposals will be returned if accompanied by SAE. Obtains new clients through queries and submissions. Commission rates of ten per cent for domestic sales (15 per cent for illustrators) and 20 per cent on foreign sales. Commission rate for illustration is 15 per cent.

* Specialises in children's authors and illustrators.

Fiction Considers General Children's and Picture book titles.

Submission Guidelines Send query letter with SAE. Does not accept scripts or poetry.

Illustration Considers full colour illustration for Picture books and Story books for 0-12 year olds.

Illustration Guidelines Send cover letter with A4 size photocopied samples.

Recent Sale(s) *Muck It Up!,* Jane Clark and Trevor Duncan (HarperCollins); *Swallowcliffe Hall* series, Jennie Walters (Simon & Schuster); *'Varjak Paw'* series, S.F.Said (David Fickling Books); *Tabitha's Terrifically Tough Tooth,* Charlotte Middleton (Gullane Children's Books)

Client(s) Josephine Poole, Hannah Webb, Polly Dunbar, Mick Gowar, Malachy Doyle, Fernando Vilela, Daniel Postgate, Jane Simmons, Trish Phillips, Tim Hopgood, Joseph Theobald, Pedro De Alcantara, Rob Childs, Sandra Ann Horn, Lucy Micklethwait, Julia Rawlinson, Sean Taylor, Peter Utton

Tips Celia Catchpole specialises in children's authors and illustrator's of picture books. Does not accept unsolicited manuscripts.

The Christopher Little Literary Agency

10 Eel Brook Studios, 125 Moore Park Road, London, SW6 4PS

☎ 020 7736 4455

☎ 020 7736 4490

✉ info@christopherlittle.net

🌐 www.christopherlittle.net

Contact Christopher Little

Established 1979

Insider Info Actively seeking clients. Considers children's non-fiction and novels, television scripts and movie scripts. Aims to respond to queries and manuscripts within six weeks. Unsuccessful proposals will be returned with SAE. Obtains new clients through queries and submissions. Commission rates of 15 per cent for domestic sales, and 20 per cent for foreign sales and film rights. Does not charge a reading fee.

Member of the Association of Authors' Agents.

Non-Fiction Considers Commercial Children's Non-Fiction.

Fiction Considers Mainstream and Literary full-length Fiction.

Scripts Mainly considers scripts from existing clients only.

Submission Guidelines Send query letter with synopsis, three sample chapters and SAE. Pages should be double-spaced, single-sided and A4 sized. No poetry, plays, science fiction, illustrated material, textbooks or short stories.

Recent Sale(s) *Demonata* series, Darren Shan; *Harry Potter* series, J.K. Rowling; *The Kingdom of the Frosty Mountain,* Angela Woolfe

Client(s) A.J. Butcher, Carol Hughes, Linda Newbery, J.K. Rowling, Darren Shan, Angela Woolfe

Tips The agency also handles merchandising, in-house legal matters, contract affairs, royalties and accounting for their clients. They offer a high level of personal, hands-on representation.

Conville & Walsh Ltd

2 Ganton Street, London, W1F 7QL

☎ 020 7287 3030

☎ 020 7287 4545

✉ firstname@convilleandwalsh.com

Contact Director, Clare Conville

Established 2000

Insider Info Seeking both new and established writers. Considers non-fiction books, children's books and novels. Unsuccessful proposals will be returned if accompanied by SAE. Obtains new clients through queries and submissions. Commission rates of 15 per cent for domestic sales and 20 per cent for foreign sales. Does not charge reading fees.
Member of the Association of Authors' Agents.
Non-Fiction Considers Children's History, Science/Technology and General Interest Non-Fiction titles.
Fiction Considers Children's and Young Adult novels.
Submission Guidelines Accepts query letter with a synopsis, three sample chapters and SAE. No scripts, short stories or poetry.
Tips Has an interest in first-time novelists.

Curtis Brown Group Ltd
Haymarket House, 28–29 Haymarket, London, SW1 4SP
☎ 020 7393 4400
☎ 020 7393 4400
✉ cb@curtisbrown.co.uk
🌐 www.curtisbrown.co.uk
Contact Janice Swanson (Children's Authors and Illustrators)
Established 1899
Insider Info Actively seeking clients. Considers children's non-fiction, novels and illustrated books. Simultaneous submissions are accepted. Aims to respond to queries and proposals within eight weeks. Unsuccessful proposals are returned if accompanied by SAE. Obtains new clients by queries and submissions. Does not charge a reading fee.
Member of the Association of Authors' Agents.
* Janice Swanson previously worked at Scholastic Children's Books and has also worked in the advertising and television industries. As well as representing children's authors and illustrators she also represents a number of estates.
Fiction Considers Children's and Young Adult novels, as well as illustrated titles.
Submission Guidelines Send query letter with SAE, a synopsis and three sample chapters. Pages should be double-spaced, single-sided and A4 sized. Address package to 'SUBMISSIONS DEPARTMENT'.
Recent Sale(s) *Star Dancer*, Beth Webb; *Going for Gold: Mel Beeby Agent Angel*, Annie Dalton
Client(s) Andrew Butcher, Nicki Cornwell, Annie Dalton, Kenneth Grahame (Estate), F.E. Higgins, A.A. Milne (Estate), Beth Webb, Jonny Zucker
Tips When submitting sample chapters make sure your name, contact number and email address are

clearly written on the cover. No stapled, bound, or emailed manuscripts.

Darley Anderson Literary, TV & Film Agency
Estelle House, 11 Eustace Road, London, SW6 1JB
☎ 020 7385 6652
☎ 020 7386 5571
✉ enquiries@darleyanderson.com
🌐 www.darleyandersonchildrens.com
Contact Julia Churchill (Children's Books)
Established 1988
Insider Info Actively seeking clients. Considers non-fiction books, children's books, novels, television and movie scripts. Receives up to 300 submissions per week. 95 per cent of clients are new or previously unpublished writers. Simultaneous submissions are accepted. Aims to respond to queries, proposals and manuscripts within one month. Unsuccessful proposals will be returned if accompanied by SAE. Obtains new clients through recommendations from others, queries and submissions.
Member of the Association of Authors' Agents.
Non-Fiction Considers Children's and Young Adult Non-Fiction.
Fiction Considers Picture book, Children's and Young Adult titles.
Scripts Considers Action/Adventure, Cartoon/Animation and Comedy scripts.
Submission Guidelines Send query letter with SAE, synopsis and the first three chapters. Also accepts queries by email or phone. Darley Anderson is hoping to begin hosting regular writing workshops. Visit their website for updates.

David Higham Associates Ltd
5–8 Lower John Street, Golden Square, London, W1F 9HA
☎ 020 7434 5900
☎ 020 7437 1072
✉ dha@davidhigham.co.uk
🌐 www.davidhigham.co.uk
Contact Anthony Goff, Alice Williams, Bruce Hunter, Lizzy Kremer, Veronique Baxter (Fiction, Non-Fiction, Children's); Caroline Walsh (Fiction, Children, Illustrators)
Established 1935
Insider Info Seeking both new and established writers. Considers children's non-fiction, fiction and picture books, film scripts, television scripts and stage plays. Simultaneous submissions are accepted. Unsuccessful proposals will be returned with SAE.

Obtains new clients through recommendations from others, queries and submissions. Commission rates of 15 per cent for domestic sales, 20 per cent for foreign sales and 15 per cent for film rights (scripts receive 10 per cent). Offers a written contract until it is terminated by either party. Does not charge a reading fee, or offer a criticism service.

Member of the Association of Authors' Agents.

Non-Fiction Considers General Interest Children's Non-Fiction titles.

Fiction Considers Children's and Young Adult Fiction, and Illustrated books.

Scripts Considers scripts for Film, Television and Theatre.

Submission Guidelines Send query letter with SAE, outline, synopsis, three sample chapters and an author biography. The agency is actively seeking good commercial and literary fiction, and general non-fiction.

Illustration Considers full colour illustration for Picture books.

Illustration Guidelines For picture books send the complete manuscript by post, complete with copies of all illustrations.

Tips According to their website David Higham is the leading agency for children's writers and illustrators in the UK. Postal submissions only.

Dorie Simmonds Agency
Riverbank House, 1 Putney Bridge Approach, London, SW6 3JD
- 020 7736 0002
- dhsimmonds@aol.com

Contact Dorie Simmonds

Insider Info Seeking both new and established writers. Considers non-fiction books, scholarly books and children's books. Unsuccessful proposals will be returned if accompanied by SAE. Obtains new clients through queries and submissions. Commission rates of 15 per cent for foreign and domestic sales. Does not charge a reading fee.

Member of the Association of Authors' Agents.

Non-Fiction Considers Educational, Scholarly and General Interest Children's Non-Fiction titles.

Fiction Considers Children's Fiction titles.

Submission Guidelines Send a query letter with SAE, synopsis and two to three sample chapters. Include any publishing history in the letter.

Tips Authors of non-fiction are to submit only an outline with their preliminary letter.

Eddison Pearson Ltd
West Hill House, 6 Swains Lane, London, N6 6QS
- 020 7700 7763
- 020 7700 7866
- enquiries@eddisonpearson.com

Contact Clare Pearson

Established 1996

Insider Info Considers children's non-fiction books, fiction and poetry. Simultaneous submissions are accepted. Aims to respond to queries and proposals within four weeks. Unsuccessful proposals will be returned with SAE. Obtains new clients through queries and submissions. Commission rates of 10 per cent for domestic sales and 15–20 per cent for foreign sales. Does not charge a reading fee.

Non-Fiction Considers General Interest Children's Non-Fiction.

Fiction Considers Children's Novels and Poetry.

Submission Guidelines Send query letter with SAE and outline.

Client(s) Valerie Bloom, Sue Heap, Robert Muchamore

Tips Query by email for up to date submission guidelines. The agency endeavours to reply promptly to all submissions.

Ed Victor Ltd
6 Bayley Street, Bedford Square, London, WC1B 3HE
- 020 7304 4100
- 020 7304 4111

Contact Executive Chairman, Ed Victor; Director, Sophie Hicks; Director, Margaret Phillips

Established 1976

Insider Info Considers non-fiction books, children's books and novels. Obtains new clients through queries and submissions. Commission rates of 15 per cent on domestic and foreign sales. Does not charge reading fees.

Member of the Association of Authors' Agents.

Fiction Considers Action/Adventure and Fantasy Children's titles.

Submission Guidelines Send query letter with SAE and synopsis. No scripts, academic or poetry titles.

Client(s) Eoin Colfer

Tips Ed Victor does not accept unsolicited manuscripts.

Elizabeth Roy Literary Agency
White Cottage, Greatford, Nr. Stamford, Lincolnshire, PE9 4PR
- 01778 560672

☎ 01778 560672
🌐 www.elizabethroyliteracyagency.co.uk
Established 1990
Insider Info Seeking both new and established writers. Considers children's non-fiction, illustrated fiction and novels. Simultaneous submissions are accepted. Unsuccessful proposals will be returned if accompanied by SAE. Obtains new clients through queries and submissions. Commission rates of 15 per cent for domestic sales and 20 per cent on foreign sales. Does not charge a reading fee.

* Specialises in children's books, both writers and illustrators.

Non-Fiction Considers Children's Non-Fiction titles.
Fiction Considers Children's and Picture book Fiction titles.
Submission Guidelines Send query letter with SAE, synopsis and two to three sample chapters.
Tips Writers should declare all the agents and publishers that their proposal has already been submitted to. Illustrators must include sample figure work with submissions. Does not accept submissions by email, on disk, or on CD.

Eunice McMullen Children's Literary Agent Ltd

Low Ibbotsholme Cottage, Off Bridge Lane, Troutbeck Bridge, Windemere, Cumbria, LA23 1HU
☎ 01539 448551
☎ 01539 442289
✉ eunicemcmullen@totalise.co.uk
🌐 www.eunicemcmullen.co.uk
Contact Director, Eunice McMullen
Established 1992
Insider Info Actively seeking clients. Considers children's non-fiction books and novels. Unsuccessful proposals will be returned if accompanied by SAE. Obtains new clients through queries and submissions. Commission rates of ten per cent on domestic sales and 15 per cent on foreign sales.

* Eunice had worked in publishing, including for the Puffin imprint of Penguin, before beginning work as an agent. In 1992 she established her own agency.
Non-Fiction Considers Children's titles.
Fiction Considers Children's and Picture book titles.
Submission Guidelines Query via telephone.
Recent Sale(s) *Septimus Heap Book 1 'Magyk'*, Angie Sage
Client(s) Wayne Anderson, Sam Childs, Ross Collins, Charles Fuge, Angie Sage, Gillian Shields, Susan Winter

Tips Telephone enquiries only before submission, no unsolicited manuscripts.

Eve White

1a High Street, Kintbury, Berkshire, RG17 9TJ
☎ 01488 657656
☎ 01488 657656
✉ evewhite@btinternet.com
🌐 www.evewhite.co.uk
Contact Eve White
Established 2003
Insider Info Seeking both new and established writers. Considers non-fiction books, children's books, novels and illustrated books. Receives over 100 manuscripts per month. Represents 90 clients, 30 of whom are new, or previously unpublished writers. Prefers to receive exclusive submissions. Aims to respond to manuscripts within two months. Unsuccessful proposals will be returned if accompanied by SAE. Obtains new clients through recommendations from others, queries and submissions. Commission rates of 15 per cent on domestic sales and 20 per cent on foreign sales and film rights. Offers a written contract until terminated by either party with 60 days notice. Does not charge a reading fee or offer a criticism service. They will sometimes suggest a literary consultancy or a specific editor if work looks promising, but not right for them at the time. Writers may be charged for printing manuscripts and for overseas postage. Member of the Association of Authors' Agents.

* Eve White has a degree in Education (with English and Drama). She worked as a teacher and then as a writer, director and actress in theatre and television. The agency will frequently get involved in the public relations side of an author's career.
Fiction Considers Picture books, Illustrated Fiction, Children's novels and Young Adult titles.
Submission Guidelines Send query letter with SAE, synopsis, sample chapters and an author biography. No poetry and no email submissions.
Recent Sale(s) *You're A Bad Man, Mr Gum!* Andy Stanton; *My Fat, Mad Teenage Diary*, Rae Earl
Client(s) Rae Earl, Abie Longstaff, Peter J Murray, Andy Stanton, Margi Hann Syme
Tips Ensure to mark submissions with 'CHILDREN'S'. Lists are currently full for children's picture books, and short stories and non-fiction for the under eights. Check the website for further details.

Felicity Bryan Literary Agency
2a North Parade, Banbury Road, Oxford, OX2 6LX

☎ 01865 513816

☎ 01865 310055

✉ agency@felicitybryan.com

🌐 www.felicitybryan.com

Contact Catherine Clarke (Children's Authors)

Established 1988

Insider Info Seeking both new and established writers, for children's fiction and illustrated fiction. Simultaneous submissions are accepted. Aims to respond to queries and manuscripts within eight weeks. Unsuccessful proposals are returned if accompanied by SAE. Obtains new clients through recommendations from others and queries/submissions. Written contract offered. Does not charge a reading fee. Does not offer a criticism service.

Member of the Association of Authors' Agents.

Fiction Considers Children's and Young Adult novels, and Illustrated Fiction.

Submission Guidelines Send query letter with SAE, outline, synopsis, sample chapters, biography and a proposal. Does not accept poetry, film, television, or play scripts, science fiction, fantasy, light romance or how-to books.

Client(s) Julie Hearn, Natasha Narayan, Meg Rosoff, Matthew Skelton

Tips Catherine Clarke handles children's fiction and has a 'small and highly successful list of new writers for children'. Does not accept authors from North America for practical reasons.

Film Rights Ltd
Mezzanine, Quadrant House, 80–82 Regent Street, London, W1B 5AU

☎ 020 7734 9911

☎ 020 7734 0044

✉ information@filmrights.ltd.uk

🌐 www.filmrights.ltd.uk

Contact Director, Brendan Davis; Director, Joan Potts

Established 1932

Insider Info Seeking both new and established writers. Currently handles television scripts, film scripts, stage plays, and radio broadcasting. Considers non-fiction, fiction, film scripts, television scripts, stage plays, and radio broadcasting. Unsuccessful proposals are returned if accompanied by SAE. Obtains new clients by queries/submissions. Commission rate of ten per cent for domestic sales and 15 per cent for foreign sales. Does not charge a reading fee.

Scripts Considers scripts for children's productions.

Submission Guidelines Send query letter with SAE.

Tips Works in association with Laurence Fitch Ltd.

Fraser Ross Associates
6 Wellington Place, Edinburgh, EH6 7EQ

☎ 0131 657 4412/0131 553 2759

✉ kjross@tiscali.co.uk

✉ linsey.fraser@tiscali.co.uk

🌐 www.fraserross.co.uk

Contact Linsey Fraser; Kathryn Ross

Established 2002

Insider Info Actively seeking clients. Currently handles children's illustrated fiction and novels. Unsuccessful proposals are returned if accompanied by SAE. Obtains new clients by queries/submissions. Commission rates of ten per cent for domestic sales and 20 per cent for foreign sales. Does not charge a reading fee.

* Both partners had careers in readership development, book selling and teaching before establishing their own agency. They also ran the Scottish Book Trust, from 1991–2002, they have been judges on panels for prizes such as the Whitbread and Fidler, and have addressed conferences on readership development worldwide. Presently they run the Pushkin Prizes, are National Co-ordinators for the Scottish Executive's Read Together initiative, and they administer the Blue Peter Awards.

Fiction Considers Children's Storybooks and Novels.

Submission Guidelines Send query letter with SAE, synopsis, three sample chapters and a biography. Pages should be one-sided, double-spaced, numbered and A4 sized. Please do not send any unfinished work.

Illustration Considers full colour illustration for Picture books and Storybooks.

Illustration Guidelines For picture books send complete manuscript with two to three sample artwork copies (colour/black and white) plus a rough storyboard/thumbnail sketches for a complete story. Alternatively, submit a dummy rough of the proposed book.

Client(s) Gill Arbuthnott, Erica Blaney, John Cresswell, Samantha David, Vivian French, Chris Higgins, Liz MacWhirter, Jack McLean, Jan and Tony Payne, Jamie Rix and Linda Strachan. Illustrators: Jo Allen, Tony Bibby, Chris Fisher, Mark Jobe and Julie Lacome

Tips If you require acknowledgement of submitted material, then a paid reply postcard must be included with the manuscript.

Futerman, Rose & Associates (FRA)
91 St. Leonards Road, London, SW14 7BL

☎ 020 8255 7755

☎ 020 8286 4860

● guy@futermanrose.co.uk
● betty@futermanrose.co.uk
ⓦ www.futermanrose.co.uk
Contact Alexandra Green (Teenage Fiction)
Established 1984
Insider Info Actively seeking clients. Currently handles teenage fiction and scripts. Unsuccessful proposals are returned with SAE. Obtains new clients by queries and submissions. Commission rates of ten per cent for domestic sales and 20 per cent for foreign sales. Does not charge a reading fee. Member of the Association of Authors' Agents.
Fiction Considers Teenage and Young Adult titles.
Scripts Considers general scripts.
Submission Guidelines Send query letter with SAE, synopsis, three sample chapters and a biography. Does not accept science fiction, poetry, young children's or textbooks.
Recent Sale(s) *My Now or Never Diary*, Liz Rettig
Client(s) Liz Rettig, Shirley Clarkson
Tips The agency will only consider young adult fiction aimed at older teenagers, not children's fiction.

Greene & Heaton Ltd
37 Goldhawk Road, London, W12 8QQ
● 020 8749 0315
● 020 8749 0318
● info@greeneheaton.co.uk
ⓦ www.greeneheaton.co.uk
Contact Linda Davis (Children's Authors/Illustrators)
Established 1963
Insider Info Actively seeking clients. Currently handles children's fiction and illustrated books. Simultaneous submissions are accepted. Aims to respond to queries and proposals within six weeks. Unsuccessful submissions returned with SAE. Obtains new clients by queries and submissions. Commission rates of 10–15 per cent for domestic sales and 20 per cent for foreign sales. Does not charge a reading fee. Member of the Association of Authors' Agents.
 * Linda Davis previously worked as a children's publisher at both HarperCollins and Dorling Kindersley.
Fiction Considers new and classic children's fiction and illustrated titles.
Submission Guidelines Send query letter with SAE, synopsis and three sample chapters. Does not accept scripts.
Recent Sale(s) *From Where I Stand*, Tabitha Suzuma
Client(s) Abby Cocovini, Amber Deckers, Joshua Doder (Josh Lacey), Tabitha Suzuma

Tips Agent Linda Davis has recently been building a list of children's authors for Greene Heaton. She is currently looking for more classic fiction for the eight to twelve age group.

The Inspira Group
5 Bradley Road, Enfield, Middlesex, EN3 6ES
● 020 8292 5163
● 0870 139 3057
● darin@theinspiragroup.com
ⓦ www.theinspiragroup.com
Contact Darin Jewell
Established 2001
Insider Info Seeking both new and established writers. Considers non-fiction books, children's books, novels, general fiction and short story collections. Represents 18 clients, 50 per cent of whom are new and previously unpublished writers. Simultaneous submissions are accepted. Aims to respond to queries within three days and manuscripts within 14 days. Unsuccessful proposals will be returned with SAE. Obtains clients through recommendations from others, queries and submissions. Has sold nine books within the last year. Commission rates of 15 per cent on domestic and foreign sales. Offers a written contract until terminated by either party with 30 days notice. Does not charge a reading fee, but does not offer a criticism service.
 * Darin pursued his doctoral research at Cambridge, England before becoming an agent. He likes to work with talented writers, whether they be first-time authors or previously published authors.
Non-Fiction Considers all types of Children's Non-Fiction.
Fiction Considers all types of Children's Fiction.
Submission Guidelines Send query letter, with SAE, entire manuscript, synopsis and an author biography. Initial queries are invited by email or phone. Actively seeking talented writers who have a passion for writing. No poetry, biographies or anthologies.
Recent Sale(s) *Follow The Fox*, Gordon Askew
Client(s) Gordon Askew, Stephanie Baudet, Tony Langham

Intercontinental Literary Agency
Centric House, 390–391 Strand, London, WC2R 0LT
● 020 7379 6611
● 020 7379 4724
● ila@ila-agency.co.uk
ⓦ www.ila-agency.co.uk

Contact Tessa Girvan (Rights for Children's and Young Adult titles Worldwide, including work with co-agents in Poland and Russia)

Established 1965

Insider Info Considers children's books and young adult titles. Works with other agents and publishers exclusively.

Member of the Association of Authors' Agents.

* Specialises in translation rights for authors from Britain, the USA and Australia.

Client(s) Elyse Cheney Literary Associates, Lucas Alexander Whitley Ltd, Luigi Bonomi Associates, Mulcahy & Viney Ltd, PDF, Turnbull Agency (John Irving), Wade & Doherty Literary Agency

Tips The ILA does not deal directly with writers, only with other agents and publishers.

Jennifer Luithlen Agency
88 Holmfield, Leicester, LE2 1SB

✆ 0116 273 8863

✆ 0116 273 5697

Contact Jennifer Luithlen (Agent); Penny Luithlen (Agent)

Established 1986

Insider Info Not currently seeking new clients. Currently handles children's fiction. Commission rate is 15 per cent for domestic sales, 20 per cent for foreign sales.

Fiction Will consider mainstream Children's Storybooks and Novels.

Tips No unsolicited manuscripts.

Jenny Brown Associates
33 Argyle Place, Edinburgh, EH9 1JT

✆ 0131 229 5334

✆ 0131 229 6695

✉ lucy.juckes@btinternet.com

🌐 www.jennybrownassociates.com

Contact Lucy Juckes (Children's & Illustrators)

Established 2002

Insider Info Actively seeking clients. Currently handles children's non-fiction, fiction and illustrated books. Accepts simultaneous submissions. Aims to respond to queries/proposals within six weeks. Manuscripts returned with SAE. Clients usually obtained through queries/submissions. Commissions rate of 12.5 per cent for domestic sales, 20 per cent for foreign sales. Does not charge a reading fee.

Member of the Association of Authors' Agents.

* Lucy Juckes was previously co-founder and Managing Director of Barrington Stoke, the children's publisher specialising in books for reluctant readers. She has also worked as Sales Director of Bloomsbury.

Fiction Considers Children's and Young Adult Fiction and Picture books.

Submission Guidelines Authors should include SAE, synopsis, sample chapters, author biography, one page synopsis and brief CV with submission, which should be double-spaced, one-sided A4, of 25 pages only. No poetry, science fiction, fantasy, sagas or academia considered.

Recent Sale(s) *Blackriggs*, Jamie Jauncey (Macmillan Children's Books); *Captives*, Tom Pow (Random House Children's Books)

Client(s) Gaby Halberstam, Diana Hendry, Jamie Jauncey, Tom Pow, John Ward

Tips Jenny Brown Associates is always looking for new authors, but will only accept submissions by post.

Johnson & Alcock Ltd
Clerkenwell House, 45–47 Clerkenwell Green, London, EC1R 0HT

✆ 020 7251 0125

✆ 020 7251 2172

✉ info@johnsonandalcock.co.uk

Contact Michael Alcock, Anna Power, Andrew Hewson, Merel Reinink

Established 1956

Insider Info Actively seeking clients. Currently handles non-fiction books, children's books and novels. Accepts simultaneous submissions. Manuscripts returned with SAE. Clients usually obtained through queries/submissions. Commission of 15 per cent on domestic sales, 20 per cent on foreign sales. Does not charge a reading fee.

Member of the Association of Authors' Agents.

Fiction Will consider Literary and Commercial Children's Fiction.

Submission Guidelines Authors should include query letter, SAE, synopsis and author biography with submissions. Include details of media/writing experience. No scripts, poetry, science fiction, academia or technical writing considered.

Tips Does not generally consider unsolicited manuscripts, but fiction writers may submit the first three chapters with first contact. Only accepts postal submissions.

Laurence Fitch Ltd
Mezzanine, Quadrant House, 80–82 Regent Street, London, W1B 5AU

✆ 020 7734 9911

✆ 020 7734 0044

○ information@laurencefitch.com
ⓦ www.laurencefitch.com
Contact Director, Brendan Davis
Established 1952
Insider Info Actively seeking clients. Currently handles television scripts, movie scripts, stage plays and radio scripts. Will consider simultaneous submissions. Unsuccessful proposals will be returned with SAE. Obtains new clients via queries/submissions. Commission rates of ten per cent by domestic sales, and 15 per cent by foreign sales. Does not charge a reading fee.
Scripts Will consider Mainstream Children's scripts.
Submission Guidelines Send proposal package with query letter, SAE, synopsis, sample chapters and three sample scenes/screens.
Recent Sale(s) *101 Dalmations; 102 Dalmations; The Hobbit* (Stage), Glyn Robbins
Client(s) Glyn Robbins
Tips No unsolicited manuscripts will be accepted. The agency works in association with Film Rights Ltd.

LAW Ltd
14 Vernon Street, London, W14 0RJ
○ 020 7471 7900
○ 020 7471 7910
ⓦ www.lawagency.co.uk
Contact Philippa Milnes-Smith (Children's and Young Adult)
Established 1996
Insider Info Actively seeking clients. Currently handles non-fiction books, children's books and novels, and illustrated titles. Will consider simultaneous submissions. Aims to respond to queries/proposals within eight weeks. Unsuccessful proposals will be returned with SAE. Obtains new clients via queries/submissions. Commission rates are 15 per cent by domestic sales and 20 per cent by domestic sales. Does not charge a reading fee.
Fiction Will consider Children's and Young Adult Fiction.
Submission Guidelines Send proposal package with query letter, SAE, synopsis, and two sample chapters or up to 30 pages in single-sided, double-spaced A4 format. No scripts, poetry or textbooks will be accepted.
Recent Sale(s) *The Demon Headmaster*, Gillian Cross
Client(s) Gillian Cross
Tips The agency may take longer than specified to reply to submissions during a busy period, and will not accept international reply coupons. Submissions by email, fax or disk will not be accepted. Is also interested in illustrated fiction for 0–16 year olds.

Lisa Eveleigh Literary Agency
c/o Pollinger Ltd, 9 Staple Inn, London, WC1V 7QH
○ 020 7404 0342
○ 020 7242 5737
○ lisaeveleigh@dial.pipex.com
Contact Lisa Eveleigh
Established 1996
Insider Info Actively seeking clients. Currently handles non-fiction books, novels and children's books. Unsuccessful submissions will be returned with SAE. Obtains new clients via queries/submissions. Commission rate is 15 per cent by domestic sales and 20 per cent by foreign sales. Does not charge a reading fee.
Non-Fiction Will consider General Interest Children's titles.
Fiction Will consider Mainstream Children's and Young Adult titles.
Submission Guidelines Send proposal package with query letter, SAE, synopsis, two to three sample chapters, and author biography. Accepts queries by email. No scripts, children's picture books, horror, science fiction or poetry titles will be accepted.
Tips Send preliminary letter only via email (no manuscripts).

London Independent Books
26 Chalcot Crescent, London, NW1 8YD
○ 020 7706 0486
○ 020 7724 3122
Contact Carolyn Whitaker
Established 1971
Insider Info Actively seeking clients. Currently handles non-fiction books and novels for adults and teenagers. Simultaneous submissions will be accepted. Unsuccessful proposals will be returned with SAE. Obtains new clients via queries/submissions. Does not charge a reading fee.
Non-Fiction Will consider General Interest and Travel titles.
Fiction Will consider Fantasy, Young Adult and Commercial Fiction.
Submission Guidelines Send proposal package with query letter, SAE, synopsis, two sample chapters, or up to 30 pages. No young children's or computer books.
Tips The agent will suggest revision and offer constructive criticism.

Luigi Bonomi Associates Ltd

91 Great Russell Street, London, WC1B 3PS

☎ 020 7637 1234

☎ 020 7637 2111

✉ info@bonomiassociates.co.uk

Contact Luigi Bonomi, Amanda Preston

Established 2005

Insider Info Actively seeking clients, currently handles teenage non-fiction books and novels. Manuscripts are returned with SAE. Clients usually obtained through queries/submissions. Commission rate of 15 per cent for domestic sales, 20 per cent for foreign sales and 15 per cent for film sales. Does not charge a reading fee.

Member of the Association of Authors' Agents.

Non-Fiction Will consider Child Guidance/ Parenting, Sports, Lifestyle and Teenage Non-Fiction titles.

Fiction Will consider Teenage and Young Adult Fiction.

Submission Guidelines Authors should submit query letter, SAE, synopsis and three sample chapters with submission. No poetry, science fiction, fantasy, scripts, or children's will be considered.

Tips Luigi Bonomi handles many celebrity authors, such as Alan Titchmarsh and Sir Terry Wogan. They are interested in new authors, especially for television tie-ins. They do not represent children's writers but will be open to writers for teenagers and young adults.

Lutyens and Rubinstein

231 Westbourne Park Road, London, W11 1EB

✉ firstname@lutyensrubinstein.co.uk

Contact Susannah Godman

Established 1991

Insider Info Currently handles non-fiction books, children's books and novels. Accepts simultaneous submissions. Aims to respond to queries/proposals and within six weeks. Manuscripts returned with SAE. Member of the Association of Authors' Agents.

Non-Fiction Considers General Interest Non-Fiction titles.

Fiction Considers Children's Fiction.

Submission Guidelines Authors should include query letter, SAE, synopsis and sample chapters with submissions. Queries accepted by email.

Maggie Noach Literary Agency

22 Dorville Crescent, London, W6 0HJ

☎ 020 8748 2926

☎ 020 8748 8057

✉ m-noach@dircon.co.uk

Established 1982

Insider Info Actively seeking clients. Considers children's books, novels and non-fiction. Prefers to receive exclusive submissions. Proposals accompanied by SAE will be returned. Commission rates of 15 per cent for domestic sales and 20 per cent for foreign sales. Does not charge a reading fee. Member of the Association of Authors' Agents.

Fiction Will consider Children's and Young Adult Fiction.

Submission Guidelines Send proposal package with SAE, synopsis and two or three sample chapters. Will not accept manuscripts for very young children or any illustrated books for children. Also, will not accept scientific, academia, specialist non-fiction, poetry, short stories or plays.

Tips Do not fax or email submissions – they will be deleted unopened.

Marianne Gunn O'Connor Literary Agency

Morrison Chambers, Suite 17, 32 Nassau Street, Dublin 2, Republic of Ireland

✉ magoclitagency@eircom.net

Contact Marianne Gunn O'Connor

Established 1996

Insider Info Seeking both new and established writers. Currently handles non-fiction books and children's novels. Proposals accompanied by SAE will be returned. Commission rates are 15 per cent for domestic sales, 20 per cent for foreign sales and 20 per cent for films.

Non-Fiction Will consider General Interest and Commercial Non-Fiction.

Fiction Will consider Children's, Literary and Commercial Fiction.

Submission Guidelines Send proposal package, including a brief synopsis and two or three sample chapters.

Tips No unsolicited manuscripts.

The Marsh Agency Ltd

11–12 Dover Street, London, W1S 4LJ

☎ 020 7399 2800

☎ 020 7399 2801

✉ enquiries@marsh-agency.co.uk

🌐 www.marsh-agency.co.uk

Contact Managing Director, Paul Marsh (Serious Non-Fiction, Literary Fiction, Client Development, Business Development and Client Account Management); Rights Director, Camilla Ferrier;

Agent, Geraldine Cooke; Agent, Jessica Woollard; Agent, Leyla Moghadam (English Language Sales)
Established 1994
Insider Info Seeking both new and established writers. Currently handles non-fiction, children's books, novels and short story collections. Proposals accompanied by SAE will be returned. Commission rates are 15 per cent for domestic sales and 20 per cent for foreign sales.

 Member of the Association of Authors' Agents.

 * Paul Marsh worked for Anthony Sheil Associates Ltd, from 1977 and became their Foreign Rights Director in 1979. He left in 1993 and went on to establish The Marsh Agency in 1994 with his wife. Camilla Ferrier worked for HarperCollins prior to joining the agency in 2002, and Geraldine Cooke was an Editor for many years at Penguin before joining in 2004. She also founded the Headline Review List. Jessica Woollard was a Director for Toby Eady Associates before joining the agency in 2006, and Leyla Moghadam worked for some time at the European Commission. Leyla is multi-lingual, speaking English, German, French and Farsi.
Non-Fiction Will consider General Interest Children's titles as well as Parenting titles.
Fiction Will consider Children's Action/Adventure, Fantasy, Science Fiction and Young Adult titles.
Submission Guidelines Send proposal package with SAE, synopsis, three sample chapters and author biography (double-spaced, numbered A4 pages). Accepts queries by email. Will not accept scripts, poetry or children's picture books.
Recent Sale(s) *Undersea Prisoner,* Duncan Falconer
Client(s) Monica Ali, Kate Atkinson, Meg Cabot
Tips When submitting manuscripts print your name, address and contact number on the front, and your name and the title on all pages.

Martinez Literary Agency
60 Oakwood Avenue, London, N14 6QL
☎ 020 8886 5829
Contact Françoise Budd, Mary Martinez
Established 1988
Insider Info Considers fiction books, non-fiction and children's books.
Non-Fiction Will consider Children's Arts and Crafts and General Interest Non-Fiction.
Fiction Will consider Children's Fiction.
Tips Martinez Literary Agency is not currently accepting any new clients.

McKernan Agency
5 Gayfield Square, Edinburgh, EH1 3NW
☎ 0131 557 1771
✉ maggie@mckernanagency.co.uk
⊕ www.mckernanagency.co.uk
Contact Maggie McKernan (Fiction)
Established 2005
Insider Info Actively seeking both new and established clients. Deals with non-fiction, children's books, fiction and anthologies. Currently working with 17 clients, around 50 per cent of whom are previously unpublished writers. Accepts queries by email. Will accept simultaneous submissions. Aims to respond to queries and proposals within two weeks and manuscripts within four weeks. Will return unwanted material with SAE. Usually obtains new clients through recommendations from others, queries and submissions.

 * A small agency, therefore clients receive very individual attention. During Maggie McKernan's career she has edited many prize winning authors, including Jim Crace, Ben Okri and Vikram Seth.
Non-Fiction Will consider all types of Children's Non-Fiction.
Fiction Will consider Children's Action/Adventure, Fantasy, Horror, Science Fiction, Mainstream and Young Adult titles.
Submission Guidelines Accepts proposal package including query letter, SAE, outline, three sample chapters, author biography and proposal. Accepts queries by email.
Tips Seeks novels of all kinds, both commercial and literary, including quality non-fiction.

Merric Davidson Literary Agency
12 Priors Heath, Goudhurst, Cranbrook, Kent, TN17 2RE
☎ 01580 212041
☎ 01580 212041
✉ md@mdla.co.uk
⊕ www.mdla.co.uk
Contact Merric Davidson
Insider Info Actively seeking both new and established clients. Deals with children's books, novels and fiction. Will consider simultaneous submissions. Will return unwanted material with SAE. Usually obtains new clients through queries and submissions.
Fiction Will consider Children's and Contemporary Fiction titles.
Submission Guidelines Accepts proposal package with query letter, SAE, synopsis, author biography. Will not accept short stories, academia or scripts.

Tips The agency is part of MBA Literary Agent Ltd. Will not accept unsolicited manuscripts.

Mulcahy and Viney Ltd
15 Canning Passage, Kensington, London, W8 5AA

- ivanmulcahy@mvagency.com
- www.mvagency.com

Contact Ivan Mulcahy, Charlie Viney, Jonathan Conway

Established 2002

Insider Info Seeking both new and established writers. Currently handles non-fiction books, novels and children's books, representing 72 clients. The agents' backgrounds include periods in journalism, publishing, printing, business and research. Accepts simultaneous submissions. Unwanted material discarded. Does not charge a reading fee.

Fiction Deals with Children's books and novels from previously published writers.

Submission Guidelines With their submission, authors should include query letter, outline, synopsis, sample chapters, biography and a summary of competitor books in the market.

Tips Unsolicited children's book proposals, but must be from previously published writers.

PFD (Peters, Fraser & Dunlop)
Drury House, 34–43 Russell Street, London, WC2B 5HA

- 020 7344 1000
- 020 7836 9539/020 7836 9541
- postmaster@pfd.co.uk
- www.pfd.co.uk/childrens

Contact Rosemary Canter (Children's Books)

Insider Info Currently handles non-fiction books, novels, children's books, illustrated books, television scripts and movie scripts. Will consider all genres of work. Prefers to receive exclusive submissions. Commission rates of ten per cent for domestic sales, and 20 for foreign sales.

Member of the Association of Authors' Agents.

 * Rosemary Canter has been an agent with PFD for 14 years and specialises in representing writers and illustrators of work for babies and children of all ages up to 13 or 14. She worked previously as a publisher in children's books, for over 15 years.

Fiction Will consider Children's novels, Picture books and stories for younger readers.

Scripts Will consider all genres.

Submission Guidelines Send query letter, SAE, synopsis, two to three sample chapters and author biography. Submission should be double-spaced, on single-sided A4. Do not bind or staple. Include a brief CV.

Recent Sale(s) *Jake Cake and the Robot Dinner Lady*, Michael Broad

Client(s) James Berry, Michael Broad, Bridget Collins, Kate Forsyth, Richard Hamilton, Sam Lloyd, Sally Nicholls, Maggie Pearson, Emma Thomson, Benjamin Zephaniah

Tips Rosemary Canter is most interested in 'heart breaking' romance or 'distinctive' fantasy for six to seven year olds. PFD has a dedicated page for illustrators at: www.pfd.co.uk/illustrators

Pollinger Ltd
9 Staple Inn, London, WC1V 7QH

- 020 7404 0342
- 020 7242 5737
- info@pollingerltd.com
- www.pollingerltd.com

Contact Managing Director/Agent, Lesley Pollinger; Agent, Joanna Devereux; Agent, Tim Bates; Consultant, Leigh Pollinger; Consultant, Joan Deitch

Established 1935

Insider Info Currently handles non-fiction books, children's books, novels, television scripts and movie scripts. Manuscripts will be returned with SAE. Clients are usually obtained through queries/submissions. Commission rate of 15 per cent for domestic sales, 20 per cent for foreign sales.

 * The agency has always been a family business.

Non-Fiction Will consider most subjects, including Children's titles.

Fiction Will consider all genres.

Scripts Will consider all genres for Television and Film.

Submission Guidelines Authors should include query letter, SAE, synopsis, three sample chapters and biography with submissions, which should be in black type, double spaced, one sided A4. No poetry or academia considered.

Recent Sale(s) *Corbenic*, Catherine Fisher

Client(s) Peter Clover, Catherine Fisher, Philip Gross

Tips No manuscripts by email or fax. Pollinger state on their website that they only rarely take on new clients, and that even then they have to be of the highest standard.

Redhammer Management Ltd
186 Bickenhall Mansions, London, W1U 6BX

- 020 7224 1748
- 020 7224 1802
- info@redhammer.info
- www.redhammer.info

Contact Managing Director, Peter Cox
Insider Info Seeking both new and established writers. Currently handles non-fiction books, fiction novels, children's books, television scripts and film scripts. Accepts simultaneous submissions. Aims to respond to queries, proposals and manuscripts within six weeks. Proposals will be returned if accompanied by SAE. Obtains new clients by queries or submissions. Commission rates of 17.5 per cent for domestic sales and 20 per cent for foreign sales. Does not charge a reading fee.
 Member of the Association of Authors' Agents.
Fiction Will consider Mainstream/Contemporary, Fantasy and Science-Fiction Children's and Young Adult books.
Scripts Will consider Children's Action/Adventure, Comedy, Contemporary, Fantasy and Science-Fiction scripts.
Recent Sale(s) *Chronicles of Ancient Darkness*, (Series) Michelle Paver; *The Joshua Files: Invisible City*, M.G. Harris
Client(s) Joe Donnelly, M.G. Harris, Amanda Lees, Michelle Paver
Tips Redhammer Management only accepts submissions from previously published writers. A limited number of unpublished writers may be approached by the agency through Litopia Writers' Colony, an internet writing community, www.litopia.com.

Rogers, Coleridge & White Ltd
20 Powis Mews, London, W11 1JN
- 020 7221 3717
- 020 7229 9084
- info@rcwlitagency.co.uk
- www.rcwlitagency.co.uk
Contact Deborah Rogers, Gill Coleridge, Pat White (Children's & Illustrated Books)
Established 1987
Insider Info Seeking both new and established writers. Currently handles children's fiction and non-fiction, and illustrated books. Aims to respond to queries and proposals within eight weeks. Proposals will be returned if accompanied by SAE. Obtains new clients by recommendation, conferences, and queries or submissions. Commission rates of 15 per cent for domestic sales and 20 per cent for foreign sales.
 Member of the Association of Authors' Agents.
 * Prior to opening the agency Deborah Rogers was an agent and also worked in publishing, while Pat White was an editor and rights director for Simon & Schuster.

Fiction Will consider most categories of Fiction, including Children's, Young Adult and Illustrated titles.
Submission Guidelines Send proposal package with SAE, synopsis, three sample chapters and author biography. No plays, screenplays, technical or educational books will be considered.
Tips Rogers, Coleridge & White does not accept submissions by fax or email.

Rosemary Sandberg Ltd
6b Bayley Street, London, N4 2EE
- 020 7304 4110
- 020 7304 4109
- rosemary@sandberg.demon.co.uk
Contact Director, Rosemary Sandberg
Established 1991
Insider Info Not currently seeking new clients. Currently handles children's books.
Fiction Will consider Children's Fiction, Picture books and Children's Illustrated titles.
Tips Rosemary Sandberg's client list is full at present, and the agency is not currently accepting unsolicited submissions of any kind.

Rupert Crew Ltd
1a King's Mews, London, WC1N 2JA
- 020 7242 8586
- 020 7831 7914
- info@rupertcrew.co.uk
- www.rupertcrew.co.uk
Contact Director, Doreen Montgomery; Director, Caroline Montgomery (Fiction)
Established 1937
Insider Info Actively seeking clients. Currently handles teenage fiction. Proposals will be returned if accompanied by SAE. Obtains new clients by queries or submissions. Commission rates of 15 per cent for domestic sales and 20 per cent for foreign sales. Does not charge a reading fee.
 Member of the Association of Authors' Agents.
Fiction Will consider Teenage and Young Adult Fiction.
Submission Guidelines Accepts query letter with SAE. No scripts, poetry, short stories, journalism, science fiction or fantasy considered.
Tips Rupert Crew tends to focus on mainstream fiction or non-fiction projects.

Sarah Manson Literary Agent
6 Totnes Walk, London, N2 0AD
- 020 8442 0396

○ info@sarahmanson.com
○ www.sarahmanson.com
Contact Sarah Manson
Established 2002
Insider Info Currently handles children's fiction books. Does not accept simultaneous submissions. Does not charge a reading fee.
Fiction Will consider Children's Fiction, Children's Picture books and Young Adult titles.
Submission Guidelines Send proposal package with SAE, synopsis, three sample chapters and author biography.
Tips Sarah Manson primarily deals with children's fiction and picture books, and prefers exclusive submissions.

Sayle Screen Ltd
11 Jubilee Place, London, SW3 3TD
○ 020 7823 3883
○ 020 7823 3363
○ info@saylescreen.com
○ www.saylescreen.com
Contact Toby Moorcroft, Jane Villiers, Matthew Bates
Established 1952
Insider Info Seeking both new and established writers. Currently handles television scripts and film scripts. Aims to respond to queries, proposals and manuscripts within three months. Proposals will be returned if accompanied by SAE. Obtains new clients by recommendation. Commission rates of ten per cent for domestic sales and 15 per cent for foreign sales. Does not charge a reading fee.
Scripts Will consider Children's and Young Adult scripts and adapted screenplays.
Submission Guidelines Send query letter with SAE, synopsis, and author biography.
Recent Sale(s) *ShoeBox Zoo*
Client(s) Mark Haddon, Joanne Harris, Sue Townsend
Tips Works in conjunction with the Sayle Literary Agency, handling film and television rights for their book titles. Sayle Screen does not accept submissions by email.

The Standen Literary Agency
41b Endymion Road, London N4 1EQ, London
○ 020 8444 1641
○ 020 8444 1641
○ info@standenliteraryagency.com
○ www.standenliteraryagency.com
Contact Yasmin Standen
Established 2004

Insider Info Not currently seeking new clients. Currently handles non-fiction books, novels and children's books. Aims to respond to queries and proposals within four months. Proposals will be returned if accompanied by SAE. Obtains new clients by queries or submissions. Commission rates of 15 per cent for domestic sales and 20 per cent for foreign sales. Does not charge a reading fee.
Non-Fiction Will consider General Interest and Children's titles.
Fiction Will consider Literary and Children's Fiction.
Submission Guidelines In general, send a query letter with SAE, synopsis and three sample chapters. For children's books of 500 words or less, send the entire manuscript. Illustrated work, science fiction titles and scripts will not be considered.
Recent Sale(s) *Ghost Rescue*, Andrew Murray (Series); *Fish for Alexander*, Kara Zane
Client(s) Kara Kane, Zoe Marriott, Andrew Murray
Tips Does not accept submissions by recorded/special delivery, or electronic submissions of any form. Always advise the agency whether submissions are exclusive or not. Overseas submissions will not be returned, but include an email address for response. Does not represent illustrators.

Uli Rushby-Smith Literary Agency
72 Plimsoll Road, London, WN4 2EE
○ 020 7354 2718
○ 020 7354 2718
Contact Uli Rushby-Smith
Established 1993
Insider Info Seeking both new and established writers. Currently handles non-fiction books, fiction, novels and children's books. Will consider simultaneous submissions. Proposals will be returned if accompanied by SAE. Commission rates of 15 per cent for domestic sales and 20 per cent for foreign sales. Does not charge a reading fee.
Non-Fiction Will consider General Non-Fiction and Children's titles.
Fiction Will consider Literary, General and Commercial Fiction.
Submission Guidelines Send query letter with SAE, outline, and two to three sample chapters. No scripts or poetry considered.
Tips Uli Rushby-Smith does not accept submissions on disk.

United Authors Ltd
11–15 Betterton Street, London, WC2H 9BP
○ 020 7470 8886

☎ 020 7470 8887

✉ editorial@unitedauthors.co.uk

Established 1998

Insider Info Seeking both new and established writers. Currently handles non-fiction, fiction and children's books. Will consider simultaneous submissions. Proposals will be returned if accompanied by SAE. Obtains new clients by queries or submissions. Commission rates of 12 per cent for domestic sales, 20 per cent for foreign sales and 15–20 per cent for film (and radio) sales. Does not charge a reading fee.

Non-Fiction Will consider General Interest and Children's Non-Fiction titles.

Fiction Will consider Mainstream and Children's Fiction.

Submission Guidelines Send query letter with SAE.

Tips Will suggest revision on any solicited manuscripts.

Vanessa Holt Ltd
59 Crescent Road, Leigh on Sea, Essex, SS9 2PF

☎ 01702 473787

☎ 01702 471890

✉ vanessa@holtlimited.freeserve.co.uk

Contact Director, Vanessa Holt

Established 1989

Insider Info Actively seeking clients. Currently handles non-fiction books, fiction, novels, and children's books. Will consider simultaneous submissions. Proposals will be returned if accompanied by SAE. Obtains new clients by queries or submissions. Commission rates of 15 per cent for domestic sales, 20 per cent for foreign sales and 15 per cent for film sales. Does not charge a reading fee. Member of the Association of Authors' Agents.

Non-Fiction Will consider General Interest Non-Fiction and Children's titles.

Fiction Will consider Mainstream and Literary Children's and Young Adult Fiction.

Submission Guidelines Send query letter with SAE. No children's illustrated books, scripts, poetry, academia or technical books will be considered.

Tips Vanessa Holt is interested in books with potential film, television or radio tie-ins. Does not accept unsolicited manuscripts.

Wade & Doherty Literary Agency Ltd
33 Cormorant Lodge, Thomas More Street, London, E1W 1AU

☎ 020 7488 4171

☎ 020 7488 4172

✉ rw@rwla.com

🌐 www.rwla.com

Contact Robin Wade (General Fiction, Non-Fiction and Children's books)

Established 2001

Insider Info Actively seeking clients. Currently handles non-fiction books, fiction, novels, children's books and anthologies. Currently represents 31 clients, around 50 per cent of whom are new or previously unpublished writers. Will consider simultaneous submissions. Aims to respond to queries and proposals within seven days, and manuscripts within 30 days. Proposals returned if accompanied by SAE. Obtains new clients by recommendation, conferences, and queries or submissions. Has sold 21 titles in the past year. Commission rates of ten per cent for domestic sales, 20 per cent for foreign sales and 20 for film sales. Written contract offered for extent of publishing, with 30 days notice required for termination. Does not charge a reading fee, and does not offer a criticism service.

Non-Fiction Will consider Children's General Interest and Educational titles.

Fiction Will consider all genres of Children's and Young Adult Fiction, including Fantasy, Science Fiction and Humour.

Submission Guidelines Send proposal package with synopsis, author biography and first 10,000 words of sample material by email.

Recent Sale(s) *Dragon Horse,* Peter Ward (Random House Children's Books)

Client(s) Steve Alton, Louise Cooper, Kimberly Greene, Adam Guillain, Lorna Read, Andrea Shavick, Peter Ward

Tips Wade & Doherty are always open for submissions and prefer submissions by email, although they will also accept them by post.

Watson, Little Ltd
48–56 Bayham Place, London, NW1 0EU

☎ 020 7388 7529

☎ 020 7388 8501

✉ office@watsonlittle.com

🌐 www.watsonlittle.com

Contact Managing Director, Mandy Little; Senior Agent, James Willis; Literary Agent, Isabel Atherton (Young Authors)

Insider Info Actively seeking clients. Currently handles non-fiction books, fiction, novels and children's books. Will consider simultaneous submissions. Proposals returned if accompanied by SAE. Obtains new clients by queries or submissions. Commission rates of 15 per cent for domestic sales, 20 per cent for foreign sales and 15 per cent for film sales. Overseas Associates are The Marsh Agency Ltd; Film and Television Associates are The Sharland Organisation Ltd and MBA Literary Agents Ltd; USA Associates are Howard Morhaim Literary Agency (Adult) and The Chudney Organisation (Children's). Does not charge a reading fee.

Member of the Association of Authors' Agents.

Non-Fiction Will consider Children's Educational, History and Science titles.

Fiction Will consider Children's and Young Adult Fiction.

Submission Guidelines Send query letter with SAE and synopsis. No scripts, poetry, short stories or pure academia considered.

Recent Sale(s) *Fat Dog Thin,* David Alderton (Hamlyn); *Maddigan's Fantasia,* Margaret Mahy (Faber & Faber)

Tips Watson, Little does not accept email queries or full-length unsolicited manuscripts. The agency also represents a small number of illustrators. Contact Mandy Little for further details.

ILLUSTRATOR'S

Advocate
39 Church Road, Wimbledon Village, London, SW19 5DQ
- 020 8879 1166
- 020 8879 3303
- mail@advocate-art.com
- www.advocate-art.com

Contact Managing Director, Edward Burns
Established 1992
Insider Info Actively seeking clients. Currently represents 200 artists and illustrators. Supplies work to book and magazine publishers, greeting card publishers and advertising agencies, usually mid-market. Obtains new clients through queries and submissions. Commission rates of 30–35 per cent. Does not offer a critiquing service.
Illustration Considers all types of illustration, including Children's books, Educational books and Non-Fiction.
Submission Guidelines Send sample work by email, as JPEG attachments.
Client(s) Alex Burnett, Astrid Kroemer, Chris Boyd, Gilad Soffer, Melanie Mitchell, Sharon Williams
Tips Advocate generally supply mid-market clients, but will go mass-market or top-end if pushed.

The Agency (London) Ltd
See entry under Literary Agents

Allied Artists
63 Sheen Road, Richmond, Surrey, TW9 1YJ
- 020 8334 1010
- 020 8334 9900
- info@allied-artists.net
- www.allied-artists.net

Contact Mary Burtenshaw, Gary Mills

Established 1983
Insider Info Currently represents 40 artists and illustrators. Supplies work to international publishers, book packagers, magazine groups, educational bodies and advertising and design studios. Commission rates of 30–35 per cent.
Illustration Considers all types of illustration, including Realistic Figure Illustrations, Stylised Work and Cartoons for Children's books.
Client(s) Cathy Menzies, Bill Crews, Brett Hudson, Helen Smith, Jo Banner, Omri Stephenson, Steve Barkess
Tips Also offers a syndication library of realistic illustrations to the book and magazine markets.

Arena
31 Eleanor Road, London, E15 4AB
- 0845 050 7600
- info@arenaworks.com
- www.arenaworks.com

Contact Tamlyn Francis, Caroline Thomson
Established 1970
Insider Info Currently represents 33 artists and illustrators. Supplies work for book covers, children's books, magazines and newspapers, designs for packaging and advertising campaigns. Commission rate of 20 per cent.
Illustration Considers all types of illustration, including Children's Picture books, Fiction and Book Covers.
Client(s) Colin Backhouse, Frances Castle, Brigid Collins, Faranak, Christopher Gibbs, Philip Hood, John Howe, Teresa Murfin, Janet Woolley
Tips Arena also handles original artwork for corporate clients and digital designs for new media.

The Art Agency (Wildlife Art Ltd)
The Lodge, Cargate Lane, Saxlingham Thorpe, Norwich, NR15 1TU

- 01508 471500
- 01508 470391
- info@the-art-agency.co.uk
- www.theartagency.co.uk

Established 1992
Insider Info Actively seeking clients. Currently represents over 30 illustrators. Clients include UK and international book and magazine publishers, packaging and advertising agencies, such as BBC Magazines, DeAgostini, Dorling Kindersley, HarperCollins, Reader's Digest and Scholastic. Receives approximately ten submissions per week. Unsuccessful proposals will be returned with SAE. Obtains new clients through queries and submissions. Commission rates of 30 per cent.
Illustration Considers all types of illustration, including Traditional Illustration and Digital Illustration, for Fiction and Non-Fiction for all age groups.
Submission Guidelines Send sample copies of illustration either as high-quality prints, or on CD (containing low resolution JPEG files, each under 500KB). Include SAE for return. Does not accept email submissions.
Client(s) Robin Carter, Rob Davis, Mike Dodd, Sally Launder, Peter Scott
Tips The Art Agency specialises in children's and young adult illustrations. They only represent illustrators, not fine artists. Does not accept illustrations for greeting cards, or prints.

Artist Partners Ltd
2E The Chandlery, 50 Westminster Bridge Road, London, SE1 7QY

- 020 7401 7904
- 020 7401 3378
- christine@artistpartners.com
- www.artistpartners.com

Contact Christine Isteed
Established 1951
Insider Info Actively seeking clients. Currently represents 68 artists and illustrators. Clients include book publishers, magazine and newspaper publishers, design and advertising agencies, film and animation studios. Unsuccessful proposals will be returned with SAE. Obtains new clients through queries and submissions.
Member of the Society of Artists Agents.
Illustration Considers all types of illustration, including Traditional, Digital, 3D and Animation.

Submission Guidelines Send image proofs, or JPEG files on a CD by post with SAE.
Client(s) Gary Blythe, Sam Hadley, Lizzie Sanders, Caroline Swanne
Tips When sending submissions be sure to mark the package 'FAO: Christine Isteed'.

Art Market
51 Oxford Drive, London, SE1 2FB

- 020 7407 8111
- 020 7407 8222
- info@artmarketillustration.com
- www.artmarketillustration.com

Contact Philip Reed
Established 1988
Insider Info Actively seeking clients. Currently represents over 35 artists and illustrators. Clients include book publishers and billboard, design and advertising agencies. Obtains new clients through queries and submissions.
Member of the Society of Artists Agents.
Illustration Considers all types of illustration, including Digital and 3D, for Billboards, Posters, Publicity & Marketing and Packaging, as well as for Children's and Adult Book Covers.
Submission Guidelines Send samples by email as JPEG files, or send a link to the online gallery.
Client(s) Petria Whelan, Gillian Martin
Tips Although not specifically an agency for children's illustrators, Art Market does work with clients in the book publishing industry. Illustrations are all contemporary in style. Art Market will only respond to successful submissions.

The Artworks
40 Frith Street, London, W1D 5LN

- 020 7734 3333
- 020 7734 3484
- lucy@theartworksinc.com
- steph@theartworksinc.com
- www.theartworksinc.com

Contact Lucy Scherer, Stephanie Alexander
Insider Info Currently represents over 40 artists and illustrators. Clients include book publishers, design and advertising agencies. Commission rates of 25 per cent.
Member of the Society of Artists Agents.
Illustration Considers all types of illustration, including Children's books and Gift books.
Client(s) Lisel Ashlock, Izhar Cohen, Heather Gatley, Sarah McMenemy, Hanoch Piven, Ai Tatebayashi, Beegee Tolpa

Tips The Artworks also has offices in New York and Japan, and works with a number of international clients.

Associated Freelance Artists Ltd
124 Elm Park Mansions, Park Walk, London, SW10 0AR
- 020 7352 6890
- 020 7352 8125

Contact Director, Eva Morris; Director, Doug FitzMaurice

Insider Info Clients include book and magazine publishers, and greeting card companies.

Illustration Considers all types of illustration, particularly for Children's Educational books.

Tips Mostly represents freelance illustrators.

Beehive Illustration
42a Cricklade Street, Cirencester, Gloucestershire, GL7 1JH
- 01285 885149
- 01285 641291
- paul@beehiveillustration.co.uk
- www.beehiveillustration.co.uk

Contact Paul Beebee (New Clients)

Established 1989

Insider Info Currently represents over 80 illustrators. Clients include children's book publishers. Commission rates of 25 per cent.

Illustration Considers all types of illustration, specialising in Children's Educational and Language Non-Fiction, and General Children's books.

Client(s) Adrian Barclay, Neil Chapman, Marie Anne Didierjean, Jane Eccles, Tina McNaughton, Martin Sanders

Tips Deals with both UK and international clients.

Caroline Sheldon Literary Agency
See entry under Literary Agents

Celia Catchpole
See entry under Literary Agents

The Copyrights Group Ltd
23 West Bar, Banbury, Oxfordshire, OX16 9SA
- 01295 672050
- 01295 672060
- enquiries@copyrights.co.uk
- www.copyrights.co.uk

Contact CEO, Nicholas Durbridge; Creative Director, Linda Pooley

Insider Info The Copyrights Group is an independent licensing organisation that represents writers, artists and the owners of quality characters and brand names for licensing to manufacturers and retailers.

Client(s) Properties include: *Fungus the Bogeyman*, *Horrible Histories*, Jacqueline Wilson, *Maisy*, *Paddington Bear*, *Peter Rabbit*, *Spot*, *The Snowman* and *The Wombles*.

Tips The Copyrights Group is not an agent, but handles the licensing of established characters for promotional purposes.

Curtis Brown Group Ltd
See entry under Literary Agents

David Higham Associates Ltd
See entry under Literary Agents

David Lewis Illustration
Worlds End Studios, 134 Lots Road, London, SW10 0RJ
- 020 7435 7762
- 020 7435 1945
- david@davidlewisillustration.com
- www.davidlewisillustration.com

Contact David Lewis

Established 1974

Insider Info Currently represents 20 illustrators. Clients include book publishers, magazine and newspaper publishers, greeting card companies, toy and games packagers, corporate bodies and animation studios. Commission rates of 30 per cent.

Illustration Considers all types of illustration, including Children's Fiction, Non-Fiction, Educational books and Multimedia content.

Submission Guidelines Send sample copies (colour or black and white) by post with SAE. Do not send samples via CD or email.

Client(s) Bruce Hogarth, Catriona Hardie, Jason Chapman, Marilyn Day, Tim Pond

Tips David Lewis' illustrators cover a wide range of genres, including fantasy and science fiction.

Eastwing
99 Chase Side, Enfield, Middlesex, EN2 6NL
- 020 8367 6760
- 020 8367 6730
- andrea@eastwing.co.uk
- www.eastwing.co.uk

Contact Andrea Plummer

Insider Info Actively seeking clients. Currently represents over 30 illustrators. Clients include publishing, editorial, design and advertising companies. Obtains new clients through queries and submissions. Commission rates of 30 per cent. Member of the Society of Artists Agents.

Illustration Considers all types of illustration, mainly with a contemporary style.

Submission Guidelines Send four or five low resolution samples by email, including a link to your website, to: representation@eastwing.co.uk

Client(s) Juliette Borda, Damian Gascoigne, Joanna Walsh

Tips Eastwing is the sister agency of Inkshed. Eastwing seems to specialise more in contemporary adult illustration, for corporate clients and marketing, rather than for children's illustration.

Elizabeth Roy Literary Agency

See entry under Literary Agents

Eve White

See entry under Literary Agents

Eye Candy Illustration

Pepperpot Corner, Manor Yard, Blithbury Road, Hamstall Ridware, Staffordshire, WS15 3RS
- 01889 504411
- info@eyecandy.co.uk
- www.eyecandy.co.uk

Established 2002

Insider Info Actively seeking clients. Currently represents over 40 artists and illustrators. Clients include book publishers, editorial and packaging companies, design and advertising agencies and greetings card manufacturers. Unsuccessful proposals will be returned with SAE. Obtains new clients through queries and submissions.

Illustration Considers Contemporary UK and International illustration.

Submission Guidelines Send printed samples by post with SAE, or email samples as 72 dpi JPEG files to: newtalent@eyecandy.co.uk

Client(s) Kenneth Andersson, Mel Croft, Joy Gosney, Adam Howling, Paul Powis

Tips Eye Candy are a successful company, who work with international clients as well as UK companies. They aim to maintain a close and flexible relationship with their illustrators.

Felicity Bryan Literary Agency

See entry under Literary Agents

FOLIO

10 Gate Street, Lincoln's Inn Fields, London, WC2A 3HP
- 020 7242 9562
- 020 7242 1816
- all@folioart.co.uk
- www.folioart.co.uk

Established 1982

Insider Info Currently represents 40 artists and illustrators. Clients include book publishers, and design and advertising agencies.

Illustration Considers all types of illustration, including Traditional, Digital and Multimedia.

Client(s) Jill Barthorpe, Maria Colino, Alex Green, Anne Sharp, Roger Watt

Tips FOLIO is particularly interested in high-quality, versatile artists, who are able to work in a variety of mediums.

Frances McKay Illustration

18 Lammas Green, London, SE26 6LT
- 020 8693 7006
- frances@francesmckay.com
- www.francesmckay.com

Contact Director, Frances McKay

Established 1999

Insider Info Currently represents 18 illustrators. Clients include book publishers and packagers, such as Barrington Stoke, Bloomsbury Children's Books, Faber & Faber and Random House Children's Books. Commission rates of 25 per cent.

Illustration Considers illustrations for Picture books and Children's books aimed at children over the age of four.

Submission Guidelines Send sample copies by post with SAE, or as JPEG files on a CD. Alternatively send low-resolution scans by email.

Client(s) Andrew Brakespeare, Elena Gomez, Francois Hall, Charlotte Hard, Chris Mould, Shan Wells

Tips Check the website for an idea of what styles the agency is interested in.

Fraser Ross Associates

See entry under Literary Agents

Graham-Cameron Illustration

The Studio, 23 Holt Road, Sheringham, Norfolk, NR26 8NB

- ☏ 01263 821333
- ☏ 01263 821334
- ✉ enquiry@graham-cameron-illustration.com
- 🌐 www.graham-cameron-illustration.com

Contact Partners: Duncan Graham-Cameron, Helen Graham-Cameron, Mike Graham-Cameron

Established 1985

Insider Info Actively seeking clients. Currently represents 42 illustrators. Clients include book publishers. Unsuccessful proposals will be returned with SAE. Obtains new clients through queries and submissions.

Illustration Considers all types of illustration, both Traditional and Digital, for Children's General and Educational books. Ages range from Younger Children to Teenage and Young Adult books.

Submission Guidelines Send sample copies by post or by email, as JPEG attachments. Alternatively, send a query by email with a link to an online gallery.

Client(s) Tim Archbold, Neil Boyce, Bridget Dowty, Lyn Gray, Britt Harcus, Peter Kent, Bob Moulder, Pip Sampson, James Walmsley

Tips Graham-Cameron specialises in illustrators for picture books and children's educational books.

Greene & Heaton Ltd

See entry under Literary Agents

Illustration

2 Brooks Court, Cringle Street, London, SW8 5BX

- ☏ 020 7720 5202
- ☏ 020 3333 5920
- ✉ team@illustrationweb.com
- 🌐 www.illustrationweb.com

Contact Mike Cowley, Juliette Lott, Harry Lyon-Smith

Established 1929

Insider Info Actively seeking clients. Currently represents over 100 artists and illustrators. Clients include book publishers, design and advertising agencies, broadcast companies and new media. Obtains new clients through queries and submissions.

Illustration Considers all types of illustration, including Traditional and Digital Art and Animation, for a range of genres. These include Children's books, Character Illustrations and Toy Packaging. Member of the Society of Artists Agents.

Submission Guidelines Fill in online form available at: www.illustrationweb.com/submit.asp

Client(s) Linda Bronson, Chris Ede, Andy Hammond, Sonia Kretschmar, John Richardson

Tips Illustration generally only accepts two to three new illustrators per year, who must have a progressive, contemporary style, as well as previous experience and success in the illustration market. All illustrators must be able to use up to date digital software, such as Photoshop and Illustrator.

The Illustration Cupboard

22 Bury Street, St. James's, London, SW1Y 6AL

- ☏ 020 7976 1727
- ✉ john@illustrationcupboard.com
- 🌐 www.illustrationcupboard.com

Contact John Huddy

Established 1995

Insider Info Currently represents over 50 artists. Specialises in the exhibition and sale of original contemporary book illustration from around the world.

Illustration Considers all types of art and illustration, including Children's Book Covers.

Tips The Illustration Cupboard mostly functions as a gallery and sales point for internationally acclaimed artists and illustrators. It hosts an annual winter exhibition, as well as many single-artist and two-man exhibitions.

Inkshed

99 Chase Side, Enfield, EN2 6NL

- ☏ 020 8367 4545
- ☏ 020 8367 6730
- ✉ abby@inkshed.co.uk
- 🌐 www.inkshed.co.uk

Contact Abby Glassfield

Established 1985

Insider Info Actively seeking clients. Currently represents 30 illustrators. Clients include publishing, editorial, design and advertising companies. Obtains new clients through queries and submissions. Commission rates of 30 per cent.
 Member of the Society of Artists Agents.

Illustration Considers all types of illustration.

Submission Guidelines Send four or five low resolution samples by email, including a link to your website, to: representation@inkshed.co.uk

Client(s) Jasmine Chin, Martin Chatterton, Lizzie Gardiner, Turinna Gren, Anne Kristin Hagesaether

Tips Due to a high volume of queries, Inkshed will generally only respond to successful submissions.

Jenny Brown Associates
See entry under UK & Irish Children's Publishers

John Hodgson Agency
38 Westminster Palace Gardens, Artillery Row, London, SW1P 1RR
- 020 7580 3773
- 020 7222 4468
Established 1965
Insider Info Currently represents six artists. Clients include book publishers. Obtains new clients through queries and submissions. Commission rates of 25 per cent.
Illustration Considers all types of illustration, especially Picture books for 0–8 year olds.
Submission Guidelines Query by phone in the first instance. When sending samples enclose SAE for return.
Tips John Hodgson is a small company, so always phone before sending any samples.

John Martin & Artists
12 Haven Court, Hatfield Peverel, Chelmsford, Essex, CM3 2SD
- 01245 380337
- bernardjma@aol.com
- www.jm-a.co.uk
Contact Bernard Bowen-Davies
Established 1956
Insider Info Currently represents 12 illustrators. Clients include book publishers.
Illustration Considers illustration for Children's Fiction, Non-Fiction and Educational books.
Submission Guidelines Send sample copies by post with SAE.

Kathy Jakeman Illustration
Richmond Business Centre, 23–24 George Street, Richmond, Surrey, TW9 1HY
- 020 8973 2000
- kathy@kji.co.uk
- www.kji.co.uk
Contact Kathy Jakeman
Established 1990
Insider Info Currently represents over 15 illustrators. Clients include children's book publishers. Commission rates of 25 per cent.
Illustration Considers all types of illustration for Children's books.

Submission Guidelines Send sample copies by post with covering letter and SAE. Does not accept email submissions.
Tips Kathy Jakeman specialises in illustrations for children's publishing. They are currently re-developing their website, so check back for submission guidelines.

LAW Ltd
See entry under Literary Agents

Linda Rogers Associates
163 Half Moon Lane, London, SE24 9JG
- 020 7501 9106
- contact@lindarogers.net
- www.lindarogers.net
Contact Linda Rogers
Established 1973
Insider Info Currently represents 57 artists and illustrators. Clients include book and magazine publishers. Unsuccessful proposals will be returned with SAE. Obtains new clients through queries and submissions. Commission rates of 25 per cent.
Illustration Considers all types of illustration, focusing on Children's books for all ages.
Submission Guidelines Send sample copies by post with SAE. Does not accept submissions by email.
Client(s) Jacey Abram, James Bourne, Elke Counsell, Alex Higlett, Edward Ripley
Tips Linda Rogers is most interested in contemporary children's illustration featuring multi-racial characters.

Maggie Mundy Illustrators' Agency
14 Ravenscroft Park Mansions, Dalling Road, London, W6 0HG
- 020 8748 2391
- maggiemundy@compuserve.com
Contact Maggie Mundy
Established 1983
Insider Info Currently represents 13 artists and illustrators. Clients include book publishers. Commission rates of 25–30 per cent.
Illustration Considers all types of illustration, including Children's books, Educational books and Non-Fiction.
Tips Maggie Mundy looks for originality, humour and detail in illustration submissions.

Meiklejohn Illustration Ltd

5 Risborough Street, London, SE1 0HF
- 020 7593 0500
- 020 7593 0501
- info@meiklejohn.co.uk
- www.meiklejohn.co.uk

Contact Charlotte Manning, Alice Wilkinson
Established 1973
Insider Info Actively seeking clients. Currently represents 43 illustrators. Clients include book publishers, design and advertising agencies, and new media companies. Unsuccessful proposals will be returned with SAE. Obtains new clients through queries and submissions.
 Member of the Society of Artists Agents.
Illustration Considers all types of illustration, including Traditional and Digital Illustration, and Photo Manipulation.
Submission Guidelines Send a CD portfolio; printed samples by post with SAE; or email up to four samples as JPEG files (at 72 dpi, no larger than 400 pixels); or your website url to: submissions@meiklejohn.co.uk
Client(s) Fred Blunt, Ken Gamage, Andrew Hamilton, Garry Parsons, Chris Simpson
Tips Meiklejohn is one of the UK's most successful illustration agencies and its artists cover a very wide range of styles and genres. Also has a sister company called New Division (www.newdivision.com) which is headed by Charlotte Manning. New Division specialises in stylish contemporary illustration.

NB Illustration Ltd

40 Bowling Green Lane, London, EC1R 0NE
- 020 7278 9131
- 020 7278 9121
- info@nbillustration.co.uk
- www.nbillustration.co.uk

Contact Charlotte Berens, Joe Najman, Paul Najman
Established 2000
Insider Info Actively seeking clients. Currently represents over 35 artists and illustrators. Clients include book publishers, magazine and newspaper publishers, and advertising agencies. Obtains new clients through queries and submissions. Commission rates of 30 per cent.
 Member of the Association of Illustrators.
Illustration Considers all types of illustration, including Children's Picture books.
Submission Guidelines Send printed samples by post with SAE, or email samples as 72dpi JPEG files (up to 1MB) to: submissions@nbillustration.co.uk

Client(s) Mark Beech, Jo Goodberry, Tom Gravestock, Martin Macrae, Nicola Taylor, Kevin Waldron
Tips NB Illustration are always looking for new talent and are happy to represent overseas illustrators.

The Organisation

69 Caledonian Road, Kings Cross, London, N1 9BT
- 020 7833 8268
- 020 7833 8269
- info@organisart.co.uk
- www.organisart.co.uk

Contact Lorraine Owen
Established 1987
Insider Info Currently represents 68 artists and illustrators. Clients include book publishers, and design, editorial, packaging and advertising agencies. Commission rates of 30 per cent.
Illustration Considers all types of illustration, including both Traditional and Digital, for Children's Picture books and Educational titles.
Client(s) Javier Joaquin, Sepia Lace, Katherine Lucas, Del Thorpe
Tips The Organisation represents international artists in a variety of media.

PFD (Peters, Fraser & Dunlop)

See entry under Literary Agents

Phosphor Art

41 The Pumphouse, Pumphouse Close, Off Renforth Street, London, SE16 7HS
- 020 7064 4666
- 020 7064 4660
- info@phosphorart.com
- www.phosphorart.com

Contact Trina/Luke
Insider Info Currently represents 49 illustrators. Clients include book publishers, design and advertising agencies and broadcast companies.
 Member of the Society of Artists Agents.
Illustration Considers all types of illustration, including a variety of Traditional styles, Digital Illustration and Animation.
Client(s) Anthony Atkinson, Claire Fletcher, Alison Lang, Darren Whittington
Tips Phosphor Art is a young company that specialises in innovative graphic digital illustration. They also have a division called 'Radiation Monkeys', for animators and digital producers.

Rogers, Coleridge & White Ltd
See entry under Literary Agents

Rosemary Sandberg Ltd
See entry under Literary Agents

SGA Children's Illustration Agency
Argyll House, 1a All Saints Passage, London, SW18 1EP
- 020 8875 8335
- 020 8875 8301
- rebecca@sgadesignart.com
- www.sgadesignart.com

Established 1985
Insider Info Actively seeking clients. Currently represents over 30 illustrators. Clients include book publishers and greeting card companies. Obtains new clients through queries and submissions. Commission rates of 30 per cent.
Illustration Considers all types of illustration, focusing mainly on Children's Picture books, Activity books, Educational titles and Board books, as well as Teenage books and Greeting Cards.
Submission Guidelines Send sample copies by post as hard copies, or on disc, or by email as JPEG files.
Client(s) Andrew Geeson, Doreen Lang, Lucy Pearce, Terry Riley
Tips SGA specialises in illustrations for the children's publishing industry and is always looking for new artists.

Specs Art
93 London Road, Cheltenham, Gloucestershire, GL52 6HL
- 01242 515951
- roland@specsart.com
- www.specsart.com

Contact Roland Berry
Established 1982
Insider Info Currently represents 30 illustrators. Clients include book publishers, advertising agencies and other visual communications companies. Commission rates of 25 per cent.
Illustration Considers all types of illustration, including Aimation work, for cChildren's books and characters.
Submission Guidelines Send up to six samples by email as JPEG files, with a covering letter.
Client(s) Roberta Angeletti, Alan Batson, Poly Bernatene, Gary Slater

Tips Specs Art are specialists in representing licenced character illustration.

Sylvie Poggio Artists' Agency
39 Haselmere Road, London, N8 9RB
- 020 8341 2722
- 020 8374 1725
- sylviepoggio@blueyonder.co.uk
- www.sylviepoggio.com

Insider Info Currently represents 38 illustrators. Clients include book publishers, design and advertising agencies, and new media companies. Member of the Association of Illustrators.
Illustration Considers all types of illustration, including Cildren's books and cCartoons.
Client(s) Anni Axworthy, Sebastian Burnett, Paco Cavero, Lisa Smith, Melanie Sharp

Temple Rogers Artists' Agency
120 Crofton Road, Orpington, Kent, BR6 8HZ
- 01689 826249
- 01689 896312

Contact Patrick Kelleher
Insider Info Clients include book and magazine publishers.
Illustration Considers illustrations for Children's Eucational books and Magazine content.

Vicki Thomas Associates
195 Tollgate Road, London, E6 5JY
- 020 7511 5767
- 020 7473 5177
- vickithomasassociates@yahoo.co.uk
- www.vickithomasassociates.com

Contact Vicki Thomas
Established 1985
Insider Info Currently represents 50 artists and illustrators. Clients include book publishers and packaging, gift and greeting card companies. Commission rates of 25–30 per cent.
Illustration Considers all types of illustration, including Children's books, Packaging and Greeting Cards, as well as Textile Design and Craft.
Submission Guidelines Send sample copies by post with covering letter and SAE.
Client(s) Mayou Alexander, Julia Hulme, Julie Lavender, Jill Moore, Rachel B. Stevens, Carol Tratt
Tips Vicki Thomas also functions as a gift design consultancy, handling textile and papercrafts.

Watson, Little Ltd
See entry under Literary Agents

CHILDREN'S THEATRES

Arts Depot

5 Nether Street, Tally Ho Corner, North Finchley, London, N12 0GA

- 020 8369 5455
- 020 8369 5467
- Online form.
- www.artsdepot.co.uk

Established 1996

Insider Info The Arts Depot is a successful receiving venue for drama, music, dance and comedy. The Arts Depot runs an extensive year round programme of children's productions.

Recent Productions *Tiddalick; Don't Let the Pigeon Drive the Bus!; Head in the Clouds.*

Tips Arts Depot advertises current vacancies on their website.

Birmingham Repertory Theatre

Centenary Square, Broad Street, Birmingham, B1 2EP

- 0121 245 2000
- stage.door@birmingham-rep.co.uk
- www.birmingham-rep.co.uk

Artistic/Editorial Director Rachel Kavanaugh

Established 1913

Insider Info The Rep stages shows specifically for children and runs theatrical initiatives like Transmissions, a young writers programme for ages 12–25, and Page to Stage, a writing development programme for young people. The Door is the theatre space dedicated to the production of new plays by aspiring writers. The Young Rep is a successful youth theatre.

Recent Productions *Hansel and Gretal; Peter Pan Christmas Production.*

Submission Guidelines First-time writers are eligible, as are established writers.

Tips The Rep will read unsolicited scripts as part of its 'attachment' scheme with the aim of developing new plays for production and giving the writer support without the pressure of a commission. For information about deadlines, contact the Literary Department on 0121 245 2045.

Buxton Opera House

Water Street, Buxton, Derbyshire, SK17 6XN

- 01298 72050
- 01298 27563
- admin@boh.org.uk
- www.buxtonoperahouse.org.uk

Contact Chief Executive, Andrew Aughton

Established 1903

Insider Info A successful receiving theatre for adults and children, which stages around 450 shows each year. Plans are in place to add a children's theatre. Boasts an impressive education and community department which organises holiday activities for children, runs school workshops and devises larger scale events such as the annual A–Z children's festival which hosts performances and drama workshops for people aged 1–19. Organises other festivals including the Buxton Fringe season as part of the Buxton festival, where new writers, emerging comedy talent and those from the cutting edge cinema scene can perform their work.

Recent Productions *Basil of the Caribbean; Potted Potter.*

Tips Contact the Education Officer Louise Kerwin on 01298 72050, or via email to education@boh.org.uk, if you have any ideas for a project in the education and community programme.

The Byre Theatre of St. Andrews

Abbey Street, St. Andrews, Fife, KY16 9LA

- 01334 475000
- 01334 475370
- rosanne.gunn@byretheatre.com
- www.byretheatre.com

Contact Programme Officer, Rosanne Gunn

Established 1933

Insider Info A modern theatre which puts on a programme of creative drama, dance and music for children and adults. It also runs an active education programme for all ages including youth theatre groups for children aged 8-11 and 12-21, and workshops and projects for people aged over 50.

Recent Productions *Olga Volt; The Electric Fairy; Monster Hits.*

Tips Runs a supportive playwright group 'Byrewriters' where writers have the chance to develop their writing skills. Some of these writers, including Chris Dolan and Bob Adams have gone on to have considerable success. Contact Elsie Lindsay for more information.

Chichester Festival Theatre
Oaklands Park, Chichester, West Sussex, PO19 6AP
- 01243 354951
- 01244 354953
- admin@cft.org.uk
- www.cft.org.uk

Artistic/Editorial Director Jonathan Church
Established 1962
Insider Info A famous flagship theatre producing a variety of shows from musicals, through to new writing. During Autumn it becomes a host to touring theatres. The theatre runs education and community projects, such as anti-bullying workshops and activities for children, over the holidays. Runs a successful youth theatre for children aged 10–19 which produces an annual Christmas show. Senior members were commissioned to devise a forum theatre piece tackling bullying in 2005. *Turning The Tide* toured ten West Sussex community youth wings and was the opening performance for the South East Anti-Bullying conference.
Tips Each month the website publishes an interview with a key member of the theatre's staff. This can be a good source of information on future plans and directions for the theatre. Writers may also email marketing@cft.org.uk with a review of one of the shows (250 words maximum). Those selected will gain free entry to a future show and their review will be published on the website. The subject line for this email should read 'Community Critic'.

Contact Theatre Company
Oxford Road, Manchester, M15 6JA
- 0161 274 0623
- Online form.
- www.contact-theatre.org

Artistic/Editorial Director John E. McGrath
Insider Info A specialist theatre based in Manchester working with ages 13–30. Contact supports young artists, as well as acting host to other touring companies. Contact is interested in all forms of new creative work including dance, theatre, spoken word, live art and music, especially from young people, however artists from all ages are welcome. Runs the Contact Young Actors Company for talented young artists.
Submission Guidelines Email proposals to sarahbates@contact-theatre.org, or telephone New Writing on 0161 274 0642, or Creative Development on 0161 274 0625. Payment for full commissions is in accordance with Writers Guild of Great Britain rates.
Tips Contact runs many projects designed to encourage emerging new talent such as RAW Rhythm and Words, a writers project for young people, and Contacting the World, a theatre exchange project for young people. Visit the website for more details.

The Egg - Theatre Royal Bath
Sawclose, Bath, BA1 1ET
- 01225 823476
- hannah.entwistle@theatreroyal.org.uk
- www.theatreroyal.org.uk/the-egg

Contact The Egg Administrator, Hannah Entwistle; Head of Education and Outreach, Jamie Luck
Established 2005
Insider Info Part of the Theatre Royal in Bath, The Egg is a new purpose built theatre for children, young people and their families. It acts as a venue for shows by children and for children.
Recent Productions *The Magnificent Flying Machine.*
Tips Runs in-school or after school drama projects, including the chance for schools to perform in The Egg. Storm on the Lawn is the Theatre Royal's annual summer school which brings together 60 young people, who work with theatre professionals to devise an outdoor theatrical play. Sunmmer 2007 hosted the commissioned fantasy piece *Boewulf.*

Everyman Theatre
Regent Street, Cheltenham, Gloucestershire, GL50 1HQ
- 01242 512515
- 01242 224305
- admin@everymantheatre.org.uk
- www.everymantheatre.org.uk

Artistic/Editorial Director Sue Colverd
Established 1891
Insider Info A presenting and producing theatre promoting a wide range of plays from ballet to traditional family Christmas Pantomimes. As well as the main theatre, seating 684, the 'Other Space' studio hosts experimental, small scale productions, education and youth work, and drama workshops.
Recent Productions *An Old Spot Nativity,* Christmas show for 2007.

Tips Everyman 'Reachout' is a community scheme which enables young and old to explore their creative abilities through youth workshops and other creative programmes. Part of Reachout's remit is to work with, and develop new writers. For more information on any Reachout scheme, contact: reachout@everymantheatre.org.uk.

Horsecross
Perth Theatre, 185 High Street, Perth, PH1 5UW
❶ 0845 612 6324
✉ jmcgregor@horsecross.co.uk
⊕ www.horsecross.co.uk
Artistic/Editorial Director Jennifer McGregor
Insider Info Horsecross is a successful arts centre that operates a wide range of theatre productions, including music, plays, films, comedy and family shows. Perth Youth Theatre is a fun and dynamic company for people aged 12–21 from the Perth area. The theatre runs extensive community and education work, including workshops and a young playwrights group.
Recent Productions *Shopping For Shoes,* a funny romantic play about teenage love written by Tim Crouch.
Tips Horsecross advertises job vacancies on their website. For more information on the playwrights group and youth theatre see the separate entry under groups.

Komodia Brighton
44 Gardner Street, Brighton, BN1 1UN
❶ 01273 647101
✉ admin@komedia.co.uk
⊕ www.komedia.co.uk
Established 1994
Insider Info The award-winning live entertainment venue hosts an eclectic mix of music, theatre, comedy, cabaret and kids shows together with a café, bistro and late bars. Acts as a venue for touring children's theatre companies. Sister groups in Bath and Edinburgh.
Recent Productions *Inside Out.*
Tips Komodia specialises in nurturing talent and promoting new work, including children's productions, from comedies through to visual theatre.

Leeds Childrens Theatre
c/o Carriageworks Theatre, The Electric Press, 3 Millennium Square, Leeds, LS2 3AD
✉ info@leeds-childrens-theatre.co.uk

⊕ www.leeds-childrens-theatre.co.uk
Established 1935
Insider Info An amateur dramatic society, run entirely by volunteers, and a member of the Leeds Civic Arts Guild. It is based at The Carriageworks Theatre in the heart of Leeds. Performs two shows per year, one in the Spring, and the other in Autumn. The LCT offers young members the chance to direct and produce a play as part of their new Greenroom initiative production, which is performed at Upstairs @ The Carriageworks, exclusively for LCT members and their families.
Recent Prodctions *Peter Pan; The Scatterbrained Scarecrow of Oz.*
Tips Runs an excellent Saturday morning drama workshop, however there is a two year waiting list for a place.

Library Theatre Company
Central Library, St. Peter's Square, Manchester, M2 5PD
❶ 0161 234 1913
❶ 0161 228 6481
✉ Online form.
⊕ www.librarytheatre.com
Artistic/Editorial Director Chris Honer
Established 1952
Insider Info One of the oldest repertory performing theatre companies in the UK. It produces a wide and varied programme of shows from children's theatre to contemporary works. Their education programme includes drama workshops for schools and work experience for young people. Library Theatre is also a touring company and acts as a venue for other touring companies, comedians and poetry performers.
Recent Productions *Tom's Midnight Garden.*
Tips The Library Theatre Education Department is happy to develop tailor made programmes for schools or organisations, from a single day to ongoing projects.

Lyric Hammersmith
Lyric Square, King Street, London, W6 0QL
❶ 08700 500 511
❶ 020 8741 5965
✉ enquiries@lyric.co.uk
⊕ www.lyric.co.uk
Artistic/Editorial Director David Farr
Insider Info The Lyric Theatre in West London comprises of two performance spaces: the main theatre, and a contemporary studio which stages new pieces. A leading producing and presenting

theatre, Lyric works with some of the most promising companies in Britain, including some of the best children's companies. The Christmas Pantomime production is of particular note. The Lyric holds a regular programme of Saturday drama club shows and runs creative learning programmes for 11–19 year olds in the UK.

Recent Productions *Christmas Claytime* and *Beauty and the Beast* are Christmas productions for 2007.

Tips The productions rarely result from unsolicited scripts, but from direct and ongoing relationships with directors, designers and companies.

The New Wolsey Theatre
Civic Drive, Ipswich, Suffolk, IP1 2AS
- 01473 295911
- 01473 295910
- info@wolseytheatre.co.uk
- ekidd@wolseytheatre.co.uk
- www.wolseytheatre.co.uk

Artistic/Editorial Director Peter Rowe
Established 2001

Insider Info After the closure of the original Wolsey Theatre, The New Wolsey Theatre opened in 2001. It is a producing and performing theatre, playing host to a number of successful touring companies with performances that include drama, music, comedy, poetry, dance and children's shows. The Wolsey Theatre runs a Youth Theatre Group for ages 13–18 with performances staged in the New Wolsey Theatre.

Recent Productions *Beneath the Waves,* by Theatre Is...; *Aesop's Fables.*

Tips For playwrights wishing to develop their ideas and scripts the theatre runs the Writer's Workshop, as well as PULSE – the fringe festival which showcases new and emergent talent.

Norwich Puppet Theatre
St James, Whitefriars, Norwich, Norfolk, NR3 1TN
- 01603 629921
- 01603 617578
- info@puppettheatre.co.uk
- http://puppettheatre.co.uk

Artistic/Editorial Director Luis Boy
Established 1979

Insider Info Norwich Puppet Theatre (NPT) produces a year round programme of puppetry shows and puppet workshops for family centred audiences at its own theatre. The NPT also tours schools, international festivals and other venues throughout the UK. The theatre aims to extend puppetry into different art forms; exploring rod, glove, shadow, objects, toys, and masks, instead of developing commercial puppetry shows.

Submission Guidelines Accepts query and synopsis. Submissions accompanied by a SAE will be returned.

Tips The company generally produce one play per year and aim to report back to writers within four weeks. Most NPT productions are created in a workshop environment, so often a script is the starting point from which the production will be created. The rights agreement and subsequent payment will depend on the resulting production, and payment will be via royalties (three per cent).

Nuffield Theatre
University Road, Southampton, SO17 1TR
- 023 8031 5500
- 023 8031 5511
- info@nuffieldtheatre.co.uk
- www.nuffieldtheatre.co.uk

Artistic/Editorial Director Patrick Sanford
Established 1964

Insider Info An award winning presenting and producing theatre for adults and children that stages shows in its main house, studio and on tours nationally and internationally, to theatres, schools and other venues. Their reputation of being a centre of creative excellence in Southampton proceeds them, with a wide repertoire from new writings, to British and foreign classics. Runs two successful Youth Theatre Groups for people aged 5–12 and 13–25.

Recent Productions *Dragons Teeth,* by Stuff and Nonsense Theatre.
Burglar Bill, by Pandoras Box.

Tips Runs an extremely successful playwrights course for aspiring writers, which meets fortnightly every Thursday evening over a two year period resulting in a full length production. Success stories include Katie Betts, winner of Channel 4's *The Play's the Thing.* Email alison.thurley@nuffieldtheatre.co.uk for application details and general information.

The Orange Tree Theatre
1 Clarence Street, Richmond, Surrey, TW9 2SA
- 020 8940 3633
- Online form.
- www.orangetreetheatre.co.uk

Artistic/Editorial Director Sam Walters
Established 1971

Insider Info The Orange Tree is a successful receiving venue for children and adults, with a policy of producing new plays, foreign works and even musicals. The seating area consists of 172 spaces. The Orange Tree runs three youth theatres for children aged 12–18, and provides Shakespeare workshops for schools.

Recent Productions *The Suitcase Kid*.

Tips Since 1986 the Orange Tree has run a highly successful Trainee Director scheme. Each year the scheme provides the important first steps for two young directors to assist on all productions, and then direct a showcase at the end of their year.

Polka Theatre for Children
240 The Broadway, Wimbledon, London, SW19 1SB

- 020 8545 8320
- 020 8545 8365
- admin@polkatheatre.com
- richardmashannon@polkatheatre.com
- www.polkatheatre.com

Artistic/Editorial Director Jonathan Lloyd

Contact Associate Director: New Writing, Richard Shannon

Established 1967

Insider Info A specialist producer and host of children's theatre based in Wimbledon, London. Audiences can expect imaginative new writers, dynamic performers, inventive adaptations of popular stories and resonant subjects. Every show is accompanied by a learning programme for schools and families which consist of workshops, online working packs and after show events. It has two auditorium spaces, the smaller of which is dedicated exclusively to early year audiences. Polka is well established and recognised in this field.

Recent Productions *There's Only One Wayne Matthews!*, a show celebrating Black culture for children aged ten and over.

Submission Guidelines Accepts unsolicited scripts. Initially an outline and five pages of the plot are required. Contact Richard Shannon by email, or telephone: 020 8545 8349

Tips There are extremely detailed guidance notes for writers on what Polka is looking for, and hints and tips on writing children's theatre, available to download on their website.

Queen's Theatre
Billet Lane, Hornchurch, RM11 1QT

- 01708 462362
- 01708 462363
- info@queens-theatre.co.uk
- www.queens-theatre.co.uk

Artistic/Editorial Director Bob Carlton

Established 1953

Insider Info Queen's Theatre has a resident company of actors and musicians who present a diverse, popular and innovative programme of eight main-house productions each year, and four Theatre in Education tours throughout the academic year. Queen's Theatre offers a wide and varied Education and Outreach Programme aimed at young people and adult groups, to inspire and provide opportunities for individual study, performance and professional development.

Recent Productions *Brum and the Big Blue Diamond Mystery*, for children over the age of three.

Submission Guidelines No unsolicited scripts. Accepts queries and synopsis. Queen's Theatre produces a mixture of musical theatre, comedy and straight drama.

Tips The Queen's Theatre New Writing Programme is full of opportunities for local aspiring playwrights to learn and develop skills, especially through the Writing Award scheme – writing courses and a writers group that runs monthly.

Redbridge Drama Centre
Churchfields, South Woodford, London, E18 2RB

- 020 8504 5451
- 020 8505 6669
- www.redbridgedramacentre.co.uk

Artistic/Editorial Director Keith Homer

Insider Info The Redbridge Drama Centre provides high quality curriculum support for schools, including children's theatre workshops and technical services, and acts as a host to touring companies. Redbridge runs its own resident Theatre In Education company, Vital Stage, which tours schools and other performing venues. Redbridge has previous handled commissions from the NSPCC.

Recent Productions *Before the City; Lets Keep Talking;Unlocking the Pyramid*.

Tips The Vital Stage theatre group provides excellent opportunities for professional actors, teachers and students to work collaboratively.

Sherman Theatre Company
Senghennydd Road, Cardiff, CF24 4YE

- 029 2064 6901
- 029 2064 6902
- admin@shermantheatre.demon.co.uk
- www.shermantheatre.co.uk

Artistic/Editorial Director Phil Clark

Contact Dinos Aristidou

Insider Info The Sherman Theatre Company, based in Cardiff, produces a wide range of productions every year, including theatre for young people, inventive adaptations of classic dramas and new writing projects. It is a touring company and a youth theatre.

Recent Productions *Beauty and the Beast,* Christmas production for 2007.

Tips Script Slam is a monthly event at which four new young writers can present a 15 minute piece of their scripts. The audience then votes for the piece they want to see developed. Submit 10 to 20 pages of script (either a full play or a sample) for up to eight actors, to Dinos Aristidou. Script Slam leaflets are also available from the theatre.

Soho Theatre
21 Dean Street, London, W1D 3NE
- 020 7287 5060
- 020 7287 5061
- writers@sohotheatre.com
- www.sohotheatre.com

Artistic/Editorial Director Lisa Goldman
Contact Literary Assistant, Rachel Taylor
Established 1969

Insider Info A leading professional theatre based in the heart of London, producing primarily adult shows. Forthcoming children's shows are scheduled throughout the year; visit the website for full listings.

Recent Productions *Men of Steel,* an award winning puppet sensation.

Submission Guidelines Submit complete manuscript, including a brief covering letter and SAE. No email submissions.

Tips What distinguishes Soho is their comprehensive writing centre. They aim to discover new and talented writers, who can also develop and improve their skills through the script reading service. Soho runs the Writers Attachment Programme, and offers awards such as the Verity Bargate Award. Writers can take advantage of the script library and the writer's rooms. Visit the website for full details.

The Theatre of Small Convenience
Edith Walk, Malvern, Worcestershire, WR14 4QH
- 01684 568933
- wctheatre@yahoo.com
- www.wctheatre.co.uk

Artistic/Editorial Director Dennis Neale
Established 1999

Insider Info This intriguing theatre is the smallest in the world seating only twelve people. Situated in Great Malvern, it hosts performances both amateur

and professional in theatre, puppetry, monologues, poetry and story-telling.

Tips The ToSC 'building' was converted from an old Victorian Gentleman's lavatory.

Traverse Theatre
10 Cambridge Street, Edinburgh, EH1 2ED
- 0131 228 3223
- philip.howard@traverse.co.uk
- www.traverse.co.uk

Artistic/Editorial Director Philip Howard
Contact Literary Assistant, Louise Stephens
Established 1963

Insider Info The Traverse Theatre is Edinburgh's new writing theatre, commissioning and supporting writers from Scotland and internationally. An essential element of the Traverse Company's work takes place within the educational sector, concentrating on the process of playwriting for young people. Class Act is a project whereby young people in schools have the opportunity to work with theatre professionals and see their work performed on the Traverse stage. Commissions six plays per year.

Submission Guidelines Submit complete manuscript. Submissions accompanied by a SAE will be returned. Aims to respond to manuscript submissions within six months.

Tips Traverse Young Writers group (ages 18–25), led by professional playwrights, has been running for over three years and meets weekly.

Tricycle Theatre
269 Kilburn High Road, London, NW6 7JR
- 020 7372 6611
- 020 7328 0795
- info@tricycle.co.uk
- www.tricycle.co.uk

Artistic/Editorial Director Nicholas Kent
Established 1980

Insider Info A successful theatre, cinema and art gallery. Tricycle runs a year-round programme of activities for young people, with dedicated theatre productions, films and workshops, as well as an active Youth Theatre and Young Artists Group.

Recent Productions *Peter and the Wolf; The Gingerbread Man; Clownderella.*

Submission Guidelines Submissions accompanied by a SAE will be returned.

Tips The local community includes such diverse cultural groups as Irish, Afro-Caribbean, Jewish and Asian, and the choice of writers and writing tends to reflect this. A fee may be charged for unsolicited scripts. Please phone or email for details.

Unicorn Theatre

147 Tooley Street, Southwark, London, SE1 2HZ
- 020 7645 0500
- 020 7645 0550
- stagedoor@unicorntheatre.com
- www.unicorntheatre.com

Artistic/Editorial Director Tony Graham
Contact Assistant to the Artistic Team, Rhona Foulis
Established 1947
Insider Info One of the leading producers and hosts of professional theatre for children, based in the heart of London. Plays host to a yearly programme of theatre, with professional casts across two main auditoriums. Runs workshops and projects for schools throughout the London area.
Recent Productions *Truckstop*, a dramatic piece of theatre about a Mother's love for her daughter. *How To Beat a Giant,* a fantasy children's piece for over sevens. *Handas Suprise* and *Duck*, Christmas productions for 2007.
Submission Guidelines No unsolicited scripts. Email artistic@unicorntheatre.com for information detailing instructions for writers, or send SAE to Unicorn. Submissions accompanied by SAE will be returned.

Unity Theatre

1 Hope Place, Liverpool, L1 9BG
- 0151 709 6502
- 0151 709 7182
- graemephillips@unitytheatre.co.uk
- www.unitytheatreliverpool.co.uk

Artistic/Editorial Director Graeme Phillips
Established 1944
Insider Info Unity hosts professional children's theatre performances and activities, attracting national and international work of the highest quality. Splatterfest is their week long children's festival, with some of the most exciting theatrical productions from all over the world. Unity also runs Splatterdays, a Saturday drama and craft workshop, aimed at five to thirteen year olds. Summer Splatts is a week long art workshop, which they hold at the beginning of Summer.
Recent Productions *Tasty Tales,* by Tangere Arts; *Drogo Island*.

Submission Guidelines Contact Artistic Director, Graeme Phillips by email provided, or tel 0151 702 7363.
Tips Unity Theatre Liverpool has an excellent track record of encouraging new writing, and supporting new companies. Many writers originally promoted by Unity have gone on to be successful in mainstream theatre.

Watford Palace Theatre

Clarendon Road, Watford, WD17 1JZ
- 01923 235455
- 01923 819664
- enquiries@watfordpalacetheatre.co.uk
- www.watfordtheatre.co.uk

Artistic/Editorial Director Brigid Larmour
Established 1908
Insider Info A theatre with wide appeal, producing modern works, comedies, adaptations of classics, and pantomimes. Also hosts children's shows.
Recent Productions *Aladdin* by Joe Graham
Submission Guidelines No unsolicited manuscripts. Submissions accompanied by SAE will be returned. Works by first-time writers, as well as established writers are accepted.
Tips There are a lot of opportunities for young people to get involved with all aspects of the theatre through 'Active', the education department at the theatre. The department encompasses two successful youth theatres, and new writing projects for adults and young people aged 15–19.

Wycombe Swan theatre

St. Mary Street, High Wycombe, Buckinghamshire, HP11 2XE
- 01494 514444
- 01494 538080
- enquiries@wycombeswan.co.uk
- www.wycombeswan.co.uk

Artistic/Editorial Director Sam McCaffrey
Established 1992
Insider Info An arts venue which consists of three theatre spaces; the Swan Theatre, the Town Hall and the Oak Room. Plays hosts to a various number of productions for children and families, as well as musicals, spoken word, comedy, adult theatre and local events.
Tips Hosts a wide range of children shows, from pantomimes to the Summer Youth Project Play - *Kiss Me Kate* is the production for 2007.

THEATRE

LISTINGS

Young Vic Theatre Company

66 The Cut, London, SE1 8LZ

- ☎ 020 7922 2800
- ☎ 020 7922 2802
- ✉ info@youngvic.org
- 🌐 www.youngvic.org

Artistic/Editorial Director David Lan
Established 1970
Insider Info Britain's leading establishment for young theatre artists - especially directors, where they can develop and practice the performing arts profession.

Recent Productions *The Member of the Wedding; Fragments; A Christmas Carol*

Tips There are extensive opportunities for young people and adults to become involved with the theatre in many capacities. Visit the website for details of schemes such as work experience and training projects. The productions tend to be fairly high profile, so unsolicited scripts are unlikely to be commissioned.

THEATRE GROUPS

Action Space Mobile

Mapplewell & Staincross Village Hall, Darton Lane, Mapplewell, Barnsley, S75 6AL

- ☎ 01226 391112
- ☎ 01226 391112
- ✉ contact@actionspacemobile.org
- 🌐 www.actionspacemobile.org

Artistic/Editorial Director Mary Turner
Insider Info Action Space Mobile (ASM) is a community arts and theatre company that specialises in disabilities and the arts. ASM offer diverse workshops, from music technology, to felt making. There are drama opportunities for people with disabilities through their inclusive theatre companies 'In the Boat' and 'Cross the Sky'. ASM also carry out work in schools, their projects range from one off workshops, to short residencies and long term projects.

Tips Action Space Mobile often commission artists to deliver a range of activities, particularly with young people. ASM will contract experienced specialists such as artists, drama and movement specialists, dancers, puppeteers, mosaic artists and other craft specialists for work. Past workshops have included mosaic art making with children, and jewellery making. If you have an idea for a school project, ASM will be happy to talk to you.

Action Track Performance Co. Ltd

The Stock Shed, Flaxdrayton Farm, Drayton, South Petherton, Somerset, TA13 5LR

- ☎ 01460 240472
- ✉ mail@actiontrack.org.uk
- 🌐 www.actiontrack.org.uk

Artistic/Editorial Director Caroline Barnes
Insider Info Action Track provides personal workshops for schools and communities, in the fields of Drama, Dance, Popular Music and Design. The scripts, songs, scenario and sets are all devised in the period of time available. The company consists of writers, musicians and singers, actors, designers, makers and dancers. A community music studio is available to hire.

Tips Contact them for information on company shadowing, work experience, and any other needs you might have.

Apples and Snakes

Battersea Arts Centre, Lavender Hill, London, SW11 5TN

- ☎ 020 7801 9022
- ✉ geraldine@applesandsnakes.org
- 🌐 www.applesandsnakes.org

Artistic/Editorial Director Geraldine Collinge
Established 1982
Insider Info Apples and Snakes is a successful theatrical poetry organisation that presents live and dynamic poetry performances across England, in new spaces and to new audiences, especially the young. Their successful 'Poetry in Education' scheme has a good ongoing relationship with many poetry artists, who are available for performances and workshops in schools, prisons, libraries and other venues.

Submission Guidelines A detailed document is available to download on their website containing their submission policy. Each regional coordinator will aim to watch the performance at a live external event. After two paid gigs are booked at Apples and Snakes, the poets are uploaded onto their website for performances and other poetry opportunities, such as new commissions and poetry events.

Tips Apples and Snakes offers a detailed information resource document for newcomers to the London performance poetry scene, including poetry venues, open mic nights and related organisations.

Arc Theatre
Orbital House, 20 Eastern Road, Romford, Essex, RM1 3DP
- 020 8594 1095
- 01279 836370
- carole@arctheatre.com
- www.arctheatre.com

Artistic/Editorial Director Carole Pluckrose
Established 1984
Insider Info Arc Theatre consists of highly skilled and trained actors, storytellers, facilitators, workshop leaders, production managers and designers, who work extensively in schools, the community, in the public sector and for businesses. Arc provides tailor made drama based workshops that incorporate the national curriculum, and address sensitive issues such as bullying, drug awareness, and pregnancy. Arc also runs the Barking & Dagenham Youth Theatre, for children over 12.
Tips Arc welcomes applications from anyone interested in performing arts for children, whether that be writer, designer, director, storyteller or a freelance actor. Email CV to Nita Bocking: nita@arctheatre.com

Big Foot Theatre Company
23 Seaford Road, Hove, BN3 4EG
- 0870 0114 914
- kevin@bigfoot-theatre.co.uk
- www.bigfoot-theatre.co.uk

Artistic/Editorial Director Kevin Holland
Insider Info Big Foot is a national drama company for young children with offices throughout the UK. It offers summer schools, youth drama workshops, school programmes, INSET training for teachers and professional theatre educators to work in schools.
Tips Bigfoot Arts has an exclusive license to franchise Bigfoot branded programmes throughout the UK and are looking for very special people who are passionate about drama in education and want to be part of a new wave of child empowerment. Send a CV and covering letter to: franchise@bigfoot-theatre.co.uk. There are many job opportunities open with Big Foot company, they welcome applications from everyone interested in Big Foot, however most applications come from the following background: trained actors with considerable facilitation experience, arts graduates with some teaching/facilitation experience and trained teachers.

Bitesize Theatre Company
8 Green Meadows, New Broughton, Wrexham, LL11 6SG
- 01978 358320
- 01978 358315
- admin@bitesizetheatre.co.uk
- www.bitesizetheatre.co.uk

Artistic/Editorial Director Linda Griffiths
Established 1992
Insider Info A Theatre in Education company which tours schools in England and Wales. Produces ten to twelve shows per year, including new writings, Shakespeare, adaptations of classic stories and entertaining seasonal shows with an ongoing national curriculum influence. Bitesize shows have three to six professional actors. Runs a youth theatre company for children aged three to nineteen, based in Wrexham which has a keen interest in children with disabilities and special needs.
Tips Visit the Bitesize website for a comprehensive list of all its past and current productions.

Devon Arts In Schools Initiative
Great Moor House, Bittern Road, Sowton Industrial Estate, Exeter, EX2 7NL
- 01392 385214
- 01392 382181
- admin@daisi.org.uk
- www.daisi.org.uk

Artistic/Editorial Director Liz Hill
Established 1992
Insider Info DAISI aims to promote the arts in Devon and Torbay schools. DAISI arranges arts education workshops for artists and students and workshops with Devon Youth Theatre.
Tips Artists are invited to register with DAISI to benefit the opportunity to work in education including artists workshops and residencies, the chance to design and direct for Devon Youth Theatre and opportunities to exhibit work in special projects. Visit their website for how to register.

Dont Feed The Poets Production
c/o The Foresters Arms, 2 Shepherd Street, St. Leonards-on-Sea, East Sussex, TN38 0ET
- 01424 436513
- info@dontfeedthepoets.com
- www.dontfeedthepoets.com

Artistic/Editorial Director John Knowles
Insider Info An up and coming poetry performance company across Eastern England which promotes events for children and adults, including readings

from acclaimed writers, open-mic nights, poetry based cabaret evenings, children's shows and spoken word theatre. Their flagship literature festival, Word About Town, runs in Hastings, St.Leonards and Rother and is now in its fourth year.

Tips Carries out extensive work in schools with 3 long term projects in East Sussex primary schools, and ongoing workshops with Hastings young people as part of 'The Street Opera Project'. A non-incorporated group they are steered by a committee of writers, performers and community representatives. Focuses on theatrical poetry, rather than straight theatre productions.

Etch Productions
29, Meerbrook Road, London, SE3 9QG
- 07979 617303
- info@etchproductions.co.uk
- www.etchproductions.co.uk

Artistic/Editorial Director Norman Murray and Suhayla Pezeshk

Established 2004

Insider Info Etch Productions works with children, adults, teachers and the community developing writing and listening skills using performance as it's tool. Runs saturday drama classes for children aged 5-16, theatre productions, storytelling and drama workshops for primary schools.

Recent Productions *Peter Pan,* an open air community production.

Tips The company plans to develop promote and support writers and their work within communities. Writers are welcome to email examples of their work to become part of their database for future opportunities such as festival work.

Giant Productions
Centre for Inclusive Arts, 100 Beith Street, Glasgow, G11 6DQ
- 0141 334 2000
- 0141 357 4100
- info@giantproductions.org
- www.giantproductions.org

Artistic/Editorial Director Katrina Caldwell

Established 1989

Insider Info Giant is an inclusive arts organisation who work with children of all abilities, including those with disabilities and special needs, in a shared creative environment. Its two main strands of work are theatre and visual arts productions and projects that are highly participatory using multi-sensory techniques such as aromatherapy, lighting and

Makaton communication. The company tours schools and other venues.

Submission Guidelines Contact Katrina Caldwell with ideas for theatrical projects at: katrina@giantproductions.org

Tips Giant offers training programmes in inclusive arts and creative play for arts professionals and teachers.

Monster Productions
Buddle Arts Centre, 258b Station Road, Wallsend, Tyne & Wear, NE28 8RG
- 0191 240 4011
- 0191 240 4016
- info@monsterproductions.co.uk
- www.monsterproductions.co.uk

Artistic/Editorial Director Laura Lindow

Insider Info A leading producer of children's theatre for the under sevens, and providers of youth theatre programmes. Produces creative theatre using puppetry, live music and participatory interaction to engage and encourage theatre in young audiences.

Tips Runs engaging workshops for children and adults, giving them priceless experience in puppetry, storytelling and musical theatre. A number of scripts from past productions are available fon their website or teachers to download.

National Youth Theatre
443–445 Holloway Road, London, N7 6LW
- 020 7281 3863
- 020 7281 8246
- info@nyt.org.uk
- www.nyt.org.uk

Artistic/Editorial Director John Hoggarth and Paul Roseby

Established 1956

Insider Info The National Youth Theatre (NYT) offers young people aged 13–21 the opportunity to participate in workshops, courses and holiday programmes. Children must audition to become members of the courses, which are held during holiday periods. They introduce students to the basic techniques of theatrical performance, including voice, movement, and delivery of text, as well as involving more specialised techniques, such as clowning, mask work and stage fighting. Once members, the students can audition for public productions.

Tips The NYT welcomes volunteers.

The New Stagers Theatre Club

St. Anne's Church Hall, St. Ann's Crescent, Wandsworth, London, SW18 2LR

☎ 07814 611239

✉ secretary@newstagers.co.uk

🌐 www.newstagers.co.uk

Established 1967

Insider Info A well established amateur drama group that produces four shows per year, ranging from family productions to serious drama and comedies. The January Pantomime production is performed from an original story scripted by the company. New Stagers normally perform at the hall of St Anne's Church in Wandsworth, but last year it celebrated a first with its production of 'The Haunting of Hill House' at the New Wimbledon Studio.

Recent Productions *Robin Hood & the Babes in the Wood; Red Riding Hood; Alladin*

Tips The company allows members to be involved with any stage of the productions. Email them for more details.

Northcott Young Company

Northcott Theatre, Stocker Road, Exeter, EX4 4QB

☎ 01392 223999

✉ artisticdirector@northcott-theatre.co.uk

🌐 www.northcott-theatre.co.uk/youngcompany.html

Artistic/Editorial Director Rachel Vowles

Established 1967

Insider Info The Northcott Young Company offers young people aged 13 to 21 weekly workshops and participation in events and shows. Previous productions have included *Blood Wedding, Oh What A Lovely War* and *Around the World in Eighty Days*.

Tips Northcott Theatre advertises jobs, including backstage designer positions on their website.

Perth Youth Theatre and Young Playwrights

Perth Theatre, 185 High Street, Perth, PH1 5UW

☎ 01738 477730

✉ jmcgregor@horsecross.co.uk

🌐 www.horsecross.co.uk

Artistic/Editorial Director Jennifer McGregor

Insider Info Perth Youth Theatre is a fun and dynamic company for young people aged 12–25, which performs at its resident theatre in Perth. PYT runs a young playwrights group for people aged up to 25, allowing older members of the youth theatre to join.

Recent Productions *The Laramie Project* and *The Tay*; A new piece by Charlotte Allan (a previous participant in the PYT Trainee Directorship Scheme)

Tips PYT runs a yearly trainee directorship scheme, for aspiring directors to work alongside established theatre professionals, in order to gain insight and experience in directing plays.

Royal Academy of Dramatic Art (RADA)

62–64 Gower Street, London, WC1E 6ED

☎ 020 7636 7076

☎ 020 7323 3865

✉ enquiries@rada.ac.uk

🌐 www.rada.org

Artistic/Editorial Director Edward Kemp

Established 1904

Insider Info RADA is one of the most prestigious drama schools in the UK, with a brilliant reputation for producing some of the country's finest acting professionals, whether it be actors, or backstage artists. The Academy offers acting, directing and technical courses, summer schools, RADA examinations and RADA youth group and acting workshops for talented younger students.

Tips RADA Enterprises is the subsidiary, money generating arm of RADA, that works for corporate, individual and institutional clients. Visit www.radaenterprises.org for more information on their services.

Scottish Youth Theatre

The Old Sheriff Court, 105 Brunswick Street, Glasgow, G1 1TF

☎ 0141 552 3988

☎ 0141 552 7615

✉ marym@scottishyouththeatre.org

🌐 www.scottishyouththeatre.org

Artistic/Editorial Director Mary McCluskey

Established 1976

Insider Info The company holds weekly drama classes in Glasgow and Edinburgh, residential courses, a national roadshow, foundation courses, the Summer Festival and special projects. SYT Productions is a highly acclaimed youth performance company for talented students.

Recent Productions *When A Star Falls;* A play that tackles nationality and identity issues that face people of all ages, written by Scottish Bafta winner, David Cosgrove

Stagecoach Theatre Arts Plc

The Courthouse, Elm Grove, Walton-on-Thames, Surrey, KT12 1LZ
- 01932 254333
- 01932 222894
- Online form.
- www.stagecoach.co.uk

Artistic/Editorial Director Stephanie Manuel
Established 1988
Insider Info Stagecoach is a global theatre company for young children, with schools in Australia, Canada, USA, Gibraltar, Germany and Spain. In the UK there are 598 theatre schools run by talented teachers in the field of dancing, drama, directing and music. Each school stages two productions a year, to family and friends. Stagecoach also runs 'Mini Stages', a mother and baby group combining play and music.
Tips Stagecoach is always seeking talented teachers and talented personnel to join the company. Email a CV to: jpugh@stagecoach.co.uk or contact them for more details.

Stagefright Drama Group

St. Luke's Church Hall Theatre, La Route du Fort, Jersey, Channel Islands, JE2 7PA
- 01534 722414
- cm.richardson@jerseymail.co.uk
- www.stagefrightdrama.co.uk

Artistic/Editorial Director Carole Richardson
Established 1990
Insider Info An amateur drama group affiliated to Jersey Youth Service. The group teaches drama, dance and music. Their aim is to help young people and adults build self confidence, make new friends, and encourage a love of the arts.
Recent Productions Snow White and the Turnips; The Selfish Giant; We Will Rock You
Tips Stagefright are currently seeking people who have experience with stage management, scenery painting, set design and costumes, and can work with sound equipment. To find out more email them, or visit their website to print off an application form.

Teach It Through Drama

- 020 8693 1472
- info@teach-it-through-drama.com
- www.teach-it-through-drama.com

Artistic/Editorial Director Olivia Carruthers and Elizabeth Fost
Insider Info Provides drama workshops, storytelling shows for children, and INSET training for teachers. All workshops follow the national curriculum, covering English, History, PSHE, Maths and Science. All are designed for whole class participation in a hall or other clear space.

Theatre Writing Partnership

c/o Nottingham Playhouse, Wellington Circus, Nottingham, NG1 5AF
- 0115 947 4361
- 0115 953 9055
- sarah@theatrewritingpartnership.org.uk
- www.theatrewritingpartnership.org.uk

Artistic/Editorial Director Sarah Francoise
Established 2001
Insider Info TWP is a pioneering new writing organisation that works in partnership with six main producing theatres across the East Midlands region: Derby Playhouse; Leicester Haymarket; New Perspectives; Nottingham Playhouse; and Royal and Derngate Theatres, Northampton.

Traverse Theatre

See entry under Children's Theatres.

Young At Art

15 Church Street, Belfast, BT1 1PG
- 028 9023 0660
- ali@youngatart.co.uk
- www.youngatart.co.uk

Insider Info Northern Ireland's Children's Arts Organisation and co-ordinator of the annual Belfast Children's Festival, showcasing a number of events; from theatre productions and workshops, to dance and digital technology. Young At Art arranges a wide variety of arts projects for children of all all ages, which include workshops, commissions, regional touring, research and the development of online resources such as 'Toolbox' – a database of arts activities for children and teachers.
Tips Information for freelance staff vacancies is advertised on the 'News and Events' section of their website. Young At Art keeps an online register of freelance artists for future opportunities; send an up to date CV with contact details to be included on the register.

Action Transport Theatre Company

Whitby Hall, Stanney Lane, Ellesmere Port, Cheshire, CH65 9AE

- 0151 357 2120
- 0151 356 4057
- info@actiontransporttheatre.co.uk
- www.actiontransporttheatre.co.uk

Artistic/Editorial Director Joe Sumison
Established 1986
Insider Info A successful children's theatre company specialising in creating new and original theatre projects for, with and by young people. Action Transport delivers high quality productions at their studio in Whitby Hall, and also tours schools and other performing venues regionally and nationally. They run two youth theatre groups, for ages 11–14 and 15–18.
Recent Productions *Tika and Gogo*, in partnership with Vulavulani Theatre Company.
The Bomb, by writer in residence, Kevin Dyer.
Tips Writer in residence Kevin Dyer runs writing workshops. Visit the website to download Kevin's helpful writing guide.

Aesop's Touring Theatre Company

The Arches, 38 The Riding, Woking, Surrey, GU21 5TA

- 01483 724633
- 01483 724633
- info@aesopstheatre.co.uk
- www.aesopstheatre.co.uk

Insider Info A theatre in education company which tours schools, art centres and theatres with plays written specifically for children of nursery, infant and junior ages. All material has a national curriculum influence. Runs workshops and parties for children.
Recent Productions *Henry VIII; World War II; The Gingerbread Man; The Hare and the Tortoise; The Story of Aesop's Fables*
Tips Aesop's has a good working relationship with many professional actors and behind the scenes staff who have considerable enthusiasm and specialist skills in 'Theatre in Education'.

Big Brum Theatre In Education Company

Pegasus Primary School, Turnhouse Road, Castle Vale, Birmingham, B35 6PR

- 0121 464 4606
- 0121 464 4605
- chris@bigbrum.plus.com
- www.bigbrum.org.uk

Artistic/Editorial Director Chris Cooper
Established 1982
Insider Info The Theatre in Education Company works in schools and colleges throughout the West Midlands region, with pupils from the ages of three to seventeen, and students in higher education. Produces two highly participatory TIE programmes per year providing engaging performances for children to enjoy and learn from.
Recent Productions *The Balancing Act; The Under Room; Separation Wall* and *Virtue*
Tips Big Brum runs a successful youth theatre, which was invited to perform a play, *One Hundred Thousand Whys,* about Jewish children growing up in the Warsaw Ghetto at The International Festival of Theatre for Children and Young People in Warsaw, in 2005. Email Ceri Townsend (ceri@bigbrum.plus.com) for general information about the youth theatre.

Big Fish Theatre Company

The Forum @Greenwich, Trafalgar Road, Greenwich, SE10 9EQ

- 020 8269 1123
- 020 8269 1115
- info@bigfishtheatre.co.uk
- www.bigfishtheatre.com

Artistic/Editorial Director Alex Cooke
Established 1997
Insider Info The London based theatre company carries out regional touring of innovative issue-based theatre productions in schools and youth settings for young people aged 11–18. Runs social impact projects such as the Southwark Youth Offending Team Project and the Southwark Unwanted Sexual Contact Project, combining drama activities and workshops to address some of the issues disadvantaged young people face, and to challenge social injustice.
Recent Productions *City Zen*, tackling Citizenship; *Them and Us*, tackling homophobia; *Running Scared*, concerning Bullying.
Tips Big Fish is committed to developing quality theatre experiences in a variety of settings and supporting new writers in this process.

Big Telly Theatre Company

The Town Hall, The Crescent, Portstewart,
Northern Ireland, BT55 7AB

- ☎ 028 7083 2588
- ☎ 028 7083 2588
- ✉ zoe@big-telly.com
- 🌐 www.big-telly.com

Artistic/Editorial Director Zoë Seaton
Established 1987
Insider Info Northern Ireland's leading theatre
company, which produces Irish heritage and cultural
plays, adaptations of classic texts and visual shows
combining dance, music, circus, magic and film. The
company tours theatre venues and festivals
throughout Ireland, the UK and abroad.
Recent Productions *Bog People,* inspired by poems
by Seamus Heaney; *The Country Boy,* based on
popular Irish classic by John Murphy; *The Little
Mermaid,* an acclaimed production of the popular
children's classic.
Tips The company offers theatrical workshops for
schools, from comedy to theatrical sets.

Big Wooden Horse Theatre for Young People

London

- ☎ 020 8567 8431
- ✉ adam@bigwoodenhorse.com
- 🌐 www.bigwoodenhorse.com

Artistic/Editorial Director Adam Bampton-Smith
Insider Info The Big Wooden Horse Theatre offers
high quality theatre for children of all ages,
nationally and internationally, performing in some of
the most successful receiving venues for children,
such as the Lyric and Theatre Royal. A prestigious
forthcoming children's show is *Don't Let The Pigeon
Drive the Bus* by Sesame Street creator Mo Willems.
Recent Productions *The Legend of Perseus*
Tips To join their mailing list visit their website.

Box Clever Theatre Company

12.G.1 The Leathermarket, Weston Street,
London, SE1 3ER

- ☎ 020 7357 0550
- ☎ 020 7357 8188
- ✉ admin@boxclevertheatre.com
- 🌐 www.boxclevertheatre.com

Artistic/Editorial Director Michael Wicherek
Insider Info A multidisciplinary touring company
led by writer in residence Michael Wicherek, which
performs in schools, colleges and theatres across the
UK. The company's school tours include new writing
on life issues and adaptations of curriculum set texts.
Michael's forthcoming writings include *SK8* and
Sweetness & Badness which will be on tour
throughout 2008.
Tips Box Clever is interested in hearing any ideas
about new projects, training opportunities, school
and theatre tours and workshops.

Cambridge Touring Theatre

- ☎ 01223 246533
- ✉ info@cambridgetouringtheatre.co.uk
- 🌐 www.cambridgetouringtheatre.co.uk

Artistic/Editorial Director Rosie Humphreys
Established 2000
Insider Info A small scale regional touring company
for children and adults across East Anglia which aims
to invest in local acting talent. Productions include
famous stories and works by Shakespeare and Dylan
Thomas. Recent emphasis has been on children's
plays and workshops, with tours of classic
children's stories.
Recent Productions *Wind in the Willows*, specially
adapted for the Cambridge Touring Theatre; *Robin
Hood*; *Alice in Wonderland*.
Tips Runs theatre workshops for Key Stage 1, 2 and 3
schoolchildren.

Catherine Wheels Theatre Company

Brunton Theatre, Ladywell Way, Musselburgh,
EH21 6AF

- ☎ 0131 653 5255
- ✉ admin@catherinewheels.co.uk
- 🌐 www.catherinewheels.co.uk

Artistic/Editorial Director Gill Robertson
Insider Info A leading professional theatre
company for children and young people, which
performs in theatres, schools and festivals
throughout the UK and abroad. A successful
production is *Martha*, which has stayed in the
company's repertoire since its first show in 1999.
Recent Productions *Lifeboat,* an award winning
play based on a true story by Nicola McCartney for
children aged eight and upwards.
A Town Called Elsewhere, a TIE production for
Primary Years 1 to 3.
Cyrano, for children aged ten and upwards.

Chain Reaction Theatre Company

3 Mills Studios, Sugar House Yard, Sugar House
Lane, London, E15 2QS

- ☎ 020 8534 0007
- ☎ 020 8534 0007

○ s.choppen@chainreactiontheatre.co.uk
⊕ www.chainreactiontheatre.co.uk
Artistic/Editorial Director Sarah Choppen
Established 1994
Insider Info A successful touring company for young people and adults. Currently it has 12 main repertoires of educational issue based theatre projects, which are accompanied by workshops and teachers resource packs. It tackles sensitive issues that young people face, such as drug abuse and sexual health. The company has recently branched out into musical theatre for adults and offers information training performances for corporate bodies and professional clients at conferences and training days.
Tips Chain Reaction welcomes new commissions for theatre projects relating to issues that affect young people today. Contact Sarah Choppen at: s.choppen@chainreactiontheatre.co.uk or via post.

Chalkfoot Theatre Arts
Central Studios, 36 Park Place, Margate, Kent, CT9 1LE
○ 01843 280077
○ 01843 280088
○ info@chalkfoot.crg
⊕ www.chalkfoot.org.uk
Artistic/Editorial Director Philip Dart
Established 2003
Insider Info Chalkfoot is a community arts group that focuses on bringing theatre to rural communities by touring schools and non-theatre venues. The company produces innovative, fresh and highly professional productions of new plays, devised work, or new approaches to classic texts, utilising strong and contemporary design techniques.
Recent Productions *Never Ever After; Alice in Wonderland; The Ragged Trousered Philanthropists*
Submission Guidelines Does not accept unsolicited scripts.
Tips Less experienced writers are encouraged to join East Kent Playwrights' Group, an independent group of local writers originally set up by Chalkfoot's Artistic Director, Philip Dart. Chalkfoot is the sister company of The Channel Theatre Company which accepts commissions for TIE performances.

Chickenshed Theatre Company
Chase Side, Southgate, London, N14 4PE
○ 020 8351 6161
○ 020 8292 0202
○ maryw@chickenshead.org.uk

⊕ www.chickenshed.org.uk
Artistic/Editorial Director Mary Ward
Established 1974
Insider Info A successful theatre company for children and adults that produces a wide variety of shows. These range from full scale productions, with a 250 plus member cast, to solo performances in its own studio theatre, as well as new works through its company workshops.
Recent Productions *Tales From A Shed,* a nationally acclaimed production for under sevens.
Tips Runs a 600 cast youth theatre workshop, and runs an annual summer school theatre workshop for non-members. Has a successful outreach and educational programme working with many schools and in the wider community. There are 19 sister 'Sheds' expanding Chickenshed's work across the UK, and internationally with a 'Shed' in St. Petersberg, Russia.

Classworks Theatre
The Junction, Clifton Way, Cambridge, CB1 7GX
○ 01223 249100
○ info@classworks.org.uk
⊕ www.classworks.org.uk
Artistic/Editorial Director Claudette Bryanston and Jenny Culank
Established 1983
Insider Info Classworks runs two youth theatres which each perform at least one production a year, and a successful touring company with a focus on new writing for young people. The company has commissioned and produced over 60 productions.
Recent Productions *Olivia,* a modern adaptation of Charles Dickens' *Oliver Twist; The Children*, aimed at 14–17 year olds; *In Limbo*, which tells the story of an adolescent boy and his friendship with an elderly seamstress set in the 60s.
Tips Classworks are always on the lookout for graphic designers, illustrators and photographers to work on their productions and youth plays. Applications from graduates just starting out are welcomed. There are many volunteer positions available in arts administration and the youth theatre. Visit the jobs section of their website for more details.

Cleveland Theatre Company
Arts Centre, Vane Terrace, Darlington, DL3 7AX
○ 01325 352004
○ 01325 369404
○ ctc@ctctheatre.org.uk
⊕ www.ctctheatre.org.uk

Artistic/Editorial Director Paul Harman
Established 1987
Insider Info Tours professional theatre productions to schools and theatre venues within Tees Valley, the North East and nationally to festivals.
Recent Productions *Big Eyes; Good Morning Mr Dickens* and *The Fool of The World*.
Tips Organises the annual Takeoff Festival for children, which is a showcase for other companies that aims to increase artist development, collaboration, teacher development, public awareness, and to provide something unusual for young audiences.

Feelgood Theatre Productions

Production House, 21 Lindum Avenue, Manchester, M16 9NQ
- 0161 862 9212
- thefolks@feelgoodtheatre.co.uk
- www.feelgoodtheatre.co.uk

Artistic/Editorial Director Caroline Clegg
Established 1994
Insider Info A northern based touring company for adults and children performing at theatres, specific sites and outdoor venues in the UK. Produces quality plays by famous writers and playwrights such as Shakespeare, as well as newly written plays. Feelgood strives to support the community with unique programmes and projects giving people the chance to be involved with the Theatre. Past projects include new writing sessions and workshops for schools tackling bullying.
Recent Productions *A Midsummer Night's Dream*.
Tips Feelgood offers internships for theatrical professionals with the aim to support emerging talent. Email Feelgood for more details.

Freehand Theatre

1 Reynard Villas, Mayfield Grove, Baildon, Shipley, West Yorkshire, BD17 6DY
- 01274 585277
- admin@freehandtheatre.co.uk
- www.freehandtheatre.co.uk

Artistic/Editorial Director Lizzie Allen
Established 1982
Insider Info A two person run company which produces puppetry shows for children aged five and over, using a mix of quality puppetry, good design, rich concepts, music and gentle humour. Freehand tours schools, theatres and community venues nationally.
Tips Freehand likes to work with collaborative artists such as directors, designers and composers. Their

play *Under One Roof* was taken on for production by the Polka Theatre in 2006.

Fuse Theatre Company

13 Hope Street, Liverpool, L1 9BH
- 0151 708 0877
- 0151 707 9950
- kathy@fusetheatre.com
- www.fusetheatre.co.uk

Artistic/Editorial Director Kathy McArdle
Established 1978
Insider Info Fuse produces adaptations, new writing productions, translations and devised work for young people in schools, libraries, community venues, theatre venues, museums and galleries.
Recent Productions *In Search of Fabulous Beasts,* a collaboration with Unity Theatre for children aged five to seven.
Tips Fuse advertises jobs for playwrights, directors, theatre artists, performers, designers and art administrators on their website.

Half Moon Young People's Theatre

43 White Horse Road, London, E1 0ND
- 020 7265 8138
- 020 7709 8914
- admin@halfmoon.org.uk
- www.halfmoon.org.uk

Artistic/Editorial Director Adam Annand
Established 1972
Insider Info A regional touring theatre company that produces and presents theatre in schools and youth settings, as well as performances at the Half Moon theatre itself. Produces two professional tours each year. Provides an extensive participatory programme for schools and community projects. Runs seven youth theatre groups embracing children from ethnic minorities and the severely disabled.
Recent Productions *Igloo Hullabaloo; Mermaid and the Mirror* and *Grubs, Slugs and Boogie Bugs*.
Tips Half Moon seeks to research and commission writings from new playwrights whose background and experiences reflect the immediate community. Offers script development support with professional directors. Alongside their aim to nurture new talent, they also offer existing children's writers ongoing workshops to develop their ideas for plays. To apply send a CV to Half Moon, or visit website for more details.

Hiss & Boo Theatre Company

1 Nyes Hill, Wineham Lane, Bolney, West Sussex, RH17 5SD

☎ 01444 881707

☎ 01444 882057

✉ ian@hissboo.co.uk

🌐 www.hissboo.co.uk

Artistic/Editorial Director Ian Liston

Established 1977

Insider Info A company specialising in music hall, pantomimes, children's theatre, light entertainment and variety. Also provides corporate entertainment and has had some success overseas. Productions are performed in theatres and other venues of all sizes across the UK and abroad. Some productions have been housed in the West End.

Submission Guidelines Accepts query and synopsis by post only, no phone calls. Submissions accompanied by a SAE will be returned.

Tips Hiss & Boo concentrates on the production of pantomimes and children's shows, but will also show interest and may consider scripts for plays, musicals and comedy thrillers. There is not much scope, however, for new writings.

Kazzum

Studio 8, 4th Floor, The Old Truman Brewery, 91 Brick Lane, London, E1 6QL

☎ 020 7539 3500

✉ info@kazzum.org

🌐 www.kazzum.org

Artistic/Editorial Director Daryl Beeton

Insider Info Kazzum is a participative arts company that runs workshops and produces plays for children with an international artistic style. Its main strands of work are: small scale touring productions for audiences eight years old or younger; larger scale productions for children over ten years old; and community and education projects – including work with refugees in the Greater London area.

Recent Productions The Sorcerer's Apprentice; Ten Suitcases; The Little Mermaid

Tips Kazzum is currently seeking talented people to join their team. Contact them via email for more details.

Kipper Tie Theatre

✉ kippertie2004@aol.com

🌐 www.molesbusiness.com

Artistic/Editorial Director Bernie C. Byrnes

Insider Info Produces high quality, educational theatre which mixes acting with dance, music, and mime. Kipper Tie often work on collaborative adult productions with other theatre companies.

Recent Productions Whiff; The Mole Who Knew It Was None Of His Business; Hillbilly Goats Gruff

Tips Kippper Tie offer educational workshops for schools, covering creative writing, acting, exam preparation and backstage work.

Krazy Kat Theatre Company

173 Hartington Road, Brighton, East Sussex, BN2 3PA

☎ 01273 692552

✉ krazykattheatre@ntlworld.com

🌐 www.krazykattheatre.co.uk

Artistic/Editorial Director Kinny Gardner

Established 1982

Insider Info A specialist touring company that introduces young people to the delights of live theatre by combining mime, dance, song, Commedia dell Arte, puppets and sign language. Performances are held in schools, arts centres, theme parks and other venues nationally and internationally. Krazy Kat offers a unique play for deaf children 'The Magic Flute'. Each performance normally has two male actors.

Tips The company runs workshops in their particular theatrical field. Visit their website for further details.

Little Angel Theatre

14 Dagmar Passage, London, N1 2DN

☎ 020 7226 1787

✉ info@littleangeltheatre.com

🌐 www.littleangeltheatre.com

Artistic/Editorial Director Peter Glanville

Established 1961

Insider Info A touring company which specialises in puppetry shows. It has its own theatre based in Islington, London. Produces imaginative and groundbreaking shows for children and their families, as well as hosting a broad range of visiting puppet companies. Their education department works with primary schools, out of school clubs, and youth and community groups, drawn from all over the capital. Runs a Saturday puppetry club for adults and children.

Submission Guidelines Specific enquiries should go to Artistic Director, Peter Glanville (peter@littleangeltheatre.com), or see the website for other members of staff.

London Bubble Theatre Company

5 Elephant Lane, London, SE16 4JD

☎ 020 7237 4434

☎ 020 7231 2366

✉ admin@londonbubble.org.uk

🌐 www.londonbubble.org.uk

Artistic/Editorial Director Jonathon Petherbridge

Insider Info A successful touring company driven by the belief that theatre can be made and enjoyed by anyone. It provides people of all ages in the London area with quality and participatory theatre. The company produces works with a range of people, from experienced actors in professional plays, to children and adults new to theatre in workshops.

Recent Productions *Spangleguts*, an adaptation of an Italian fairytale.

Tips London Bubble runs Youth Theatre Groups for children aged 5–17.

Lyngo Theatre Company

2 Clare House, 129 Eardley Road, London, SW16 6DB

☎ 0039 041 721384

✉ patrick@lyngo.co.uk

🌐 www.lyngo.co.uk

Artistic/Editorial Director Patrick Lynch

Established 2003

Insider Info A successful Italy-based company bringing new and innovative theatre to the UK and Ireland. Marcello Chiarenza directs and designs all of Lyngo's theatre productions with his very distinctive 'object theatre' style. All shows are performed by actor and writer Patrick Lynch, founder of Lyngo.

Recent Productions *The Fish's Wife; Egg & Spoon; Watch the Birdy.*

Tips Patrick Lynch is currently appearing in CBBC's *Razzle Dazzle* and was shortlisted for a 2007 Arts Foundation Award, for outstanding work in the field of young people's theatre.

M6 Theatre Company

Studio Theatre, Hamer County Primary School, Albert Royds Street, Rochdale, Lancashire, OL16 2SU

☎ 01706 355898

☎ 01706 712601

✉ info@m6theatre.co.uk

🌐 www.m6theatre.co.uk

Artistic/Editorial Director Dot Wood

Established 1977

Insider Info An award winning touring company designed to encourage the development of theatre for young people. M6 caters for all age groups, with productions designed specifically for the very young, such as multi-sensory productions, to issue based drama that affects older children. M6 tours schools, community centres and arts venues, mainly in the North West. They aim to push the boundaries of children's theatre in new and exciting ways, in order to enrich and inspire the imaginations of young people.

Recent Productions *The Garden in Winter*, a multi-sensory show for young children.
Take 3, a play combining movement, film and mime.

Tips M6 has its own 92 capacity studio theatre, bringing many creative benefits to the company and the local community.

Multi Story Theatre Company

The Barns, Bestridge, Swimbridge, Barnstaple, EX32 0PY

☎ 01271 830147

✉ multistory@hotmail.com

🌐 www.multistorytheatre.co.uk

Artistic/Editorial Director Bill Buffrey

Established 2000

Insider Info A small scale theatre company based in the South West which produces theatre for children and adults touring schools, arts venues and small theatres across the UK. The company is mainly concerned with the power of story, performing adaptations of old plays to new audiences. The company often tours abroad, most recently in South America.

Recent Productions *Tattercoats; The Magicians Daughter.*

Tips Runs diverse workshops for school children in theatre skills, poetry performance and play making. It recently launched a modest fringe festival as part of the North Devon festival, where eight companies participated with 16 successful performances.

Nottingham Playhouse Roundabout

Nottingham Playhouse, Wellington Circus, Nottingham, NG1 5AF

☎ 0115 947 4361

☎ 0115 947 5759

✉ Online form.

🌐 www.nottinghamplayhouse.co.uk

Artistic/Editorial Director Giles Croft

Established 1975

Insider Info Nottingham Playhouse Roundabout is the resident Theatre in Education company at

Nottingham Playhouse. Their remit is to produce plays and workshops with a national curriculum influence for children, young people and support teachers. Since their beginning, Roundabout has produced over 250 plays, for nearly half a million children.

Tips The company runs its own Young Critics scheme for students, which aims to attract young people to the theatre and stimulate a response to plays. Each student attends a workshop, then watches a performance at the Nottingham Playhouse and forms a formal review of the show.

Oily Cart
Smallwood School Annexe, Smallwood Road, London, SW17 0TW
- 020 8672 6329
- 020 8672 0792
- Online form.
- www.oilycart.org.uk

Artistic/Editorial Director Tim Webb
Established 1981
Insider Info A highly specialist touring theatre which caters for babies and children with disabilities, touring schools and venues across the UK. Produces highly imaginative and interactive shows using multi-sensory techniques, such as visual effects, live music, puppetry and video projection.
Recent Productions *Baby Balloon*, a show for very young children aged six months to two years. *Blue*, a specialist show for children with disabilities.
Submission Guidelines At present new scripts are generated from inside the company, but they may consider scripts for the future.

The People's Theatre Company
12e High Street, Egham, Surrey, TW20 9E
- 01784 470439
- admin@ptc.org.uk
- www.ptc.org.uk

Artistic/Editorial Director Steven Lee
Insider Info The Peoples Theatre Company produces some of the best new shows and children's theatre, and runs extensive Theatre in Education programmes consisting of tailor made workshops and after school clubs.
Recent Productions *The Witches Bogey*; *Bink & The Riddles of the Sphinx*.
Tips The Peoples Theatre Company runs a careers development programme for theatre professionals. If you are interested in applying email a CV and a covering letter. Registering with Peoples Theatre Company enables career development

opportunities and other benefits. Visit the website for details.

Pilot Theatre
c/o York Theatre Royal, St. Leonards Place, York, YO1 7HD
- 01904 635755
- 01904 656378
- info@pilot-theatre.com
- www.pilot-theatre.com

Artistic/Editorial Director Marcus Romer
Established 1981
Insider Info One of Britain's most successful touring companies for young people and national resident at York Theatre Royal. The company is responsible for successful productions of *Lord of the Flies*, *Beautiful Thing*, *East is East*, *Rumble Fish* and *Sing Yer Heart Out for the Lads*. Pilot theatre has a successful education and outreach programme that consists of the Pilot Youth Theatre, education packs and a new initiative, 'Magic Net Youth Encounter', bringing European actors and the youth members together to devise a play.
Recent Productions *Sing Yer Heart Out for the Lads*; *Looking for JJ*, based on Anne Cassidy's award winning novel.
Tips For a full listing of previous shows and current productions, visit their website.

Pop-Up Theatre
27a Brewery Road, London, N7 9PU
- 020 7609 3339
- 020 7609 2284
- mike@pop-up.net
- www.pop-up.net

Artistic/Editorial Director Michael Dalton
Established 1982
Insider Info Pop-Up is a prestigious children's theatre company that works with some of the most successful children's writers of our time. The company performs to an annual audience of over 25,000; in theatres, art centres, schools and nurseries, both in the UK and overseas. Their other strands of work are 'Equal Voices', an extensive training package for young people, which promotes self respect and self expression, and 'Dramatic Links', which is a continuing project to help professional writers develop scripts that are relevant to children's experiences and perceptions.
Recent Productions *Heaven Eyes*; *Starry Starry Night*; *Me and My Monsters*. The production for 2008 is *Britain's Next Top Family*, an interactive family show.

Tips If you are interested in being involved in 'Dramatic Links' then email a script and CV, including details or any previous writing experience. Pop-Up often undertakes collaborative projects with other theatre companies to produce new plays and workshops exploring children's theatre.

Premier Stage Productions
4 Haywood, Bracknell, Berkshire, RG12 7WG
- 01344 453888
- 01344 305151
- info@premier-productions.co.uk
- www.premier-productions.co.uk

Artistic/Editorial Director Jason Francis
Established 1997
Insider Info A successful, well run touring company, with a good reputation for producing quality children's shows. Premier Stage has secured rights to present *Mr Men* and *Little Miss, Brum* and *Barney* stories for the stage.
Recent Productions *Little Red Riding Hood; Peter Pan; Goldilocks.*
Tips All Premier Stage Productions utilise exciting, colourful sets, stunning costumes and engaging actors to more strongly appeal to children.

Proteus Theatre Company
Queen Mary's College, Cliddesden Road, Basingstoke, Hampshire, RG21 3HF
- 01256 354541
- 01256 356186
- info@proteustheatre.com
- www.proteustheatre.com

Artistic/Editorial Director Mary Swan
Established 1979
Insider Info Proteus is a South East based touring company, producing approximately three plays per year. Many shows are inter-disciplinary, including photography, film, dance, music and visual arts. Touring venues are mainly village halls and community spaces.
Recent Productions *Sprout,* a new commission by Phil Smith.
Peter Pan, utilising multimedia and static trapeze techniques.
Submission Guidelines No unsolicited manuscripts. Proposals must include a synopsis, cast breakdown and a CV. A cast of approximately four actors is normally employed, although there can be more than four characters in the play.
Tips The subject matter of the plays must appeal to families.

Quicksilver Theatre
4 Enfield Road, London, N1 5AZ
- 020 7241 2942
- 020 7254 3119
- talktous@quicksilvertheatre.org
- www.quicksilvertheatre.org

Artistic/Editorial Director Guy Holland and Carey English
Established 1977
Insider Info Quicksilver specialises in new writing for children. An emphasis is placed on bold visual style and strong narratives to produce exciting and educational theatre for young audiences. Quicksilver usually split their audience into two groups; three to five year olds who like small productions in intimate venues, based on things that matter to their lives; and older children who require challenging plays with thought provoking storylines.
Recent Productions *Upstairs In The Sky; Teddy in his Rucksack,* by Carey English and Guy Holland.
Tips A unique writing project for Quicksilver 'Primary Voices' will bring children, writers and Quicksilver staff together to devise a new play with the children's ideas at the forefront of the storyline. The script will tour in 2008.

Rainbow Theatre
66 Ham Road, Worthing, BN11 3HP
- 01903 203598
- 01903 203598
- nicolas.young@rainbow-theatre.co.uk
- www.rainbow-theatre.com

Artistic/Editorial Director Nick Young
Established 1983
Insider Info A Theatre in Education company, with branches in London and the West Country. Rainbow Theatre offers a wide range of projects, from fairytale and historical plays, to schools workshops. The company performs annual Shakespeare plays to family audiences.
Tips The company works with a team of professional actors.

Red Ladder Theatre Company
3 St. Peter's Buildings, York Street, Leeds, LS9 8AJ
- 0113 245 5311
- 0113 245 5351
- firstname@redladder.co.uk
- www.redladder.co.uk

Artistic/Editorial Director Rod Dixon
Established 1969

Insider Info A leading new writing theatre company based in Leeds, performing in theatres and other venues across the UK. Red Ladder runs Red Grit, a yearly development project where ten northern members devise a new piece of exciting theatre for children. Also runs the Asian Theatre School, an annual theatre training programme for young Asian girls in Yorkshire.

Recent Productions *Doors,* a modern piece of absurd theatre by award winning playwright Madani Younis for children over 13.

Submission Guidelines Writers new to the company are advised to make contact with the Artistic Director before submitting any written material.

Tips Red Ladder supports new writers; Emma Adams' *Forgotten Things* debut tour launched in September 2007. She was a previous participant of a new writing project in 2005 between Red Ladder and Contact Theatre in Manchester.

For enquiries about Red Grit 2008, email: leyla@redladder.co.uk

TAG Theatre

119 Gorbals Street, Glasgow, G5 9DS

- 0141 429 5561
- 0141 429 7374
- info@tag-theatre.co.uk
- www.tag-theatre.co.uk

Artistic/Editorial Director Guy Hollands
Established 1967

Insider Info TAG (Theatre About Glasgow) represents young people's theatre productions as part of the internationally acclaimed Citizens Theatre. It is also a successful national and international touring company. All work is supported by education programmes. It runs the Citizens YOUNG Company, for people aged 16–21. They stage performances at Citizens Theatre and run weekly drama classes for children.

Recent Productions *Yellow Moon,* written by Scottish writer David Greig, a modern Bonnie and Clyde tale for children aged 15 and over.

Submission Guidelines The company is not looking for 'issue based' plays. Visit their website for instructions for unsolicited manuscripts.

Tall Stories

Compass Theatre, Glebe Avenue, Ickenham, UB10 8PD

- 01895 638922
- 01895 638857
- firstname@tallstories.co.uk

- www.tallstories.org.uk

Artistic/Editorial Director Olivia Jacobs and Toby Mitchell
Established 1997

Insider Info Tall Stories produces modern, participatory theatre with a fresh take on old, new and timeless stories. Tall Stories performs at theatre venues across the UK and internationally at festivals.

Recent Productions *Monster Hits; Does a Monster...?; Mum & The Monster; The Snow Dragon; The Gruffalo; Snow White.*

Tips Tall Stories can offer tailor made workshops for children and adults. Contact them for more details, or with ideas for a workshop.

Tamasha Theatre

2nd Floor, 18 Rupert Street, London, W1D 6DE

- 020 7734 5988
- admin@yellowearth.org
- www.yellowearth.org

Artistic/Editorial Director David Tse
Established 1995

About An Asian culture theatre company, that produces a wide variety of shows, including adaptations of classic literature, new writing, improvised comedy and musicals. The company has only recently started branching out into theatre for children.

Submission Guidelines Writers new to the company are advised to make contact with the Artistic Director before submitting any work for consideration. Include SAE.

Recent Productions *Child Of The Divide;* A dramatic show by Sudha Bhuchar aimed at children, addressing culture and religion

Tips The company has a strong new writing policy.

Tell Tale Hearts

89 High Street, Penistone, Sheffield, S36 6BR

- 01226 761450
- info@telltalehearts.co.uk
- www.telltalehearts.co.uk

Artistic/Editorial Director Natasha Holmes
Established 1997

Insider Info A Theatre in Education company, delivering creative, multi-sensory theatre productions exclusively for early years and primary children, across schools, theatres and other venues in Britain.

Recent Production *Beneath The Waves,* an interactive performance for children aged 3–7, incorporating a beautiful set, live music and video animation.

Rumpelstiltskin, a Christmas piece in collaboration with Figment Theatre, for children aged 5–11.

Tips Runs drama consultancy programmes for teachers, designed to enhance learning through play across the curriculum.

Theatre Centre
Shoreditch Town Hall, 380 Old Street, London, EC1V 9LT

- 020 7729 3066
- 020 7739 9741
- admin@theatre-centre.co.uk
- www.theatre-centre.co.uk

Artistic/Editorial Director Natalie Wilson

Established 1953

Insider Info Theatre Centre is a new writing and touring company that produces and commissions new theatre for young people. The company produces approximately four new productions per year. Performance sites include schools, theatres and other arts venues that are accessible for young people.

Recent Productions *God is a DJ*; A powerful tale of people betrayed by their dreams, by writer Oladipo Agboluaje

Journey to the River Sea; Adapted by Carl Miller from the award winning novel by Eva Ibbotson, aimed at children aged seven and older.

Tips The company has a strong new writing policy. As part of its equal opportunities philosophy, new writing from young people, women, Black, Asian, gay, and disabled people is welcomed. The theatre currently commissions plays by firstly approaching writers of whom they have been made aware.

Theatre Is...
The Innovation Centre, College Lane, Hatfield, AL10 9AB

- 01707 281100
- info@theatreis.org
- www.theatreis.org

Artistic/Editorial Director Stuart Mullins

Insider Info A creative new theatre company throughout the East of England that produces, commissions and curates new work by, for and with young people.

Recent Productions *Apple Cart*; A collaborative production between Apples and Snakes and Oily Cart. A highly creative multisensory show for children who have verbal difficulties

Master Juba; A collaborative piece with Greenwich and Lewisham Young People's Theatre, which is based on the real life story of an amazing black dancer freed from slave heritage

Submission Guidelines At present new scripts are generated from inside the company, but they may consider scripts for the future.

Tips Theatre Is... has developed a professional training project with Apple Cart to support regional artists, and to improve theatre for very young children and children with disabilities and learning difficulties.

Theatre of Widdershins
Marshmangle, Bull Street, Potton, Sandy, Bedfordshire, SG19 2NR

- 01767 262767
- widdershins@ntlworld.com
- www.theatre-of-widdershins.co.uk

Artistic/Editorial Director Andy Lawrence

Insider Info A successful puppet theatre that brings highly visual and innovative puppetry to theatres, schools, community halls and festivals. The company also provides puppet making workshops.

Recent Productions *Furry Tails*; *Rumplestiltskin*; *The Elves and The Shoemaker*; *The Kings Got Donkey Ears*

Tips All productions are designed in-house at the present time, with artwork and music developed by friends of the company.

Theatre Workshop
34 Hamilton Place, Edinburgh, EH3 5AX

- 0131 225 7942
- 0131 220 0112
- firstinitiallastname@twe.org.uk
- www.theatre-workshop.com

Artistic/Editorial Director Robert Rae

Established 1965

Insider Info Theatre Workshop is a producing theatre that includes disabled actors in its main productions, paying special attention to access and inclusion issues. The theatre itself seats 155.

Recent Productions *Endgame*; A collaborative piece with Sharmanka

Tips Theatre Workshop regularly commissions new writing. As the theatre is located in Scotland, Scottish writers, or pieces relevant to modern Scottish life are popular. Scripts should take into account that actors and others involved may be disabled, as well as able bodied. The theatre enjoys working with minority group organisations.

Theatr na n'Og

Unit 3, Millands Road Industrial Estate, Neath, Wales, SA11 1NJ

- 01639 641771
- 01639 647941
- cwmni@theatr-nanog.co.uk
- www.theatr-nanog.co.uk

Artistic/Editorial Director Geinor Styles

Insider Info A Theatre In Education company for schools in Neath, Port Talbot, Swansea and Bridgend. Also a professional touring company to general audiences, in venues across the UK. Runs a drama club and a youth theatre for young children to develop their theatre skills.

Recent Productions *Kapow,* a musical play for under 8s.

Tips Theatr na n'Og runs workshops and drama programmes. If you have an idea for a workshop contact them via email at: sam@theatr-nanog.co.uk

Travelling Light Theatre Company

13 West Street, Old Market, Bristol, BS2 0DF

- 0117 377 3164
- 0117 377 3167
- jude@travellinglighttheatre.org.uk
- www.travlight.co.uk

Artistic/Editorial Director Jude Merrill

Insider Info A professional touring company that performs in schools, festivals and theatres throughout the UK and Europe. Presents new commissions, devised pieces and adaptations of plays that are relevant to young people.

Recent Productions *Clown;* Adaptation of the book by Quentin Blake, in association with the Bristol Old Vic

Shadow Play; A mix of music, dance, mime and design, inspired by the way children use play to investigate the world around them

Tips Travelling Light has an extensive education and community programme that consists of workshops for children, a youth theatre, youth summer courses and a young writers project called 'Short Sharp Shots' in secondary schools. For more information on the youth theatre, email Jen Camillin at: jen@travellinglighttheatre.org.uk

Visible Fictions

Suite 325–327, 4th Floor, 11 Bothwell Street, Glasgow, G2 6LY

- 0141 221 8727
- 0141 221 3944
- firstname@visiblefictions.co.uk
- www.visiblefictions.co.uk

Artistic/Editorial Director Douglas Irvine

Insider Info One of the UK's leading theatre companies, with an international reputation for creating innovative and memorable theatre experiences for young people and adults. Visible Fictions have international theatre projects with Minneapolis Children's Theatre Company and Seattle Children's Theatre.

Recent Productions *Monster;* Based on the award winning novel by Walter Dean Myers for young adults aged eleven and upwards

Song From The Sea; A puppetry show by Mike Kenny for children aged four and upwards

Wild Things; A dramatic story telling show about a little boy's adventure, for children aged four and upwards, written by Visible Fictions

Shopping for Shoes; A romantic comedy about teenage love for children aged ten and upwards, by Tim Crouch

Tips Visible Fictions runs community and education projects, which encompass workshops, residencies, long term youth theatres, and education resources that support each production.

Wee Stories

c/o The Kings Theatre, 2 Leven Street, Edinburgh, EH3 9LQ

- 0131 221 0606
- info@weestoriestheatre.org
- www.weestoriestheatre.org

Artistic/Editorial Director Andy Cannon

Established 1995

Insider Info A story telling company, based in Scotland, that visits schools and other venues nationally. Produces four productions for schools each year.

Recent Productions *Jack and the Beanstalk,* Christmas show for 2007 at the Traverse in Edinburgh; *Is this a Dagger,* based on Shakespeare's Macbeth; *Treasure Island.*

Submission Guidelines Wee Stories does not have the staff to take the time to read and/or comment on scripts. Writers and Playwrights with work that is of interest are welcome to contact them, but there is no need to send in a script.

Tips Wee Stories won the Equity Award for 'Best Show for Children and Young People' in the 2004 TMA Theatre Awards for their production of *Arthur: The Story of a King.*

Whirlwind Theatre Productions

54 High Road, Halton, Lancaster, LA2 6PS
- ☎ 01524 811025
- ✉ enquiries@whirlwindtheatre.org.uk
- 🌐 www.whirlwindtheatre.org.uk

Artistic/Editorial Director Myette Godwyn

Insider Info A small scale touring company for children aged six to twelve that produces theatre with good storylines, adaptations of folk tales, or new writing for children. Whirlwind uses traditional and historical ways of staging a play.

Tips The founders are deeply committed Christians and all their work has a religious influence.

SET DESIGN

3D Creations

9a Bells Road, Gorleston, Norfolk, NR31 6BB
- ☎ 01493 657093
- ☎ 01493 443124
- ✉ info@3dcreations.co.uk
- 🌐 www.3dcreations.co.uk

Contact Scenic Designer, Ian Westbrook

Insider Info 3D creations are international scenic specialists that create tailor made creative design solutions for the theatre. The company offers set design, props, model and sculpture making, backcloths and scenic painting, and designs for museums and galleries.

Client(s) *Theatre Royal Plymouth*– entire set design for *Snow White and the Seven Dwarfs*

Birmingham Stage Company– a 7ft high Mummy case which had actors hiding inside and body parts for the embalming scenes of the *Horrible Histories* tour

Theatre Royal Norwich– the opening backdrop scene for their production of *Aladdin*

Theatre Royal Norwich– the painted backcloth (40ft wide x 20ft drop) for *Robinson Crusoe* Pantomime

Alison Hargreaves Management

27 Hamilton Road, Dollis Hill, London, NW10 1NS
- ☎ 020 8438 0112
- ✉ agent@alisonhargreaves.co.uk
- 🌐 www.alisonhargreaves.co.uk

Contact Director, Alison Hargreaves

Insider Info A theatre agency that solely represents emergent and established Set and Lighting Designers and Directors. Clients work for commercial and subsidised theatre and opera companies throughout the UK, Europe and the USA.

Client(s) Keith Baker: *James and the Giant Peach*, *Young Europe Season (Sweet Peter, Little Angels and Kadouma's Island) Just So, Boy, Stargazer, Silver Sword* and *The Snow Lion* at Polka Theatre, *Peter Pan* for Proteus Theatre Company.

Will Hargreaves: *Spot's Birthday Party* at Oxford Playhouse, *Dick Whittington*, *Sleeping Beauty*, *Cinderella*, *Robin Hood*, *Beauty & The Beast* and *Robinson Crusoe* at Bury St Edmunds.

Tips All set designers have links to their own websites, where it is possible to view more of their work.

Amanda Howard Associates

21 Berwick Street, London, W1F 0PZ
- ☎ 020 7287 9277
- ☎ 020 7287 7785
- ✉ mail@amandahowardassociates.co.uk
- 🌐 www.amandahowardassociates.co.uk

Contact Agents: Amanda Fitzalan Howard; Kate Haldane; Mark Price; Kirsten Wright; Darren Rugg; Chloe Brayfield

Insider Info Talent and Literary agents representing Theatre Designers and Directors and many more.

Client(s) Colin Richmond: *Hansel and Gretal* at Northampton Theatre Royal.

Jason Southgate: *James and the Giant Peach*, *Peter Pan*, and Puppets created for *Charlotte's Webb* at Citizens Theatre.

Emma Wee: *How To Beat A Giant* at Unicorn Theatre.

Naomi Wilkinson: *Aladdin* and *The Firework Maker's Daughter* at Lyric Theatre.

Tips All set designers have downloadable CV's and links to their own websites, whee it is possible to view more of their work.

Associated Arts

8 Shrewsbury Lane, Shooters Hill, London, SE18 3JF
- ☎ 020 8856 4958
- ☎ 020 8856 8189
- ✉ karen@associated-arts.co.uk
- 🌐 www.associated-arts.co.uk

Contact Director, Karen Baker

Insider Info An arts agency for Set, Lighting, Sound Designers and Directors.
Client(s) Carol Betara: As Associate Designer at Contact Young Persons Theatre she designed Allan Bleasedales *No More Sitting On The Old School Bench* and many 'Theatre in Education' productions. She has designed many productions for young people with Inter-Action, Roundabout, TEAM, Second Age Theatre Company and Barnstorm.
 Sue Condie: *Aladdin* and *Sleeping Beauty* at Everyman Theatre, *Tongues Will Wag* at Greenwich Young Persons Theatre, *Can't See the Woods for the Trees* for Roundabout TIE, and *Oliver Twist* and *Beauty and the Beast* as Associate Designer at New Victoria Theatre. Sue has designed many other projects for Action Transport Theatre Company.
Tips Visit website for set designers gallery portfolios and links to their own websites.

Clare Fox Associates
9 Plympton Road, London, NW6 7EH
- ☎ 020 7328 7494
- ☎ 020 7372 2301
- ✉ cimfox@yahoo.com
- ⊕ www.clarefox.co.uk
Contact Director, Clare Fox
Insider Info A small, low-skey agency for Set and Lighting Designers and Directors.
Client(s) Liz Ascroft: *Alice's Adventures In Wonderland*, *The Snow Queen*, *Kipling's Jungle Book Stories*, *Robin Hood*, *Beauty And The Beast*, and *Neville's Island* at Dukes Playhouse, Lancaster.
Tips All set designers have links to their own websites to view more of their work.

Creative Media Management
3b Walpole Court, Ealing Studios, London, W5 5ED
- ☎ 020 8584 5363
- ☎ 020 8566 5554
- ✉ enquiries@creativemediamanagement.com
- ⊕ www.creativemediamanagement.com
Contact Founder/Agent, Jacqui Fincham; Agent, Owen Massey; Agent, Chris Calitz
Established 1999
Insider Info A leading technical and literary agency representing a wide range of professionals in the theatre, film and television industries. Theatre workers include Set, Costume, Lighting, Hair & Make-up and Set Decorators.
Client(s) Susie Caulcutt: *Babe-The Sheep Pig* and *Fantastic Mr Fox* at Regents Open Air Theatre,

Charlotte's Web at Forum Theatre & UK Tour, *BFG* and *The Witches* for David Wood, UK Tours.
 Gemma Fripp: *Stuart Little* and *Double Act* at Polka Theatre.

Curly Willy Productions Ltd
The Warehouse, Durham Street, Ilkeston, Derbyshire, DE7 8FQ
- ☎ 0115 9442299
- ✉ carol@curlywilly.co.uk
- ⊕ www.curlywilly.co.uk
Contact Directors, Andrew and Carol
Insider Info Curly Willy offers Costume and Prop Making, Character Heads, Scenery Design, Mascots and Design Consultancy for Theatre, TV, Film, Education and Promotional events. Design credits have included work for West End shows, Disney and the Royal Shakesphere Company.
Tips Visit their website to view pictures of their design projects.

Dennis Lyne Agency
108 Leonard Street, London, EC2A 4RH
- ☎ 020 7739 6200
- ☎ 020 7739 4101
- ✉ info@dennislyne.com
- ⊕ www.dennislyne.com
Contact Director, Dennis Lyne
Insider Info A theatrical and talent agency that represents emergent and established Theatre and Lighting Designers and Directors.
Client(s) Kate Burnett: *The Ghosts of Scrooge*, *Merlin* and *Beauty and the Beast* at the Library Theatre, *The Little Mermaid* at Sheffield Crucible. While working as Head of Design at Contact Theatre she won the Manchester Evening News Award for *The Power of Darkness*, *To Kill a Mockingbird* and *The Little Prince*. Kate also won the Time Out Award for *Doctor Faustus* at the Young Vic and was designer in residence for the Manchester Arts Education Festival for five years.
 Fred Mellor: Designs for Unicorn Theatre. She has an interest in designing in unconventional spaces other than theatre buildings, such as an old hospital, a jam factory, a mortuary, a disused brothel, labyrinthine Victorian town hall cellars, a supermarket distribution complex and the biggest potting shed in Europe.

The Designers Formation
20 Gorsey Road, Nottingham, NG3 4JL
- ☎ 0115 969 2633

✉ jill@designersformation.com
🌐 www.designersformation.com
Contact Director, Jill Westby
Insider Info A theatre agency which solely represents Theatre, Lighting and Costume Designers. The agency lists all the designers forthcoming, current and recent productions for viewing on the website.
Client(s) Nettie Scriven: *The Secret Garden* at Nottingham Playhouse, *A Little Princess* Yvonne Arnaud, *The Snow Spider* and *Aesop's Fables* at Sherman Theatre.
Helen Fownes-Davies: She has designed sets for Nottingham Playhouse, Roundabout Theatre and New Perspectives theatre.
Steve Denton: *Jane Eyre*, *Nothing Compares 2 U* and *Moll Flanders* for the Royal Welsh College of Music & Drama, where he holds a part-time lecturing post. He has designed sets for TIE, youth theatre and education projects with companies across the UK.
Tips All set designers have images of their work on the website.

Jeffrey Cambell Management
11a Greystone Court, South Street, Eastbourne, East Sussex, BN21 4LP
☎ 01323 411444
☎ 01323 411373
✉ cambell@theatricaldesigners.co.uk
🌐 www.theatricaldesigners.co.uk
Contact Director, Jeremy Campbell
Insider Info A theatre agency representing Theatre, Lighting, Costume, Sound Designers, Directors and Choreographers. Jeffrey Cambell Management is an international company and has clients working in the UK, America, Canada, Australia, Europe, Russia, Argentina, South Africa, Hong Kong and Japan.
Client(s) Russell Craig: *Sleeping Beauty* at the Unicorn Theatre for Children, London. Russell also has wide teaching and lecturing experience and is an accomplished prop maker.

Loesje Sanders Ltd
Pound Square, North Hill, Woodbridge, Suffolk, IP12 1HH
☎ 01394 385260
☎ 01394 388734
✉ loesje@loesjesanders.org.uk
🌐 www.loesjesanders.com
Contact Agent, Loesje Sanders
Insider Info A successful theatrical agency for Set Design, Lighting & Costume Designers, Choreographers and Directors. The company lists all forthcoming designers work on their website.
Client(s) Alex Lowde: *The Gentle Giant* at The Clore Studio, *Tobias and the Angel* at The Young Vic.
Tips All set designers have CVs available to view.

Make It So
Flat 3, The Lodge, 18–19 Upper Lewes Road, Brighton, BN2 3FJ
☎ 01273 279995
✉ info@makeitso.gb.com
🌐 www.makeitso.gb.com
Contact Director, Stephen Holroyd
Established 2005
Insider Info Make It So is an arts and entertainment company that provides many different types of theatre services, including; Script Writing, Lighting Design, Directing, Musical Directing, Dance, Choreography and Stage Management. The company can produce large scale theatre productions incorporating external artists and staff, or provide the entire artistic service. Previous theatrical productions include *The Adventures of Sindbad*, plays for the New Dubai Community Theatre in the United Arab Emirates; *Alladdin* at the Jumeria Beach Hotel Group in Dubai; and *Guys and Dolls* a community production with the Worthing Musical Comedy Society.
Tips The company has an archive of many of the productions it has worked on, from January 2006 to present. Many of its productions are international.

Paragon Creative
Unit 8, Harrier Court, The Airfield, Elvington, York, YO41 4EA
☎ 01904 608020
☎ 01904 608011
✉ mark@paragon-creative.co.uk
🌐 www.paragoncreativeltd.co.uk
Contact Managing Director, Peter Holdsworth; Production Director, Stephen Jackson
Insider Info Paragon offer Model Making, Prop Making, Scenic Design, Set Dressing, Scenic Painting, Sculpting and Metalwork, serving a range of venues, from Theatres and Museums, to Aquariums. The Paragon team consists of 35 highly talented staff, who have worked on 600 projects worldwide.
Client(s) Richmond Theatre, Cadbury Land, *Ice Age* Movie Park in Bottrop, Germany, *Slime* at The Deep, Hull.
Tips Visit the website to view pictures of their projects.

Perry Scenic Limited

Unit D & E, 100 Dudley Road, East Oldbury, West Midlands, B69 3EB

- ☎ 0121 552 9696
- ⊕ 0121 552 9697
- ✉ enquiries@perryscenic.com
- 🌐 www.perryscenic.com

Insider Info Perry Scenic is a multi-talented, technically skilled company, dedicated to the creation and construction of large scale Art and Scenic Effects; for Theatres, Concerts, Television, Themed Environments, Presentations and Events.

Tips Perry Scenic also works with high profile music clients, such as the Rolling Stones and The Cure.

PFD Peters, Frasers & Dunlop

Drury House, 34–43 Russell Street, London, WC2B 5HA

- ☎ 020 7344 1000
- ⊕ 020 7836 9539
- ✉ postmaster@pfd.co.uk
- 🌐 www.pfd.co.uk

Contact Director (Theatre Dept.), Kenneth Ewing; Agents: Rose Cobbe; Nicki Stoddart; St John Donald

Insider Info A successful international literary and talent agency, with a sister company in New York. Represents professionals from a broad spectrum of industries, including Sets, Lighting, Sound & Costume Designers, Directors, Playwrights and more.

Client(s) Liz Cooke: *Yikes* at Unicorn Theatre for Children, *Peter Pan* at Oxford Playhouse, *The Little Mermaid* at Sphinx Theatre Company.

Isla Shaw: *Does A Monster Live Here?/Monster Hits* and *The Gruffalos Child* for Tall Stories Theatre Company, *Pippi Longstockings* for Dragon Black Productions.

Ben Stones: *Pinnochio* at Theatre Royal Northampton.

Polly Sullivan: *The Snow Dragon* for Tall Stories Theatre Company, *The Bear Stories* at Polka Theatre for Children.

Tips PFD are always happy to consider unsolicited theatre material but will only represent writers and directors who are based in the UK or Ireland.

Scenic Design

- ✉ scenicdesign.org@hotmail.com
- 🌐 www.scenicdesign.org.uk

About Scenic Design offers Theatre Design, Prop Making, Costume Design, Model Making, Shop Window Displays, Injection Mould Making, Sculpture Making, and Lightweight Installation in Yorkshire, Leeds, Sheffield, Harrogate and York. Scenic Design will develop prototype ideas for Stage, Set or Window Displays, and even mass manufacture the product.

Recent Products The company has previously made papier maché Frankenstein heads, gargoyles, vampires and tombstones. Entire sets have been made out of paper, and they have produced trophies and other props such as rocking horses, hedgehogs, masks and snowmen.

Tips Initial correspondence occurs through email. Can supply props and scenes for theatre production.

Tornado Designs

54 High Road, Halton, Lancaster, LA2 6PS

- ☎ 01524 811025
- ✉ enquiries@whirlwindtheatre.org.uk
- 🌐 www.whirlwindtheatre.org.uk

Contact Co-founders, Mike Whalley and Myette Godwyn

Insider Info Tornado designs can offer complete design solutions from set and costume design, through to prop and mask making, scenic construction, lighting and/or sound design, costume making and scenic painting.

Clients *Curzon Productions:* Set construction of *Carousel.*

Denholm Elliott Project, Ibiza: Costume design for *At The Sea's Edge.*

TOY & PACKAGING MANUFACTURERS

Anthony Peters Manufacturing Company Ltd

Thorpe Road, Melton Mowbray, Leicestershire, LE13 1SL

☎ 01664 481882
☎ 01664 481883
✉ cynthiahoggett@anthonypeters.com
🌐 www.anthonypeters.com

Contact Managing Director, Mike Austin; Product Development - Sales & Marketing Manager, Cynthia Hoggett

About Anthony Peters are designers and manufacturers specialising in arts and crafts materials and tools, paint accessories and kits. Products are aimed mostly at the educational market and include *The Young Gardener* range, Christmas activities and sponge cutting sets. Undertake both own-brand label design for arts and crafts as well as contract production jobs.

Recent Products *Chinese New Year Activity Pack* (Festival and Season Arts & Crafts).

Atomic Design

Spooner House, 116a Ashley Road, Hale, Cheshire, WA14 2UN

☎ 0161 929 7221
☎ 0161 929 7216
✉ studio@atomicdesign.co.uk
🌐 www.atomicdesign.co.uk

Contact Andrew Fairley

About Atomic Design offers illustration and packaging design, and other design services, for websites through to corporate branding. Atomic has designed and illustrated children's packaging in the toy and confectionary markets.

Recent Products *Fizzy Lizzy*: Character concepts for McCowens as part of Atomics ongoing packaging design for the company.

Tips For current vacancies visit their website. Send in a CV and samples of illustrations and work.

Bandai UK Ltd

Jellicoe House, Botleigh Grange, Hedge End, Southampton, SO30 2AF

☎ 0845 602 8782
🌐 www.bandai.co.uk

Parent Bandai Co.

About A subsidiary of the third largest toy company in the world, Bandai Co. Ltd. Produces licenced toys and characters including *Power Rangers*, *Pokémon*, *Digimon*, *Gundam* and *Thunderbirds*, as well as original products such as the worldwide phenomenons *Tamagotchi* and *Badge IT!*. Products include action figures, confectionary, visual content, video game software, DVDs, amusement machines and mobile phone network content. Works closely with other media companies, such as television and film studios, to which many of its characters are licensed. Corporate partners include 4Kids Entertainment, Disney Consumer Products, DIC Entertainment, Universal Studios Consumer Products, Warner Bros and Sanrio.

Recent Products *Ben 10: Action Figure*: Includes a collectible Lenticular card and bonus animation disc. *Squirt Alert Action Game*: Electronic game for 2–4 players.

Benjamin Toys Ltd

Unit 8, Fulton Close, Argyle Way, Stevenage, SG1 2AF

☎ 01438 726002
☎ 01438 347444
✉ contact@benjamintoys.co.uk
🌐 www.benjamintoys.co.uk

Contact Sales, Vanessa Conrad

About Benjamin Toys Ltd manufactures and distributes science and discovery toys, radio control cars and other vehicles, boys toys, outdoor toys, jigsaws, and sea monkeys, as well as various licensed character products across the UK, Ireland and overseas.

Recent Products *Antzone*: Watch ants at work inside a see-through container. The kit includes a magnifier, tweezers, water dropper, ant-size watering hole and poster. (Science and Nature) *Bubblemax 300*: Includes a bubble solution dipping cup. (Summer Fun) *Porsche 911 GT2*: A radio-controlled car. (Boys Toys)

Brain-ed Ltd

250 Cygnet Court, Centre Park, Warrington,
WA1 1PP

- 01925 412636
- 01925 412638
- sales@brain-ed.co.uk
- www.braingymuk.com

Contact Sales, Caroline Seston

About Invents and manufactures highly educational
games and puzzles for retail, educational and
corporate sectors.

Recent Products *The Kaleidoscope Classic:* a brain-
teasing puzzle which won the Smart Puzzle award at
Toyfair '06.
Belly Busters: a healthy eating game for children.
Feel Good Faces: a non competitive game that
encourages confidence and self esteem for children
aged 5+. (Social skills game)

Brio

Sutton House, Bishop Meadow Road,
Loughborough, Leicestershire, LE11 5RE

- 01509 231874
- info@brio.co.uk
- www.brio.co.uk

About A global manufacturer of educational toys,
designed to stimulate children's minds from an early
age. Best known for railway-themed toys. Products
include games, building blocks, pull-alongs and
push-alongs.

Britannia Games

BIC House, Innova Park, Electric Avenue, Enfield,
EN3 7XU

- 020 8350 1264
- 020 8350 1351
- info@britanniagames.com
- www.britanniagames.com

Contact Sales, Ralph Patmore

About A manufacturer of licensed TV board games,
educational and children's games, travel games,
interactive DVD games, trading cards and gifts.
Britannia is well known for TV themed games such as
Family Fortunes, Blankety Blank, Catchphrase and *Play
Your Cards Right.*

Recent Products *Engie Benjy:* a memory game for
Children aged 3+.
Hammer Horror: an interactive DVD game for
Children aged 8+ and adults.

Cassidy Brothers Plc

Cornford Road, Blackpool, Lancashire, FY4 4QQ

- 01253 766411
- 01253 691486
- help@casdon.com
- www.casdon.co.uk

Contact Chairman & Managing Director, Paul M.
Cassidy; Sales, Roger Howard

About Cassidy brothers is famous for its licensed toy
miniatures of household favourites such as Dyson
and Henry hoovers, irons and ironing boards, and
many more. Other products include activity play,
dolls accessories and nursery products. The team are
always on the look out for new ideas that use the
latest technology to produce stimulating products
for children. Specifically avoid toys linked
with violence.

Recent Products *Dyson Vacuum Cleaner DC08:* a
unique small-scale version of the famous Dyson for
3–8 year olds.
Post Office: includes all the accessories you would
expect from a local post office.

Centre Line Design

Hexgreave Hall, Upper Hexgreave, Farnsfield,
Nottinghamshire, NG22 8LS

- 01623 884300
- 01623 884301
- enquiries@cldesignltd.com
- www.cldesignltd.com

Contact Founder, Steve Wagstaff

About Centre Line offers a professional service for
packaging and product design, 2D graphic design
and injection mould design. Also offers other design
services, such as website and logo design. Centre
Line Design has worked for Lego, MV and Tomy.

Recent Products *Bob the Builder: Scoop the Digger:* A
'Sit and Ride' children's toy designed for MV Sports.
Activity Sounds Flower Nursery Toy:
Designed for Tomy.
Duplo Bricks Range: Toy packaging
designed for Lego.

Tips For all recruitment vacancies and student
placements please email: iwantajob@
cldesignltd.com

Cochranes of Oxford Ltd

29 Groves Industrial Estate, Shipton Road,
Milton under Wychwood, Chipping Norton,
Oxfordshire, OX7 6JP

- 01993 832868
- 01993 832578

○ cochranes@mailbox.co.uk
ⓦ www.cochranes.co.uk

About Producers and designers of educational products and kites. Educational kits are aimed at pre-school, primary, secondary and tertiary education levels and cover subjects such as maths, science, design and technology. Cochranes also acts as a contract manufacturer for toys and models and will undertake individual commissions.

Recent Products *Orbit Small DNA Kit*: a build-your-own DNA helix. (Education/Science)
UFO-SAM: a holographic foil kite that reflects the light as it flies. (Recreational Kite)

Tips If you have an idea or design contact them by phone, email or via their website.

Corinthian
1st Floor Stirling House, Stirling Road, Cressex Business Park, High Wycombe, Buckinghamshire, HP12 3RT
○ 01494 478200
○ 01494 523847
○ enquiry@corinthianplc.com
ⓦ www.corinthianplc.com

About Corinthian is a marketing and manufacturing company dealing with both toys and confectionary. Licensed brands include *'Puppy in my Pocket'*, *'Kitty in my Pocket'*, the *'FA'* (Football Association) and *'Marvel Micros'*. Products include figurines, games and children's packaged jewellery. Corinthian also contributes to international promotions with brands such as Kelloggs, Coca-Cola and McDonalds.

Recent Products *Micro Stars Series 15 Triple Pack*: contains three top player figurines and six Milk Chocolate Footballz.
Puppy Salon: features a neat, fold-up carry case with hairdryer, flip-up mirror, swivelling chair and four puppies.

Crayola
Binney & Smith (Europe) Ltd, Saturn Facilities Ltd, Bedford Heights, Manton Lane, Bedford, MK41 7PH
○ 01702 208170
○ consumers@vividimag.co.uk
ⓦ www.crayola.co.uk

About International producers of children's arts and crafts materials including crayons, markers, coloured pencils, paints, modelling compounds and activity products in three distinct brands: 'Crayola Mini Kids', 'Crayola' and 'Crayola Creations'. Aimed at both the educational and consumer markets.

Recent Products *Mess-Free Colour Wonder*: includes special Colour Wonder markers that only show up on Colour Wonder paper.
Create a Story: allows Children to devise a 4 page picture story, record their own voice commentary and then wipe clean and re-use the specials screens.

Creativity International!
Narrowboat Way, Hurst Business Park, Brierley Hill, West Midlands, DY5 1UF
○ 01384 485550
○ 01384 485551
○ sales@cilimited.co.uk
ⓦ www.cilimited.co.uk

About Previously known as Bemiss Jason International Limited. Producers of children's arts and crafts materials for the retail and educational markets. Licensed products include *Fadeless* paper and *Bordette* display Rolls.

Recent Products *Fadeless Seasonal Display Packs*: includes paper that comes in an assortment of different colours that represent the colours of the seasons.

Drummond Park Ltd
PO Box 12607, West Lothian, EH52 6DZ
○ info@drummondpark.com
ⓦ www.drumondpark.com

About The UK's leading manufacturer of children's and adult's board games including the *Deal or No Deal* branded games, *Balderdash* and *Doh Nutters*.

Recent Products *Jack and the Beanstalk*: A shaking, quaking action game for children aged four and upwards.
Doh Nutters: A fun filled energetic game for all the family, for ages four and upwards.

Flair Leisure Products PLC
Anne Boleyn House, 9–13 Ewell Road, Cheam, Surrey, SM3 8BZ
○ 020 8643 0320
○ 020 8642 8462
○ sales@flairplc.co.uk
ⓦ www.flairplc.co.uk

About Focuses on heritage products such as *Sticklebricks* and *Sylvanian Families*, rather than brand new products. Produces a range of toys around licensed brands, which include *Angelina Ballerina* and *Funky Chicks*. Flair is responsible for launching Tomy and K'NEX in the UK. Own-brand products include *Flairgames* heritage game boards such as

Ghost Castle and *Flairplay* a fantastic range of game books for babies and young children.
Recent Products *Fairy Tale World: Goldilocks Book*: a play-set of Goldilocks' house, with a roof that doubles up as a beautiful illustrated book.

Fuzzy Felt
Hornbeam House, Wootton Road, Tiptoe, Lymington, SO41 6FT
- 07050 097498
- Online form.
- www.fuzzyfelt.com

About Designers and producers of the classic children's felt toys. A simple yet effective design using felt artwork to create a playful scene on a hardback board. Designs are aimed at children aged 3–6 years.
Recent Products Fuzzy Felt comes in a range of product types including classic set, playscenes and teaching aids. Visit website for a full list of products.

Galt Education
Johnsonbrook Road, Hyde, Cheshire, SK14 4QT
- 0845 120 3005
- 0800 056 0314
- enquiries@galt-educational.co.uk
- www.galt-educational.co.uk

Parent Company Galt Toys
Contact Managing Director, John McDonnell
About Designs and creates innovative educational products for babies to six year olds and caters for special needs. Produces jigsaws and games, furniture, music toys and kits, science, special needs products, numeracy, physical play, sand and water, arts and more.
Recent Products *The 123 Farm Set*: Features a farmers barn, two tractors and a wagon, mother and father, horse and rider, shepherd with sheep and a farmer with cows on a summer meadow set. Suitable for children aged 18+ months. (Imaginative Play)
 IBM Centre For Young Learners: A first of its kind, an all inclusive software solution that is simple to set up, easy for children to use and encourages pre-school learning.

Galt Toys
Sovereign House, Stockport Road, Cheadle, Cheshire, SK8 2EA
- 0161 428 9111
- 0161 428 6597
- mail@galt.co.u

- www.galt.co.uk
Contact Managing Director, John McDonnell; Senior Product Manager, Diana Hall; Product Managers Peter Nicholls and Bethan Parry.
About Designs and manufactures arts and craft toys, puzzles, activity products and in recent years has branched out and become a specialist in early years products and play nests. Galt toys are sold in the UK and globally. It has a two subsidiaries; *Galt Education* and *Living & Learning* that manufactures educational products for early years and older children.
Recent Products *Beady Modelling*: A fascinating air drying modelling material made from small coloured foam beads. (Creative crafts)
 Brilliant Badges: Features badge mould, plaster moulding powder, 6 x 5ml acrylic paints, paintbrush, 3 badge pins, 2 magnets, guide. (Activity craft pack)

Games Workshop Group
Willow Road, Lenton, Nottingham, NG7 2WS
- 0115 914 0000
- info@games-workshop.com
- www.games-workshop.com

About Games Workshop Group PLC is the largest and most successful tabletop fantasy and futuristic battle games company in the world. It designs, manufactures and dispatches three core gaming systems: *The Lord of The Rings*, *Warhammer* and *Warhammer 40,000*. They also produce specialist games systems for the more enthusiastic hobbyist. They run a publishing company that publishes action novels, art books, background books and other items, all set in the dark and gothic worlds of *Warhammer* and *Warhammer 40,000*.
Recent Products *Chaos Space Marine Army Set*: Contains one Chaos Terminator Lord, five Chaos Terminators, fifteen Chaos Space Marines, eight Khorne Berzerkers, five Possessed Chaos Space Marines, two Chaos Spawn and one Chaos Defiler. Includes the new Codex: Chaos Space Marines.
Tips Editors are needed for Games Workshop's long running monthly hobby magazine *White Dwarf*. Available jobs at Games Workshop in the UK and overseas are advertised on their website.

Genie Toys Plc
25 Imperial Square, Cheltenham, Gloucestershire, GL50 1QZ
- 01242 236322
- 01242 238322
- admin@genietoys.com
- www.genietoys.com
Contact Sales, Casey Norman

About Genie Toys is primarily an originator, developer, manufacturer and licenser of toys. Genie offers a full range of design, illustration, sculpting, model-making, engineering and production services for toy companies to fulfil their need for new toy concepts.

Recent Products *Fashion Annie*: Distributors include Playmates, Epoch, Bandai and Stadlbauer.
Dragonball Z Secret Saiyan: Distributors include Irwin, Jakks and Giochi Preziosi.
Halloween Barbie: Licensee Mattel, Inc.

Tips Genie does not distribute toy products or sell directly to consumers.

Geoff Bullen Electronics UK Ltd

Ascot House, Mulberry Close, Goring, West Sussex, BN12 4QY

- 01903 244500
- 01903 700715
- info@gbelectronics.com
- www.gbelectronics.com

About GB Electronics and their affiliated company, GBE Designs Ltd are a specialist electronic design consultancy, that provides full support in product and prototype design. GBE provides consultancy on the design of electronic toys.

Recent Products *Jumpsmart: The Electronic Trampoline*: GBE created a trampoline with sensor pads in the jumping matt to monitor how many bounces a child can make and sound effects to accompany bouncing. The toy proved hugely successful, with further developments to introduce to the European market.

Green Board Games

Unit 112a, Cressex Business Park, Coronation Road, High Wycombe, Buckinghamshire, HP12 3RP

- 01494 538999
- 01494 538646
- enquiry@greenboardgames.com
- www.greenboardgames.com

Contact Managing Director Gary Wyatt

About Produces environmentally friendly educational toys. Products include Educational Snap and Pairs, Memory and Matching games, Board games, Card games, Playing cards, Travel games, Wikki Stix, Jigsaws, Art and Craft, Science in Action and Puzzle and Activity Books.

Recent Products *Blokus Trigon:* A strategic-thinking game for children aged seven plus.

More Word Winks: A visual/word play puzzle book where phrases and expressions are represented by illustrated words.

Hasbro

2 Roundwood Avenue, Stockley Park, Uxbridge, UB11 1AZ

- 020 8569 1234
- careers@hasbro.co.uk
- www.hasbro.co.uk

About Hasbro is a leading manufacturer of toys and games, with products including *Trivial Pursuit, Monopoly, Action Man* and *My Little Pony*. Careers, including those in design, are advertised on the site. CVs may be submitted speculatively for positions within Hasbro.

Recent Products *Transformers: Magatron Figure* (Movie Tie-In).

Hillside Designs

6 Hillside Close, Teignmouth, Devon, TQ14 9XE

- 01626 774881
- info@hillsidedesign.co.uk
- www.hillsidedesign.co.uk

Contact Managing Director, Chris Howsam

About A small scale design and development company that offers initial concept design, through to total product development using 3D CAD modelling and analysis; product visualisation and animation; and prototype build and production detailing. Hillside has experience in toy design, products for the disabled, exhibition displays, furniture and more.

Recent Products *Action Man Boomerang Extreme*: Developed a throwing arm prototype for a television advert.
Top Trumps Pack: Developed client concept using CAD and rapid prototyping. Prepared tooling data and control drawings.

Tips Hillside is accepting CVs for designer and model maker jobs. Email a text-only CV, or post the entire CV.

Hornby Hobbies

Westwood Industrial Estate, Margate, Kent, CT9 4JX

- 01843 233525
- online submission form
- www.scalextric.com

About Hornby is a household name in Britain, a leading manufacturer and distributor of model railways and locomotives, accessories and digital

command control train sets. Hornby also produces *Scalextric, Scalextric Digital, Scalextric Sport World* and *Micro Scalextric* and *Thomas and Friends* railway sets.
Recent Products *Percy Circus Electric Train Set*: Includes Percy the Saddle Tank Engine and electric power accessories.
Scalextric: C1196 Pro Rally Championship: Featuring World Rally Championship cars from Ford and Subaru.

Hutton and Partners
Borough House, 32 West Borough, Wimborne Minster, Dorset, BH21 1NF
- 0845 230 3004
- 01202 885251
- info@huttonpartners.com
- www.huttonpartners.com
Contact Founder and Director, Steve Hutton
Insider Info A graphic design company that offers creative solutions for packaging design, plus other soltuions for websites to product branding. Hutton and Partners has designed packaging and branding logos for toy and craft clients such as; *Hunbrol, Hazel Mill Toys* and the *Toy and Hobby Association*.
Recent Products *Hunbrol's* Packaging for *Young Scientist; Human Science, Microscope Lab, Astronomy and Chemistry.*
Hazel Mill Toys, Packaging for *Extra Wide Puzzles and Giant Floor Games.*

Hyphen Design
15–20 The Oval, Bethnal Green, London, E2 9DX
- 020 7739 8010
- 020 7739 8764
- enquiries@hyphendesign.com
- www.hyphendesign.com
Contact Mike
About Hyphen is a product design consultancy that can offer full product development from scratch, design a portion of the product, or come up with a design idea for a totally new product. Services include research and innovation, ergonomics, engineering specialities, prototype and model making and manufacturing needs. Hyphen's clientele include *Tomy* and *Hasbro*.
Recent Products *Megasketcher*. Hyphen were asked to update one of Tomy's best known products.
Get a Letter. The most recent design for Tomy.
Micro Machines Rally Mountain: Hyphen developed idea a compact, folding race track for Hasbro.
Remote control sumo wrestlers: Mechanical fighting toys for the Marks and Spencer toy range.

Tips Visit Hyphen's website to download a job application form.

Invicta Ltd
Harborough Road, Oadby, Leicester, LE2 4LB
- 0116 272 0555
- 0116 272 0626
- invicta.sales@dial.pipex.com
- www.invictagroup.co.uk
Contact Sally Smith
About Invicta are designers and manufacturers of plastic display and packaging materials and educational products. They offer a proven service covering design, value engineering, print, production and just in time delivery of in-store displays, product packaging and end to end solutions. Offers bespoke moulding of plastic toys.
Recent Products Invicta educational products include plastic art containers, abacuses and plastic microscopes.
Tips Invicta advertises job vacancies on their website.

Juice Factory
24 College Road, Maidenhead, Berkshire, SL6 6BN
- 01628 789769
- info@juice-factory.co.uk
- www.juice-factory.co.uk
Contact Jasper Williams
About Juice Factory is a design and marketing consultancy that offers a full range of creative and production services. Juice Factory offers packaging design solutions, which cover areas as diverse as toy packaging, to household care and confectionary.
Recent Products Own label toy packaging for Mothercare.

Lego UK
33 Bath Road, Slough, SL1 3UF
- www.lego.com
About The UK branch of the famous Danish stacking brick toy. Brands include *Duplo* and *Technic Lego*. Lego also produces licenced products such as *Star Wars, Bionicle* and *Batman*.
Recent Products *Bionicle Toa Kongu*: includes building instructions
Tips Careers within Lego, including artist and designer jobs are advertised on their website.

Living and Learning

Sovereign House, Stockport Road, Cheadle, Cheshire, SK8 2EA

☎ 0161 428 9111

🖷 0161 428 6597

✉ mail@galt.co.u

🌐 www.galt.co.uk

Parent Company Galt Toys

Contact Managing Director, John McDonnell; Senior Product Manager, Diana Hall; Product Managers Peter Nicholls and Bethan Parry

About Develops and researches educational products for older children, producing manufactured licensed science and history kits; *Horrible Science Series & Horrible Histories* and other products, such as puzzles and games, family games, start kits and products that use sound as a tool for learning.

Recent Products *Horrible Science: Explosive Experiments*; Based on Scholastic's best selling books, the kit incorporates slimy slush, rockets and miniature volcanoes to make science stuff fun.
Times Tables Soundtrack; A unique listening game that encourages learning of times tables. Features a board game, a CD and counters. Children must listen to the question and give an answer to see who is right, in order to move along the board.

Mattel UK Ltd

Mattel House, Vanwall Business Park, Vanwall Road, Maidenhead, Berkshire, SL6 4UB

☎ 01628 500000

🖷 01628 500075

✉ enquiries@mattel.ciom

🌐 www.mattel.com

Contact Chairman and Chief Executive Officer, Bob Eckert

About A leading international distributor and manufacturer of children's toys. Mattel owns Fisher Price, which is in command of the entire pre-school and infant toy line at Mattel, they also own Corgi, a UK based toy car company, Tyco Toys, Bluebird Toys and more. Mattel is responsible for leading brands, such as *Barbie* and *Hot Wheels* and has licensing agreements with *Harry Potter, Max Steel* and *Barney*. Their website contains links to Barbie, and Fisher Price.

Recent Products *Hot Wheels; Flip N Go Spin City Playset; Barbie: The Island Princess*

Tips Mattel advertises jobs on their website.

Milestone Designs

1 The Highway, Beaconsfield, Buckinghamshire, HP9 1QD

☎ 01494 676436

🖷 01494 676438

✉ info@milestonedesign.co.uk

🌐 www.milestonedesign.co.uk

About Milestone offers Packaging, Branding and Identity, Web Design, Promotional Literature, Poster and Display, Business to Business, Logo and 3D designs.

Recent Products *Action Man James Bond Limited Edition*: Front of pack illustration for Hasbro.
K'NEX: Milestone designed completely new packaging with the K'NEX logo running up the side of the box for Hasbro.

Mother Media

23 Park View, Swynnerton, Stoke on Trent, Staffordshire, ST15 0QG

☎ 01782 796137

✉ contact@mothermedia.co.uk

🌐 www.mothermedia.co.uk

About Mother Media is a collective design agency specialising in Illustration, Website design, Graphic design, Photography, Video, Multimedia and Bespoke marketing solutions.

Recent Products *Wagtails Catnip Dancing Christmas Chums*: Packaging and illustration for pet toys.

MotionTouch

Dunsfold Park, Cranleigh, Surrey, GU6 8TB

☎ 01483 204754

🖷 01483 275691

✉ info_d@motiontouch.com

🌐 www.motiontouch.com

Contact Managing Director, Henry Powell

About Motion Touch is a leading design and manufacturing company which provides a full development service, from initial concept, through to manufacturing and marketing. Skilled designers can work on any concept using a wide variety of materials form plastic to electronics. The company owns manufacturing factories in Asia and China that offer cost effective manufacturing equipment. Alternatively Motion Touch can source an appropriate manufacturing factory for the client's needs.

Recent Products *Child Development Programme*: An innovative product designed for Mentis XL. The product targets the whole spectrum of skills: physical development, communication, social and perceptual. The pack includes an instruction manual and DVD, a wrist strap, 108 coloured shapes, a ladder, soft ball, four feet templates, two coloured discs and a turtle beanie. The main distributor was Boots.

Tips The company has offices across the whole of the UK and internationally in America and Poland. Visit their website for contact details.

Playmobil UK Ltd

6 Argent Court, Sylvan Way, Southfields Business Park, Basildon, Essex, SS15 6TH
- 01268 490184
- 01268 548181
- Online submission form
- www.playmobil.de

About Playmobil is a global manufacturer and distributor of commercial children's toys. The headquarters in Zirndorf, Germany, carry out research, development and advertising, and manufacturing occurs in Dietenhofen. Products include plastic dolls, figurines, railways, cars, farm animals, zoo animals, forts and castles, pirates and buildings. Playmobil owns fun parks in America and throughout Europe.

Recent Products *RC-Cargo Engine with Light*: Includes remote control, and opening doors. Ages 5+
Prince & Princess Fairy Tale Set: Ages 4+

Seymourpowell

327 Lillie Road, London, SW6 7NR
- 020 7381 6433
- 020 7381 9081
- design@seymourpowell.com
- www.seymourpowell.com

Contact Founder, Dick Powell; Partner, Richard Seymour

About A design and new product development company, with a team of 60 highly skilled designers who work across a wide variety of products. These include leisure items like *Action Man* toy designs, to more conceptual designs, such as the ENV hydrogen fuel cell powered motorcycle.

Recent Products *Action Man: Rocket Bike*; Seymourpowell designed a Rocket Bike for Hasbro's classic and ever popular *Action Man* Line.

Tips Seymourpowell Foresight is a research unit run by eight people, that can offer a future product strategy for consumer companies.

Small World Design

72a Pope Lane, Penwortham, Lancashire, PR1 3DA
- 01772 750885
- 01772 750885
- Online form
- www.smallworlddesign.co.uk

Contact Partners, David Peet and Sue Chadwick
Established 1995

About A freelance design company who write, illustrate, design and package all manner of children's material and merchandise, including pre-school material, novelty books, big books, games, jigsaw puzzles, activity packs, licenced products, creative and educational products and more. Customers include children's book publishers, packagers, wholesalers, toy and game manufacturers and educational suppliers across the UK, Europe and worldwide. They also offer product licensing for their designs.

Recent Products *Game Plan*: A newly-created, researched and designed, word and chasing game for Edu-Science Hong Kong. Also created *In Gear* for Edu-Science. Other products include *Hopping Hare Children's Exercise Mats* and a range of bright, colourful children's furniture in an alphabet theme, designed in conjunction with TFT Educational Ltd.

Southbank Design

Suite B Millbridges, Newton Lane, Romsey, Hampshire, S051 8HJ
- 01794 500123/4
- 01794 500125
- enquiries@southbank-design.co.uk
- www.southbank-design.co.uk

About A graphic design company that creates design solutions for a number of clients in many business sectors, from individual traders to multinationals. Provides solutions for packaging, illustrations and artworks, and other services such as website design.

Recent Products *Betty Spaghetty* and *Tamagotchi* toy range: Southbank worked for the Bandai toy company to design the packaging and point of sale ideas for these phenomenal products. Southbank also managed the clients print requirements for the *Tamagotchi* project.
Archie's World Leisure centre: Colourful, bright and modern pop-up and exhibition stands.

Tips For enquiries about designer and illustrator jobs, email query and CV.

MULTIMEDIA

LISTINGS

The Studio Blackheath Ltd

72a Old Dover Road, Blackheath, London, SE3 8SY

- ☎ 020 8853 8531
- ☎ 020 8853 8532
- ✉ Online form.
- 🌐 www.thestudio-london.com

Contact Sally Smith

About The Studio is a versatile design company, with specialisms in designing toy products and luxury brand marketing. The Studio works closely with major toy manufacturers to produce new products for global markets. They handle all aspects of the design procedure, from first instance prototypes, to the finished article and packaging solutions. The Studio also offers website design, exhibition stands, logo design, leaflets and pamphlets and direct marketing fulfilment.

Recent Products *Oba!*: Wooden Toy Product design for Halsall International.
Barbie '12 Dancing Princesses': A range of Barbie Christmas decorations for Mattel Inc.
Station Dash: A board game design for Halsall International in conjunction with the television series *Underground Ernie*.

Tips The Studio advertises designer and illustrator jobs jobs on their website. Enquire about available positions via email: jobs@thestudio-london.com

Vivid Imaginations

Ashbourne House, The Guildway, Old Portsmouth Road, Guildford, Surrey, GU3 1LS

- ☎ 01483 449944
- ☎ 01483 446336
- ✉ info@vividimag.co.uk
- 🌐 www.vividimaginations.co.uk

Contact Founders: Nick Austin and Alan Bennie

About Vivid is the number one toy and gift product developer, responsible for some of the most popular toys on the market. Brands include, *I Love Ponies, Animal Hospital, Pirates of the Caribbean*, Disney's *Winnie the Pooh* and *Bratz*. Current licensing partners include Hasbro, Crayola, Disney and Playmates. Own brand includes *Vivid Games*.

Recent Products *No Brainer!*: A game of Yes or No answers.
WWE Stunt Action Ring.
Winnie The Pooh Baby 'Woodland' Cosy Play Gym.

Zapf Creation (UK) Ltd

21 Chestnut House, Blenheim Park, Medlicott Close, Oaklay Hay Corby, Northamptonshire, NN18 9NF

- ☎ 01536 462809
- ☎ 01536 460917
- ✉ info@zapf-creation.co.uk
- 🌐 www.zapf-creation.com/uk

Contact Marketing Manager, Vicky Colburn

About Zapf Creation is a German owned leading brand manufacturer and designer of dolls and accessories. Products include fashionable dolls, mini dolls, and play and functional dolls for girls aged three to eight. *BABY Born, Baby Annabell* and *CHOU CHOU* are its most popular lines.

Recent Products *BABY Born: Ethnic With Magic Eyes; BABY Born Bathtub; Crawling CHOU CHOU.*

STORY BOOKS & AUDIO PUBLISHING

Abbey Home Media

435–437 Edgware Road, London, W2 1TH

- ☎ 020 7563 3910
- ☎ 020 7563 3911
- ✉ anne.miles@abbeyhomemedia.com
- 🌐 www.abbeyhomemedia.com

Contact Managing Director/Acquisitions & Programme Development, Anne Miles; Director Audio, Video & DVD Sales, Emma Evans

About Abbey Home Media are a children's multimedia publishing company. They produce spoken word, audiobook and music titles on CD and cassette, including the audio work of Michael Rosen.

Barefoot Books Ltd

124 Walcot Street, Bath, BA1 5BG

- ☎ 01225 322400
- ☎ 01225 322499
- ✉ info@barefootbooks.co.uk
- 🌐 www.barefootbooks.co.uk

Contact Publisher, Tessa Strickland

Established 1993

About Barefoot Books is a children's book publisher in both the UK and US that specialises in cultural themes and the worlds diversity. They publish audiobooks, music titles, and book and audio titles on CD, including the popular *Storyteller's Caravan* audiobook range.

Barrington Stoke

18 Walker Street, Edinburgh, EH3 7LP

- 0131 225 4113
- 0131 225 4140
- barrington@barringtonstoke.co.uk
- www.barringtonstoke.co.uk

Contact Managing Director, Sonia Raphael; Editorial Manager, Kate Paice

Established 1998

About Barrington Stoke publishes books reluctant readers or children with reading difficulties. They also publish limited audiobook material, usually as cassette tapes with accompanying books.

BBC Audiobooks

St. James House, The Square, Lower Bristol Road, Bath, BA2 3BH

- 01225 335336
- 01225 310771
- nick.forster@bbc.co.uk
- www.bbcaudiobooks.co.uk

Contact Managing Director, Paul Dempsey; Children's Commissioning Editor, Kate Walsh, Sales and Marketing Manager Nick Forster

Established 2003

About BBC Audiobooks publishes a wide range of spoken word and audio material on CD and cassette. Children's imprints include Chivers Children's Audiobooks, and BBC Cover to Cover (Children's). Publishes BBCchildren's TV Tie-Ins such as the 'Tweenies' and 'Bob The Builder'.

BBC Cover to Cover (Children's)

St. James House, The Square, Lower Bristol Road, Bath, BA2 3BH

- 01225 878000
- 01225 310771
- bbcaudiobooks@bbc.co.uk
- www.bbcaudiobooks.co.uk

About Cover to Cover is an imprint of BBC Audiobooks. It publishes unabridged audiobook versions of bestselling children's books, from authors such as Philip Pullman and Jacqueline Wilson.

Bloomsbury Publishing Plc

36 Soho Square, London, W1D 3QY

- 020 7494 2111
- 020 7434 0151
- csm@bloomsbury.com
- www.bloomsbury.com/audiobooks

About Bloomsbury publishes a large list of children's fiction and non-fiction audiobook titles, including picture books and unabridged novels.

Bolinda Publishing

2 Ivanhoe Road, London, SE5 8DH

- 020 7733 1088
- marisa@bolinda.com
- www.bolinda.com

Contact Publisher, Marisa McGreevy

Established 2003

About Bolinda are an international publisher of large print and unabridged audiobooks. They publish fiction and non-fiction titles for children and adults on cassette, CD and MP3-CD, and are preparing to launch a new downloadable service for audiobooks on iPod's and MP3 players. The main office is based in Australia.

Chivers Children's Audiobooks

St. James House, The Square, Lower Bristol Road, Bath, BA2 3BH

- 01225 878000
- 01225 310771
- bbcaudiobooks@bbc.co.uk
- www.bbcaudiobooks.co.uk

About Chivers is an imprint of BBC Audiobooks, publishing bestselling and classic fiction audiobooks for both adults and children. Publishes on cassette and CD.

Cló Iar-Chonnachta

Inverin, Connemara, County Galway, Ireland

- 00353 91 593307
- 00353 91 593362
- cic@iol.ie
- www.cic.ie

Contact General Manager, Deirdre N' Thuathail; Literary Editor, Lochlainn í Tuairisg

Established 1985

About Publishes books and audiobooks for adults, teenagers and children, mostly in the Irish language. They publish both fiction, including short stories and poetry, and non-fiction. The publisher is also a traditional Irish music label.

CSA WORD

6a Archway Mews, London, SW15 2PE

- 020 8871 0220
- 020 8877 0712
- info@csaword.co.uk

@ www.csaword.co.uk

Contact Managing Director, Clive Stanhope; Audio Commissioning Editor, Victoria Williams

Established 1989

About An independent audiobook publisher focusing on classic texts that work well in audio, such as *Just William* and *Hilaire Belloc*. Publishes on cassette and CD, and also offers a download service. CSA also produces radio programming for the BBC.

Dref Wen

28 Church Road, Whitchurch, Cardiff, CF14 2EA

- 029 2061 7860
- 029 2061 0507
- gwilym@drefwen.com

Contact Managing Director, Gwilym Boore

Established 1970

About Dref Wen is a Welsh book publisher that also produces audiobooks in both the Welsh, and English language. The books are generally aimed at Welsh language learners.

The Educational Company of Ireland

Ballymount Road, Walkinstown, Dublin 12, Ireland

- 00353 1 450 0611
- 00353 1 450 0993
- info@edco.ie
- www.edco.ie

Contact Publisher, Frank Fahy

About An educational publisher that also produces audio material on cassette and CD. Most audiobooks are Irish language teaching resources or educational titles.

HarperAudio

77–85 Fulham Palace Road, London, W6 8JB

- 020 8741 7070
- 020 8307 4517
- enquiries@harpercollins.co.uk
- www.harpercollins.co.uk

Contact Chief Executive Officer and Publisher, Victoria Barnsley

Established 1990

About An imprint of HarperCollins. Publishes a wide range of bestselling fiction and non-fiction audiobooks for adults and children. All titles are read by famous actors, or other celebrities.

Hodder Headline Audiobooks

338 Euston Road, London, NW1 3BH

- 020 7873 6000
- 020 7873 6024
- Online form
- www.hodderheadline.co.uk

Established 1994

About An imprint of Hodder Headline. Publishes a range of bestselling titles from Hodder Headlines children's and adult lists, such as *Wallace & Gromit* and *Magic Roundabout* audiobooks.

Ladybird Books Ltd

Penguin Group UK, 80 Strand, London, WC2R 0RL

- 020 7010 3000
- 020 7010 6707
- ladybird@uk.penguingroup.com
- www.ladybird.co.uk

About Ladybird Books is an established publisher of books and audiobooks for children aged 0–8. Titles are produced on cassette and CD, with accompanying books, and include fairytales nursery rhymes, fiction and licenced character stories.

Macmillan Audio Books

20 New Wharf Road, London, N1 9RR

- 020 7014 6000
- 020 7014 6001
- audiobooks@macmillan.co.uk
- www.panmacmillan.com

Contact Audio Publisher, Alison Muirden

Established 1995

About An imprint of Pan Macmillan. Publishes children's and adult's audiobooks, in both cassette and CD formats. Has an extensive backlist of over 400 titles. Visit website to download an audio catalogue.

Naxos AudioBooks

3 Wells Place, Redhill, Surrey, RH1 3SL

- 01737 645600
- 01737 644327
- Online form
- www.naxosaudiobooks.com

Contact Managing Director, Nicolas Soames

Established 1994

About Naxos is an audiobook publisher that produces fiction and non-fiction for children on their Junior Classics list. They have over 350 titles available in both CD and downloadable MP3 formats.

Orion Audiobooks

Orion House, 5 Upper St Martin's Lane, London, WC2H 9EA

- 020 7240 3444
- 020 7240 4822
- pandora.white@orionbooks.co.uk
- www.orionbooks.co.uk

Contact Audio Manager, Pandora White
Established 1998
About An imprint of the Orion Publishing Group. Publishes audiobooks in cassette, CD and MP3 formats for children and adults. The children's audiobook list has over 150 titles.

Penguin Audiobooks

80 Strand, London, WC2R 0RL

- 020 7010 3000
- audiobooks@penguin.co.uk
- www.penguin.co.uk/audio

Contact Audio Publisher, Jeremy Ettinghausen
Established 1993
About An imprint of Penguin that publishes a wide range of audiobooks for children and adults, including fiction, non-fiction, poetry and life writing. Also has an imprint: Puffin Audiobooks.

Puffin Audiobooks

80 Strand, London, WC2R 0RL

- 020 7010 3000
- audiobooks@penguin.co.uk
- www.penguin.co.uk/audio

Contact Audio Publisher, Jeremy Ettinghausen
About Puffin Audiobooks is an imprint of Penguin Audiobooks. It publishes top classic and contemporary literature, for children and teenagers.

Random House Audiobooks

20 Vauxhall Bridge Road, London, SW1V 2SA

- 020 7840 8541
- 020 7233 6127
- audiopublicity@randomhouse.co.uk
- www.randomhouse.co.uk/audio

About An imprint of Random House that publishes a wide range of fiction and non-fiction audiobooks, read by distinguished recording artists, popular actors or, in many cases, the author. Categories include fantasy and adventure with titles by Phillip Pullman and Christopher Paolini. Generally has over 200 titles in stock.

SmartPass

15 Park Road, Brighton, BN2 7HL

- 01273 300742
- info@smartpass.co.uk
- www.smartpass.co.uk

Contact Managing Director, Phil Viner; Creative Director, Jools Viner
Established 1999
About SmartPass publishes educational audiobooks and material for teachers and students. SmartPass has worked with the Royal Shakespeare Company, the National Theatre, and the BBC radio repertory, presenting unabridged plays, poetry, and guided dramatisations of novels.

Usborne Publishing Ltd

Usborne House, 83–85 Saffron Hill, London, EC1N 8RT

- 020 7430 2800
- 020 8636 3758
- mail@usborne.co.uk
- www.usborne.co.uk

Contact Founder, Peter Usborne; Publishing Director, Jenny Tyler
Established 1973
About Usborne publishes a limited amount of audiobooks, audio language dictionaries and music for children.

Walker Books

87 Vauxhall Walk, London, SE11 5HJ

- 020 7793 0909
- 020 7587 1123
- editorial@walker.co.uk
- www.walkerbooks.co.uk

Contact Publisher, Lorraine Taylor
About Walker Books publishes a variety of fiction and non-fiction audiobooks for children and teenagers on cassette and CD. Categories include Action, Fantasy, Sc-fi, Movie Tie-Ins, Early Readers and Series such as the Alex Rider Adventures.

Walking Oliver Productions

Jasper Lodge, Ferrers Road, Lewes, East Sussex, BN7 1PY

- 01273 475532
- info@walkingoliver.com
- www.walkingoliver.com

Contact Founder, Paul Austin Kelly
Established 2003

About Walking Oliver develops, creates and records quality music for children and their families. They are a children's music label, but also produce musical audiobooks, including poetry from Michael Rosen.

DVDS

4Mation Educational Software
First Floor, 63 Boutport Street, Barnstaple, Devon, EX32 2BA
- ☎ 01271 325353
- ☎ 01271 322974
- ✉ sales@4mation.co.uk
- 🌐 www.4mation.co.uk

About 4Mation designs, develops, and publishes educational software for use within schools and at home. Covers all curriculum subjects, including Maths, English, Science and History. For full product listings visit their website.

Recent Products *Maths Circus Act 5*, part of the Maths Circus Series which features tasks, activities and printable worksheets for Key Stage 1–4

Tips 4Mation distributes products to Australia.

Alternative View Studios
Unit 2B Leroy House, 436 Essex Road, London, N1 3QP
- ☎ 020 7688 1864
- ☎ 020 7688 1860
- ✉ neilthompson@avstudios.com
- 🌐 www.avstudios.com

Contact Directors: Andy Moss and Neil Thompson

About Alternative View Studios is an award winning interactive media and animation company. The company consists of a team of talented designers, illustrators and animators. They have technical experience in creating e-learning solutions for young children, delivered via CD-ROMs, DVDs and the internet. Alternative View provide broadcast animation and online flash game design. Clients include *Bitesize*, *Cbeebies*, *The FA* and *Harcourt Education*. Alternative View is very experienced in illustrating characters for CD-ROMs.

Recent Products *Pearson Broadband: Skulldiggery Digitext*: Alternative View illustrated and animated an interactive story for Year 6 pupils, based on the writing style of Jeremy Strong, published on CD-ROM.

Harcourt: The Lost Purse: An illustrated interactive story as part of the multimedia CD-ROM series for Key Stage 1 literacy students.

BBC: The Tweenies and The Fimbles: Alternative View designed 3D graphics - in identical format to the television characters - for worldwide CD-ROM distribution for young children.

Tips Alternative View is seeking freelance designers, developers and flash trained animators.

AVP
School Hill Centre, Chepstow, Monmouthshire, NP16 5PH
- ☎ 01291 625439
- ☎ 01291 625439
- ✉ info@avp.co.uk
- 🌐 www.avp.co.uk

Contact Mark

About A leading supplier and publisher of educational resources for schools throughout the UK. AVP publishes CD-ROMS, Audio CDs, DVDs, online resources and classroom equipment. Covers all curriculum subjects, after school software and special needs.

Recent Products *3D Amazing Animals*: features compelling activities and games with two animal books, stickers and a ready to assemble mobile, ages five to nine.

Word World: Animals: one of a series featuring activities to develop vocabulary in early years, ages two to five.

Tips The company welcomes ideas for software publication, email: eureka@avp.co.uk

BBC Active
See Entry under Educational Publishers

Birchfield Interactive plc
The Media Centre, Culverhouse Cross, Cardiff, CF5 6XJ
- ☎ 0800 915 6616
- ☎ 0800 138 8895
- ✉ enquiries@birchfield.co.uk
- 🌐 www.birchfield.co.uk

About A leading publisher of educational software for primary, secondary and tertiary education, covering all curriculum subjects.

Recent Products *Ace's Monkey Art Adventure*: for children aged three to five.

Ace's Monkey Science: for children aged four to seven. All software packages contain fun graphics, quizzes and narration to present the information in an entertaining manner.

Black Cat Software

The Chiswick Centre, 414 Chiswick High Road, London, W4 5TF

- 020 8996 3333
- 020 8742 8390
- info@granada-learning.com
- www.blackcatsoftware.com

Parent Company Granada Learning Company
Contact Danielle Morgan
About Black Cat is a successful imprint that publishes educational software for primary schools, with particular emphasis on packages that support the teaching of maths, ICT, science and literacy.
Recent Products *Science Activity Builder* and *Numbers, Words and Pictures 2*: software for Key Stage 1 and early years education that teaches data-handling, graphs, painting, turtle graphics and word processing tools.

BNM Interactive

Unit 37, The Enterprise Centre, James Street, Carlisle, Cumbria, CA7 5BB

- 01228 546622
- info@bnm-interactive.co.uk
- www.bnm-interactive.co.uk

Contact Paul Batey
About BNM offers CD-ROM design, website design, virtual guides, search engine optimisation and graphic design for print.
Recent Products *Outward Bound Xperience*: A CD-ROM design for young school children promoting outdoor education and leadership skills. The CD-ROM was distributed to 3,000 schools.
Tips Please call Paul Batey, or email paul@bnm-interactive.co.uk, for more info on CD-ROM design.

CATS Educational Software

Unit 12 Lightburn Trading Estate, Lightburn Road, Ulverston, Cumbria, LA12 7NE

- 01229 588114
- 01229 588115
- info@cats-edu.co.uk
- www.cats-edu.co.uk

About Specialists in Educational software for Key Stage 1–4, covering Literacy, Numeracy and Science subjects. Titles include their own brand *Splatt* series.

Recent Products *Splatt: Numeracy; Splatt: Literacy; Splatt: Science; Splatt: Revision*.
Tips All *Splatt* software features activities, games and quizzes presented in a fun and exciting format to aid learning.

Channel 4 Learning

PO Box 400, Wetherby, LS23 7LG

- 0870 124 6444
- 0870 124 6446
- 4learning.info@channel4.co.uk
- www.channel4.com/learning

Contact London Representative, Sue Bell
About Channel 4 publishes and distributes a vast range of multimedia resources for schools, colleges, and home learners on video, DVD, CD-ROM, online and via broadband.
Recent Products *Living & Growing DVD pack*: for ages 5–11. Features three units of the *Living and Growing* series, plus resource books.
Maths Mansion CD-ROM: based on the television series for children aged 9–10.

Creative Jar Ltd

The Old Bakehouse, 26 High Street, Twyford, Berkshire, RG10 9AG

- 0118 934 4069
- 0118 934 3066
- info@creative-jar.com
- www.creative-jar.com

About Creative Jar is a multimedia design agency that offers CD-ROM design, website design, flash animation and game design.
Recent Products *Pearson Education*: Creative Jar delivered a slick educational CD-ROM for secondary school students.
Tips Creative Jar actively seek freelancers and contractors to join their team. Vacancies are advertised via their website.

E Business Engineers

1 Richmond Hill, Bournemouth, Dorset, BH2 6HE

- 0845 260 0186
- 0845 260 0187
- info@e-businessengineers.com
- www.e-businessengineers.com

About A website design company that designs CD-ROMs, offering custom design, educational projects and e-learning CD-ROMs for students.

Evolution Creative

Studio 5, East Wing, The Maltings, Bridge Square, Farnham, Surrey, GU9 7QR

☎ 01252 724339

✉ Online form.

About A software development company that offers CD and DVD creation using cutting edge graphics, animation and video, DVD authoring services, packaging design, multimedia applications for CD-ROM and website design and hosting.

Recent Products *Rugrats In Paris Promo CD; The Rugrats Movie Interactive Educational Guide.*

Fat Flash

19 Castle Hill, Lancaster, Lancashire, LA1 1YN

☎ 01524 590430

✉ info@fatflash.co.uk

🌐 www.fatflash.co.uk

Parent Company Fat Media

About Fat Flash are a design company that provide internet marketing solutions throughout the UK. Fat flash offer promotional CD-ROM and multimedia production, viral and flash game design, website animation, modelling and bespoke animation.

Recent Products *Brentwood Borough Council*: An educational CD-ROM aimed at children aged 10–14, tackling drugs, crime, recycling and CCTV. It included many innovative features such as video, questionnaires and games. Graphics for the CD-ROM were a space theme, which are available to view on their website.

Kebab Challenge: The game features a Kebab with wings that flies through the skies. Featured on a national student accommodation website *Cityblock plc.*

Feel Design Limited

2 South Barn, Midgeley Lane, Goldsborough, North Yorkshire, HG5 8JN

☎ 01423 860733

☎ 01423 860733

✉ enquiries@feeldesign.co.uk

🌐 www.feeldesign.co.uk

Contact Head Designer, James Blundell

About Services include CD-ROM and DVD design, web design, flash game design and graphic design. Caters for individual businesses, to large corporations.

Recent Products *Yellow Door Children's books*: CD-ROMS to accompany educational materials and children's books featuring animated stories, activities, music and storytelling for use in schools.

Tips The company works with a number of freelance artists to tailor any specific needs for a project.

Focus Multimedia

The Studios, Lea Hall Enterprise Park, Wheelhouse Road, Rugeley, Staffordshire, WS15 1LH

☎ 01889 570156

✉ fmgeneral@focusmm.co.uk

🌐 www.focusmm.co.uk

About A leading publisher of PC CD-ROM software, Focus Multimedia has established itself over the last decade as the UK's premier value software company. CD-ROMs are the UK's best-selling range, often topping the PC chart. Publishes PC and CD-ROMs on Games, Lifestyle, Children, Knowledge, Travel, Creativity and Productivity. Focus publishes educational products for children including Encyclopedias, Dictionaries and Thesauruses, Astronomy, Literacy, Maths and Music. Licensed brands for children include Lego, Teaching You, Oxford University Press and Encyclopedia Britannica. Focus is also a publisher licensed PC games for children.

Recent Products *Story Wizard*: CD-ROM for young budding authors. Features an ideas generator, dictionary and thesaurus and supports Key Stage 2, 3 and 4.

Oxford First Encyclopedia: features seven separated sections that represent a young child's interests and fun illustrations, and photos and text that can be pasted into other software packages.

Crazy Chicken Heart of Tibet: a pc game featuring advanced graphics.

Fusion Media

Unit B5.03, LCB Depot, 31 Rutland Street, Leicester, LE1 1RE

☎ 0116 261 6828

✉ info@fusionmedia.com

🌐 www.fusionmedia.co.uk

About A creative design agency that offers CD-ROM design, website design, graphics and packaging, flash games and animation and DVD menu design.

Recent Products *Educational CD-ROM: Cardiff University*: Aimed at 9–12 year olds, educating them on the dangers of drinking too much alcohol. It features a 2D interactive cartoon, a game and quizzes.

Global Software Publishing

Meadow Lane, St. Ives, Cambridgeshire, PE27 4LG

- 01480 496666
- 01480 460206
- mike.corbett@gsp.cc
- www.gspsoftware.co.uk

About GSP is the UK's leading consumer software publisher with a range of over 400 CD-ROM titles, many of which dominate the PC charts. GSP publishes licensed games, educational and reference brands. Some brand names include Sega, Letts, DK publishers and BBC titles.

Recent Products *Big Cook, Little Cook Fairytale Fun*: Features educational games, recipes and puzzles.

Granada Learning

The Chiswick Centre, 414 Chiswick High Road, London, W4 5TF

- 020 8996 3333
- 020 8742 8390
- info@granada-learning.com
- www.granada-learning.com

Contact Chris Brown

Imprints ASE (Staff Assessments)
BlackCat Educational Software (Primary Software)
Granada Learning Software (Educational Software)
Granada Learning Professional Development (Professional Training)
nferNelson (Education Assessments)
SEMERC (Special Needs)
The Skills Factory (Teachers Resources)

About A leading publisher of curriculum based resources for teachers and students in the UK and abroad. It boasts an impressive catalogue of over 800 software programs, which span the syllabus of primary and secondary schools. Black Cat is the educational software developer for primary school children (see separate entry).

Recent Products *Phoneme Factory Sound Sorter*: Features activities that develops children's awareness of sounds in speech (Publisher: SEMERC).
Simulation Explorer: Features interactive science experiments and worksheets (Publisher: Granada Learning).

Tips For more information on the imprint companies visit the website.

Idigicon Educational Software

Ashfield House, Ashfield Road, Balby, Doncaster, DN4 8QD

- 01302 310800
- 01302 314001
- sales@idigicon.com
- www.idigicon.com

About A leading publisher of children's educational PC software. Brands include 'Encyclopaedia Britannica Education Series', 'Kid's Academy', 'Garfield', 'Full Marks' and 'Skills For Success'.

Recent Products *Garfield: Letters and Words*: ages 3–4 (PC).
Kids Academy: Early Numeracy and Mental Maths (PC)

Tips Also publishes PC games for children.

Illumina Digital Media

8 Canham Mews, Canham Road, London, W3 7SR

- 020 8600 9300
- 020 8600 9333
- Online form.
- www.illumina.co.uk

Contact Managing Director, Andrew Chitty; Editorial Director, Mike Flood Page; Director of Design and Development, David McGirr

About Illumina is an award winning new media company with a broad client base spreading across the education, information and entertainment sectors. Services include CD-ROM production, documentary programming for digital and terrestrial television, web design for commercial and public sector clients, and services and applications for interactive television and broadband technologies. Clients include the BBC, the National Theatre, RSC, Channel 4, the Welsh Assembly and the DfES.

Recent Products *Tobu: Learning Japanese*: An online KS3 Japanese language course with an accompanying CD-ROM as part of the 'DfES Curriculum Online' project.

Tips Currently seeking freelance and permanent designers, developers, web designers and producers to join their team. Email a CV to jobs@illumina.co.uk, or visit their website for more details.

Indigo Learning Ltd

3 Cabot House, Compass Point Business Park, Stocks Bridge Way, St. Ives, Cambridgeshire, PE27 5JL

- 01480 354335
- 01480 354345
- info@indigolearning.com
- www.indigolearning.com

Contact Managing Director, Paul

About Indigo Learning develops and publishes software tools that inspire creativity for young children. Their most popular product is Dazzle 03, an exciting cross curricular art package, which features beautiful illustrations and can be customised for nursery age children, right up to Key Stage 2.

Recent Products *Indigo Illustrations*: Illustrations on the human body, British history, planet earth and animals.

Indigo Creative Suite: Three top products: *Dazzle 03, Centre Stage* and *Buzz Webz*, in one package.

iweb Design Solutions

10 Parker Court, Dyson Way, Staffordshire Technology Park, Staffordshire, ST18 0WP

- 01785 279920
- 01785 223514
- services@iwebsolutions.co.uk
- www.iwebsolutions.co.uk

About iweb provides CD-ROM design, web design, illustration, education resources and print design. iweb combines video, audio, illustrations, animations and text to provide high quality CD-ROM design. iweb has specialist expertise in designing educational CD-ROMs - clients include Harcourt Education and Oxford University Press. iweb can design character, storyboards and animations for educational resources.

- www.iwebsolutions.co.uk

The Association for Science Education: CD-ROM resource packages, aiming to enthuse and excite young people, whilst supporting their learning about science. Distributed throughout all secondary schools in the UK.

Twenty First Century Science CD-ROM: A commission by *Oxford University Press*.

Harcourt Education: National Literacy CD-ROM for primary students.

Harcourt Education: Digital illustration for an educational multimedia project for young children.

Knowledge Media Design

Faculty of Art and Design, De Montfort University, Leicester, LE1 9BH

- 0116 257 7173
- 0116 250 6101
- sbrown@dmu.ac.uk
- kmd.dmu.ac.uk

Contact Professor Stephen Brown

About Knowledge Media Design is an interdisciplinary grouping within the Faculty of Art and Design at De Montfort University. The centre comprises of three specialist groupings: The Learning Zone; The Interactive Zone; and The Vision Zone (who work on commercial projects). Their expertise lies in educational technology and

learning design. Visit their website for more information on the zones.

Submission Guidelines Contact Stephen via email to discuss any ideas for a new project.

Recent Products *Coin Street CD-ROM*: A historical educational CD-ROM for students based on the Coin Street area in Waterloo, London.

Tips Knowledge Media Design is a centre for educational technology research. They are a acknowledged leader in the development of remote learning, using video conferencing, and virtual distributed classrooms.

Logotron Ltd

124 Cambridge Science Park, Milton Road, Cambridge, CB4 0ZS

- 01223 425558
- 01223 425349
- info@logo.com
- www.logotron.co.uk

About Logotron is one of the UK's most successful and largest publishers of educational software tools and applications for early years to secondary level. Logotron has research and publishing links with Microsoft Research in Europe, Widgit Software for special needs and Cambridge Software Publishing.

Recent Products *Revelation Natural Art*.

Viewpoint: a data handling package.

Simulation Insight: a Science modelling programme.

Tips Logotron advertises vacancies on their website.

Lunar Multimedia Ltd

Gressingham, Lancaster

- 01524 222335
- john@lunar.co.uk
- www.lunar.co.uk

Contact Managing Director, John

About A multimedia design company with specialities in CD-ROM and DVD design and authoring, graphics, web design and 360 degree tours.

Recent Products *It's Your Goal*: An award winning children's educational health CD-ROM. Developed in partnership with Indigo Multimedia Ltd. Distributed in schools in the UK.

NHS & NUFC: A children's CD-ROM full of fun learning games and information on how to lead a healthy lifestyle with on-screen guidance videos from Bobby Robson. Distributed in schools across Tyneside.

Tips The company is a one man operation, that seeks freelancers when needed.

Microsoft Education UK

Microsoft Campus, Thames Valley Park, Reading, RG6 1WG

- 0870 607 0800
- askedu@microsoft-contact.co.uk
- www.microsoft.com/uk/education

About Microsoft has developed technology, tools, programmes and solutions to help address education challenges, while improving teaching and learning opportunities. Microsoft desktop, multimedia, server and online products, such as *Microsoft Windows Vista, Microsoft Office 2007* and *Microsoft Student 2007* are used throughout the education system.

Recent Products *Encarta Standard 2007*: Students can explore a world of knowledge that's accurate, engaging and up to date. Over 36,000 articles, tens of thousands of pictures and sound clips, videos, animations, games, maps and more.

Mindscape

41 Basepoint Business Centre, Metcalf Way, Crawley, West Sussex, RH11 7XX

- 01553 84904
- enquiries@mindscape.co.uk
- www.mindscape.co.uk

About The Mindscape group is a major publisher in the CD-ROM market, covering games, educational topics for kids, and lifestyle.

Recent Products *Mindscape's Brain Trainer*: 15 Mind Enhancing Activities.
My Pony Club: A game that allows players to design their own pony.

MotivatEd

9–12 Bennell Court, West Street, Camberton, Cambridge, CB23 7EN

- 01223 265617
- info@MotivatEd.ltd.uk
- www.motivated.ltd.uk

Contact Pete Gilmour

About A leading company that designs and develops e-learning resources. MotivatEd consists of a talented team of designers, flash game designers and developers with experience in educational software design and coding for CD-ROMs, games design, 3D animation and multimedia publishing.

Oui3 Design and Multimedia

2 Satellite Park, Macmerry Business Park, Tranent, EH33 1RY

- 01875 616926
- 01875 616924
- www.oui3design.com
- Online form.

About Oui3 Design offers CD ROM design, packaging design, brand design, website design and exhibition stands.

Recent Products *Crunchy the Croc*: CD ROM designed to help teach young children the importance of oral hygiene. It features educational games, funky graphics and printable worksheets. The CD was distributed to all nurseries, and child and family centres across Lothian.

Ransom

51 Southgate Street, Winchester, Hampshire, SO23 9EH

- 01962 862307
- ransom@ransom.co.uk
- www.ransom.co.uk

Contact Managing Director, Jenny Ertle

About Ransom publishing is an independent and specialist publisher of software and books for reluctant and struggling readers.

Submission Guidelines Visit their website for detailed writing guidelines for authors. Illustrators should send samples of work via email, and include a CV and covering letter.

Recent Products *The Letter Detective*: Helps young children learn the alphabet. For ages four to six (CD-ROM).
Dark Man Interactive Software: Set One: Interactive activities to enhance reading skills for older children (CD-ROM).
In Bloom: From the 'Just In Rhyme' series. Interactive books to help children explore rhyme (CD-ROM).

Tips Ransom also publishes children's fiction and non-fiction (see entry under UK & Irish Publishers).

Robert Powell Publications

56 Stockton Lane, Stafford, ST17 0JS

- 01785 664600
- 01785 661822
- info@robertpowelltraining.co.uk
- www.robertpowellpublications.com

Contact Managing Directors, Robert Powell and Isobel Powell

About An educational publisher that specialises in interactive CD-ROMs for schools. Its *Raising Achievement* series and its *Blockbusters* range are available in 11 subjects for ages 7–16. Subjects range from Art and Design, to Science.

Tips Publishes Self help books for teachers.

Sherston Publishing Group

Angel House, Sherston, Malmesbury, Wiltshire, SN16 0LH

- education@sherston.co.uk
- shop.sherston.com

Contact Russell Mabon and Jamie Bayliss

About A leading educational software publishing company for primary schools, with titles that cover the whole of the curriculum, including some of the UK's most popular software, such as *Tizzy's Toybox*, *The Crystal Rain Forest*, and *The Map Detectives*. Sherston has partnerships with major education specialists, including BBC Worldwide Children's Learning, Oxford University Press, and LDA.

Recent Products *Foundations In ICT Pack*: Includes nine CD-ROMs and a scheme of work book.

Jellybods: Features fun and short activities for young children to help develop early learning skills.

Tips Sherston is currently seeking people to join their team. For more details contact Katie Taylor via email: katie.taylor@sherston.co.uk

Software Production Associates (SPA)

AVP, School Hill Centre, Chepstow, NP16 5PH

- 0845 230 1305
- 01291 629671
- Online submission form
- www.spasoft.co.uk

About Develops educational software for early years through to A-Level. Covers Early Learning, English and Creative, Languages and Humanities, Mathematics and ICT, and Science. A subsidiary of AVP Educational Software, see separate entry.

Recent Products *Muddles,* Mike Blamires; Features literacy activities suitable for all ages, including children with special needs (CD-ROM).

Storm Educational Software

The Education Barn, Holm and Ivy, St. James, Shaftesbury, Dorset, SP7 0JA

- 01747 858323
- 01747 858323
- storm@stormeducational.co.uk
- www.stormeducational.co.uk

About A well established educational software publishing company for children aged four and over. Best known for their *Smudge The Dog* series, which covers numeracy, literacy, science, geography and punctuation.

Recent Products *Smudge's Early Compass and Map Skills*; Features map and compass activities, ages 4–9

Smudge the Scientist; Features activities covering science topics, ages 4–8

The Roman Adventure; Features stimulating maths exercises, ages 7–11

Tips Many of the activities from the Smudge CD-ROMs are available as individual titles in the web browser range.

Strange Software

Burnt Street, Wells next the Sea, Norfolk, NR23 1HL

- 01328 711486
- tboy@strange.co.uk
- www.strange.co.uk

Contact Carl Phillips and Max Phillips

About Strange Software offers a wide range of internet design, with expertise in software publishing and CD-ROM projects.

Recent Products *Proms Safari*: An interactive children's CD-ROM for BBC Proms, with radio play, information and music sequencer, distributed to UK schools.

Studio 24

Hope Street Yard, Hope Street, Cambridge, CB1 3NA

- 0870 241 6159
- 0870 094 0375
- info@studio24.net
- www.studio24.net

About A new media design consultancy that designs websites, and works on CD-ROM development and e-commerce stores. Studio 24 work for a variety of sectors, including educational, charitable, government, e-commerce and commercial.

Tips The company advertises current vacancies on their website.

Tmax Productions

18 Park House, 16 Northfields, London, SW18 1DD

- 020 8874 6995
- Online submission form
- www.tmaxproductions.co.uk

Parent Tmax Media

About A multimedia design company that offers CD-ROM and DVD production and design, 3D modelling and animation and web design.

Tips The company consists of creative designers, artists, programmers and filmmakers, who combine their skills to produce multimedia solutions for a wide variety of clients, such as Warner Brothers and Disney.

Topologika

1 South Harbour, Eastwood Road, Harbour Village, Penryn, Cornwall, TR10 8LR
- 01326 377771
- 01376 376755
- brian@topologika.co.uk
- www.topologika.com

Contact Managing Director, Brian Kerslake

About A successful educational software publishing company for primary and secondary pupils and teachers, Covers English, Science, Maths and Numeracy, Music, Early learning and ICT.

Submission Guidelines Contact Brain via email to discuss any ideas for a new project.

Recent Products *Mathmania 2,* ages 7–11 (PC) *Music Box 2,* features activities that get children making music, ages 5–15 (PC)

Tips The company consists of experienced teachers, researchers, programmers and graphic designers.

Xigen Design

Bedford i-Lab, Priory Business Park, Stannard Way, Bedford, MK44 3RZ
- 0845 230 5188
- 0845 230 5199
- info@xigen.co.uk
- www.xigen.co.uk

About Xigen Design are successful new media specialists, that offers CD-ROM development, web design, 3D animation presentations, and videoing. To view their multimedia portfolio of work visit their website.

Tips The company advertises current vacancies on their website, including designer and developer jobs.

ELECTRONIC GAMES

Activision Europe

3 Roundwood Avenue, Stockley Park, Uxbridge, UB11 1AF
- 020 3060 1000
- hr@activision.co.uk
- www.activision.com/en_GB/home/home.jsp

Parent Company Activision Inc

Contact President and Chief Executive Officer, Michael J. Griffith; Co-Chairman and Director, Brian Kelly

Insider Info Activision Europe is an international developer, publisher and distributor of interactive software. The company has created, licensed and acquired a huge number of highly successful games that make them one of the most successful companies in the games business. Activision has acquired rights to develop games for Marvel Comics, Dreamworks, MGM Studios and Hasbro. Activision will be developing *James Bond* games up to 2014.

Submission Guidelines No unsolicited game ideas, only agented material will be accepted. They welcome contact from game developers and members of the development community for future projects.

Recent Title(s) *Fantastic Four*

Tips Visit the jobs section of the website for possible creative jobs in design and game development. For

jobs in Europe, submit CV to recruiteurope@activision.co.uk

Aqua Pacific Ltd

7 Clarendon Place, Royal Leamington Spa, Warwickshire, CV32 5QL
- 0870 428 2687
- info@aqua-pacific.com
- www.aqua-pacific.com

Insider Info Aqua Pacific is a well established computer and video game development house, specialising in conversions for PC to Playstation, Playstation to PC, and GameBoy Color. They have over 50 commercial titles published for companies such as In2games, Infogrames, Sales Curve Interactive, Ubi Soft and Dreamcatcher.

Recent Title(s) *I-Soccer* (Windows CE)

Tips Aqua Pacific also develop content for Games Based Learning, and have have developed titles for the UFI (Learn Direct), The British Council (Beijing), The Learning and Skills Council, and Boston Scientific.

Asylum Entertainment UK Ltd

300 Upper Street, Islington, London, N1 2TU
- 020 7354 7303

○ 020 7354 7304

○ info@asylum-entertainment.com

○ www.asylum-entertainment.com

Insider Info Asylum Entertainment is an award winning computer game developer focusing primarily on the major brand name children's market. Asylum has completed over 20 titles on multiple platforms for some of the biggest publishers and licence holders in the world, including Electronic Arts, Riverdeep, Vivendi, BBCW and Cartoon Network.

Recent Title(s) *Jungle Rumble Pinball* (PC); *Kid Ninja* (Wii)

Tips Asylum is focused on the children's and family entertainment markets, and do not develop adult games.

Atari UK Ltd

Landmark House, Hammersmith Bridge Road, London, W6 9EJ

○ 020 8222 9700

○ Online submission form

○ www.uk.atari.com

Insider Info Atari is a global publisher and distributor of video games and PC software for all major platform consoles. Their catalogue includes popular franchises such as *Alone In The Dark* and *V Rally* and many international licenses like *Dragon Ball Z* and *Dungeons & Dragons*. Atari owns many games development companies such as Accolade, GT Interactive, Humongous Entertainment, Hasbro Interactive, Ocean Software Ltd, Microprose and Wizardworks. The UK branch of Atari develops video games at its development studio - edengames - in France.

Submission Guidelines An online form is available to receive information on their publishing details.

Recent Title(s) *The Witcher* (PC); *Dragon Ball Z: Goku Densetsu* (Nintendo DS); *Tamagotchi Party On!* (Wii)

Tips Atari advertises vacancies on their website. Video game developers are needed to join edengames, to apply for a position email a CV to: job@edengames.com

---

Atomic Planet Entertainment Ltd

72–80 Corporation Road, Middlesbrough, TS1 2RF

○ 01642 871100

○ info@atomic-planet.com

○ www.atomic-planet.co.uk

Contact Managing Director, Darren Falcus

Insider Info Atomic Planet Entertainment (APE) is a video games development studio offering a range of services, including full product development, conception, design, artwork, programming, and audio in any genre of game. APE develops content on virtually every game platform, including Microsoft Xbox and Xbox 360, Nintendo DS, Gameboy Advance, Gamecube and Wii, PC, Sony PlayStation 2, PlayStation 3, and PSP, plus Flash, Shockwave and Java.

Recent Title(s) *An Arctic Tale* (Nintendo DS, Gameboy Advance, Wii); *Bob The Builder Festival of Fun* (Nintendo DS, PS2); *Sea Monsters* (Nintendo DS, Wii, PS2)

Tips Atomic Planet handle a lot of licenced material, including educational projects for companies such as National Geographic.

Blitz Games

PO Box 186, Leamington Spa, Warwickshire, CV23 5TX

○ 01926 880000

○ 01926 887209

○ gameon@blitzgames.com

○ www.blitzgames.com

Contact Chief Executive Officer, Philip Oliver; Chief Technical Officer, Andrew Oliver

Insider Info Blitz is one of the top five independent European games development companies. The company has 17 completed titles across all major platforms. Clients include famous corporations such as Warner Bros, Disney Inter Active, Nickelodeon, Mattel and 4Kids Entertainment.

Recent Title(s) *Spongebob Squarepants: Creature from Krusty Krab* (PS3, Xbox 360, Wii); *Pocketbike Racer* (Xbox, Xbox 360)

Tips Blitz are passionate about the future of the games industry and keen on helping the next generation of games developers. They hold presentations at English universities and schools, run competitions for budding gamers and support 'women in games'. Blitz advertises designer, artist and programmers jobs on their website. To apply, email demo work to: jobs@BlitzGames.com

---

Broadsword Interactive Ltd

8 Science Park, Aberystwyth, Ceredigion, SY23 3AH

○ 01970 626299

○ 01970 626291

○ enquiries@broadsword.co.uk

○ www.broadsword.co.uk

Contact Managing Director, John Jones-Steele; Development Director, Jim Finnis; Studio Manager, Nick Court

Insider Info Broadsword Interactive designs and produces computer software for the computer and console games industry. They also provide a conversion service to and from PC, PS2, PSP, PS3, Xbox, Xbox 360, Gamecube, DS and Wii formats.
Recent Title(s) *The Quest for Aladdin's Treasure*
Tips Broadsword are often looking for new staff. Check the vacancies page on the website, or email: jobs@broadsword.co.uk

Capcom Europe
CE Europe, 9th Floor, 26–28 Hammersmith Grove, London W6 7HA
- feedback@capcom-europe.com
- www.capcom-europe.com
Insider Info A well established global games company. Designed *Street Fighters*and *Resident Evil.*
Submission Guidelines Capcom does not accept unsolicited ideas from members of the public.
Recent Title(s) *MotoGP 07* (PS2); *Monster Hunter Freedom 2* (PSP); *Mega Man ZX* (Nintendo DS)
Tips For job opportunities send CVs via email, to go on file for future job opportunities.

Climax Racing Ltd
15 West Street, Brighton, BN1 2RE
- 01273 740800
- 01273 740800
- www.disney.go.com/disneyinteractivestudios/brighton
Parent Company The Walt Disney Company
Insider Info A UK branch of the interactive entertainment division of Disney. Develops new, original racing game franchises.
Submission Guidelines No public submissions policy, but the jobs section of the website often advertises vacancies that may be of interest, including for artists.
Tips Deals with vehicle and racing game concepts only. For the wider range of Disney Games, see the entry for Disney Interactive Studios UK.

Codemasters
PO Box 6, Leamington Spa, Warwickshire, CV47 2ZT
- 01926 814132
- 01926 817595
- custservice@codemasters.com
- www.codemasters.co.uk
Contact Director, Designer and Programmer, Paul Carrington; Director, Designer and Writer, Lisa Tunnah

Insider Info Codemasters develops and publishes world-class video games for the Xbox 360, PS3, PC and Nintendo Wii. They also develop and host online games and - through Codemasters Mobile - produce content for mobile phones and handhelds.
Submission Guidelines Accepts submissions from development teams with designs or prototypes to be developed to completion. Email submissions to: acquisitions@codemasters.com
Recent Title(s) *Bubble Bobble Double Shot* (Nintendo DS); *Micro Machines V4* (Nintendo DS)
Tips Codemasters only accept submissions from development teams with professional standard prototypes.

The Communications Group
Graffix House, Newtown Road, Henley on Thames, Oxfordshire, RG9 1HG
- 020 7381 6000
- enquiries@commsgrp.com
- www.thecommunicationsgroup.com
Insider Info The Communications Group is a professional IT and communications company that offers flash game design for businesses and corporations. All artwork, code and design work is custom made and developed in-house.
Recent Title(s) *Crazy Frog Remix*
Tips Ideas for games are welcomed for a proposal meeting. Some of their games require Shockwave, which is available to download via their website.

Core Design
2 Roundhouse Road, Pride Park, Derby, DE24 8JE
- 01332 227800
- 01332 227801
- jobs@core-design.com
- www.core-design.com
Parent Company Rebellion and Eidos Design
Insider Info Core Design's greatest achievement is the development of the *Tomb Raider* series, with the creation of Lara Croft as a world famous cyber star. Games are developed for all major console games.
Submission Guidelines See Eidos for submission details.
Recent Title(s) *Smart Bomb* (PSP); *Free Running*
Tips To apply for Programmer and Artist jobs send a CV to them via post or email. Current vacancies are advertised on their website.

D3 Europe Ltd
Poseidon House, Castle Park, Cambridge, CB3 0RD

☎ 01223 322015
✆ 01223 347800
✉ d.hope@d3p.us
🌐 www.d3p.us

Parent Company D3 Inc.

Contact Managing Director D3 Europe, David Hope

Insider Info Publishes and distributes a wide range of video games for all major console platforms. Works with external and internal developers with a focus on consumer friendly, mass-market games. The main bases are in Tokyo (D3 Inc.) and Los Angeles (D3 Publisher).

Submission Guidelines Strictly no unsolicited suggestions or ideas.

Recent Title(s) *Naruto: Ninja Council 3* (Nintendo DS); *Earth Defense Force 2017,* (Xbox)

Tips D3 will not review any creative suggestions, including artwork, notes, ideas, stories, concepts, designs, films or anything similar. For employment opportunities, check the jobs section of the website.

Denki UK

9 West Bell Street, Dundee, DD1 1HG

☎ 01382 308645
✆ 01382 308239
✉ denki@denki.co.uk
🌐 www.denki.co.uk

Insider Info Denki develops digital toys for GameBoy Advance, GameBoy Color, mobile phones, set top boxes, and PCs and the internet. Denki's main focus is on games for set top boxes at the present time. Licensed brands include *Shrek The Third, Spongebob Squareppants, Hot Wheels, Carol Vorderman's Mind Aerobics* and *Barbie Princess*. Denki also deliver their own brand named products, which include *Denki Blockers*.

Recent Title(s) *Shrek the Third* (Sky Active TV games); *Go Go Beckham: Adventure on Soccer Island*, (GameBoy Advance)

Tips Detailed instructions for positions at Denki are contained on their website.

Disney Interactive Studios UK

3 Queen Caroline Street, Hammersmith, London, W6 9PE

☎ 020 8222 1000
🌐 www.disney.go.com/disneyinteractivestudios

Parent Company The Walt Disney Company

Insider Info The UK arm of the interactive entertainment division of Disney. Develops interactive game content based on existing Disney property and original concepts. Games cover all major console and computer platforms. The main offices are in the US.

Submission Guidelines There is no public submission policy, however they do run a graduate scheme for artists and writers (in the US). For further details email: internships@disstudios.net For all other Disney opportunities, visit the careers site at: http://dcpcareers.disney.go.com/dcpcareers

Recent Title(s) *Cars; Chicken Little: Ace in Action; Cinderella: Dollhouse 2*

Tips Another UK site, Climax Racing Ltd, recently acquired by Disney, is located in Brighton. See separate entry for details.

Eidos

Wimbledon Bridge House, 1 Hartfield Road, Wimbledon, London, SW19 3RU

☎ 020 8636 3000
✆ 020 8636 3001
✉ Online form
🌐 www.eidos.com

Parent Company SCi Entertainment Group

Insider Info A games developer and publisher, with brands including *Tomb Raider* and *Championship Manager*. Games are created for all major console platforms.

Submission Guidelines Submissions of games and character ideas are accepted and will be reviewed, although it must be made clear whether the material needs returning or not. All persons submitting material and information will be required to sign a submission letter (as part of a form provided by Eidos), as a condition of evaluating any material or information submitted. To enquire further, visit the corporate website.

Recent Title(s) *Pony Friends; Tomb Raider Anniversary*

Tips Never send original material, and read the detailed submission statement at the bottom of the Eidos website for information on the copyright policy for submitted ideas.

Electronic Arts (EA)

2000 Hillswood Drive, Chertsey, Surrey, KT16 0EU

🌐 www.electronicarts.co.uk

Insider Info An independent games developer and manufacturer, working on original concepts as well as film and television tie-ins, such as *Harry Potter*. The main focus is on fantasy, action, strategy and sports games, with major brands such as *FIFA* and *The Sims*.

Submission Guidelines There is no public submission policy, however their job site contains various opportunities for their UK sites in Chertsey, Guildford and London.

Recent Title(s) *Harry Potter & the Order of the Phoenix; The Sims Pet Stories; UEFA Champion's League 2006–7*

Elite Systems Ltd
12a Lombard Street, Lichfield, Staffordshire, WS13 6DR
- 0703 115 1536
- steve.wilcox@elite-systems.co.uk
- www.elite-systems.co.uk

Insider Info Elite is a highly specialised developer of game software products for hand-held, mobile and wireless systems. Provides Java games for companies such as T-Mobile and Vodafone.

Submission Guidelines Send demos of software, artwork, or music, by post with a covering letter.

Recent Title(s) *Atlantis Quest*, *Paperboy*

Tips Elite accepts submissions of demos by post, they are particularly keen on ideas for Java games for mobiles.

Empire Interactive Europe
The Spires, 677 High Road, North Finchley, London, N12 0DA
- 020 8343 7337
- 020 8343 7447
- generaljobs@empire.co.uk
- www.vulcan.co.uk

Contact Chief Executive Officer, Ian Higgins; Managing Director, Simon Jeffrey

Insider Info Empire Interactive is a well established global games software publishing company, with operations worldwide. Empire develops licensed brand titles, as well as own brand titles for all major platform consoles including PC and CD-ROM.

Submission Guidelines At the present time all ideas are developed in-house by the team.

Recent Title(s) *Space Empires V*, ages 3+ (PC); *Hello Kitty Roller Coaster Rescue*, ages 3+ (Gamecube, XBOX)

Tips Visit their website for job vacancies. Razorworks Studio is the UK development team for Empire, visit www.razorworks.com for job listings.

Eurocom Entertainment Software
Eurocom House, Ashbourne Road, Mackworth, Derby, DE22 4NB
- 01332 825100
- 01332 824823
- Online form

- www.eurocom.co.uk

Insider Info Eurocom offers a full development service across Sony, Microsoft and Nintendo platforms, and PC. Previous Eurocom developments have included games based on James Bond, Harry Potter, Ice Age, Buffy the Vampire Slayer, Batman, Crash Bandicoot, Spyro, and Tarzan. They also create original material such as the critically acclaimed *Sphinx* and *The Cursed Mummy* for THQ.

Submission Guidelines Eurocom does not accept game submissions of any kind.

Recent Title(s) *Pirates of the Caribbean: At World's End* (Xbox360, PS3, Wii, PS2, PSP, PC)

Tips Eurocom is one of the UK's leading independent games developers. They work primarily with licenced material.

Eutechnyx Ltd
Metro Centre East Business Park, Waterside Drive, Gateshead, Tyne and Wear, NE11 9HU
- 0191 460 6060
- 0191 460 2266
- Online form
- www.eutechnyx.com

Contact Managing Director, Brian Jobling; Executive Producer, Dave Thompson; Creative Manager, Mark Barton

Insider Info Eutechnyx is one of the leaders in UK games development, specialising in driving games. Eutechnyx works with major computer games publishers such as Codemasters, Namco and THQ.

Recent Title(s) *Cartoon Network Racing* (PS2)

Tips Eutechnyx specialise in driving games, but focus mainly on adult titles.

Evolution Studios
Manor Farm Road, Near Runcorn, Cheshire, WA7 1HR
- 01928 570 400
- joinus@evos.net
- www.evos.net

Contact Managing Director, Mick Hocking

Insider Info One of the most prolific motor sports games development companies in the UK - the designers of the successful *World Rally Championship* video games. The future project for Evolution is *Motorstorm* on PS3.

Submission Guidelines At the present time all ideas are developed in-house by the team.

Recent Title(s) *World Rally Championship: Rally Evolved* (PS2)

Tips Evolution Studios advertises jobs for artists, designers and programmers on their website.

Frontier Develpments

306 Science Park, Milton Road, Cambridge, CB4 0WG

- ☎ 01223 394300
- ☎ 01223 420005
- ✉ enquiriesx@frontier.co.uk
- ⊕ www.frontier.co.uk

Contact Founder, David Braben

Insider Info An award winning independent games developer for all major platform consoles including PC games. Frontier holds the publishing rights for Aardman Animations' *Wallace and Gromit* characters on mobile phones. Frontier's success lies in the development of expansion packs for *Roller Coaster Tycoon*, the seminal game *Elite* in the early 80s, and *Frontier* - which was the best selling home computer game in the early 90s.

Recent Title(s) *Thrillriville* (PS2, PSP, Xbox)

Tips Frontier advertises artist, animator, designer and producer jobs on their website. For more information contact them via email: artistjobs@frontier.co.uk or send a showreel CD-ROM.

The Games Factory Europe

Sintrupvej 12, 8220 Brabrand, Denmark

- ☎ 0045 89 442200
- ☎ 0045 89 442222
- ✉ sales@gamefactorygames.com
- ⊕ www.gamefactorygames.eu

Parent Company K.E Media

Insider Info An international publisher of licensed games for Playstation, Nintendo and PC. Brands include Garfield, Postman Pat, Franklin, Noddy, Strawberry Shortcake, Little Miss Spider, Code Lyoko, Biker Mice From Mars and more.

Submission Guidelines Strictly no unsolicited suggestions or ideas only licensed material.

Recent Title(s) *Bratz Ponyz* (Nintendo DS)

Tips The Games Factory is also a successful distributor of toys, apparel, candy, home furnishing products for children, board games, and multimedia software.

Glu Mobile Ltd

Beaumont House, Kensington Village, Avonmore Road, London, W14 8TS

- ☎ 020 3100 1122
- ☎ 020 3100 1133
- ✉ info.emea@glu.com
- ⊕ www.glu.com

Parent Company Glu Mobile Inc

Contact CEO, Denis Guyennot

Insider Info Glu is a leading global publisher of mobile games. Its titles are often based on major brands from partners including Atari, Activision, Konami, Hasbro, SEGA and Sony.

Recent Title(s) *Transformers*; *Ice Age 2: Arctic Slide*

Tips Glu are always looking for talented, creative individuals with an interest in the future of mobile technology to join their team. Email a CV and covering letter.

HotGen Studios

7th Floor, Sunley House, Bedford Park, Croydon, Surrey, CR0 2AP

- ☎ 020 8603 0555
- ☎ 020 8603 0521
- ✉ info@HotGen.com
- ⊕ www.hotgen.com

Contact President, Fergus McGovern

Insider Info HotGen is a toy and games developer for successful entertainment corporations. HotGen designs and develops games for the major platform consoles, including handheld gaming devices, digital networks and 'Plug it in and Play' television games. Brands include Star Wars, Indiana Jones, Barbie, Tony Hawks, The Lion King, Aladdin and SpongeBob Square Pants.

Recent Title(s) *Barbie Pet Rescue* (GameBoy Colour); *Avatar the last Airbender* (Interactive Television); *Matt Hofman's Pro BMX 2* (GameBoy Advance)

Tips HotGen welcomes applications. Email a CV to: human.resources@HotGen.com

Ideaworks3D

1 East Poultry Avenue, London, EC1A 9NX

- ☎ 020 7762 3333
- ☎ 020 7762 3330
- ✉ bizdev@ideaworks3d.com
- ⊕ www3.ideaworks3d.com

Insider Info Ideaworks3D is the world's leading developer of advanced mobile games and production software for cross platform mobile game development. Platforms include BREW, Java, Symbian OS, Linux and Windows Mobile.

Recent Title(s) *Need for Speed Underground 2* (EA Mobile); *The Sims 2 Mobile* (EA Mobile)

Tips For information on jobs email: jobs-enquiriea@ideaworks3d.com

Konami Europe

Konami Digital Entertainment BV, Uxbridge, Middlesex

- 020 8987 5733
- 020 8987 5734
- james@konami.co.uk
- www.am.konami-europe.com

Contact Chief Executive Officer, Kagamesa Kozuki; Product Manager, James Anderson

Parent Konami Corporation

Insider Info The European arm of Konami - a global games, toy, online and multimedia publisher. Famous for the *Yu Gi Oh!* series.

Recent Title(s) *Yu Gi Oh! World Rally Championship 2007* (Nintendo DS); *Dewy's Adventure* (Wii); *Castlevania: Dracula X Chronicles* (PSP)

Kuju Entertainment

Unit 10, Woodside Park, Catteshall Lane, Godalming, Surrey, GU7 1LG

- 01483 414344
- 01483 414287
- kuju@kuju.com
- www.kuju.com

Parent Catalis N.V.

Insider Info A leading European games developer for all major platform consoles including PC, handheld games and online gaming. Kuju operates five studios in the UK, each with their own expertise.

Recent Title(s) *Crush* (PSP); *Batallion Wars II*; *Buzz: The Mega Quiz* (PS2)

Tips Kuju is always looking to recruit talented gamers. Email a CV to: jobs@kuju.com including examples of previous work, or check out the studio websites for Kuju London, Zoe Mode, Kuju Surrey, Kuju Chemistry and Rail Simulator for individual job listings.

Magenta Software Ltd

Unit 34, The Colonnades, Albert Dock, Liverpool, L3 4AA

- 0151 709 1669
- info@magentasoftware.com
- www.magentasoftware.com

Insider Info Magenta software work for some of the leading video game publishers to develop cutting edge interactive entertainment software for licensed brands. The company consists of talented programmers, artists and designers.

Recent Title(s) *Buzz Junior: Jungle Party; Buzz Junior: Robo Jam* (PS2); *Stuart Little 3: Big Photo Adventure* (PS2)

Tips Magenta advertises current vacancies on their website.

Midas Interactive Entertainment Ltd

Unit 14, Stansted Distribution Centre, Start Hill, Bishops Stortford, Hertfordshire, CM22 7DG

- Online form
- www.midasinteractive.com

Insider Info Midas Interactive is an international publisher of video games for the leading gaming platforms, including PlayStation, PlayStation 2, PC CD-ROM, handheld computers and mobile phones.

Recent Title(s) *Clever Kids: Pony World* (Nintendo DS, PC, PS2); *Heracles: Chariot Racing* (PS2)

Tips Midas Interactive Entertainment have been most successful with their budget range of games for the PlayStation and PS2.

Midway Games UK

43 Worship Street, London, EC2A 2DX

- 020 7382 7720
- info@midway.com
- www.midway.com

Parent Midway Games Inc

Insider Info Midway is a global games developer and publishing company that has designed some of the most popular games of all time, the most notable being *Mortal Kombat*.

Recent Title(s) *Big Buck Hunter* (PC); *Ed, Edd n' Eddy* (PS2, Xbox, Nintendo Gamecube); *Happy Feet* (PS2, Xbox)

Tips Midway Games advertise jobs on their website, they also have another office in Newcastle.

Morpheme

4th Floor, Linton House, 39–51 Highgate Road, London, NW5 1RS

- 020 7428 7703
- 070 5069 5392
- contact@morpheme.co.uk
- www.morpheme.co.uk

Contact Andy Fitter, Lucy Reed, Matt Spall

Insider Info Morpheme provides wireless entertainment services for WAP, SMS and Java. Morpheme is developing wireless content for release on all current and forthcoming mobile devices.

Recent Title(s) *Croc Mobile Pinball; Bluetooth Biplanes; Everything Explodes*

Tips Morpheme are winners of the Best Mobile Studio and Innovation Award 2005.

Namco Bandai Europe Limited

Acton Park Estate, The Vale, London, W3 7QE

- 020 8324 6101
- 020 8324 6116
- ntakeda@namco.co.uk
- www.namco.co.uk

Contact Games Development Manager, Nobuo Takeda

Insider Info Namco Bandai Games manufactures and distributes coin operated games and other leisure equipment throughout Europe. Namco Bandai USA and Japan publish and distribute video games for all major platform consoles. 'Brent Sales' is the UK and Ireland distributor of arcade games.

Recent Title(s) *Mario Kart Arcade GP 2*; *Chicken Coop*

Tips Bandai Europe can supply revamped second hand arcade games, visit their website for more details.

Nintendo UK

Mansour House, 188 Bath Road, Slough, Berkshire, SL1 3GA

- 0870 606 0247
- 023 9238 3444
- www.nintendo-europe.com

Parent Company Nintendo Co. Ltd

Insider Info The UK branch of the international console games developer and publisher whose brands include the DS and Wii. Characters include *Super Mario Bros* and *Donkey Kong*. Full games catalogue is available online.

Submission Guidelines No public submissions policy, but the jobs section of the website offers a speculative application form as well as specific opportunities.

Recent Title(s) *Yoshi's Island: Super Mario Advanced 3; The Legend of Zelda: The Wind Waker; Shrek; Smash 'n' Crash Racing*

Rare

Manor Park, Watery Lane, Twycross, Atherstone, Warwickshire CV9 3QN

- 01827 883400
- editor@rareware.com
- www.rare.co.uk

Contact Founders, Tim and Chris Stamper

Parent Microsoft Game Studios

Insider Info Rare was set up in the early nineties to study and develop for the Nintendo Entertainment System. The company has developed over 60 games for Nintendo and Gameboy, the most notable being *Donkey King Kong*. Since the acquisition of Microsoft,

Rare has expanded its development capabilities to include Xbox 360 titles.

Recent Title(s) *Viva Piñata: Party Animals*, Based on the smash hit TV show, ages 3 + (Xbox 360); *DiddyKong Racing DS*, (Nintendo DS, Gameboy Advance)

Real Time Worlds

152 West Marketgait, Dundee, DD1 1NJ

- 01382 202821
- 01382 228188
- enquiries@realtimeworlds.com
- www.realtimeworlds.com

Contact CEO and Creative Director, Dave Jones; President, Tony Harman

Insider Info A creative software development company that has worked on some of the most successful video games in the world, including *Lemmings*. Real Time Worlds is focusing on online gaming as the way forward in the games industry.

Submission Guidelines Real Time has no submission policy.

Recent Title(s) *Crackdown* (Xbox 360)

Tips For Art and Design vacancies visit their website for details. Send all applications, including a portfolio to: jobs@realtimeworlds.com

SEGA Europe Ltd

27 Great West Road, Brentford, Middlesex, TW8 9BW

- acquisitions@soe.sega.co.uk
- www.sega-europe.com

Insider Info Publishes and distributes a wide range of video games for all major console platforms. Video games include the hugely successful *Sonic The Hedgehog* series and a number of film tie-ins and licenced character products.

Submission Guidelines Submit ideas and CVs via email.

Recent Title(s) *Charlotte's Web* (PC, Nintendo DS, GameBoy Advance); *The Golden Compass* (Nintendo DS, PS2, Wii)

Tips SEGA Europe is looking to sign high quality products from developers across Europe. More specifically, SEGA are looking to broaden their range of products, particularly across multiple formats.

Sony Entertainment Europe

10 Great Marlborough Street, London, W1F 7LP

- 020 7859 5000
- help@uk.playstation.com
- www.scee.com

Contact President and Chief Executive Officer, David Reeves, Executive Vice President, Phil Harrison

Insider Info Sony computer entertainment is a global computer games company that is responsible for sales, marketing, distribution and software development for the PlayStation, PSP and PlayStation 2 and 3. Sony Entertainment has three design and development studios based in London, Liverpool and Cambridge. See separate entries. The Cambridge studio develops titles for an older age range.

Recent Title(s) *Eye Toy: Play Astro Zoo*, ages 3+ (PS2)

Tips For job opportunities at Sony, email: HRadmin@scee.net

Sony advertises current vacancies on their website.

Spiral House Ltd

Spiral House Ltd, Digital Inc, 2nd Floor, Baird House, Liverpool, L7 9NJ

- 0151 907 2915
- contact@spiralhouse.co.uk
- www.spiralhouse.co.uk

Insider Info Spiral is an independent games developer for all major platform consoles, including PC and wireless. Spiral House have a new game in development for PSP and DS, currently titled *Sleeper*, an action/puzzle game for young children.

Recent Title(s) *Ghost Master: The Gravenville Chronicles* (PS2, XBOX)

Silver (PC)

Tips Spiral advertises jobs for artists, designers, character modellers, animators and programmers on their website.

Studio Liverpool

Napier Court, Stephenson Way, Wavertree Technology Park, Liverpool, L13 1HD

- 020 7859 5000
- help@uk.playstation.com
- www.development.scee.net

Contact Executive Vice President, Phil Harrison

Parent Sony Computer Entertainment Europe

Insider Info Studio Liverpool is part of the development arm at Sony Entertainment, its seminal game series *Wipeout* was hugely successful, placing Studio Liverpool at the forefront of the games development industry for Playstation games.

Submission Guidelines At the present time all ideas are developed in-house by the team.

Recent Title(s) *Wipeout Pure 2005* (PSP)

Tips Studio Liverpool currently employs close to 100 members, and also houses a number of additional departments which contribute to the high production values that are evident in their titles.

Studio London

15 Great Marlborough Street, London, W1F 7HR

- 020 7859 5000
- help@uk.playstation.com
- www.development.scee.net

Contact Executive Vice President, Phil Harrison

Parent Sony Computer Entertainment Europe

Insider Info Studio London is part of the development arm at Sony Entertainment, its award winning social gaming titles are *Singstar* and *Eye Toy* and popular franchise *The Getaway*.

Submission Guidelines At the present time all ideas are developed in-house by the team.

Recent Title(s) *Singstar: Pop* (PS2)

Tips Studio London currently employs 225 members.

Superscape

Regus Centaur House, Ancells Business Park, Ancells Road, Fleet, Hampshire, GU15 2UN

- 01256 745745
- 01256 745777
- Online submission form
- www.superscape.com

Contact Chief Executive Officer, Kevin J. Roberts

Insider Info Superscape is the world's leading publisher of 3D mobile games and 3D technology, for organisations such as Sony Pictures Mobile, and Disney. The games are downloadable from over 40 network providers.

Recent Title(s) *Zaak The Little Wiz,* by Meantime Mobile creations (Orange, T Mobile)

Tips Superscape has offices in the USA, Japan and Russia. Further details on working at Superscape can be obtained from Human Resources on 01256 745745, or use their online contact form.

Supersonic Software

23 Adelaide Road, Leamington Spa, Warwickshire, CV31 3PD

- 01926 881140
- 01926 882240
- help@supersonic-software.com
- www.supersonic-software.com

Insider Info A well established games company that designed the *Micro Machines* series and original title *Mashed*. Supersonic specialises in fun, playable, multi-player games, for young teenage players.

Submission Guidelines At the present time all ideas are developed in-house by the team.
Recent Title(s) *Micro Machines V4* (PS2, PSP, DS and PC)
Tips Supersonic are in the development stage of a new game for Nintendo Wii, called *Scoot*.

Take Two Interactive UK Ltd
Saxon House, 2–4 Victoria Street, Windsor, Berkshire, SL4 1EN
- 01753 496600
- take2@europesupport.com
- www.take2games.co.uk

Contact International Managing Director, James Ellingford
Insider Info Take Two Interactive is a leading worldwide publisher, developer and distributor of interactive entertainment software, hardware, and accessories across all gaming formats. Subsidiaries include Gathering Games, Globalstar Games and Rockstar Games.
Recent Title(s) *Scaler* (Xbox, PS2); *Tokobot* (PSP)
Tips Take Two focus mainly on high profile adult games, such as the *Grand Theft Auto* series. Their child friendly games are more often developed for current generation consoles, or the digital and handheld markets.

Team17 Software Ltd
Longlands House, Wakefield House, Ossett, West Yorkshire, WF5 9JS
- 01924 267776
- 01924 267658
- webmaster@team17.com
- www.team17.com

Insider Info Team17 are a popular independent studio famed for creating the *Worms* franchise. and the re-launch of *Lemmings* on the PSP. They have over 40 titles and over 130 releases across 16 gaming formats. They are currently developing titles for current, next generation, digital platforms and handheld technology.
Submission Guidelines Team17 accept proposals for original game concepts, and are also able to take an outline, interim concept to full production on a wide variety of gaming platforms.
Recent Title(s) *Worms* (Xbox 360 Live Arcade); *Worms Open Warfare* (Nintendo DS, PSP)
Tips Contact Team17 directly with proposals. For licenced productions contact them for a competitive cost analysis, outline schedule and quote.

THQ (UK) Ltd
Cedar House, 78 Portsmouth Road, Cobham, Surrey, KT11 1AN
- 0870 608 0047
- eursupport@thq.com
- www.thq-games.com

Insider Info THQ is among the fastest growing video game publishers in the world, developing products for all viable current and next-generation game systems. THQ owns 15 internal studios worldwide, including Relic Entertainment, Volition Inc., Rainbow Studios and Juice Games.
Recent Title(s) *Purr Pals* (Nintendo DS); *SpongeBob and Friends: Battle for Volcano Island* (PS2, Nintendo DS)
Tips THQ has a dedicated jobs page for current vacancies in the UK. They are often on the lookout for illustrators/animators with experience of work in the computer game industry.

TT Games
Canute Court, Toft Road, Knutsford, Cheshire, WA16 0NL
- 01565 757300
- Online form
- www.ttgames.com

Contact Director, Designer and Programmer, Paul Carrington; Director, Designer and Writer, Lisa Tunnah
Insider Info TT Games was established in 2005 with the merger of publisher Giant Interactive and the developer Traveller's Tales. The aim of the company is to be the leading publisher of interactive entertainment for young gamers and their families. TT Games specialises in licenced material and franchise, including *LEGO Star Wars*, *Toy Story* and *Transformers*, as well as a range of Disney/Pixar movie tie-ins.
Recent Title(s) *Transformers: The Game* (Xbox 360, PS2, PS3, Wii, PSP); *LEGO Star Wars II: The Original Trilogy* (Xbox 360, Xbox, PS2, PC, Nintendo Gamecube, Nintendo DS, GameBoy Advance, PSP, Apple)
Tips TT Games specialise in titles aimed at young people and children. They are frequently looking for artists and animators, check the jobs page on their website.

Ubisoft
1st Floor, Chertsey Gate East, London Street, Chertsey, Surrey, KT16 8AP
- 01932 578000

☎ 01932 578001
🌐 www.ubi.com/uk
Contact Managing Director (Northern Europe), Rob Copper
Insider Info Ubisoft is a leading international developer, publisher and distributor of multi-format games. It is the second largest games company in the world with 11 studios across 15 countries, and a back catalogue of over 1,000 titles. Previous successes include the *Petz* series, *The Settlers* series, and the *Rayman* franchise.
Recent Title(s) *Rayman: Raving Rabbids 2* (Wii, Nintendo DS)
Tips Ubisoft work with licenced characters and franchise, but also have a history of producing world class original material. They are often looking for designers or programmers, check the website for details.

Ugly Studios
2 Taverner's Square, Silver Road, Norwich, NR3 4SY
☎ 01603 767684
☎ 01603 768731
📧 info@uglystudios.com
🌐 www.uglystudios.com
Insider Info Ugly Studios deliver digital and non-digital artwork for print, multimedia, computer games, television and film.
Tips Ugly Studios are currently re-developing their website.

Vivendi Games
PO Box 2510, Reading, RG2 0ZJ
☎ 0871 075 2621
🌐 www.sierra.com/uk
Insider Info Vivendi Games is a global developer, publisher and distributor of multi-platform interactive entertainment. They are a market leader in the subscription based massively multi-player online (MMO) games category, and hold leading positions in the PC, console, handheld and mobile games markets. Vivendi Games divisions include: Blizzard Entertainment; Sierra Entertainment; Vivendi Games Mobile; and Sierra Online. Vivendi works with industry leading content partners, including Universal Music Group, NBC Universal, Twentieth Century Fox, and Ludlum Entertainment, and has developed over 700 titles including the *Crash Bandicoot*, *Spyro the Dragon* and *Simpsons* series'.
Recent Title(s) *Eragon*
Tips For job vacancies in the UK, submit a CV and covering letter to: jobsuk@vugames.co.uk

Vulcan Software
Vulcan House, Portsmouth, Hampshire, PO3 5ET
☎ 023 9267 0269
📧 paul@vulcan.co.uk
🌐 www.vulcan.co.uk
Contact Director, Designer and Programmer, Paul Carrington; Director, Designer and Writer, Lisa Tunnah
Insider Info Vulcan initially designed award winning games for the Amiga computer and now focuses purely on the development of PC Software. Using PC development tools; Mother 3D, 3D Voice News and the Vulcan Portal, Vulcan are developing PC games that include *Timekeepers*, *Hybrid* and *Valhalla3D*.
Submission Guidelines At the present time all ideas are developed in-house by the team.
Recent Title(s) *Valhalla Classic Speech Adventures* (PC)
Tips Vulcan are currently looking for freelance texture artists, 3d model builders and sound fx creators to join the development of *Valhalla3D* and *Hybrid*, please contact Paul for more information.

4C Charity Christmas Card Council

Cards World Ltd, 49 Cross Street, Angel Islington, London, N1 2BB
- 0845 230 0046
- 4c@charitycards.org
- www.charitycards.org

Insider Info A charitable not-for-profit organisation that publishes high quality Christmas cards for businesses and organisations. All money generated is donated to named charities, visit their website for more information on which charities they support. Member of the Greeting Card Association.

Submission Guidelines Submit artwork copies on CD-ROM or transparencies.

Tips All designs are a mix of classic and contemporary images.

Abacus Cards

Gazeley Road, Kentford, Newmarket, Suffolk, CB8 7RH
- 01638 552399
- 01638 554082
- submissions@abacuscards.co.uk
- www.abacuscards.co.uk

Contact Art Editor, Liz Ellis

Insider Info Publishes a wide range of cards specialising in fine art and pets illustrations. The *100% Kids* range features bold, fun and funky graphics. Publishes Age, General, Relation, Birthday, and Occasion cards. Member of the Greeting Card Association.

Submission Guidelines Currently seeking fine art, photography, contemporary illustrations and design submissions. Do not send original artwork. Accepts colour copies, transparencies, digital prints and images on CD-ROM. Work may also be sent by email, or as a link to your website.

Tips There are no requirements for the service of verse writers at the present time. Much of Abacus Cards design is kept in-house, however they are seeking Christmas themed imagery, animals and pets, flowers, gardens and landscapes, floral photography, and commercial ideas for contemporary cards.

Anker International Plc

Howard House, Howard Way, Interchange Park, Newport Pagnell, Buckinghamshire, MK16 9PX
- 01908 618811
- 01908 612612
- info@anker.co.uk
- www.theankergroup.com

Contact Chief Executive Officer, Paul Fineman

Established 1971

Insider Info A global publisher and designer of Christmas, Valentine and Occasion cards, Gift wrap, Stationary, Calendars, Diaries, Photo albums and Frames, Picture, Canvas, and Disney licensed stationery, and designer stationery for children.

Recent Products *Funky Stuff:* My Secret Diary *Micky Mouse:* A4 Ring Binder

Tips Advertises current vacancies on their website.

Blue Frog Publications Ltd

331 Kemp House, 152–160 City Road, London EC1V 2NX
- 020 7060 0870
- 020 8588 0772
- info@bluefrogcards.co.uk
- bluefrogcards.co.uk

Contact Directors, Segun and Luisa

Insider Info Led by a team of talented designers, the company publishes beautifully drawn or painted cards aimed at children featuring themes such as; Dinosaurs, Animals, Magic, Horoscopes and Nursery rhymes. Also publishes Seasonal, Occasion and Blank cards. Member of the Greeting Card Association.

Tips Explore the website to view more of their cards. Blue Frog are always willing to discuss any ideas for a new project.

Card Connection Ltd

Park House, South Street, Farnham, Surrey, GU9 7QQ
- 01252 892300
- 01252 892339
- carrie-clatworthy@card-connection.co.uk
- www.card-connection.com

Contact Managing Director, Simon Hulme; Product Manager, Carrie Clatworthy

Established 1992

Insider Info Publishes Birthday and Occasion cards in a range of designs and styles including: Humour, Age and Relations, Blank, Photographic, Contemporary and Gender, Seasonal cards, Wrapping paper, Gift tags and Bottle bags. Member of the Greeting Card Association.

Recent Products *Animul Kingdum;* features animal photography with bright and brash typography and fun captions

Submission Guidelines Submit six colour copies of some styles. Include a covering letter and SAE. They are seeking good quality jokes, humorous copy and sentimental verse suitable for greeting cards. Send a selection of examples to the product department.

Carlton Cards
Mill Street East, Dewsbury, WF12 9AW
- 01924 465200
- 01924 453908
- customerfeedback@ukgreetings.co.uk
- www.carltoncards.co.uk

Contact Product Manager, Susan Gitto
Parent American Greeting
Insider Info Publishes all types of cards including commercial licensed cards. Children's brands include 'Scooby Doo', 'Pic N Mix', 'Lemon Squeezy' and 'La Di Da' Juvenile. Also publishes Handmade cards, Online cards and 'Bubblegum' cards, that are fun, funky, bright, youthful and suitable for all occasions. Member of the Greeting Card Association.
Submission Guidelines Send designs and verse samples via post to the product manager. They will respond if interested. Accepts submissions by email, but prefers postal submissions.
Recent Products
La Di Da, features soft pastel colours, embossing, glitter and romantic patterns.
Tips Carlton is a major player in youth trends and their choice of design tends to reflect this. Carlton advertises jobs on their website.

Caroline Gardner Publishing
283 Lonsdale Road, London, SW13 9QB
- 020 8288 9696
- 020 8288 9697
- info@carolinegardner.com
- www.carolinegardner.com

Contact Caroline Gardner
Insider Info Publishes quirky, yet sophisticated children's Birthday cards and 'Thank you' cards, using effective traditional printing techniques like letter press and dye stamping. Member of the Greeting Card Association.
Tips The company is currently branching out into the clothes market, designing handbags, purses, make-up bags and other accessories.

Carte Blanche Greetings Ltd
Unit 3, Chichester Business Park, Tangmere, Chichester, West Sussex, PO20 2XZ
- 0870 600 0441
- 0870 600 0442
- Online form
- www.cbg.co.uk

Contact Chief Executive, Stephen Haines; Creators of 'Tatty The Teddy,' Mike Payne, Stuart Mort-Hill and Ceri Lewis
Established 1987
Insider Info Publishes own brand 'Me To You' cards and products featuring 'Tatty The Teddy', the adorable bear with the blue nose. Member of the Greeting Card association.
Tips To view the 'Me To You' range of cards, visit: www.metoyou.com

Caspari Ltd
9 Shire Hill, Saffron Walden, Essex, CB11 3AP
- 01799 513010
- 01799 513101
- keith@caspari.co.uk
- www.casparionline.com

Insider Info A global greeting card publisher that specialises in traditional fine art, classic images and seasonal cards.
Submission Guidelines Accepts transparencies, CD-ROMs, originals, or high resolution colour copies. Aims to respond in six to eight weeks. Member of the Greeting Card Association.
Tips Does not accept photographic submissions.

Clare Madicott Publications
Foldgate Farm, Ludlow, Shropshire, SY8 4BN
- 01584 878484
- 01548 848480
- sales@maddicott.com
- www.maddicott.com

Contact Director, Richard Maddictt
Insider Info Publishes a diverse range of high quality, stylish Cards, Postcards, Stationery, Notebooks and Gift Wrap. Brands include 'Clare Maddicott', 'Rum & Raisin', 'Urbansqmo', 'On The Mantelpiece', 'Harold's Planet' and 'Steven Appleby'. Member of the Greeting Card Association.
Recent Products *'Clare Madicott: Tutti Frutti'*, features youthful illustrations of animals, wizards, and nature etc.
Tips Visit their website to explore the full range of products on offer. Distribution capabilities in the US, Canada and Europe.

Double Trouble Publishing

The Design Exchange, 34 Peckover Street, Little Germany, Bradford, BD1 5BD

- ☎ 01274 742483
- 🖶 01274 729680
- ✉ info@doubletroublepublishing.com
- 🌐 www.doubletroublepublishing.com

Established 2003

Parent Ellis Creative

Insider Info A relatively new design company that has been extremely successful with its debut range 'The Adventures of Molly & Macy' in the UK and abroad. The brand features stylish black and white photography of two little girls with the subtle use of red. Other brands include 'Zoo Zoo' and 'Little Creatures'. Member of the Greeting Card Association.

Recent Products *Little Creatures; Happy Birthday;* Features youthful digital animation of loveable creatures

Gemma International Ltd

Linmar House, 6 East Portway, Andover, Hampshire, SP10 3LU

- ☎ 01264 388400
- 🖶 01264 366243
- ✉ sales@gemma-international.co.uk
- 🌐 www.gemma-international.co.uk

Contact Directors, L. Rudd-Clarke, A. Parkin, T. Rudd-Clarke

Established 1984

Insider Info Publishes licensed brands for kids such as 'Barbie' and 'Disney', non-licensed children's cards, and gift wrap. Gemma International also supplies party products. Member of the Greeting Card Association.

Submission Guidelines Particularly interested in sentimental and cute verse. Send design, verse or copy submissions via post, or email to: k.bishop@gemma-international.co.uk

Hallmark Cards Plc

Hallmark House, Bingley Road, Heaton, Bradford, Yorkshire, BD9 6SD

- ☎ 01274 252000
- 🖶 01274 252401
- ✉ lpalil2@hallmark-uk.com
- 🌐 www.hallmarkuk.com

Established 1958

Insider Info A global company that publishes all types of greetings cards in classic, funny, contemporary and cute designs. Brands include 'Forever Friends', 'Tippi', 'Dylan & Thomas', 'Coronation Street'. Produces approximately two billion cards each year. Member of the Greeting Card Association.

Tips Hallmark advertises vacancies on their website. For information on submissions contact them via email or telephone.

Nigel Quiney Publications

Cloudesley House, Shire Hill, Saffron Walden, Essex, South East, CB11 3FB

- ☎ 01799 520100
- 🖶 01799 520100
- ✉ info@nigelquiney.com
- 🌐 www.nigelquiney.com

Contact Product and Marketing Director, Alison Butterworth

Insider Info Publishes a wide range of cards for all occasions, such as Birthday, Seasonal, Valentines and General in many styles, including Children's, Contemporary, Humorous, Fine art, Photographic, Cute and Handmade. Member of the Greeting Card Association.

Submission Guidelines Accepts colour copies, transparencies, photocopies or pencil rough. Include SAE.

Tips In addition to pursuing freelance artwork they welcome concept ideas.

Noel Tatt Group

Appledown House, Barton Business Park, New Dover Road, Canterbury, Kent, CT1 3TE

- ☎ 01227 811600
- 🖶 01227 811601
- ✉ catherine@noeltatt.co.uk
- 🌐 www.noeltatt.co.uk

Categories A successful greeting card publisher that has its own in-house design team - The Blue Room - which creates most of the card ranges. Publishes all types of cards for all occasions, in many styles such as; Cute, Humorous, Contemporary and Gender specific. Also publish Seasonal cards, Blank cards, Age and Relation cards. Member of the Greeting Card Association.

Submission Guidelines Send colour copies, digital prints, photographs, transparencies and images saved on CD-ROM. Aims to respond as soon as possible.

Tips Seeking fine art and photography of landscapes, animals, floral, and imaginative fresh imagery. Also seeking Christmas themes, especially robins and snow scenes.

Noi Publishing

115b Cottenham Park Road, Wimbledon, London SW20 0DS

- 020 8944 6122
- info@noipublishing.com
- www.noipublishing.com

Contact Tracey, Peter and Paul Francis

Insider Info Publishes and designs contemporary stylish cards for all occasions such as; Birthdays, Engagement, Thank you and Seasonal. The ranges include Children's, 'Slinky Noi', 'Naughty Noi', the Spring collection and Embossed cards.

Recent Products 'Dinki Girl and Kooki Boy'; Birthday Cards

The Paper House

Waterwells Drive, Gloucester, West Midlands, GL2 2PH

- 01452 888999
- 01452 888912
- sales@paperhouse.co.uk
- www.paperhouse.co.uk

Contact Creative Director, Matthew Jeanes

Insider Info One of the largest greeting card publishers in the UK, with over 5,000 choices of designs. Publishes a wide range of cards for all occasions in a wide range of styles such as Contemporary, Cute, Children's, Humour, Fine Art, Photography, Trend, and Graphics. Publishes 12 new ranges a year.

Submission Guidelines Accepts colour photocopies, photographs or computer print outs, as well as images on CD-ROM. Do not send originals. Include SAE. They negotiate a fee for the world-wide reproduction rights of each design separately. Accepts verses and humour submissions via post.

Tips Seeking all types of design submissions and copywriter's submissions for humorous and traditional cards.

Really Good

Old Mast House, The Square, Abingdon, Oxfordshire, OX14 5AR

- 01235 537888
- 01235 537779
- potatoes@reallygood.uk.com
- www.reallygood.uk.com

Contact Managing Director, David Hicks; Production Manager, Charley Russell

Established 1987

Insider Info Design and publish a range of stylish and humorous cards. Also; Gift wrap, Stationary and Gifts for pets, Christmas and Babies. Member of the Greeting Card Association.

Recent Products *Thoughts of Edward Monkton*; Humorous cards and other products including books, stationery and badges

Ripe; A range of bright and vibrant age cards

Love From Me x, Greeting cards suitable for both adults and children, featuring young, observant and often to the point captions for all occasions, including birthdays

Submission Guidelines Seeking imaginative and creative submissions capable of commercial success. Send samples with SAE, email low resolution images, or provide a link to a website to view your work/ products.

Regent Greeting Cards

Regent House, Dockfield Road, Shipley, West Yorkshire, BD17 7SF

- 01274 580555
- 01274 586293
- sales@regent-group.com
- www.regentgreetingcards.co.uk

Categories Publishes Children's cards, Gender cards, Contemporary cards, Cute cards, Wedding and Occasion cards and Hand Made cards. Member of the Greeting Card Association.

Recent Products *Nik Naks,* Best selling children's range, features Birthday gender designs

Tips Explore the website, or obtain the catalogue using the online submission form.

Riverdale Publishing

Riverside Works, Keighley Road, Silsden, North Yorkshire, BD20 0EH

- 01535 650020
- 01535 650021
- phillip.needham@riverdalepublishing.co.uk
- www.riverdalepublishing.co.uk

Contact Chief Executive, Phillip Needham

Insider Info A leading publisher and designer of greeting cards and gift wrap in the UK and Ireland. Consists of a couple of design studios that develop thousands of Riverdale's titles every year. Publishes Seasonal cards, Occasion cards, and Children's cards - including the 'Underground Ernie' licensed brand. Visit individual studio websites to view their cards. Member of the Greeting Card Association.

Tips Riverdale advertises current vacancies for artists, designers and editors on their website.

Riverside Cards Ltd

Jubilee Way, Grange Moor, Wakefield, WF4 4TD

- 01924 840500
- 01924 840600
- sales@riversidecards.com
- www.riversidecards.com

Contact Design Manager, Suzanne Pickles

Insider Info A publisher, designer and supplier of greeting cards in the UK. Clients include BP, Esso, Londis, Aramark, Booker, Nisa, Costcutter and independent retailers. Publishes an extensive range of cards including cards for all occasions such as Weddings, Birthdays, Engagement and Seasonal. Ranges include 'Max' - fun based character cards and 'New Dimensions' - large eye catching designs. Member of the Greeting Card Association.

Submission Guidelines Accept colour copies, transparencies, digital prints and images on CD-ROM. Include SAE. Alternatively, email images to: design@riversidecards.com

Simon Elvin Ltd

Wooburn Green, Buckinghamshire, HP10 0PE

- 01628 526711
- 01628 531483
- sales@simonelvin.com
- www.simonelvin.com

Contact Art Director, Isabel Scott Evans; Studio Coordinator, Rachel Bradley

Established 1978

Insider Info Publishes all types of cards in the Seasonal, Christmas and Everyday collections, own brand 'Isabel' titles and Handmade cards. Member of the Greeting Card Association.

Recent Products *Planet Happy;* Age and Badge Birthday Cards

Submission Guidelines Send a small collection of good quality colour copies or prints, or send by CD or email include SAE. Aims to respond in 15 days. One off payment for the rights to the cards.

Tips The company employs a team of designers, writers and machine operators to manufacture the cards from scratch, through to the very end.

Soul Trader Cards

3 Broomfield Hall, Enmore, Bridgwater, Somerset, South West, TA5 2DZ

- 01278 671679
- 01278 671535
- sales@soultraderuk.com
- www.soultraderuk.com

Insider Info Soul Trader promotes greeting cards and other paper products, with 11 beautiful and original ranges. 'The Fairy Way' are blank cards with beautiful watercolour illustrations of the world of fairies, 'Poetry Cards' is a selection that features humorous and inspiring poetry by known and unknown poets and 'Moocards' features illustrations of character cows having fun.

Recent Products *The Fairy Way;* Birthday Cake

Tips Other ranges include 'Masha D'yans', 'Deborah Cavenaugh', 'Marja Leena', 'Collage', 'Patience Brewster', 'The Wayward Gene', 'Cats Rule!' and 'Once upon a Time...' Visit their website to view more of their card designs.

Splimple Cards

PO Box 2973, Stratford upon Avon, Warwickshire, CV37 1ZP

- 01789 415545
- 01789 264296
- wow@splimple.com
- www.splimple.com

Contact Resident Writer, Stuart Caldwell

Insider Info Publishes clever, humorous greeting cards in a quirky and distinctive manner. Stuart Caldwell is the talented writer behind the Splimple range. The children's range is 'Splimplings'; age cards with a canny sense of children's humour, such as bodily functions, smelly things and elementary anatomy. Other brands include 'Faulkners Gallery', amusing illustrations of daily lives and relationships, '...Love You Really', 'Harry No Thumbs Clagg' and the 'Christmas' range. Visit the website to view these exceptional cards. Member of the Greeting Card Association.

Recent Products *Christmas Exposed,* a range of 12 cards that explain what people are really thinking during the festive period.

Tigerprint

Bingley Road, Heaton, Bradford, BD9 6SD

- 020 7758 0200
- 020 7758 0222
- info@tigerprint-uk.com
- www.tigerprint.uk.com

Established 1996

Insider Info A designer of cards, stationery, toys and gifts, gift wrap and a Christmas range. Tigerprint is the main supplier to the card shop at Marks and Spencer, which is the fourth biggest retailer of greetings cards. Member of the Greeting Card Association.

Tips Tigerprint is running a design competition for budding card designers. To submit your artwork register online, then follow the competition instructions. The winner gets their work published and has the chance of a placement at Tigerprint.

Wishing Well Studios

Kellet Close, Martland Park, Wigan, Lancashire, WN5 0LP

- 01942 218888
- 01942 218899
- info@wishingwell.co.uk
- www.wishingwell.co.uk

Established 1996

Insider Info An award winning publisher of greeting cards. Publishes Seasonal cards, Humorous cards, Occasion cards such as Birthday, Valentine and Get Well cards, Photography and Artwork cards and licensed titles such as 'Hammer Films' featuring photographs of iconic films and clever captions.

Submission Guidelines Send photocopies - not originals - of design ideas to the Art Director, or email to: nickyh@wishingwell.co.uk

Verse writers should send work to the Editorial department, or email: susie.linley@wishingwell.co.uk

Recent Products *Bring Me Sunshine*; Licensed photographic card range

Tips Seeking artwork, illustrations and photography that will lend itself to commercial success. Also humorous verse and jokes covering the regular old favourite subjects, to more topical matters. Verses should be kept between 4–24 lines, but the majority they use are 8, 12 or 16 lines.

WEBSITES FOR CHILDREN

A Kid's Life

- www.kidslife.com

About Website that features life lessons and advice by children, for children.

Ask for Kids

- www.askforkids.com

About A search engine for children, hosted by Ask.com. Formerly known as Ask Jeeves for Kids.

Bedtime-Story

- www.the-office.com/bedtime-story

About An online resource of bedtime stories, designed for business people to read to their children over the phone.

Build-it-Yourself

- www.build-it-yourself.com

About A site that has guides for children to build things ranging from decorations to toys.

Cbeebies

- www.bbc.co.uk/cbeebies

About The official Cbeebies website. Makes use of plenty of animated licenced characters. Features stories, puzzles, games, articles and clips from Cbeebies programmes.

Citv

- www.citv.co.uk

About The official website of the Citv television service. The website includes articles, reviews, puzzles, games and a creative gallery. It also makes use of illustrated/animated, and licenced characters.

Cool-Reads

- www.cool-reads.co.uk

About The Cool-Reads website features book reviews by 10–15 year olds for other children.

Cyberkids

- www.cyberkids.com

About An online portal for children featuring fun and games, search facilities and forums.

CyberSleuth Kids

- http://cybersleuth-kids.com

About A search engine for children. Also features puzzles, games and downloadable colouring pages.

Fact Monster

- www.factmonster.com

About A massive online reference resource for children.

Family Friendly Search

ⓦ wwwfamilyfriendlysearch.com

About A metasearch engine for children and families that searches several other sites, such as Yahooligans and Ask for Kids.

Funbrain

ⓦ www.funbrain.com

About A website featuring educational games, puzzles and blogs for children of all ages.

Funorama

ⓦ www.funorama.com

About Funorama is an online activity centre and bookstore for children. It has educational projects and articles for download or print.

Games Kids Play

ⓦ www.gameskidsplay.net

About An online resource that includes the rules of hundreds of games that children like to play, from card games to playground games.

Global Children's Art Gallery

ⓦ www.naturalchild.org/gallery

About A website that allows children to post their art in an online gallery. The site currently has over 1,000 pictures from children all over the world.

Homework Elephant

ⓦ www.homeworkelephant.co.uk

About A site offering over 5,000 resources to aid children and teenagers with homework assignments.

Ithaki 4 KiDS

ⓦ www.ithaki.net/kids

About A metasearch engine for children.

Jetix

ⓦ www.jetix.co.uk

About Website of the Jetix television channel. Contains articles, games, puzzles, creative pages and details of all Jetix shows. The site contains lots of animations and licenced characters.

KiddONet

ⓦ www.kiddonet.com

About KiddONet offers children an online space with high quality content and web tools that allow them to create, learn, play and communicate safely.

Kidlink

ⓦ www.kidlink.org/english

About Kidlink is a social network for children aged between 10 to 15 years old, from over 174 different countries. It also features free educational programmes.

KidsClick!

ⓦ www.kidsclick.org

About A web search engine for children, designed and maintained by librarians. Offers a search facility and a wide range of categories for browsing.

KidSites.com

ⓦ www.kidsites.com

About A guide to the best websites for children.

KidsJokes.co.uk

ⓦ www.kidsjokes.co.uk

About A website with hundreds of jokes for children.

KidsReads.com

ⓦ www.kidsreads.com

About An online resource for children's books and reading. Features include reviews, new releases, interviews, articles and podcasts.

LinkOpedia

ⓦ www.linkopedia.com/kids.html

About A diverse list of websites suitable for children aged three to ten years old.

Make-Stuff

ⓦ www.make-stuff.com/kids

About The children's section of the Make-Stuff website. Has instructions for easy craft projects, such as making bird feeders.

NASA for Kids
🌐 www.nasa.gov/audience/forkids
About A website for children hosted by NASA, the space agency. It has educational, space-themed games, art, photography, stories, interviews and articles.

National Geographic Kids
🌐 http://kids.nationalgeographic.com
About An educational website for children from National Geographic. Features include science/natural world articles, puzzles, games, videos and stories.

Nick
🌐 http://nick.co.uk
About The Nickelodeon website contains puzzles, games, review and flash animations featuring licenced characters.

Stories from the Web
🌐 www.storiesfromtheweb.org
About A website for children, teenagers and young adult writers to post their stories and poetry on. Also features reviews from young readers, articles about the latest books, and a range of activities and games.

SuperKids
🌐 www.superkids.com
About A site for children and parents with reviews of educational software, education resources and articles.

topmarks
🌐 www.topmarks.co.uk
About A site for parents and children featuring a wide range of homework help, revision websites and educational sites. Also has educational games, puzzles and stories.

TryScience
🌐 www.tryscience.org
About An educational science and technology site for children.

Webtime Stories
🌐 www.kn.pacbell.com/wired/webtime
About An online story resource for children, featuring several dedicated sections, such as 'Storytime', 'Myths, Fables & Legends', 'Great Books', 'Young Adults' and 'Just for Fun'. The site also includes a range of story based resources and audio downloads.

Yahoo! Kids
🌐 www.yahooligans.com
About A search engine for children, hosted by Yahoo! The site also features reviews, video clips, new releases and a range of jokes, articles and games.

Yucky Kids
🌐 http://yucky.kids.discovery.com
About An interactive children's museum with more than 400 'hands on' exhibits.

WRITING & PUBLISHING COURSES

The Academy of Children's Writers
PO Box 95, Huntingdon, Cambridgeshire, PE28 5RL
- 01487 832752
- 01487 832752
- enquiries@childrens-writers.co.uk
- www.childrens-writers.co.uk

Courses Writing for Children
About The Academy of Writers offers a correspondence course package, either fully tutored or untutored. The Academy of Writers is the trading name of Per Ardua Ltd. Visit their website to view a synopsis of the course.

Arvon Foundation
Lumb Bank - The Ted Hughes Arvon Centre, Heptonstall, Hebden Bridge, West Yorkshire, HX7 6DF
- 01422 843714
- l-bank@arvonfoundation.org
- www.arvonfoundation.org

Contact Centre directors, Stephen May and Caron May
Courses Writing for Children. Contact Linda Newbery, t-barton@arvonfoundation.org
Writing for Young Adults. Contact Malorie Blackman, l-bank@arvonfoundation.org
Poetry (for children). Contact Carol Ann Duffy, m-mhor@arvonfoundation.org
About The Arvon Foundation runs week long residential writing courses across four properties in Devon, Scotland, Shropshire and West Yorkshire. Visit the website for contact details of individual offices. Carries out extensive work within schools, colleges and youth groups to encourage creative writing in younger people.

Bath Spa University
School of English and Creative Studies, Bath Spa University, Newton Park Campus, Bath, BA2 9BN
- 01225 875743
- 01225 875503
- www.bathspa.ac.uk

Courses BA Creative Writing (single or joint honours). Contact Richard Kerridge, r.kerridge@bathspa.ac.uk
MA Creative Writing. Contact Richard Kerridge, r.kerridge@bathspa.ac.uk
MA Writing for Young People. Contact Julia Green, j.a.green@bathspa.ac.uk
PhD Creative Writing. Contact Dr. Tracey Brain, t.brain@bathspa.ac.uk

City Lit
Keeley Street, Covent Garden, London, WC2B 4BA
- 020 7492 2600
- 020 7492 2735
- humanities@citylit.ac.uk
- www.citylit.ac.uk

Courses HW102: Ways into Writing for Children. Contact Elizabeth Hawkins.
HW022: Writing for Children. Contact Elizabeth Hawkins.
HW045: Writing for Children (Workshop). Contact Elizabeth Hawkins.
HW206: Writing for Children's TV. Contact Phil O'Shea.
About City Lit offers a wide range of part-time courses on all aspects of writing and the arts, including several courses on writing for children.

Essex Live Literature Courses
Essex Libraries, Goldlay Gardens, Chelmsford, Essex, CM2 6WN
- 01245 436759
- malcolm.burgess@essexcc.gov.uk
- www.essexlivelit.org.uk

About Essex Live Literature is funded by the Essex County Council and hosts various literature events, including writing courses. Contact Malcolm Burgess.

Falmouth College of Arts
Woodlane, Falmouth, Cornwall, TR11 4RH
- 01326 370444
- business@falmouth.ac.uk

www.falmouth.ac.uk
About Summer schools on novel writing, and writing for children.

ICS (International Correspondence Schools)
Skypark 5, 1st Floor, Finnieston Street, Glasgow, G3 8JU
0800 056 3983
icscourseadvisors@ics-uk.co.uk
www.icslearn.co.uk
Courses ICS Writing Books for Children
About ICS is the world's largest distance learning organisation. The course covers five different age ranges.

Kingston University
River House, 53–57 High Street, Kingston upon Thames, Surrey, KT1 1LQ
020 8547 2000
admissions-info@kingston.ac.uk
www.kingston.ac.uk
Courses MA Creative, Fiction or Travel Writing. Contact Susan Henry, fasspostgrad-info@kingston.ac.uk
MA Writing for Children. Contact Susan Henry, hsundergrad-info@kingston.ac.uk
MA Poetry. Contact Susan Henry, hsundergrad-info@kingston.ac.uk
MA Publishing Studies. Contact Susan Henry, hsundergrad-info@kingston.ac.uk
MA Making Plays: Writing and Devising for the Stage. Contact Susan Henry, hsundergrad-info@kingston.ac.uk

The National Extension College
The Michael Young Centre, Purbeck Road, Cambridge, CB2 8HN
01223 400200
courses@nec.ac.uk
www.nec-courses.co.uk
Courses NEC Creative Writing
About The NEC is a large not for profit organisation that provides accessible home learning courses. The Creative Writing course includes some instruction on writing for young people.

Open College of the Arts
The Michael Young Arts Centre, Unit 1B Redbrook Business Park, Wilthorpe Road, Barnsley, S75 1JN
01226 730495
01226 730838
open.arts@ukonline.co.uk
www.oca-uk.com
Courses CW2: Making 'Magic' Happen. Contact Beth Webb.
About The Open College of the Arts offers a correspondence course of approximately nine months in length. Small bursaries are available for applicants receiving benefit, or on low incomes.

Oxford University Summer School
Oxford University Department for Continuing Education, Rewley House, 1 Wellington Square, Oxford, OX1 2JA
01865 270360
01865 270309
oussa@conted.ox.ac.uk
www.conted.ox.ac.uk/oussa
About July summer school which runs a variety of week-long writing courses and workshops. Bursaries may be available for applicants receiving benefit, or on low incomes.

Roehampton University
Erasmus House, Roehampton Lane, London, SW15 5PU
020 8392 3232
020 8392 3470
enquiries@roehampton.ac.uk
www.roehampton.ac.uk
Courses BA Creative Writing (single or joint)
MA Creative and Professional Writing. Contact Jeff Hilson, j.hilson@roehampton.ac.uk
MA Children's Literature. Contact Lisa Sainsbury, l.sainsbury@roehampton.ac.uk

Ty Newydd
National Writers Centre for Wales, Llanystumdwy, Criceth, Gwynedd, LL52 0LW
01766 522811
post@tyneyd.org
www.tynewydd.org
Courses Writing for Children: Tales of Old, Retold
About Ty Newydd is the National Writers' Centre for Wales, and offers a wide range of writing courses and events.

University of Winchester
West Hill, Winchester, SO22 4NR
01962 841515

☎ 01962 842280
✉ course.enquiries@winchester.ac.uk
🌐 www.winchester.ac.uk
Courses BA Creative Writing
MA Creative and Critical Writing
MA Writing for Children

The Writers Bureau
Sevendale House, 7 Dale Street, Manchester, M1 1JB
☎ 0161 228 2362

☎ 0161 236 9440
✉ advisory@writersbureau.com
🌐 www.writingforchildrencourse.com
Courses Writing for Children
About The Writers Bureau is accredited by The Open & Distance Learning Quality Council and is a member of the British Learning Association. The course covers everything from children's novels to picture books, non-fiction to poetry. Details are free on request and a 15 day trial period is available, as well as the option for a full refund if not successful.

ILLUSTRATION COURSES

Anglia Ruskin University
Bishop Hall Lane, Chelmsford, Essex, CM1 1SQ
☎ 0845 271 3333
☎ 01245 251789
✉ answers@anglia.ac.uk
🌐 www.anglia.ac.uk
Courses BA Illustration
BA Illustration and Animation

The Arts Institute at Bournemouth
Wallisdown, Poole, Dorset, BH12 5HH
☎ 01202 363225
☎ 01202 537729
✉ admissions@aib.ac.uk
🌐 www.aib.ac.uk
Courses BA Illustration

Coventry University
The Student Centre, 1 Gulson Road, Coventry, CV1 2JH
☎ 024 7615 2222
☎ 024 7615 2223
✉ info.rao@coventry.ac.uk
🌐 www.coventry.ac.uk
Courses BA Illustration
BA Fine Art and Illustration
BA Graphic Design and Illustration

De Montfort University
The Gateway, Leicester, LE1 9BH
☎ 0116 255 1551
☎ 0116 250 6204
✉ enquiries@dmu.ac.uk

🌐 www.dmu.ac.uk
Courses BA Graphic Design and Illustration

Doncaster College
The Hub, Chappell Drive, Doncaster, South Yorkshire, DN1 2RF
☎ 01302 553610
✉ he@don.ac.uk
🌐 www.don.ac.uk
Courses BA Illustration and Animation (Top up), contact Joanne Crapper.

Herefordshire College of Art and Design
Folly Lane, Hereford, HR1 1LT
☎ 01432 845327
☎ 01432 341099
✉ undergrad@hereford-art-col.ac.uk
🌐 www.hereford-art-col.ac.uk
Courses BA Illustration. Contact Dawn Pemberton: d.pemberton@hereford-art-col.ac.uk

Hull College
Queen's Gardens, Hull, HU1 3DG
☎ 01482 329943
☎ 01482 598733
✉ info@hull-college.ac.uk
🌐 www.hull-college.ac.uk
Courses FdA Creative Arts
BA Illustration

Kingston University
Cooper House, 40–46 Surbiton Road, Kingston upon Thames, KT1 2HX
- 020 8547 7053
- 020 8547 7080
- admissions-info@kingston.ac.uk
- www.kingston.ac.uk

Courses BA Illustration & Animation

The Manchester Metropolitan University
All Saints Building, All Saints, Manchester, M15 6BH
- 0161 247 2000
- 0161 247 6871
- www.mmu.ac.uk

Courses BA Illustration with Animation

Middlesex University
North London Business Park, Oakleigh Road South, London, N11 1QS
- 020 8411 5555
- 020 8411 5649
- admissions@mdx.ac.uk
- www.mdx.ac.uk

Courses BA Illustration

Newcastle College
Rye Hill Campus, Scotswood Road, Newcastle upon Tyne, NE4 7SA
- 0191 200 4000
- 0191 200 4349
- enquiries@ncl-coll.ac.uk
- www.newcastlecollege.co.uk

Courses FdA Animation and Illustration. Contact Paul Sisterton, paul.sisterson@ncl-coll.ac.uk

Northbrook College Sussex
Littlehampton Road, Goring by Sea, Worthing, West Sussex, BN12 6NU
- 0800 183 6060
- 01903 606073
- enquiries@nbcol.ac.uk
- www.northbrook.ac.uk

Courses HND Illustration

The North East Wales Institute of Higher Education
Plas Coch, Mold Road, Wrexham, LL11 2AW
- 01978 293439
- 01978 290008
- enquiries@newi.ac.uk
- www.newi.ac.uk

Courses BA Design: Illustration
BA Design: Illustration for Children's Publishing

The Norwich School of Art and Design
Francis House, 3–7 Redwell Street, Norwich, NR2 4SN
- 01603 610561
- 01603 615728
- admissions@nsad.ac.uk
- www.nsad.ac.uk

Courses BA Illustration

Southampton Solent University
East Park Terrace, Southampton, Hampshire, SO14 0RT
- 023 8031 9039
- 023 8022 2259
- enquiries@solent.ac.uk
- www.solent.ac.uk

Courses BA Illustration
BA Illustration (with Foundation)

Staffordshire University
College Road, Stoke on Trent, ST4 2DE
- 01782 292753
- 01782 292740
- admissions@staffs.ac.uk
- www.staffs.ac.uk

Courses BA Illustration

Staffordshire University Regional Federation
Staffordshire University, College Road, Stoke on Trent, ST4 2DE
- 01782 292753
- 01782 292740
- admissions@staffs.ac.uk
- www.surf.ac.uk

Courses HND Illustration

Swansea Institute
Mount Pleasant Campus, Swansea, SA1 6ED
- 01792 481000
- 01792 481061
- dale.dewitt@sihe.ac.uk
- www.sihe.ac.uk

Courses BA General Illustration

Swindon College

North Star Avenue, Swindon, Wiltshire, SN2 1DY
01793 498308
01793 430503
full-timeenquiries@swindon-college.ac.uk
www.swindon-college.ac.uk
Courses BA Sequential Illustration
HND Sequential Illustration
HND Illustration

University College Falmouth

Woodlane, Falmouth, Cornwall, TR11 4RH
01326 211077
01326 213880
admissions@falmouth.ac.uk
www.falmouth.ac.uk
Courses BA Illustration

University College for the Creative Arts

(Canterbury, Epsom, Farnham, Maidstone, Rochester)
Falkner Road, Farnham, Surrey, GU9 7DS
01252 892696
01252 892624
admissions@ucreative.ac.uk
www.ucreative.ac.uk
Courses BA Illustration
BA Illustration (Four years)

University of Bedfordshire

Park Square, Luton, Bedfordshire, LU1 3JU
01582 489286
01582 489323
admissions@beds.ac.uk
www.beds.ac.uk
Courses BA Illustration

The University of Bolton

Deane Road, Bolton, BL3 5AB
01204 900600
01204 399074
enquiries@bolton.ac.uk
www.bolton.ac.uk
Courses BA Animation & Illustration
BA Animation & Illustration & Creative Writing
BA Animation & Illustration & Fine Arts

University of Brighton

Mithras House, Lewes Road, Brighton, BN2 4AT
01273 644644
01273 642825
admissions@brighton.ac.uk
www.brighton.ac.uk
Courses BA Illustration
FdA Illustration

University of Central Lancashire

University of Central Lancashire, Preston, Lancashire, PR1 2HE
01772 201201
01772 894954
uadmissions@uclan.ac.uk
www.uclan.ac.uk
Courses BA Illustration

University of Cumbria

Bowerham Road, Lancaster, Lancashire, LA1 3JD
01524 384384
www.cumbria.ac.uk
Courses BA Illustration
FdA Wildlife Illustration

University of Derby

Kedleston Road, Derby, DE22 1GB
01332 593216
01332 597724
enquiries-admissions@derby.ac.uk
www.derby.ac.uk
Courses BA Illustration
BA Illustration for Animation

University of Dundee

Nethergate, Dundee, DD1 4HN
01382 384160
01382 388150
srs@dundee.ac.uk
www.dundee.ac.uk
Courses BA Illustration

University of East London

Docklands Campus, 4–6 University Way, London, E16 2RD
020 8223 2835
020 8223 2978
admiss@uel.ac.uk
www.uel.ac.uk

Courses BA Creative & Professional Writing with Illustration
BA Illustration/Graphic Design (joint)
BA Illustration with Graphic Design

The University of Gloucestershire
Hardwick Campus, St Paul's Road, Cheltenham, Gloucestershire, GL50 4BS
- 01242 714501
- 01242 543334
- admissions@glos.ac.uk
- www.glos.ac.uk
Courses BA Illustration. Contact Brian Miller.

University of Hertfordshire
College Lane, Hatfield, Hertfordshire, AL10 9AB
- 01707 284800
- 01707 284870
- www.herts.ac.uk
Courses FdA Illustration

The University of Huddersfield
Queensgate, Huddersfield, HD1 3DH
- 01484 473969
- 01484 472765
- admissionsandrecords@hud.ac.uk
- www.hud.ac.uk
Courses BA Character Design
BA Creative Imaging (Illustration)

University of Lincoln
Brayford Pool, Lincoln, LN6 7TS
- 01522 886644
- 01522 886880
- enquiries@lincoln.ac.uk
- www.lincoln.ac.uk
Courses BA Illustration

University of Northampton
Park Campus, Boughton Green Road, Northampton, NN2 7AL
- 0800 358 2232
- 01604 722083
- admissions@northampton.ac.uk
- www.northampton.ac.uk
Courses BA Illustration

University of Plymouth
Drake Circus, Plymouth, PL4 8AA
- 01752 232137
- 01752 232014
- admissions@plymouth.ac.uk
- www.plymouth.ac.uk
Courses BA Design: Illustration. Contact Exeter Campus, ead-admissions@plymouth.ac.uk
FnD Illustration. Contact North Devon College, Barnstaple

University of Portsmouth
University House, Winston Churchill Avenue, Portsmouth, PO1 2UP
- 023 9284 8484
- 023 9284 3082
- admissions@port.ac.uk
- www.port.ac.uk
Courses BA Illustration

University of Sunderland
The Student Gateway, Chester Road, Sunderland, SR1 3SD
- 0191 515 3000
- 0191 515 3805
- student-helpline@sunderland.ac.uk
- www.sunderland.ac.uk
Courses BA Illustration and Design

University of the Arts, London
65 Davies Street, London, W1K 5DA
- 020 7514 6197
- 020 7514 6198
- c.anderson@arts.ac.uk
- www.arts.ac.uk
Courses BA Illustration
FnD Illustration for Sequence & Interaction

University of the West of England, Bristol
Frenchay Campus, Cold Harbour Lane, Bristol, BS16 1QY
- 0117 328 3333
- 0117 328 2810
- admissions@uwe.ac.uk
- www.uwe.ac.uk
Courses BA Illustration. Contact Dianne Francombe.

University of Wales Institute, Cardiff
PO Box 377, Llandaff Campus, Western Avenue, Cardiff, CF5 2SG
- 029 2041 6070
- 029 2041 6286
- admissions@uwic.ac.uk
- www.uwic.ac.uk

Courses BA Illustration

University of Westminster
35 Marylebone Road, London, NW1 5LS
- 020 7911 5000
- 020 7911 5858
- admissions@wmin.ac.uk
- www.wmin.ac.uk

Courses BA Illustration

University of Wolverhampton
Compton Road West, Wolverhampton, West Midlands, WV3 9DX
- 01902 321000
- 01902 323744
- enquiries@wlv.ac.uk
- www.wlv.ac.uk

Courses BA Illustration
 BA Joint Honours Degrees in Art and Design Subjects - (Illustration)

WRITER'S & ILLUSTRATOR'S GROUPS

Airedale Children's Book Group
Leeds, West Yorkshire
◉ steven.weeks@ntlworld.com
Contact Josie Weeks
About The Airedale Children's Book Group is a member of The Federation of Children's Book Groups (FCBG). Aimed largely at children, the group organises a variety of events, along with local schools and libraries. These events may include bringing authors and illustrators to schools, story telling activities, and other book related activities for children.

Aldbourne Children's Book Group
Neals, South Street, Aldbourne, Wiltshire, SN8 2DW
☎ 01672 540716
◉ caroline@matrix-s.com
🌐 www.aldbourne.org.uk
Contact Caroline Knighton
Meetings Meeting time: Irregular events
About A group of people of all ages whose aim is to bring children and books together. The group organises book orientated events for children and adults. Fees are £12 for local members, £14 for postal members.

Anderida Writers
The Sheldon Hotel, Burlington Place, Eastbourne, East Sussex, BN21 4AS
☎ 01323 640483
◉ ann@jaapann.freeserve.co.uk
◉ pjesampson@tiscali.co.uk
Contact Mrs Ann Botha
7 Fraser Avenue
Eastbourne
East Sussex
BN23 6BB
Vice Chairman, Mr Peter Sampson
Old Mill Cottage
Lower Dicker
Hailsham
East Sussex
BN27 4BU

Meetings Meeting time: 8pm, second Tuesday of each month
About New members are welcome; please contact Ann Botha for details. Covers fiction, non-fiction, short stories, poetry, children's and travel writing, and members are encouraged to eventually produce a piece of work of a publishable standard. Current members are both published and unpublished. The group holds an annual short story competition and a Christmas dinner. A voluntary fee of £1 per meeting is expected from attendees.

Barrowby & Grantham Children's Book Group
North Leicestershire
◉ julia@cognitivefitness.co.uk
Contact Julia Jones
Meetings Meeting time: Irregular events
About The Barrowby & Grantham Children's Book Group organises visits to local schools by well known children's authors and illustrators, as well as holding local family events for members. Is one of twelve regional groups that tests books for the Red House Children's Book Awards.

Birmingham Children's Book Group
Bromsgrove, Worcestershire
☎ 0121 458 3706
◉ bevarcher@lineone.net
Contact Bev Archer
About A member of The Federation of Children's Book Groups (FCBG).

Blaenau Gwent Children's Book Group
Cartref, Heol Ganol, Brynmawr, Blaenau Gwent, South Wales, NP23 4TJ
☎ 01495 315130
◉ lipippin@aol.com
Contact Lisa Tippings
About A member of The Federation of Children's Book Groups (FCBG).

Brighton Illustrators Group (BIG)

Castor & Pollux Gallery, 165–166 King's Road Arches, Brighton, BN1 1NB

✉ jo@jomo.co.uk

🌐 www.brightonillustratorsgroup.com

Contact Chairman, Jo Moore

Meetings Meeting time: 8pm, last Thursday of every month

About A group of freelance illustrators in and around the Brighton area. Covers many styles of illustration and has regular social events. Fees are £40 for full membership.

Central West SCBWI

Birmingham area

☎ 0121 442 6224

✉ centralwest@britishscbwi.org

🌐 www.britishscbwi.org/networks

Contact Clare Bell, Donna Vann

About The central west network group for the SCBWI (Society of Children's Book Writers and Illustrators). Organises open access events about children's literature and illustration.

Children's Book Discussion Group

Wrexham Library, Rhosddu Road, Wrexham, LL11 1AU

☎ 01978 292643

Contact Shan Kensall

Meetings Meeting time: Twice per term.

About Aimed at adults interested in children's literature. This group meets to discuss recently published children's books.

Dudley Children's Book Group

Dudley, Birmingham, West Midlands

☎ 01384 376292

✉ info@fcbg.org.uk

Contact Ros Bartlett

Meetings Meeting time: Irregular events

About The Dudley Children's Book Group is a member of the FCBG and organises frequent literary events for children and adults interested in children's books. Events are often free.

Dundee & Area Children's Book Group

Tayside, Dundee, Scotland

☎ 01307 463888

✉ info@fcbg.org.uk

Contact F. Dakers

Meetings Meeting time: Irregular events

About A member of the FCBG, the Dundee & Area group aims to promote books and reading to children and their parents and carers, and to raise the profile and status of children's books.

Harrogate Children's Book Group

c/o Penny Dolan, 10 Woodside, Harrogate, North Yorkshire, HG1 5NG

☎ 01423 563561

✉ penny@pennydolan.com

Contact Penny Dolan

Meetings Meeting time: Irregular events

About A member of The Federation of Children's Book Groups (FCBG).

Illustrators Direct

Online

✉ info@illustratorsdirect.co.uk

🌐 www.illustratorsdirect.co.uk

About Illustrators Direct is an established group of top freelance illustrators and cartoonists. The group is more of a business venture than an illustration group, and functions in a similar way to an agency - except that it is run by the artists themselves, not agents. Not currently accepting new members.

Ipswich Children's Book Group

c/o Sarah Jenkins, 23 Westerfield Road, Ipswich, IP4 2UE

☎ 01473 255380

✉ sarah@jenkins24.fsnet.co.uk

Contact Sarah Jenkins

Meetings Meeting time: Irregular events

About Organises events for children and adults interested in children's literature. The group is a member of The Federation of Children's Book Groups (FCBG).

Lewes Children's Book Group

c/o Diana Rogers, 48 South Way, Lewes, East Sussex, BN7 1LY

☎ 01273 474964

Contact Diana Rogers

About The group aims to promote interest in children's books. They also donate books to legal and medical waiting rooms, and special needs groups, and organise a half-term book swap at the Nutty Wizard cafe in Lewes.

Lincoln SCBWI

Waterstone's Bookstore, High Street, Lincoln
☎ 01724 711191
🖰 www.britishscbwi.org/networks
Contact Addy Farmer
About The Lincoln branch of the SCBWI (Society of Children's Book Writers and Illustrators) meets on a regular basis to discuss and critique writing and illustrating for children.

Northern SCBWI

El Piano, 15–17 Grape Lane, The Quarter, York
☎ 01724 711191
🖰 northern@britishscbwi.org
🖰 www.britishscbwi.org/networks
Contact Addy Farmer, Alan Gidney
Meetings Meeting time: 2:30pm, first Sunday of every other month
About The Northern Network group of the SCBWI (Society of Children's Book Writers and Illustrators). Holds regular 'coffee and chat' meetings in York.

North Norfolk Children's Book Group

Greatwood Cottage, Marsham, Norwich, Norfolk, NR10 5QQ
☎ 01603 871628
🖰 gwynneth60@aol.com
Contact Gwynneth Bailey
About A member of The Federation of Children's Book Groups (FCBG).

Oxford Children's Book Group

c/o Louise Stothard, 55 Wappenham Road, Helmdon, Northamptonshire, NN13 5QA
☎ 01295 760518
🖰 louisestothard@aol.com
🖰 www.ocbg.org.uk
Contact Louise Stothard
Meetings Meeting time: Every six weeks
About A diverse group of local parents, teachers, librarians, students, authors, illustrators, and publishers who are all interested in children's literature. As well as regular meetings, the group also organises storytellings, library sessions, and other family friendly events. Runs a biannual day conference with guest speakers. Linda Newbery, winner of the Costa Award for Children's Books, is a long standing member.

Oxted Children's Book Group

c/o Fiona Owen, 2 The Waldrons, Oxted, Surrey, RH8 9DY
☎ 01883 722464
Contact Fiona Owen
About A member of The Federation of Children's Book Groups (FCBG).

Plymouth Children's Book Group

c/o Julia Pugh, 62 Hermitage Road, Plymouth, PL3 4RY
☎ 01752 511716
🖰 www.plymouthcbg.ndo.co.uk
Contact Treasurer, Julia Pugh
Meetings Meeting time: Irregular events
About One of many book groups around the country which make up the Federation of Children's Book Groups. The group is for anyone interested in finding out more about good children's books, whether they are parents, teachers, librarians or booksellers. Events include talks and discussions, including author visits, regular story times and other children's activities. Welcomes new members, fees are £8 for annual membership. Members receive discounted entry to events and three copies of *Carousel* magazine.

Solihull Children's Book Group

c/o Pat Tate, 51 Highwood Avenue, Solihull, B92 8QY
☎ 0121 247 8637
🖰 p.tate@virgin.net
Contact Pat Tate
About A member of The Federation of Children's Book Groups (FCBG).

South Buckinghamshire Children's Book Group

c/o Chris Davis-Foster, 47 Hillview Road, High Wycombe, Buckinghamshire
☎ 01494 523046
🖰 chris@davis-foster.wanadoo.co.uk
Contact Chris Davis-Foster
Meetings Meeting time: Irregular events
About The group runs book related events for children and parents/carers throughout the year. Fees are £12 for annual membership, which includes three issues of *Carousel* magazine and a newsletter.

Southeast SCBWI

Costa Coffee, 11 High Street, Canterbury

- southeast@britishscbwi.org
- www.britishscbwi.org/networks

Contact Jane Clarke

Meetings Meeting time: 10:30am, first Saturday of every month

About The South Eastern Network group of the SCBWI (Society of Children's Book Writers and Illustrators). Runs a regular monthly meeting in Canterbury for both writers and illustrators which is open to anyone. Bring samples of work for peer review and critique. Also holds regular critique sessions in Deal and Brighton.

Southhampton Children's Book Group

c/o Kim Wherry, 5 Dimond Hill, Southampton, SO18 1JF

- 023 8055 1251
- jkjkwherry@btinternet.com

Contact Kim Wherry

About A member of The Federation of Children's Book Groups (FCBG).

South West Illustrators (SWILL)

Member's Homes, Bath and Bristol

- www.swillustrators.co.uk

Contact Kate Davies

Meetings Meeting time: Irregularly, four or five times per year

About A group of professional illustrators in the South West of England, mainly around Bath and Bristol. Currently has about 20 members, and welcomes new members. Meetings are generally informal, including much 'chatting, nibbling and imbibing'. Contact details for members are available on the website.

Southwest SCBWI

- southwest@britishscbwi.org
- www.britishscbwi.org/networks

Contact Ellen Renner

About The Southwest Network group of the SCBWI is still in the process of getting up and running. Contact Ellen Renner to lend your support.

St. Albans Children's Book Group

c/o Andrea Goodall, 45 Wick Avenue, Wheathampstead, Hertfordshire, AL4 8PZ

- apenny@waitrose.com

- www.users.waitrose.com/~apenny/page3.html

Contact Membership Secretary, Andrea Goodall

Meetings Meeting time: Irregular events

About St. Albans Children's Book Group accepts family, school and individual members. A full events calender is available on the website. Fees are £12 for annual membership, which includes three issues of *Carousel* magazine.

Sutton Writers

Civic Offices, St. Nicholas Way, Sutton, SM1 1EA

- teresa.tipping@tesco.net
- www.suttonwriters.info

Contact Teresa Tipping
24 Twickenham Close
Beddington
Croydon
CR0 4SZ

Meetings Meeting time: 7.30pm–10pm, second Friday of each month

About New members are welcome, either to attend meetings month by month, or to become a full member. All types of creative writing are covered, including poetry, articles, short stories, writing for children and novels. Various workshops for full members are run in members' homes. Any level of experience is welcome, whether writing for pleasure, or for profit. Fees for full members are £18 per annum, which entitles them to free meetings, workshops, in-house competitions and copies of the newsletter. Members who cannot attend the meetings, but wish to enter competitions and receive the newsletter are charged £9 per annum. Visitors are charged £3 per meeting, but may apply to become full members.

Worcestershire Children's Book Group

c/o Julie Benkwitz, Wulstan's Farm Barn, Shrawley, Worcestershire, WR6 6TQ

- 01299 890022
- jbenkwitz@aliceottley.com
- www.wcbg.co.uk

Contact Julie Benkwitz

Meetings Meeting time: Irregular events

About A newly formed, charitable group of parents, teachers, librarians and booksellers, all with a passion for children's books. Aims to help make authors, illustrators, poets and storytellers accessible to the local community, through school visits, family activity days, competitions and trips. Fees are £12 for annual membership, which includes three issues of *Carousel* magazine.

York Children's Book Group

c/o Liz Bellwood, 144 York Road, Haxby, York,
YO32 3EL

☏ 01904 763437

✉ ycbg@mac.com
🌐 www.yorkchildrensbookgroup.co.uk
Contact Liz Bellwood
About A member of The Federation of Children's
Book Groups (FCBG).

FORUMS

Absolute Write Water Cooler

🌐 www.absolutewrite.com/forums
About A community of writers and editors of all
levels, hosted by Absolute Write. The forum has a
dedicated section for children's writing. Registration
is free. The site is funded by voluntary donations.

achukachat

🌐 www.achuka.co.uk/achukachat
About A small forum run by the ACHUKA children's
book website. Registration is free.

Art for Artists

🌐 http://groups.myspace.com/artforartists
About A MySpace group where artists and
illustrators can network creatively. Has over
30,800 members.

ArtForums.co.uk

🌐 www.artforums.co.uk
About A massive forum for artists and illustrators to
meet online. Also offers artists the opportunity to sell
their work online.

Artists Network

🌐 http://forum.artistsnetwork.com
About Artists Network is an online forum covering a
wide range of art and illustration subjects. It also
offers artists the chance to submit their work for a
possible critique from a professional.
Registration is free.

Artists United

🌐 http://groups.myspace.com/artistsunited
About A MySpace group for artists and illustrators.
The group aims to unite artists from across the world
for networking, constructive feedback and the
chance to get together to work on group projects.
Has over 5,300 members.

BellaOnline Children's Book Writing Forum

🌐 www.bellaonline.com/site/childrensbookwriting
About A small forum for children's writers, run by
Bella magazine. Registration is free.

Book Chat/Writers Chat

🌐 www.4-lane.com/bookchat
About An online chat service for book lovers. Also
contains Writers Chat, a chat service for
creative writers.

ButterflyQuill.com

🌐 www.butterflyquill.com
About A discussion forum for writers of all types,
include freelance reporters and article writers. Also
has a range of resources including job
market listings.

Children's Writers & Illustrators Chat Board

🌐 www.verlakay.com/boards
About An absolutely massive online forum, hosted
by author Verla Kay. Has advice on writing for
children, resource links and genre discussions, as
well as many other sections. Registration is free.

enCompass Culture Discussion Boards

🌐 www.encompassculture.com/discussionboards
About The discussion boards of the enCompass
Culture global reading group. Categories for adults,
children aged 12–18, and younger children to
discuss books and reading. Registration is free.

Fiction Fanatics

🌐 http://groups.myspace.com/fictionfanatics
About A MySpace group for fiction writers of all
types. Has over 1,800 members.

FictionPost
ⓦ www.fictionpost.com/forums
About A general community writing forum where authors can exchange stories and poetry. Registration is free.

FreelanceWriting
ⓦ www.freelancewriting.com/forums
About The discussion forum of FreelanceWriting.com with subjects of interest to freelance writers. Also has links to job opportunities and resources. Registration is free.

MoreWriting
ⓦ www.morewriting.co.uk
About A community site that offers friendly writing support and reviews, as well as resource links and chat rooms. Registration is free.

The Readers Circle
ⓦ http://groups.myspace.com/readerscircle
About A MySpace group where users can discuss and share books that they have read. Has over 9,000 members.

Serious writers+poets
ⓦ http://groups.myspace.com/serious
About A MySpace discussion group that aims to read and respond to other user's work, and offer constructive criticism. Covers poetry, stories and song lyrics. Has over 10,000 members.

UnknownWriters.net
ⓦ www.unknownwriters.net
About An online forum, offering free registration, which runs competitions and publishes winning writing online.

Untitled
ⓦ www.everyauthor.com/forum
About A writing forum for critical discussion, hosted by Every Author. Contains a wide range of writing and publishing topics, including challenges and games. Registration is free.

WBBS Forums
ⓦ www.writersbbs.com/forums
About The Writer's BBS forums were founded 1996. They cover a large range of writing subjects, including dedicated sections for 'Writing for Children', 'Writing for Young Adults' and 'Children's Writing Critiques'. Registration is free, although a 'Gold' registration for $15 per year grants access to extra resources.

WetCanvas
ⓦ www.wetcanvas.com
About A discussion forum for all types of artists and illustrators, with nearly six million images archived.

Wordtrip
ⓦ www.wordtrip.com
About Wordtrip is a large forum for all types of creative writing. It also runs various writing competitions within the forums. Registration is free.

WritersCafe
ⓦ www.writerscafe.org
About An online writing community. Allows users to create their own author profiles, post their writing, get reviews, join writing groups, and befriend other authors. Registration is free.

Writer's Digest
ⓦ www.writersdigest.com/mbbs/forum
About A forum hosted by the Writer's Digest. Covers all aspects of writing and literature, including writing for children. Registration is free.

Writers' Dock
ⓦ www.writersdock.org
About Writers' Dock is a popular forum that was formed after the closure of the BBCs 'Get Writing' site in 2005. It has a lively forum and runs various competitions.

The Writers Hangout
ⓦ www.writershangout.com/forum
About An online message board and forum that allows users to share their poems, stories, and other writing, comment on the works of others, and participate in general discussion. Registration is free.

Writers In Touch
ⓦ www.writersintouch.com
About A general writer's forum that discusses all forms of creative writing. Registration is free.

The Writer's Lounge
⊕ http://groups.myspace.com/writerslounge
About A MySpace group for the discussion of literature and poetry. Offers constructive criticism and a bulletin board. Has over 7,300 members.

Writers Notebook
⊕ www.sfnorthwest.org/notebook
About A small forum for creative writing discussion. Registration is free.

Writers Resource
⊕ http://writersresource.tribe.net
About Writers Resource offers a forum and discussion community that aims to provide inspiration and support for struggling writers.

The Writing Bridge
⊕ www.thewritingbridge.org
About The Writing Bridge was formed in 2003 to provide a close-knit community for writers. Membership must be applied for.

Writing.com
⊕ www.writing.com
About Writing.com runs a small forum as part of its site, with occasional topics on children's books and writing. Registration is free.

Writing Forums
⊕ www.writingforums.com
About A forum for writers of all types. Allows users to to talk with other writers, get feedback on work, discuss ideas, share tips and tricks, and network. Registration is free.

Writing/Writers
⊕ http://writingwriters.group.stumbleupon.com
About A forum to discuss writing and writers. Has over 1,800 members.

WW Forums
⊕ www.wwforums.com
About The online community forums for readers and writers of children's literature. The forum is hosted by Writer's Write Inc and contains a wide range of discussion topics, including publishing and marketing advice. Registration is free.

ONLINE RESOURCES

About Children's Books
⊕ www.childrensbooks.about.com
About A section of About.com, this site contains up to date news and information on the international children's book trade, links to interviews with popular authors, reviews, and new releases. It also publishes a free weekly newsletter.

ACHUKA Children's Books UK
⊕ www.achuka.co.uk
About ACHUKA is an online guide to children's books and children's book publishing. It covers the latest news, interviews, releases and reviews, and also has a blog and chat forum.

Amazon
⊕ www.amazon.co.uk
About The UK site for the famous online retailer. Amazon's book section offers millions of books, used and new, at discount prices, as well as new release notification service. The site also includes reader reviews, book information and constantly updated bestseller charts.

Armadillo
⊕ www.armadillomagazine.com
About A literary e-zine covering children's book reviews, interviews and articles. Old material is archived and made available to non-subscribers. Armadillo covers every aspect of the children's book trade and is always looking for new reviewers, but does not pay a fee. Instead, contributors may keep their review copies. See entry under Magazine Publishers.

Art Originals

ⓦ www.artoriginals.co.uk

About Art Originals is an advertising space for cartoonists, animators and illustrators, graphic and digital artists, photographers, film animators and more. The website allows consumers, companies and the general public to view artwork online, and buy or commission a piece of work directly from the artist.

Artscape

ⓦ www.artscape.org.uk

About The Artscape directory features organisations and individual artists who undertake educational work. All art forms and regions are covered and many more artists and organisations are currently being added.

Association of Illustrators

ⓦ www.theaoi.com

About Website of the London based Association of Illustrators. Contains a massive range of information for professional illustrators and agencies, including member profiles, news, reviews, event listings, articles and a newsletter.

BBC Children's

ⓦ www.bbc.co.uk/cbbc

About The CBBC website is an entertainment site for children. It has sections on children's books and art, including information on the Blue Peter Book Awards.

BBC Schools

ⓦ www.bbc.co.uk/schools

About The BBC's education website contains a wealth of information on the current national curriculum. Although aimed at young people, the information is also important to anyone working in educational publishing.

BBC Teens

ⓦ www.bbc.co.uk/teens

About BBC Teens is a portal page for teenagers, providing links to various teen-related sections of the BBC website. Also contains educational and national curriculum links, and links to current creative initiatives.

The Best Kids Book Site

ⓦ www.thebestkidsbooksite.com

About A US site that covers children's books, crafts, games, blogs, podcasts, online video and web resources. Has many links to children's book awards, series fiction and author websites, and also provides access to the Book Wizard, an information tool for tracking down children's books.

Bookheads

ⓦ www.bookheads.org.uk

About The website of the Booktrust Teenage Prize for Fiction. It contains author interviews, reviews, competitions and details of previous Booktrust winners, as well as providing information on the current prize.

BookHive

ⓦ www.bookhive.org

About A US site that acts as a guide to children's books and literature. It is aimed at parents and teachers, as well as children, and contains book reviews and recommendations.

Book Reviews by Kids

ⓦ www.bookreviewsbykids.com

About A website dedicated to children's book reviews, written by children. It provides guidance for children on how to write a review and allows them to send their own reviews in via an online form, or by email. Provides a good idea of what children really think about the books that are aimed at them.

Books4Publishing

ⓦ www.books4publishing.com

About Books4Publishing is a showcase website which hosts authors' synopsis and first chapters and promotes them to publishers and agents. The site is membership based and costs £10 to register. It costs a further £2 for every publisher you wish to send your manuscript to, using the site's service.

Booktrusted

ⓦ www.booktrusted.co.uk

About The website for the children's division of Booktrust. It provides free resources and recommendations for teachers, librarians and parents about books for young people of all ages, including information on events and competitions, reviews, interviews and news.

British SCBWI

☉ www.britishscbwi.org

About Official website of the British Isles Region of the Society of Children's Book Writers and Illustrators. Contains resources, reviews, critiques, member networks, event listings and a newsletter.

Canadian Children's Book Centre

☉ www.bookcentre.ca

About The Canadian Children's Book Centre is a not for profit organisation that exists to promote, support and encourage the reading, writing and illustrating of Canadian books for children and teenagers. The website contains information on the Canadian children's book trade, author interviews, illustrator profiles, new book releases and a calendar of events. It also features writing tips from well known authors.

Chapter One Promotions

☉ www.chapteronepromotions.com

About A writers' site, which is also a literary agency and consultancy. Writers and illustrators may display their work on the site for a fee. There are details of events and competitions, and a section on resources for children.

The Children's Book Council

☉ www.cbcbooks.org

About The website of the American Children's Book Council organisation. Dedicated to encouraging children to enjoy reading and to increasing awareness of the importance of reading for educational purposes. Contains book reviews, releases, author profiles and interviews and an author/illustrator directory. Also has a number of articles about writing for children and getting published, and lists of competition and prize details.

Children's Books Central

☉ www.eleanorsbooks.com

About Maintained by Eleanor's Books, this site contains information on children's book and illustrations. Content includes articles, news, discussion forums, directories and links.

Children's Books Online: The Rosetta Project

☉ www.childrensbooksonline.org

About The internet's largest collection of illustrated antique books. All the children's books can be read online or downloaded.

Children's Literature

☉ www.childrenslit.com

About A US site that aims to help parents, teachers and librarians choose suitable books for children. The site contains featured interviews and children's book news and also has a fully searchable archive of over 300,000 children's book reviews.

The Children's Literature Web Guide

☉ www.acs.ucalgary.ca/~dkbrown

About The Children's Literature Web Guide aims to gather together and categorise the growing number of internet resources related to books for children and young adults. Provided by the University of Calgary, in Canada.

Classic Children's Stories

☉ www.childhoodreading.com

About An online archive of classic children's stories, complete with illustrations. Allows searches by author or illustrator.

Contemporary Writers

☉ www.contemporarywriters.com

About A searchable database, supported by the British Arts Council, that contains up to date profiles of some of the UK and Commonwealth's most important living writers. Features include biographies, bibliographies, critical reviews, prizes and photographs.

Cool Reads

☉ www.cool-reads.co.uk

About A children's books website featuring reviews by readers aged 10–15.

The Drawing Board

☉ http://members.aol.com/thedrawing

About The Drawing Board for Illustrators website contains a large archive of information for illustrators, including articles on how to get published, links and dedicated children's illustration pages.

Education Guardian

🌐 www.educationguardian.co.uk

About The Guardian newspaper's education pages online. Provides the latest news from the education and teaching industry, including national curriculum information.

EnCompassCulture

🌐 www.encompassculture.com

About EnCompassCulture is a global online reading group with sections for children's books and books for 12–18 year olds. It provides up to date information about the latest book releases and authors, as well as reviews and book trade news. The site also functions like a large reading group and users can discuss the latest books in the group forums.

EunetArt

🌐 www.eunetart.org

About EunetArt is the European network of theatre for young people. It is a place to meet, exchange and learn, develop co-operation projects, a platform to raise issues, and a voice for children's and young people's arts in Europe.

Guy's Read

🌐 www.guysread.org

About Guy's Read is a US site that aims to help boys find books they will like to read. Also contains book suggestions from other Guy's Read visitors.

Kids' Bookline

🌐 www.cllc.org.uk

About Part of the Welsh Books Council's children's books department. The website contains a range of literary activities for children, in both English and Welsh language, and also contains a small directory of Welsh authors and illustrators.

KidSpace

🌐 www.ipl.org/div/kidspace/browse/rzn0000

About Part of the Reading Zone section of the Internet Public Library (IPL). Contains a range of articles and fiction pages from the IPL, as well as links to other literary websites.

Kids' Reads

🌐 www.kidsreads.com

About A US website featuring information, reviews, author profiles and news from the children's book trade. Also produces podcasts.

Learning and Teaching Scotland

🌐 www.ltscotland.org.uk

About A site containing details about the education system in Scotland, including the Curriculum for Excellence and the Intranet for Scottish Schools.

The Looking Glass

🌐 www.the-looking-glass.net

About The Looking Glass is an online children's literature journal featuring a range of articles about children's books and writing. Aimed at academics, librarians, teachers, parents and anyone interested in children's literature.

MarksWorks

🌐 www.marksworks.co.uk

About Website of Graham Marks, Children's Editor for the Publishing News. Contains reviews of the latest children's books, author profiles, articles and children's book trade news.

Mrs Mad's Book-a-Rama!

🌐 www.mrsmad.com

About A large archive of children's book reviews and author links from an independent reviewer. Has a very fun and light hearted approach.

National Curriculum Online

🌐 www.nc.uk.net

About Contains in-depth details about the current National Curriculum as well as links to online teaching resources.

National Literacy Trust

🌐 www.literacytrust.org.uk

About The official website of the National Literacy Trust. Contains information on all of its campaigns, including: *Reading Is Fundamental, UK*, the *National Reading Campaign, Talk To Your Baby, Reading The Game, Reading Connects*, and the *Vital Link*. Results of research into specific areas of concern to do with literacy can be found on the website. The site also provides a rich range of resources to help with reading, and it also links to many other organisations.

National Reading Campaign
ⓦ www.readon.org.uk

About The website of the National Reading Campaign, which aims to promote reading for pleasure across the nation and to provide a support network to bring the reading community together. Also offers free access to *Read On* magazine. Part of the National Literacy Trust.

On-Lion for Kids!
ⓦ http://kids.nypl.org

About The New York Public Library children's book site, featuring a range of articles and book reviews.

Picturing Books
ⓦ http://picturingbooks.imaginarylands.org

About A website about picture books, containing articles about writing and publishing picture books, resources, reviews and a links page.

Play! Illustration for Toys and Interactive Games
ⓦ www.playillustration.com

About Play! is an advertising space for toy and interactive game artists. Play is especially designed for creative departments, advertising agencies and design firms for toy and interactive game companies. The annual resource is published in book form and a companion website is available.

Quentin Blake
ⓦ www.quentinblake.com

About The official website of famous children's illustrator Quentin Blake. Contains information on new books and exhibitions, downloads for children, and teaching materials. Also contains a great deal of information about Blake and his art.

The Reading Agency
ⓦ www.boox.org.uk

About The website of The Reading Agency (TRA), an organisation whose aim is to inspire a reading nation, by working in new ways with readers, writers, libraries and their partners. Contains trade news, resources and information on all current TRA projects.

Reading Is Fundamental
ⓦ www.rif.org.uk

About RIF is an initiative of the National Literacy Trust. It aims to promote an interest in reading for pleasure, by donating books to children living in disadvantaged areas. RIF hopes to address the cycle of under achievement of children in the UK. So far RIF has donated over 750,000 books.

Ricochet-Litterature Jeunesse
ⓦ www.ricochet-jeunes.org

About A library website offering identification sheets about books, authors, illustrators, and film adaptations of children's and young people's literature. The site also contains reader comments and links to excerpts.

The Roald Dahl Club
ⓦ www.roalddahlclub.com

About A website about Roald Dahl's children's books. Includes a section for teachers and an online magazine called *The Gobblefunk Gazette*.

SLAINTE
ⓦ www.slainte.org.uk

About SLAINTE is a Scottish website that incorporates the websites of the Chartered Institute of Library and Information Professionals in Scotland (CILIPS) and the Scottish Library and Information Council (SLIC). It aims to support individuals and organisations working within library and information services in Scotland.

Society of Artists Agents
ⓦ www.illustratorsagents.co.uk

About Website of the Society of Artists Agents (SAA), with links to a number of member illustrator agencies and artists.

Society of Illustrators
ⓦ www.societyillustrators.org

About Official website of the American Society of Illustrators, containing information on members, illustration links, news and event listings.

Stories from the Web
ⓦ www.storiesfromtheweb.org

About A website for children, teenagers and young adult writers to post their stories and poetry on. Also features reviews from young readers, articles about the latest books, and a range of activities and games.

Storybook Web

⊕ www.ltscotland.org.uk/storybook

About A website containing literary activities for children aged five to eight. Also features audio and video clips of authors reading excerpts and answering questions about their writing. Includes a parent/teacher section.

Storyzone

⊕ www.storyzone.co.uk

About A form of e-book publisher that makes classic and contemporary children's stories available for download. It costs £5 to download 5 stories, £10 for 12 stories, £20 for 25 stories, and £40 for 50 stories.

Teen Reads

⊕ www.teenreads.com

About The sister website of Kids' Reads, Teen Reads focuses on books for teenagers and the young adult market. Contains news, reviews, interviews and features.

TeenSpace

⊕ www.ipl.org/div/teen/teenread

About Sister site to KidSpace, and part of the Internet Public Library (IPL). Contains a range of articles and fiction pages from the IPL, as well as links to other literary websites. Also contains articles about school and careers for teenagers.

Trace

⊕ http://tracearchive.ntu.ac.uk

About A free online resource linked to Nottingham Trent University. Trace provides a space for writers to meet, communicate, discuss work and be creative. Also offered through the site are courses, a consultancy service, and a children's area.

UK Children's Books

⊕ www.ukchildrensbooks.co.uk

About A large site containing links to many publishers and authors of children's books, as well as other helpful organisations. The site is affiliated with Word Pool, a resource site centred around children's books.

The Word Pool

⊕ www.wordpool.co.uk

About Contains articles about writing children's books, coping with reluctant readers and author profiles. Has a 'Parent's Corner' page, and offers a free monthly newsletter.

World of Reading

⊕ www.worldofreading.org

About A website hosted by the Ann Arbor District Library in America. Contains book reviews written by and for children around the world, as well as event listings, research and media pages.

Write4Kids

⊕ www.write4kids.com

About US site with many free resources and articles on writing for children. The site also has a free newsletter.

FOR WRITERS AND ILLUSTRATORS

Academi
Main Office: 3rd floor, Mount Stewart House, Mount Stuart Square, Cardiff, CF10 5FQ
- 029 2047 2266
- 029 2049 2930
- post@academi.org
- www.academi.org

Contact Chief Executive, Peter Finch
About Academi is the trading name of the Welsh National Literature Promotion Agency and Society for Authors. It works to promote the literature of Wales both in Wales and elsewhere. It hosts literary events and competitions, including the Cardiff International Poetry Competition and the Wales Book of the Year awards. It also provides bursaries and grants, and hosts various writing and literature courses.

AccessArt
38 Mill Lane, Impington, Cambridge, CB4 9XN
- 01223 520213
- info@accessart.org.uk
- www.accessart.org.uk

About AccessArt is a charity committed to furthering the advancement of education in the visual arts. AccessArt designs and delivers creative projects in the community and in schools, working with learners of all ages. This learning and teaching is then developed and shared via the AccessArt website, which is aimed at pupils, students and lifelong learners, as well as teachers, gallery educators and artists. The website contains teaching and education resources, online workshops, events guides and a forum.

American Society of Composers, Authors & Publishers (ASCAP)
One Lincoln Plaza, New York, NY 10023, USA
- 001 212 621 6000
- 001 212 724 9064
- Online form
- www.ascap.com

Contact President and Chairman, Marilyn Bergman

About ASCAP is a membership association of more than 300,000 American composers, songwriters, lyricists, and music publishers of every kind of music. It represents artists in rights agreements, and offers a wide range of advice.

The Arthur Ransome Society
Abbott Hall Museum, Kendal, Cumbria, LA9 5AL
- 01539 722464

Contact President, Norman Willis
Established 1990
About The Arthur Ransome Society aims to promote the study and appreciation of the life and works of Arthur Ransome, author of the *Swallows and Amazons* series. The society also encourages children and adults to become interested in adventurous activities.

Arts Council England
14 Great Peter Street, London, SW1P 3NQ
- 0845 300 6200
- 020 7973 6590
- enquiries@artscouncil.org.uk
- www.artscouncil.org.uk

Contact Chairman, Sir Christopher Frayling; Chief Executive, Peter Hewitt
About Arts Council England works to develop and promote the arts across England, acting as an independent body at arm's length from Government. They distribute money from the Government and the National Lottery and provide Grants for the Arts, which are open to individuals, organisations and other art based bodies.
 Arts Council England has a central office in London and nine regional offices:
EAST
Eden House, 48–49 Bateman Street, Cambridge, SW1P 3NQ
- 0845 300 6200
- 0870 242 1271
Executive Director, Andrea Stark
EAST MIDLANDS
St. Nicholas Court, 25–27 Castle Gate, Nottingham, NG1 7AR

- ☎ 0845 300 6200
- ☏ 0115 950 2467
- Executive Director, Laura Dyer
- LONDON

2 Pear Tree Court, London, EC1R 0DS
- ☎ 0845 300 6200
- ☏ 020 7608 4100
- Executive Director, Sarah Weir
- NORTH EAST

Central Square, Forth Street, Newcastle upon Tyne, NE1 3PJ
- ☎ 0845 300 6200
- ☏ 0191 230 1020
- Executive Director, Mark Robinson
- NORTH WEST

Manchester House, 22 Bridge Street, Manchester, M3 3AB
- ☎ 0845 300 6200
- ☏ 0161 834 6969
- Executive Director, Michael Eakin
- SOUTH EAST

Sovereign House, Church Street, Brighton, BN1 1RA
- ☎ 0845 300 6200
- ☏ 0870 242 1257
- Executive Director, Felicity Harvest
- SOUTH WEST

Senate Court, Southernhay Gardens, Exeter, EX1 1UG
- ☎ 0845 300 6200
- ☏ 01392 229229
- Executive Director, Nick Capaldi
- WEST MIDLANDS

82 Granville Street, Birmingham, B1 2LH
- ☎ 0845 300 6200
- ☏ 0121 643 7239
- Executive Director, Sally Luton
- YORKSHIRE

21 Bond Street, Dewsbury, West Yorkshire, WF13 1AX
- ☎ 0845 300 6200
- ☏ 01924 466522
- Executive Director, Andy Carver

Arts Council Ireland
70 Merrion Square, Dublin 2, Ireland
- ☎ 00353 1 618 0200
- ☏ 00353 1 676 1302
- ⊙ Online form
- ⊕ www.artscouncil.ie

Contact Arts Programme Director, John O'Kane; Grants Executive, Mary Ellen Greene; Grants Executive, Kevin Healy

About The Arts Council of Ireland is the Irish Government agency for developing the arts. They work in partnership with artists, arts organisations, public policy makers and others to build a central place for the arts in Irish life. They aim to offer support and funding to artists and art organisations across the country.

Arts Council of Northern Ireland
77 Malone Road, Belfast, BT9 6AQ
- ☎ 028 9038 5200
- ☏ 028 9066 1715
- ⊙ info@artscouncil-ni.org
- ⊕ www.artscouncil-ni.org

Contact Chief Executive, Roisin McDonough; Literature Officer, Damian Smyth; Visual Arts Officer, Iain Davidson; Visual Arts Officer, Suzanne Lyle

About The Arts Council is the lead development agency for the arts in Northern Ireland. They aim to support artists and arts organisations by offering a broad range of funding opportunities through Exchequer and National Lottery funds, and by promoting and encouraging the arts through a range of events.

Arts Council of Wales
9 Museum Place, Cardiff, CF10 3NX
- ☎ 029 2037 6500
- ☏ 029 2022 1447
- ⊙ info@artswales.org.uk
- ⊕ www.artswales.org.uk

Contact Chief Executive, Peter Tyndall; Arts Director, David Alston

About The Arts Council of Wales is responsible for funding and developing the arts in Wales. They receive funding from the National Assembly and the National Lottery and use it to support regional arts activities and organisations. The council also provides grants and funding for individual Welsh artists and writers.

Arts Council of Wales has a central office in Cardiff and three regional offices:

MID & WEST WALES OFFICE

6 Gardd Llydaw, Jackson Lane, Carmarthen, SA31 1QD
- ☎ 01267 234248
- ☏ 01267 233084
- Acting Director, Amanda Loosemoore
- NORTH WALES OFFICE

36 Princes Drive, Colwyn Bay, LL29 8LA
- ☎ 01492 533440
- ☏ 01492 533677
- Director, Sian Tomos

SOUTH WALES OFFICE
9 Museum Place, Cardiff, CF10 3NX
- 029 2037 6525
- 029 2022 1447
Director, David Newland

Association for Library Service to Children
50 East Huron, Chicago, Illinois, 60611, USA
- 001 800 545 2433
- 001 312 944 7671
- library@ala.org
- www.ala.org

About The American Library Association (ALA) is the oldest and largest library association in the world, with more than 65,000 members. It aims to promote the highest quality library and information services and public access to information. The ALA offers professional services and publications to members and non members, including online news stories from American Libraries, and analysis of crucial issues from the Washington Office.

Association for Scottish Literary Studies (ASLS)
c/o Department of Scottish Literature, University of Glasgow, 7 University Gardens, Glasgow, G12 8QH
- 0141 330 5309
- d.jones@scothist.arts.gla.ac.uk
- www.asls.org.uk

Contact General Manager, Duncan Jones
About The Association for Scottish Literary Studies aims to promote the study, teaching and writing of Scottish literature, and to further the study of the languages of Scotland. Publishes a range of Scottish literature magazines, journals and e-zines, and also hosts three or more conferences per year.

Association of American Publishers (AAP)
2nd Floor, 71 Fifth Avenue, New York, NY 10003, USA
- 001 212 255 0200
- 001 212 255 7007
- pschroeder@publishers.org
- www.publishers.org

Contact President and CEO, Patricia Schroeder
About The Association of American Publishers (AAP) represents publishers of all sizes and types across America. It is the principal trade association of the US book publishing industry.

Association of Authors Agents
20 John Street, London, WC1N 2DR
- 020 7405 6774
- 020 7831 2154
- aaa@johnsonandalcock.co.uk
- www.agentsassoc.co.uk

Contact President, Clare Alexander; Vice President, Derek Johns; Secretary, Anna Power
About The Association exists to provide a forum for member agents to discuss industry matters, to represent the interests of agents and their clients and to uphold a code of good practice. The majority of established agencies in the UK belong to the Association. Most writers will never need to have direct contact with the Association, but all receive indirect benefits.

Association of Authors' Representatives (AAR)
676a, Suite 312, 9th Avenue, New York, NY 10036, USA
- 001 212 840 5777
- www.aar-online.org

About The Association of Authors' Representatives is a not for profit organisation of qualified literary agents, and dramatic representatives of authors, dramatists and other creators and owners of intellectual property. It aims to provide information, education and support to members, and works to protect the best interests of its clients.

Association of Booksellers for Children
ABC National Office, 62 Wenham Street, Jamaica Plain, Massachusetts, 02130, USA
- 001 617 390 7759
- 001 617 344 0540
- kristen@abfc.com
- www.abfc.com

Contact Executive Director, Kristen McClean
About The ABC is a national membership association, that offers a support network for professional independent children's booksellers. The association is for all booksellers who share the goal of encouraging quality and service within the American children's book industry.

Association of Canadian Publishers (ACP)
Suite 306, 174 Spadina Avenue, Toronto, Ontario, M5T 2C2, Canada

001 416 487 6116

001 416 487 8815

admin@canbook.org

www.publishers.ca

Contact Executive Director, Margaret Eaton

About The Association of Canadian Publishers represents Canadian owned book publishers, with members from all provinces and publishing sectors, including literary, general trade, scholarly and education. It primarily aims to encourage the writing, publishing, distribution and promotion of Canadian books.

Association of Illustrators (AOI)

2nd Floor, Back Building, 150 Curtain Road, London, EC24 3AT

020 7613 4328

020 7613 4417

info@theaoi.com

www.theaoi.com

Contact Manager, Silvia Baumgart

About The AOI is a non-profit making trade association, which aims to advance and protect illustrator's rights and encourage the promotion of illustration. They maintain a detailed client directory of illustrators, agents and other organisations and also publish *Varoom* magazine.

The Audiobook Publishing Association

18 Green Lanes, Hatfield, Hertfordshire, AL10 9JT

07971 280788

charlotte.mccandlish@ntlworld.com

www.theapa.net

Contact Chairman, Jo Forshaw; Administrator, Charlotte McCandish

About The APA is the UK trade association for the audiobook industry. Membership is open to all those involved in the publishing of spoken word audio, including publishers, producers, abridgers, agents, actors and studios. It aims to increase the profile of audiobooks in the media and to provide a forum for general discussion.

Australia Council for the Arts

372 Elizabeth Street, Surry Hills, New South Wales, 2010, Australia

0061 2 9215 9000

0061 2 9215 9111

mail@ozco.gov.au

www.ozco.gov.au

Contact Chairman, David Gonski

About The Australia Council for the Arts is the Australian Government's arts funding and advisory body. It supports and promotes the practice and enjoyment of the arts including Aboriginal arts, community development, dance, literature, music, theatre and visual arts, and crafts.

Australian Copyright Council

245 Chalmers Street, Redfern, New South Wales, 2016, Australia

0061 2 8815 9777

0061 2 8815 9799

info@copyright.org.au

www.copyright.org.au

Contact Chairman, Peter Banki; Executive Officer, Libby Baulch

About The Australian Copyright Council is an independent, not for profit organisation that provides information, advice and training about copyright in Australia.

Australian Publishers Association (APA)

60–89 Jones Street, Ultimo, New South Wales, 2007, Australia

0061 2 9281 9788

0061 2 9281 1073

maree.mccaskill@publishers.asn.au

www.publishers.asn.au

Contact CEO, Maree McCaskill; Project Manager (Children's Publishing), Libby O'Donnell

About The Australian Publishers Association is the peak industry body for Australian book, journal and electronic publishers. It acts as an advocate for all Australian publishers, and aims to ensure publishers' interests are defended on defamation, copyright, competition policy and taxation issues.

Australian Writers' Guild (AWG)

8/50 Reservoir Street, Surry Hills, New South Wales, 2010, Australia

0061 2 9281 1554

0061 2 9281 4321

admin@awg.com.au

www.awg.com.au

Contact Executive Director, Jacqueline Woodman

About The AWG is the professional association for all Australian performance writers, including writers for film, television, radio, theatre, video and new media. It represents members in their negotiations, and supports them in the development of their craft.

Barnardo's Photographic Archive

Tanners Lane, Barkingside, Ilford, Essex, IG6 1QG

- ☎ 020 8498 7345
- ☎ 020 8550 0429
- ✉ stephen.pover@barnardos.org.uk
- 🌐 www.barnardos.org.uk/photo_archive

Contact Marysa Dowling; Stephen Pover

About An ongoing archive of photographs and videos covering the history of the Barnardo's organisation. The collection mainly relates to child care, and is used primarily to locate photographs of former residents, but is also available for use by the media and the public.

The Beatrix Potter Society

c/o The Lodge, Salisbury Avenue, Harpenden, Hertfordshire, AL5 2PS

- ☎ 01582 769755
- ✉ beatrixpottersociety@tiscali.co.uk
- 🌐 www.beatrixpottersociety.org.uk

Contact President, Brian Alderson

Established 1980

About The Beatrix Potter Society exists to promote the study and appreciation of the life and works of Beatrix Potter. The society organises regular conferences, meetings and other events in the UK and USA.

Book Publishers Association of New Zealand (BPANZ)

Private Bag 102 902, North Shore City, 0745, New Zealand

- ☎ 0064 9 442 7426
- ☎ 0064 9 479 8536
- ✉ anne@bpanz.org.nz
- 🌐 www.bpanz.org.nz

Contact Association Director, Anne de Lautour

About The BPANZ is the trade association of book publishers and distributors in New Zealand.

The Booksellers Association

Minster House, 272 Vauxhall Bridge Road, London, SW1V 1BA

- ☎ 020 7802 0802
- ☎ 020 7802 0803
- ✉ mail@booksellers.org.uk
- 🌐 www.booksellers.org.uk

Contact Chief Executive, Tim Godfray

About The Booksellers Association represents over 95 per cent of booksellers in the UK and Ireland. Its website will be of interest to writers for its overall information about the book and publishing industry, and for its statistical information on numbers of book published, etc.

Booktrust

Book House, 45 East Hill, London, SW18 2QZ

- ☎ 020 8516 2977
- ☎ 020 8516 2978
- ✉ query@booktrust.org.uk
- 🌐 www.booktrust.org.uk

About Booktrust is an independent national charity that encourages people of all ages and cultures to discover and enjoy reading. It administers seven book prizes, including the Orange Prize for Fiction, the Booktrust Teenage Prize and the Nestlé Prize. It has many ongoing projects that promote reading, including the appointment of the Children's Laureate. The website contains up to date information on the children's book trade. The trust also runs the national Bookstart initiative which gives advice and books to parents.

The British Council

10 Spring Gardens, London, SW1A 2BN

- ☎ 0161 957 7755
- ☎ 0161 957 7762
- ✉ general.enquiries@britishcouncil.org
- 🌐 www.britishcouncil.org

Contact Director General, Sir David Green; Director of Literature, Susanna Nicklin; Director of Arts, Leigh Gibson

About The British Council is the UK's international organisation for educational opportunities and cultural relations. Its purpose is to build mutually beneficial relationships between people in the UK and other countries, and to increase appreciation of the UK's creative ideas and achievements. For writers, this might mean your book or ideas being promoted, perhaps in one of the Council's exhibitions or publications, or in one of its libraries. The council has over 180 libraries in 110 countries across the world.

The British Council publishes a number of journals and essays as well as the *New Writing* anthology of short stories. Literature resources on the council website include a literary portal (www.literature.britishcouncil.org), various directories of writing and literature courses, a directory of literature conferences, information on active writers (www.contemporarywriters.com), and links to a number of translation resource sites (www.literarytranslation.com; www.youngtranslators.com). It also hosts a global

online bookclub for children and adults at www.encompassculture.com.
Check the website for the latest information from the British Council.

British Museum
Great Russel Street, London, WC1B 3DG
- ☎ 020 7323 8000
- ☎ 020 7323 8616
- ✉ information@thebritishmuseum.ac.uk
- 🌐 www.thebritishmuseum.ac.uk

About The museum collection is available for researchers of all levels, and museum facilities are accessible to members of the public wishing to carry out their own work, through its libraries, study rooms and collection. The collection can also be accessed online in the 'Explore' section of the website, which contains detailed information about more than 4,000 objects.

Canadian Authors Association
320 South Shores Road, Campbellford, Ontario, K0L 1LO, Canada
- ☎ 001 705 653 0323
- ☎ 001 705 653 0593
- ✉ admin@canauthors.org
- 🌐 www.canauthors.org

Contact President, Joan Eyolfson Caadham
About The Canadian Authors Association (CAA) is Canada's national writing organisation. It aims to support and develop the Canadian writing community by hosting events, conferences and awards, and by providing resources on the website.

The Canadian Children's Book Centre (CCBC)
Suite 101, 40 Orchard View Boulevard, Toronto, M4R 1B9, Canada
- ☎ 001 416 975 0010
- ☎ 001 416 975 8970
- ✉ info@bookcentre.ca
- 🌐 www.bookcentre.ca

About The Canadian Children's Book Centre (CCBC) is a national, not for profit organisation, dedicated to encouraging, promoting and supporting the reading, writing and illustrating of Canadian books for young readers.

Canadian Publishers' Council
Suite 203, 250 Merton Street, Toronto, Ontario, M4S 1B1, Canada
- ☎ 001 416 322 7011
- ☎ 001 416 322 6999
- ✉ pubadmin@pubcouncil.ca
- 🌐 www.pubcouncil.ca

Contact Executive Director, Jacqueline Hushion
About The Canadian Publishers' Council is Canada's main English language book publishing trade association. It represents the interests of publishing companies that publish books and other media for elementary and secondary schools, colleges and universities, professional and reference markets, and the retail and library sectors.

Canadian Society of Children's Authors, Illustrators & Performers (CANSCAIP)
Lower Level Entrance, 104–40 Orchard View Boulevard, Toronto, Ontario, M4R 1B9, Canada
- ☎ 001 416 515 1559
- ✉ office@canscaip.org
- 🌐 www.canscaip.org

Contact President, Gillian Chan; Illustrators' Representative, Sean Cassidy; Performers' Representative, Celia Lottridge
About CANSCAIP is a not for profit support network for children's authors, illustrators and performers. They organise newsletters, workshops, meetings and other information programs for authors, parents, teachers, librarians, and publishers.

Careers Writers' Association
16 Caewal Road, Llandaff, Cardiff, CF5 2BT
- ☎ 029 2056 3444
- ☎ 029 2065 8190
- ✉ secretary@careerswriters.co.uk
- 🌐 www.careerswriters.co.uk

Contact Membership Secretary, Ann Goodman
About The CWA attracts professionals who work in careers writing. Membership is only open to writers with an established reputation for providing objective and up to date careers information. Many draw on expertise gained as specialist information providers in careers services, as employment researchers, or as careers consultants to the national press. The CWA believes that providing thoroughly researched, accurate and up to date information is essential to help individuals of all ages - including young adults - make informed choices of courses and careers.

The Center for Children's Books (CCB)

Graduate School of Library and Information Science, University of Illinois at Urbana-Champaign, 501 East Daniel Street, Champaign, Illinois, 61820, USA

- 001 217 244 9331
- ccb@uiuc.edu
- http://ccb.lis.uiuc.edu

Contact Director of the Center for Children's Books, Dr. Christine Jenkins

About The Center for Children's Books (CCB) houses a non-circulating collection of more than 16,000 recent and historically significant trade books for children, plus review copies of nearly all trade books published in the US in the current year. The CCB houses over 1,000 professional and reference books on the history and criticism of literature for youth, literature based library and classroom programming, and storytelling. Although the collection is non-circulating, it is available for examination by scholars, teachers, librarians, students, and other educators.

Centre for Literacy in Primary Education (CLPE)

Webber Street, London, SE1 8QW

- 020 7401 3382
- 020 7928 4624
- info@clpe.co.uk
- www.clpe.co.uk

Contact Director, Julia Eccleshare; Director, Sue Ellis

About The Centre for Literacy in Primary Education (CLPE) is an educational centre for schools and teachers, parents, teaching assistants and other educators. CLPE has a national and international reputation for its work in the fields of language, literacy and assessment. It contains a reference library and a range of teaching resources, as well as publishing book lists and literacy teaching materials.

The Children's Book Circle (CBC)

Euston House, 24 Evershot Street, London, NW1 1DB

- www.childrensbookcircle.org.uk

About The CBC is a not for profit organisation, run entirely by volunteers. It provides a forum for writers, illustrators, publishers, librarians, agents, teachers and anyone else interested in children's literature. They hold regular conferences and meetings in and around the London area, and also host the Elanor Farjeon Award, for outstanding contribution to children's literature.

The Children's Book Council (CBC)

2nd Floor, 12 West 37th Street, New York, NY 10018, USA

- 001 212 966 1990
- 001 212 966 2073
- Online form
- www.cbcbooks.org

About The Children's Book Council is the non-profit trade association of publishers and packagers of trade books and related materials for children and young adults in America. It aims to make the reading and enjoyment of children's books an essential part of America's educational and social goals, and to support literacy and reading programmes across the country.

Children's Book Council of Australia

PO Box 765, Rozelle, New South Wales, 2039, Australia

- 0061 2 9818 3858
- 0061 2 9810 0737
- office@cbc.org.au
- www.cbc.org.au

About The Children's Book Council of Australia aims to raise the profile of children's and young adult literature in the wider community. They host a range of conferences and events, including various awards and competitions for children's writers.

Children's Books History Society

25 Field Way, Hoddesdon, Hertfordshire, EN11 0QN

- 01992 464885
- 01992 464885

About The CBHS is interested in the historical perspective of children's books and aims to study their history, bibliography and content. The society publishes its own newsletter and hosts the Harvey Darton Award, a biennial award given by the Society for any book which contributes fresh and detailed knowledge to the history of British children's books published during the previous two years.

Children's Books Ireland

17 North Great Georges Street, Dublin 1, Ireland

- 00353 1 872 7475
- 00353 1 872 7476
- info@childrensbooksireland.com
- www.childrensbooksireland.com

Contact Director, Mags Walsh

About Children's Books Ireland is the national children's book organisation of Ireland. It aims to promote quality children's books and reading throughout the country, with a range of conferences, events and awards.

Children's Literature Association (ChLA)
PO Box 138, Battle Creek, Michigan, 49016, USA
- 001 269 965 8180
- 001 269 965 3568
- www.childlitassn.org
- info@childlitassn.org

Contact President, Roberta Seelinger Trites
About The Children's Literature Association exists to encourage high standards of criticism, scholarship, research, and teaching in children's literature in America.

CLƒ - Irish Book Publishers' Association
25 Denzille Lane, Dublin 2, Ireland
- 00353 1 639 4868
- www.publishingireland.com
- info@publishingireland.com

Contact President, Tony Farmar
About The CLƒ is an information sharing forum of Irish publishers. It provides contact details for distributors, agents, booksellers, wholesalers, media contacts, arts organisations and sister organisations in other countries to its members, as well as weekly newsletters and general trade information. Full membership of CLƒ is currently open to anyone who is a publisher of books (with at least two titles already published) and who can show evidence of a publishing programme,

Comhairle nan Leabhraichean/The Gaelic Books Council
22 Mansfield Street, Glasgow, G11 5QP
- 0141 337 6211
- 0141 353 0515
- www.gaelicbooks.net
- brath@gaelicbooks.net

Contact Chairman, Professor Roibeard O' Maolalaigh
About Comhairle nan Leabhraichean, or the Gaelic Books Council, is an organisation set up in 1968 to promote Gaelic books. It is a charitable company, and its main funding comes from the Scottish Arts Council. The organisation has its own Gaelic

bookshop and book club, and provides grants and funding for new books and editorial services.

Department for Children, Schools & Families
Sanctuary Buildings, Great Smith Street, London, SW1P 3BT
- 0870 000 2288
- 01928 794248
- info@dcfs.gsi.gov.uk
- www.dfes.gov.uk

About Formerly the Department for Education and Skills, the DCSF aims to raise standards of education so that more children and young people reach their expected levels. They hope to lift more children out of poverty and re-engage disaffected young people. The department will lead work across Government in order to improve outcomes for children, including work on children's health and child poverty.

Discover
1 Bridge Terrace, London, E15 4BG
- 020 8536 5555
- team@discover.org.uk
- www.discover.org.uk

Contact Director, Sally Goldsworthy; Community and Education Manager, Clare Lewis
Established 1998
About Discover is a registered charity that aims to provide creative, play and learning opportunities based around story building. It particularly targets families in circumstances of social and economic disadvantage, and ensures that children are listened to, and can participate in decisions that affect their lives. The charity runs a variety of community centres and outreach programmes with schools and libraries around the the UK, including the Story Garden and the Story Trail.

The Edith Nesbit Society
21 Churchfields, West Malling, Kent, ME19 6RJ
- mccarthy804@aol.com
- www.the-railway-children.co.uk

Established 1996
About A society dedicated to the life and works of Edith Nesbit, author of *The Railway Children*. Organises regular talks, visits and events, and publishes a newsletter.

Educational Publishers Council

The Publishers Association, 29B Montague Street, London, WC1B 5BW

- 020 7691 9191
- 020 7691 9199
- mail@publishers.org.uk

About Acts as a forum for publishers of printed and digital educational resources for schools and colleges. It provides information services and hosts regular events and conferences for its members.

English Association

University of Leicester, University Road, Leicester, LE1 7RH

- 0116 252 3982
- 0116 252 2301
- engassoc@le.ac.uk
- www.le.ac.uk/engassoc

Contact President, Professor Elaine Treharne; Chief Executive, Helen Lucas

About The aim of the English Association is to further knowledge, understanding and enjoyment of the English language and its literatures, and to foster good practice in its teaching and learning at all levels. Based at the University of Leicester, the Association awards four prizes a year in specialist areas, and organises and participates in academic conferences.

The Enid Blyton Society

93 Milford Hill, Salisbury, Wiltshire, SP1 2QL

- 01722 331937
- www.enidblytonsociety.co.uk

Contact Anita Bensoussane

About The Enid Blyton Society aims to provide a focal point for collectors and enthusiasts of Enid Blyton through its magazine, *The Enid Blyton Society Journal*, issued three times a year; its annual Enid Blyton Day; and its website. The society no longer accepts queries by email, but does maintain an active forum on the website.

The Federacion de Gremios de Editores de Espana (Spanish Association of Publishers Guilds)

Cea Bermudez, 44-2° Dcha., 28003, Madrid

- 0034 91 534 5195
- 0034 91 535 2625
- fgee@fge.es
- www.federacioneditores.org

Contact President, D. Jordi òbeda i Baulo

Established 1978

About The FGEE is a non-profit, private professional association created to represent and defend the interests of Spanish publishers on a national, European and international level.

Federation of Children's Book Groups

2 Bridge Wood View, Horsforth, Leeds, LS18 5PE

- 0113 258 8910
- info@fcbg.org.uk
- www.fcbg.org.uk

Established 1968

About The Federation of Children's Book Groups is a registered charity that act as an umbrella organisation for local autonomous children's book groups all around the UK. The book groups organise a variety of activities in their localities, often in conjunction with their local schools and libraries. These may include, bringing authors and illustrators to schools, story-telling sessions, and other book-related activities for children. The Federation produces a regular newsletter and numerous specialised booklists. Also, it organises National Share A Story Month each year in May, holds an Annual Conference in the Spring, and owns and coordinates The Red House Children's Book Award.

Federation of European Publishers

31 Rue Montoyer box 8, B – 1000 Brussels, Belgium

- 0032 2 770 11 10
- 0032 2 771 20 71
- cdambrosio@fep-fee.be
- www.fep-fee.be

Contact Director, Anne Bergman-Tahon

Established 1967

About FEP is an independent, non-commercial umbrella association of book publishers associations in the European Union that deals with legislation and advises publishers' associations on copyright and other legislative issues. FEP represents 26 national associations of book publishers of the European Union and of the European Economic Area.

Federation of Indian Publishers

18/1–C Institutional Area, Aruna Asaf Ali Marg, New Delhi, 110067, India

- 0091 2685 2263
- 0091 2686 4054
- fip1@satyam.net.in

Established 1972

About The Federation of Indian Publishers aims to encourage and support the publishing industry in India by hosting seminars and conferences and providing a national support network. The Federation also hosts the annual Delhi Book Fair.

The Greeting Card Association
United House, North Road, London, N7 9DP
- ☎ 020 7619 0396
- ✉ gca@max-publishing.co.uk
- 🌐 www.greetingcardassociation.org.uk

About The GCA is the trade association for greeting card publishers. It provides help, support, advice and a range of other benefits to its members. It publishes the *Progressive Greetings* magazine, and also has an online resource feature that contains a wealth of information about greeting card publishers, and writing/illustrating for greeting cards.

Guernsey Arts Council
La Fontaine, Courtil de la Fontaine, Kings Road, St. Peter Port, Guernsey, GY1 1QB
- ☎ 01481 254144
- ✉ tdguernsey@cwgsy.net
- **Contact** Chairman, Terry Domrille

About The Arts Council of Guernsey, in the Channel Islands.

Imaginate
45a George Street, Edinburgh, EH2 2HT
- ☎ 0131 225 8050
- ☎ 0131 225 6440
- ✉ info@imaginate.org.uk
- 🌐 www.imaginate.org.uk
- **Contact** Director, Tony Reekie

About Imaginate is an arts organisation that promotes and develops the performing arts for children and young people in Scotland. One of its chief aims is that children and young people, aged up to 18, have regular access to a diverse range of high quality performing arts activity, from home and abroad, that will entertain, enrich, teach and inspire them. Imaginate also hosts the annual Bank of Scotland Children's International Theatre Festival & Tour, among other events.

The Imperial War Museum
Lambeth Road, London, SE1 6HZ
- ☎ 020 7416 5320
- ☎ 020 7416 5374
- ✉ mail@iwm.org.uk
- 🌐 www.iwm.org.uk

About Books, pamphlets, periodicals, maps, technical drawings, propaganda leaflets, song sheets and army forms are among the items that can be viewed in the Reading Room of the Imperial War Museum, a major national gallery and archive. Open to any member of the public. Also has an online collections archive.

Independent Publishers Guild
PO Box 93, Royston, Hertfordshire, SW7 5BD
- ☎ 01763 247014
- ☎ 01763 246293
- ✉ info@ipg.uk.com
- 🌐 www.ipg.uk.com
- **Contact** Executive Director, Bridget Shine

About The IPG celebrates, encourages and represents the interests of independent publishers in the UK. It provides advice, ideas and information, and gives independent companies the support they need to keep their businesses growing.

International Board on Books for Young People (IBBY)
Nonnenweg 12, Postfach, CH-4003, Basel, Switzerland
- ☎ 0041 61 272 2917
- ☎ 0041 61 272 2757
- ✉ ibby@ibby.org
- 🌐 www.ibby.org
- **Established** 1953

About The International Board on Books for Young People (IBBY) is a non-profit organisation which represents an international network of people from all over the world who are committed to bringing books and children together. Its main aims are to encourage the publication and distribution of quality children's books, especially in developing countries, to give children everywhere the opportunity to have access to books with high literary and artistic standards. It also works to provide support and training for those involved with children and children's literature, and to stimulate research and scholarly works in the field of children's literature.

International Publishers Association
3 avenue de Miremont, 1206 Geneva, Switzerland
- ☎ 0041 22 346 3018
- ☎ 0041 22 347 5717
- ✉ secretariat@ipa-uie.org

www.ipa-uie.org

Contact President, Ana Maria Cabanellas; Secretary General, Jens Bammel; Director, Freedom to Publish, Alexis Krikorian

About The IPA's aims are to uphold and defend the right of publishers to publish and distribute the works of the mind in complete freedom. It promotes and protects the principles of copyright, and works to overcome illiteracy, lack of books and of other education materials. It has links to many other publishing organisations and international governing bodies and governments. Writers will find its website links useful in research.

Irish Educational Publishers Association
c/o Gill & Macmillan Ltd, Hulme Avenue, Park West, Dublin 12, Ireland

☎ 00353 1 500 9509

☎ 00353 1 500 9598

About An association which represents Irish publishers of educational material and resources.

Irish Writers' Centre
19 Parnell Square, Dublin 1, Republic of Ireland

☎ 00353 1 872 1302

☎ 00353 1 872 6282

✉ info@writerscentre.ie

www.writerscentre.ie

Contact Director, Cathal McCabe; Tutor, Anthony Anatoly Kudryavitsky

About A national organisation for the promotion of Irish writers and literature. It hosts various events and community based literary schemes, including a writing group for refugees and asylum seekers.

The Kipling Society
c/o Jane Keskar, 6 Clifton Road, London, W9 1SS

☎ 020 7286 0194

✉ jane@keskar.fsworld.co.uk

www.kipling.org.uk

Contact Hon. Secretary, Jane Keskar

Established 1927

About The Kipling Society is a Registered Charity and a voluntary, non-profit-making organisation. Its organises regular lectures and other events, maintains the Kipling Library and publishes the quarterly Kipling Journal.

The Lewis Carroll Society
50 Lauderdale Mansions, Lauderdale Road, London, W9 1NE

◉ Online form

www.lewiscarrollsociety.org.uk

About The Lewis Carroll Society aims to encourage research into the life and works of famous children's author Lewis Carroll (Charles Lutwidge Dodgson). The Society has members around the world, including many leading libraries and institutions, authors, researchers and many who simply enjoy Carroll's books. They publish a range of newsletters and society magazines.

The Livesey Museum for Children
682 Old Kent Road, London, SE15 1JF

☎ 020 7635 5829

✉ info@liveseymuseum.org.uk

www.liveseymuseum.org.uk

About The Livesey Museum is one of the UK's leading children's museums, with annual interactive exhibitions that are designed to support the National Curriculum at Foundation Stage, Key Stage 1 and Key Stage 2.

Museum of London
150 London Wall, London, EC2Y 5HN

☎ 0870 444 3852

☎ 0870 444 3853

✉ info@museumoflondon.org.uk

www.museumoflondon.org.uk

Contact Managing Director, Kate Starling

About The Museum of London is part of the Museum of London Group, which covers a range of institutions within the city. It has collections, events and exhibitions of interest to both children and adults.

The Mythopoeic Society
PO Box 320486, San Francisco, California, 94132, USA

✉ correspondence@mythsoc.org

www.mythsoc.org

Contact Corresponding Secretary, Edith Crowe

Established 1967

About The Mythopoeic Society is a non-profit international literary and educational organisation for the study, discussion, and enjoyment of fantastic and mythic literature, particularly the works of J.R.R. Tolkien, C.S. Lewis, and Charles Williams. Membership in the Mythopoeic Society is open to all scholars, writers, and readers of these literatures. The Society sponsors three periodicals; Mythprint is a monthly bulletin of book reviews, articles, events and other notices of interest to Society members. Mythlore is the Society's peer-reviewed journal that publishes scholarly articles on mythic and fantastic literature. Finally, Mythic Circle is a literary annual of original poetry and short stories. The society also hosts the Annual Mythopoeic Conference.

National Art Library

Victoria & Albert Museum, South Kensington, Cromwell Road, London, SW7 2RL
- 020 7942 2400
- 020 7942 2401
- nal.enquiries@vam.ac.uk
- www.vam.ac.uk/nal

About Major public reference library for the fine and decorative arts, focusing on arts, craft and book design. Material must be consulted in one of the library's reading rooms.

National Association for the Teaching of English (NATE)

50 Broadfield Road, Sheffield, S8 0XJ
- 0114 255 5419
- 0114 255 5296
- info@nate.org.uk
- www.nate.org.uk

Contact Publications Manager, Anne Fairhall; Publications Coordinator, Julie Selwood

About An association for education professionals. NATE provides information, publications and resource material as well as funding opportunities for research and training. NATE holds annual and regional conferences, and also provides a newsletter and a number of different magazines and resource books with membership.

National Association of Writers' Groups (NAWG)

The Arts Centre, Biddick Lane, Washington, Tyne and Wear, NE38 2AB
- 01262 609228
- nawg@tesco.net
- www.nawg.co.uk

About NAWG aims to bring cohesion and fellowship to isolated writers' groups and individuals, promoting the study and art of writing in all its aspects. It runs a variety of annual competitions and events including the NAWG/Writers' News short

story competition and the annual Festival of Writing, in Durham.

National Association of Writers in Education (NAWE)

PO Box 1, Sheriff Hutton, York, YO60 7YU
- 01653 618429
- paul@nawe.co.uk
- www.nawe.co.uk

Contact Director, Paul Munden

About The National Association of Writers in Education seeks to support those working in writing related occupations within education industry. The writing can cover any form, area or genre. The website provides extensive information and links for all interested in this field, including a database of funding opportunities, and, as part of its Higher Education Network, a list of all writing courses in the UK.

National Centre for Research in Children's Literature (NCRCL)

Roehampton University, Froebel College, Roehampton Lane, London, SW15 5PJ
- 020 8392 3008
- 0181 392 3819
- ncrcl@roehampton.ac.uk
- www.ncrcl.ac.uk

About A research centre within the School of Arts at Roehampton University. The NCRCL works to research the whole area of children's literature. It has PhD students, runs an MA, and holds conferences. The centre also holds several collections of children's literature and childhood studies. Writers will find the links on its website of use.

National Centre for Research in Children's Literature (NCRCL)

University of Reading, Bulmershe Court, Reading, RG6 1HY
- 0118 378 8820
- ncll@reading.ac.uk
- www.ncll.org.uk

Contact Director, Professor Viv Edwards

About NCRCL is an independent organisation that supports teachers, parents and governors with an extensive collection of resources, publications, courses and conferences.

National Library for the Blind (NLB)
Far Cromwell Road, Bredbury, Stockport, SK6 2SG
- 0161 355 2000
- 0161 355 2098
- enquiries@nlbuk.org
- www.nlb-online.org

About The National Library for the Blind is a leading agency in the provision of library and information services for visually impaired people. The library holds Europe's largest collection of Braille and Moon books, and provides a free postal library service to blind and partially sighted people worldwide. It also has a large collection of Braille music scores, giant print books, e-resources and reference materials, and publishes a wide range of magazines for visually impaired children and teenagers.

National Literacy Association
87 Grange Road, Ramsgate, Kent, CT11 9QB
- 01843 239952
- 01843 239952
- wendy@nla.org.uk
- www.nla.org.uk

Contact Director, Jo Klaces; Project Manager, Paula Edmondson; Administration Manager, Wendy Easthope
About The National Literacy Association is a small charity that works to promote awareness of and support children's literacy needs. One of their primary aims is to support children and young people who find it difficult to speak, listen, read and write. They produce various publications which include *The Guide to Literary Resources*.

National Literacy Trust
Swire House, 59 Buckingham Gate, London, SW1E 6AJ
- 020 7828 2435
- 020 7931 9986
- contact@literacytrust.org.uk
- www.literacytrust.org.uk

Contact Director, Jonathan Douglas; Trust Administrator, Jacky Taylor
About The National Literacy Trust is dedicated to building a literate nation. Among its campaigns to this end are: *Reading Is Fundamental, UK*, the *National Reading Campaign*, *Talk To Your Baby*, *Reading The Game*, *Reading Connects*, and the *Vital Link*. Results of research into specific areas of concern to do with literacy can be found on the website. The site also provides a rich range of resources to help with reading, and it also links to many other organisations.

National Museum Wales
Cathays Park, Cardiff, CF10 3NP
- 029 2039 7951
- 029 2057 3321
- Online form
- www.museumwales.ac.uk

About An organisation and website bringing together all of Wales' national museums. The website has links to other institutions, details of upcoming events and an archive of collections.

National Society for Education in Art & Design (NSEAD)
The Gatehouse, Corsham Court, Corsham, Wiltshire, SN13 0BZ
- 01249 714825
- 01249 716138
- johnsteers@nsead.org
- www.nsead.org

Contact General Secretary, Dr John Steers; President, Glen Coutts
Established 1984
About The National Society for Education in Art and Design is the leading national authority concerned with promoting and defending art, craft and design across all phases of education in the United Kingdom. Its publications include the *Journal of Art & Design* and *Start* magazine, for primary schools.

Natural History Museum, Library and Information Services
Cromwell Road, London, SW7 5BD
- 020 7942 5000
- Online form
- www.nhm.ac.uk/research-curation/library

About The Natural History Museum Library and Archive holds the world's premier collections of literature, original drawings and manuscripts relating to natural history. The library is a reference source for the biological and earth sciences and is comprised of over one million books dating from 1469. It holds 25,000 periodical titles and half a million artworks, together with extensive map, manuscript and photographic collections. The museum archives are made up of over one million items, relating to the history and work of the museum. Much of the library catalogue is online. By appointment only, researchers should contact the relevant subject department and contact details are given on the website.

Newcastle University Library
Robinson Library, Newcastle upon Tyne, NE2 4HQ
- 0191 222 7662
- lib-readersservices@ncl.ac.uk
- www.ncl.ac.uk/library

About The Newcastle University Library is home to a number of archives of historical children's books and other material relating to the history of childhood and education. It has over 100 collections of rare book archives, illustrations and woodblocks from the 15th to 21st century, and is also home to The Booktrust Collection, Seven Stories Archive and Special Collections.

The Booktrust Collection
The Booktrust Collection contains roughly 6,000 items, including picture books, children's and young adult fiction and non-fiction, toy and board games, and other items related to children's literature. It also includes a range of information on children's illustration and photography. The collection, maintained by the Booktrust organisation, is fully open-access, so that the items may be viewed and researched by the public.

Seven Stories Archive
The Seven Stories Archive, founded in 1997, is a growing collection of manuscripts and illustration for children from post-war Britain. It includes items from popular authors and illustrators, and also includes the Ladybird Archive, the Kaye Webb Archive and the Robert Westall Archive. Part of the Seven Stories Archive is housed at Newcastle University Library.

The Special Collections
A number of important collections of rare and historical children's books, focusing mainly on items from the 18th to 20th century. Special Collections includes the Robert White Collection, the Wallis Collection, the Crawhall Collection and the Bradshaw-Bewick Collection.

For more information see: www.ncl.ac.uk/library/specialcollections

New Producers Alliance
The NPA Film Centre, Unit 1.07, The Tea Building, 56 Shoreditch High Street, London, E1 6JJ
- 020 7613 0440
- 020 7729 1852
- queries@npa.org.uk

- www.npa.org.uk

Established 1993

About The NPA is a national membership organisation and registered charity that provides training and networking opportunities to new filmmakers.

New Writing North
Culture Lab, Grand Assembly Rooms, Newcastle University, King's Walk, Newcastle upon Tyne, NE1 7RU
- 0191 222 1332
- 0191 222 1372
- mail@newwritingnorth.com
- www.newwritingnorth.com

About New Writing North is the writing development agency for the North East of England (the area covered by Arts Council England North East). It aims to create an environment in the North East in which new writing in all genres can flourish and develop. It merges individual development work with writers across all media, and with educational work and the production of creative projects. It works with writers from different genres and forms to develop career opportunities, new commissions, projects, residencies, publications and live events. NWN manage the Northern Writers' Awards and the Northern Rock Foundation Writers' Award (currently the largest literary award in the UK) and supports writers at all stages of their careers by mentoring and by the creation of professional development training initiatives and projects.

Office for Standards in Education (OFSTED)
Alexandra House, 33 Kingsway, London, WC2B 6SE
- 0845 640 4045
- 020 7421 6707
- enquiries@ofsted.gov.uk
- www.ofsted.gov.uk

About A Governmental department responsible for inspecting schools, colleges and other educational facilities. Also handles the regulation of childcare providers for over 150 local authorities.

The Publishers Association
29b Montague Street, London, WC1B 5BW
- 020 7691 9191
- 020 7691 9199
- mail@publishers.org.uk
- www.publishers.org.uk

Contact Chief Executive, Ronnie Williams; Director of Educational, Academic & Professional Publishing, Graham Taylor

About The Publishers Association is the leading organisation working on behalf of book, journal and electronic publishers based in the UK. It brings publishers together to discuss the issues facing the industry, and the practical policies which will drive lobbying and campaigns in the UK and internationally. The aim of The Publishers Association is to ensure a secure future for the UK publishing industry.

Publishing Scotland
Scottish Book Centre, 137 Dundee Street, Edinburgh, EH11 1BG
- 0131 228 6866
- 0131 228 3220
- enquiries@scottishbooks.org
- www.scottishbooks.org

Contact Director, Lorraine Fannin; Information & Professional Development Administrator, Katherine Naish

About Publishing Scotland, previously The Scottish Publishers Association, is a trade association of almost 80 Scottish publishers. It is the voice and the network for publishing in Scotland. It works to help its members with the marketing of their books to the widest possible readership within the UK and overseas. On members' behalf, it attends many national and international book fairs and exhibitions. It also co-ordinates bookshop and library promotions, and other marketing initiatives.

REACH: National Advice Centre for Children with Reading Difficulties
2 Station Road, Gerrards Cross, Buckinghamshire, SL9 8EL
- 01753 888688
- 01753 888699

About Maintains an open access collection of resources, books and materials on children's reading disabilities, and offers support and assistance.

Roald Dahl Foundation
81a High Street, Great Missenden, Buckinghamshire, HP16 0AL
- 01494 890465
- 01494 890459
- www.roalddahlfoundation.org
- admin@roalddahlfoundation.org

Contact President, Quentin Blake

About The Roald Dahl Foundation is a UK based registered charity, offering a programme of grant-giving to charities, hospitals, and individuals in the UK only. The organisation offers funding and assistance in three main areas: Haematology; Neurology; and Literacy. The website also contains a wealth of information about Roald Dahl's life and work, and the illustrations of Quentin Blake.

The Roald Dahl Museum and Story Centre
81–83 High Street, Great Missenden, Buckinghamshire, HP16 0AL
- 01494 892192
- www.roalddahlmuseum.com
- admin@roalddahlmuseum.org

Established 2001

About The Roald Dahl Museum and Story Centre is a registered charity that handles the Roald Dahl archive and provides an interactive gallery space for children and adults. One of its aims is to encourage creative writing in future generations.

Scattered Authors Society
c/o Yvonne Coppard, 35 Thornton Way, Girton, Cambridge, CB3 0NL
- yvonnecoppard@aol.com

About A society for children's writers that aims to provide an informal discussion forum and contact network.

School Library Association
Unit 2, Lotmead Business Village, Lotmead Farm, Wanborough, Swindon, SN4 0UY
- 01793 791787
- 01793 791786

About The SLA promotes the development of school and college libraries and literacy. It publishes resources, training services and book lists for libraries. Also publishes a quarterly journal.

Science Museum
Exhibition Road, London, SW7 2DD
- 0870 870 4868
- sciencemuseum@nmsi.ac.uk
- www.sciencemuseum.org.uk

About The Science Museum has various exhibitions of science and technology, which appeal to both adults and children. It is also home to the Science Museum Library and Archives.

Scottish Arts Council

12 Manor Place, Edinburgh, EH3 7DD

- 0131 226 6051
- 0131 225 9833
- help.desk@scottisharts.org.uk
- www.scottisharts.co.uk

Contact Chairman, Richard Holloway; Head of Literature, Dr Gavin Wallace; Head of Visual Arts, Amanda Catto

About The Scottish Arts Council is the lead body for the funding, development and advocacy of the arts in Scotland. They use Scottish Executive and National Lottery funds to support and promote arts and creativity, and also award grants and bursaries.

Scottish Book Trust

Sandeman House, Trunk's Close, 55 High Street, Edinburgh, EH1 1SR

- 0131 524 0160
- 0131 524 0161
- info@scottishbooktrust.com
- www.scottishbooktrust.com

Contact CEO, Marc Lambert; General Manager, Jeanette Harris

About Scottish Book Trust is Scotland's national agency for reading and writing. It promotes reading and books. Under its umbrella is Live Literature Scotland, a national initiative that enables Scottish citizens to engage with the nation's authors, playwrights, poets, storytellers and illustrators. It is the only writer bursary scheme of its kind in the UK, subsidising the cost of 1,200 community visits by writers in all areas of Scotland, and is extremely popular. More than 500 writers who are available to conduct readings and literary events in Scotland are listed and searchable on the SBT database.

The Scottish Storytelling Centre (SSC)

The Scottish Storytelling Forum, 43–45 High Street, Edinburgh, EH1 1SR

- 0131 557 5724
- 0131 557 5224
- reception@scottishstorytellingcentre.com
- www.scottishstorytellingcentre.co.uk

Contact Director, Donald Smith; Programme and Events Manager, Esther Kent

About The SSC is Scotland's national charity for oral storytelling, and supports a range of live storytelling, theatre, literature, visual arts, craft and multimedia events. The SSC programme aims to promote storytelling as a vibrant contemporary art form and celebrate Scotland's rich storytelling heritage. The group has over 100 professional storytellers across Scotland.

Society for Editors & Proofreaders (SfEP)

Riverbank House, 1 Putney Bridge Approach, London, SW6 3JD

- 020 7736 3278
- 020 7736 3318
- administration@sfep.org.uk
- www.sfep.org.uk

Contact Honorary President, Judith Butcher

Established 1988

About SfEP works towards high standards in the editing and proofreading industries and represents editorial professionals in legal matters. The society has about 1,400 members and associates (mostly in the UK) providing editorial services to publishers and a wide range of companies, government agencies and other bodies. The SfEP provides training and professional Accreditation and Registration services. It also publishes the award winning, bi-monthly magazine, *Editing Matters* and a directory of members' services.

Society for Storytelling (SfS)

PO Box 2344, Reading, RG6 7FG

- 0118 935 1381
- sfs@fairbruk.demon.co.uk
- www.sfs.org.uk

About The SfS is an open organisation which welcomes anyone with an interest in oral storytelling. It aims to provide an information network for oral storytelling, stories, storytellers and storytelling clubs, and organises storytelling events, such as storytelling festivals. The SfS publishes *Storylines* magazine and the quarterly *Directory of Storytellers*.

Society of Artists Agents

21c Montpellier Row, London, SE3 0RL

- jennieward@btopenworld.com
- www.illustratorsagents.co.uk

Contact Administrator, Jennifer Ward

Established 1992

About The Society of Artists Agents (SAA) represents a number of artists and illustrators agents in all matters, aiming to promote the use of illustration, and to unify and improve the working practices between illustrators, agents and clients. Also hosts the Society of Artists Agents Illustration

Awards, an annual competition that showcases the best and most innovative contemporary illustration.

The Society of Authors

The Society of Authors, 84 Drayton Gardens, London, SW10 9SB

☎ 020 7373 6642
🖷 020 7373 5768
✉ info@societyofauthors.org
🌐 www.societyofauthors.org

Contact Chair, Tracy Chevalier; General Secretary, Mark Le Fanu

About The Society of Authors is an independent trade union, representing authors' interests in all aspects of the writing business, including publishing, theatre, broadcast, film and translation. It currently has over 8,000 members. Membership is only open to authors who have had a full-length work published, or accepted for publication. Within the society there are a number of self-regulating groups including, The Children's Writers and Illustrators Group. Members receive membership to all groups within the society and are able to take advantage of a wide variety of events, gatherings, conferences and awards administered by the society.

Society of Children's Book Writers and Illustrators (SCBWI)

56 Ackroyd Road, Forest Hill, London, SE23 1DL

✉ info@britishscbwi.org
✉ illustrators@britishscbwi.org
🌐 www.britishscbwi.org

Contact Regional Advisor, Natascha Biebow; Illustrator Coordinator, Anne-Marie Perks

About The British arm of the Society of Children's Book Writers and Illustrators is part of an international organisation offering a variety of services to people who write, illustrate, or share an interest in children's literature. SCBWI acts as a network for the exchange of knowledge between writers, illustrators, editors, publishers, agents, librarians, educators, booksellers and others involved with literature for young people. There are currently more than 12,000 members worldwide, in over 70 regions, making it the largest children's writing organisation in the world. The organisation also offers members support, information and education at a local level.

The British SCBWI runs two annual conferences – an Illustrator's Day in the spring, and a Writer's Day in the autumn. They also publish a quarterly newsletter, *Words and Pictures*, which includes up to date events and marketing information for UK and American publishers, and present the Golden Kite Award for the best fiction and non-fiction books. See the website for a full list of regional network contacts.

Society of Editors

University Centre, Granta Place, Mill Lane, Cambridge, CB2 1RU

☎ 01223 304080
🖷 01223 304090
✉ info@societyofeditors.org
🌐 www.societyofeditors.co.uk

Contact Executive Director and Company Secretary, Bob Satchwell

About Formed from the merger of the Guild of Editors and the Association of British Editors; the society campaigns and lobbies to fight for media freedom. It has more than 400 members made up of Editors, Managing Editors, Editorial Directors, Training Editors, Editors in Chief and Deputy Editors in national/regional/local newspapers, magazines, radio, television/new media, lawyers, and academics in journalism education. Its values are: the promotion of press and broadcasting freedom and the public's right to know; the universal right to freedom of expression; the vitality of the news media in a democratic society; and the commitment to high editorial standards. The society influences debate on press and broadcasting freedom, ethics, and the culture and business of news media.

Society of Young Publishers

c/o The Bookseller, Endeavour House, 189 Shaftesbury Avenue, London, WC2H 8TJ

✉ membersec@thesyp.org.uk
🌐 www.thesyp.org.uk

Contact Chairman, Doug Wallace; Membership Secretary, Claire Morrison

About The Society of Young Publishers maintains a database of job opportunities within the publishing industry and also organises monthly speaker meetings to discuss current events in the publishing industry. It is open to anyone in publishing or a related trade (in any capacity) – or who is hoping to be soon. Anyone interested or working in the publishing industry is welcome to join. The only exception is that those who have been in the industry for more than ten years are not able to stand on the committee. There are two branches – in London and Oxford. Both branches have regular events and meetings, and both are run by volunteers.

Speaking of Books

105 John Humphries House, 4 Stockwell Street, London, SE10 9JN

☎ 020 8858 6616

About An organisation that arranges talks and visits by writers, illustrators and storytellers, to schools and colleges across the UK.

Syndicat National de l'Edition (French Publishers' Association)

115 Boulevard St Germain, F-75006, Paris, France

☎ 0033 1 44 41 40 50

☎ 0033 1 44 41 40 77

✉ www.sne.fr

About The French Publishers Association (SNE) is France's trade association of book publishers. It represents approximately 400 member companies, as a member of both the Federation of European Publishers (FEP), and the International Publishers Association (IPA).

Teenage Magazine Arbitration Panel (TMAP)

28 Kingsway, London, WC2B 6JR

☎ 020 7400 7520

☎ 020 7404 4167

✉ kerry.neilson@ppa.co.uk

✉ www.ppa.co.uk/tmap

Contact TMAP Secretariat, Kelly Neilson

About The Teenage Magazine Arbitration Panel (TMAP) is the magazine industry's self-regulatory body, which ensures that the sexual content of teenage magazines is presented in a responsible and appropriate manner. TMAP works in conjunction with magazine publishers, editors and retailers.

Theatre Collections Online

Theatre Museum, 1e Tavistock Street, London, WC2E 7PR

☎ 020 7943 4700

☎ 020 7943 4777

✉ tmenquiries@vam.ac.uk

✉ http://theatremuseum.org

Contact Director of the Theatre Museum, Geoffrey Marsh; General Manager, Sara Cunningham; Head of Education, Adrian Deakes

About The online collections of the Theatre Museum. Contains a diverse collection of manuscripts, playbills, programmes, prints, photographs, videos and press cuttings related to performers and theatre productions from the 17th century onwards. The Theatre Museum's reading room has now been closed to the public in preparation for a move to premises at the V&A Collections Centre, in Kensington.

The Tolkien Society

c/o Sally Kennett, 210 Prestbury Road, Cheltenham, Gloucester, GL52 3ER

✉ membership@tolkiensociety.org

✉ www.tolkiensociety.org

Contact Secretary, Sally Kennett

Established 1969

About The Tolkien Society aims to promote the life and works of J.R.R. Tolkien. It acts as a forum for members and also organises events and conferences for Tolkien fans around the world.

Union of Welsh Publishers & Booksellers

c/o Gomer Press, Llandysul, Ceredigion, SA44 4BQ

☎ 01559 362371

☎ 01559 363758

About The Union of Welsh Publishers & Booksellers represents member companies in all matters, and provides a network of support and communication.

United Kingdom Literacy Agency (UKLA)

4th Floor, Attenborough Building, University of Leicester, Leicester, LE1 7RH

☎ 0116 229 7450

☎ 0116 229 7451

✉ admin@ukla.org

✉ www.ukla.org

Established 1963

About UKLA is a registered charity, whose sole objective is the advancement of education in literacy. UKLA is committed to promoting good practice nationally and internationally in literacy and language teaching and research. It is run by its members, which include researchers, teachers, teacher educators, literacy consultants, LEA advisers, inspectors, independent consultants, publishers and librarians. The UKLA organises a range of conferences and events, research programmes and award schemes and also acts as a public voice on literacy in education issues.

V&A Museum of Childhood
Cambridge Heath Road, London, E2 9PA
- 020 8980 2415
- 020 8983 5225
- www.museumofchildhood.org.uk

About The V&A Museum of Childhood is part of the V&A family of museums, and houses the National Childhood Collection. The galleries are designed to show the collections in a way which is accessible to adults and children of all ages. The museum runs various exhibitions, displays and seasonal events, and also runs an education programme with popular teaching sessions and resources linked directly to the National Curriculum.

Voice of the Listener & Viewer (VLV)
101 King's Drive, Gravesend, Kent, DA12 5BQ
- 01474 352835
- 01474 351112
- info@vlv.org.uk
- www.vlv.org.uk

Contact Executive Director, Peter Blackman; Membership Secretary, Sue Washbrook
About VLV represents the citizen and consumer interest in broadcasting, and works for quality and diversity in British broadcasting. It campaigns for high quality radio and television programmes, and in particular for the principles of public service broadcasting. It is influential, and attracts big names as speakers and contributors to its conferences and events. It represents the interests of listeners, viewers, citizens and consumers and works to keep listeners and viewers informed about current developments in British broadcasting. These include proposed new legislation, public consultation on broadcasting policy and the likely impact of digital technology. The VLV is entirely independent and is funded by its own members.

Volunteer Reading Help (VRH)
VRH Central Office, Charity House, 14–15 Perseverance Works, 38 Kingsland Road, London, E2 8DD
- 020 7729 4087
- 020 7729 7643
- info@vrh.org.uk
- www.vrh.org.uk

Established 1973
About Volunteer Reading Help (VRH) is a national charity that helps disadvantaged children develop a love of reading and learning. Volunteers work one-on-one in schools and colleges around the UK.

Welsh Animation Group (WAG)
c/o Georgia Anderegg, 13 Bangor Street, Cardiff, CF24 3LQ
- 029 2048 1420
- georgia.anderegg@virgin.net
- http://wag.sequence.co.uk

Contact Chair, Robin Lyons; Treasurer, Georgia Anderegg
Established 1999
About The Welsh Animation Group provides a forum for animators and artists in Wales. They aim to to promote Welsh animation, both nationally and throughout the world.

Welsh Books Council
Castell Brychan, Aberystwyth, Ceredigion, SY23 2JB
- 01970 624151
- 01970 625385
- castellbrychan@wbc.org.uk
- www.wbc.org.uk

Contact Director, Gwerfyl Pierce Jones
About The Welsh Books Council is a national body, funded by the Welsh Assembly Government, which provides a focus for the publishing industry in Wales. It provides a number of specialist services (in the fields of editing, design, marketing and distribution), with a view to improving standards of book production and publication in both Welsh and English. For writers, its main interest may be that it aims to assist and support them, by providing services and by awarding grants/commissions which are channelled through publishers. See the website for further details.

Working Group Against Racism in Children's Resources
Unit 34, Eurolink Business Centre, 49 Effra Road, London, SW2 1BZ
- 020 7501 9992
- www.wgarcr.org.uk

Established 1983
About The Working Group Against Racism in Children's Resources is a voluntary organisation that aims to train parents, teachers and carers in the identification and elimination of racist images, language and stereotypes in children's material.

Writernet
Cabin V, Clarendon Buildings, 25 Horsell Road, London, N5 1XL

020 7609 7474
020 7609 7557
www.writernet.co.uk

Contact Chair, Bonnie Greer

About Writernet provides writers of all forms of live and recorded performance, with a range of services to help their careers. It also provides a wide range of producers who employ writers with the opportunity to make more informed choices to meet their needs. It is a national, not-for-profit organisation, operating strategically across four areas - professional development, international work, cultural diversity and third sector: co-producing, publishing, providing information, advice and guidance, dramaturgical and other development support - in partnership with a wide range of organisations.

Writers Advice Centre for Children's Books

16 Smiths Yard, Summerley Street, London, SW18 4HR

07979 905353
info@writersadvice.co.uk
www.writersadvice.co.uk

Contact Editorial Director, Louise Jordan

About A literary consultancy service offering professional editorial and marketing advice to new and published children's writers, on a fee basis. The Writers Advice Centre for Children's Books is the only manuscript agency in the UK specialising solely in children's publishing. Its manuscript assessment service provides new, and published children's writers with critical feedback that can increase chances of publication. The Writers Advice Centre is open to everyone writing for children, whether they be complete beginners, or published authors. It will look at all types of writing for children. This could include picture books, early readers, short stories, novels for older children, non-fiction and poetry. The centre also provides self-publishing services under its own imprint.

The Writers' Guild of Great Britain

15 Britannia Street, London, WC1X 9JN

020 7833 0777
020 7833 4777
admin@writersguild.org.uk
www.writersguild.org.uk

Contact President, David Nobbs; Chair, Katharine Way; General Secretary, Bernie Corbett; Deputy General Secretary, Anne Hogben; Assistant General Secretary, Naomi MacDonald

About The Writers' Guild of Great Britain is the trade union representing writers in television, radio, theatre, books, poetry, film and video games. In television, film, radio and theatre, the Guild is the recognised body for negotiating minimum terms and practice agreements for writers. It campaigns and lobbies on behalf of all writers, and is influential up to government level. Its voice is listened to, and its views are respected. Any writer who has received payment under a contract in terms at, or above the Writers' Guild minimum terms for at least one piece of work is entitled to become a full member.

Young Libraries Group (YLG)

Bromley Central Library, High Street, Bromley, BR1 1EX

020 8461 7193
020 8313 9975
ian.dodds@bromley.gov.uk

Contact Secretary, Ian Dodds

About The YLG aims to provide library services for children and provides training courses and support for library staff. It also helps to judge the CILIP Carnegie, and Kate Greenaway Awards every year, and publishes the *Youth Library Review*.

FOR WRITERS AND ILLUSTRATORS

Angus Book Award
County Buildings, Forfar, DD8 3WF
- 01307 461460
- 01307 462590
- cultural.services@angus.gov.uk
- www.angus.gov.uk/bookaward

Established 1995

Insider Info An award designed to encourage reluctant readers. A shortlist of five new paperback novels for teenagers is voted for by Angus secondary school children. The children also help to arrange other aspects of the award, including the ceremony. This award is designed to encourage older children to take an active interest in books and is held annually. Sponsored by Angus Council. The winning author receives a replica of the Aberlemmo Serpent stone and £500.

Genres Fiction, Novels and Teenage Fiction

Submission Guidelines Titles must be previously published.

Tips To be eligible for this award, books must have been written by UK authors.

Askews Torchlight Children's Book Award
218–222 North Road, Preston, Lancashire, PR1 1SY
- 01772 555947
- 01772 254860
- roberts@askews.co.uk
- www.askews.co.uk

Insider Info The Askews Torchlight Award encourages wider reading, by introducing young readers to new authors. The competition takes place annually and is awarded to an author who has not already been shortlisted for other major awards.

Genres Children's Fiction for 9–12 year olds.

Tips The Torchlight Award is voted for by primary and secondary school children across the country, and is designed to encourage an interest in reading.

The Astrid Lindgen Memorial Award
Swedish National Council for Cultural Affairs, Box 27215, SE-102 53 Stockholm, Sweden
- 0046 8 5192 6400
- 0046 8 5192 6499
- literatureaward@alma.se
- www.alma.se

Competition/Award Director Director, Anna Cokorilo

Established 2002

Insider Info An award to commemorate the work of Astrid Lindgren, one of Sweden's most popular authors. The award, of five million Swedish crowns (roughly £360,000), is the world's largest for children's and youth literature, and the second largest literature prize in the world. Authors, illustrators, storytellers and promoters of children's literature are all eligible for the award, which is given to one or more recipients every year. The award is for lifetime achievement, rather than for a single piece of work. Award winners may be of any nationality, but must be living in order to be eligible. Entrants to the award must be selected by nominating bodies around the world, or nominated by members of the judging panel, they may not nominate themselves, or be nominated by any other organisation.

The Aventis Prizes for Science Books
The Royal Society, 6–9 Carlton House Terrace, London, SW1Y 5AG
- 020 7451 2513
- 020 7451 2693
- sciencebooks@royalsoc.ac.uk
- www.sciencebookprizes.com

Established 1988

Insider Info The Royal Society Prizes for Science Books celebrates the best in popular science writing for adults and children. They aim to encourage the writing, publishing and reading of good and accessible popular science books. The have grown to become one of the UK's most prestigious non-fiction literary prizes. The competition takes place annually and has a Junior category, for books written for children aged under 14. The winner of the junior prize receives £10,000 and up to five short-listed entrants from each category each receive £1,000. Books must be written in English and published for the first time in the year of the award.

Genres Scientific Non-fiction titles for General and Junior readerships.

Submission Guidelines All entries must be submitted by publishers.

Tips Entries may cover any aspect of science and technology, but educational textbooks published are not eligible.

Bardd Plant Cymru (The Welsh Language Children's Poet Laureate)

Welsh Books Council, Castell Brychan, Aberystwyth, Ceredigion, SY23 2JB

- ☎ 01970 624151
- ✆ 01970 625385
- ⊛ www.cllc.org.uk

Established 2000

Insider Info Bardd Plant Cymru aims to raise the profile of poetry amongst children in Wales, and to encourage them to compose and enjoy their own poetry. The appointed laureate holds workshops and email workshops in Wales throughout the year.

Basic Skills Book Awards

Welsh Books Council, Castell Brychan, Aberystwyth, Ceredigion, SY23 2JB

- ☎ 01970 624151
- ✆ 01970 625385
- ⊛ www.cllc.org.uk

Established 2006

Insider Info Part of the Welsh Assembly Government's National Basic Skills Strategy, the Basic Skills Book Awards are for educational publishers in Wales. There are a number of categories, including Primary Age-group, Secondary Age-group and Adult books.

Genres Welsh Education and Literacy books.

Tips A number of awards are given to Welsh publishers of education and literacy books across the age ranges.

Blue Peter Book Awards

c/o Awards Administrator, Fraser Ross Associates, 6 Wellington Place, Edinburgh, EH6 7EQ

- ☎ 0131 553 2759
- ✆ 0131 553 2759
- ◉ lindsey.fraser@tiscali.co.uk
- ◉ kjross@tiscali.co.uk
- ⊛ www.bbc.co.uk/cbbc/bluepeter/bookclub/awards

Established 2000

Insider Info A shortlist of books for young people is put together by a panel of celebrity judges. The winners are then decided by a selection of young judges, chosen through a selection process. Categories are: The Best Book with Facts; The Book I Couldn't Put Down; and The Best Illustrated Book to Read Aloud. From these three winning titles, a Book of the Year is selected. These awards are presented annually, and winners receive a trophy.

Genres Children's Fiction and Non-fiction

Submission Guidelines The awards take place in June each year. Titles must be previously published.

Tips Previous winners include high profile books such as *Harry Potter and the Philosopher's Stone* by J.K. Rowling and *Private Peaceful* by Michael Morpurgo.

BolognaRagazzi Award

Piazza Constituzione 6, Bologna, 40128, Italy

- ☎ 0039 51 615 4463
- ✆ 0039 51 587 0552
- ◉ bookfair@bolognafiere.it
- ⊛ www.bookfair.bolognafiere.it

Insider Info A prize awarded at the Bologna Children's Book Fair every year. There are three categories: Fiction; Non-fiction; and 'New Horizons' (books from emerging countries). The books are judged on their creativity, design and educational value and winners are displayed for the duration of the book fair.

The Booktrust Early Years Awards

Book House, 45 East Hill, Wandsworth, London, SW18 2QZ

- ☎ 020 8516 2972
- ✆ 020 8516 2978
- ◉ tarryn@booktrust.org.uk
- ⊛ www.booktrust.org.uk

Established 2004

Insider Info Sponsored by Booktrust. This annual award has three categories: Best book for babies under one year old; Best Picture Book for pre-school children up to five years of age; and Best New Illustrator, again up to five years old, for the illustrator's first ever published pre-school picture book. The winners will each receive a cheque for £2,000 (to be shared between author and illustrator if appropriate) and a crystal ornament. In addition, the Best New Illustrator will receive a specially commissioned award. The publishers of the winning titles will be presented with an award naming them as one of the Booktrust Early Years Awards Publishers of the Year. The aim of the prize is to celebrate, publicise and reward the exciting range of books being published today for babies, toddlers and pre-school children. Another aim is to promote and make these books accessible to as wide an audience as possible. The publishers of all three books will also receive a crystal ornament pronouncing them as one of the Booktrust Early Years Awards Publishers of the Year. There is a panel of five, chaired by Wendy Cooling, Children's Book Consultant. She is joined each year by a representative from the library service, the health service, a parent from the National Bookstart programme and a children's illustrator. The prize is only open to UK citizens, but other nationalities are eligible to enter, as long as they have been in the British Isles for at least five years.

Genres Juvenile, Baby books

Submission Guidelines Deadline for entry is June, this date may change. There is no entry fee. Work should be published previously, between September 1 and August 31.

Tips Entries are invited from publishers only.

Book Trust Teenage Prize
Book House, 45 East Hill, London, SW18 2QZ
- 020 8516 2986
- 020 8516 2978
- hannah@booktrust.org.uk
- www.bookheads.org.uk

Established 2003

Insider Info Recognises the best works of Teenage Fiction in the UK in the preceding year. The competition is held annually and the winner receives £2,500. It is open to residents of the UK, as well as citizens of the UK. Works must be in English but can be in any genre, providing they are aimed at children.

Genres Story Collections and Fiction for 13–16 year olds

Submission Guidelines Submissions must be received by the end of March each year and should be previously published between July 1 of the previous year and June 30 of the current year.

Tips Entries are invited from publishers only.

Bookworms Short Story Competition
3 Yeomanry Road, Battlefield Enterprise Park, Shrewsbury, Shropshire, SY1 3EH
- 01743 360573
- 01743 443388
- kazbamail-fern@yahoo.co.uk
- beanpolebooks.co.uk

Competition/Award Director Karen Lowe

Established 2006

Insider Info This competition is sponsored by Beanpole Books and involves submitting a 1,500 word short story, suitable for general reading on a public website. The title is chosen from the crossword titles in *50 Bookworms Crosswords*, to give an opportunity to a new or little-published writer to share their work with a wider public. This competition takes place annually and the prize is £150 and publication on the Beanpole Books website for a year. Entries are judged by Karen Lowe and a guest judge (will vary each year). Entry to the competition assumes Beanpole Books has the right to publish the winning story on its website for twelve months. This competition is open to any UK based writer.

Genres Fiction and Short Stories

Submission Guidelines Submissions must be received by October 30. Entry form is included with purchase of *50 Bookworms Crosswords*, £3.99. Short stories must be previously unpublished.

Tips View the website to see previous winners. The story should be suitable for general viewing on a public website which may be accessed by children. No science fiction, violence, explicit sex, or strong language. This is a new competition. Details may vary in future years.

The Branford Boase Award
Library and Information HQ, 81 North Walls, Winchester, SO23 8BY
- 01962 826658
- anne.marley@tiscali.co.uk
- www.branfordboaseaward.org.uk

Insider Info Annually awarded for the most promising first novel by a new writer of a book for young people. The winner receives £1,000 and a handcrafted box. Writers may have been published before in other fields, but must enter their first, unpublished, book for children.

Genres Fiction, Novels for young people aged seven plus.

Submission Guidelines Entry deadline is December. Guidelines available on website. Work should be published previously, between January 1 and December 31.

Tips Entries are invited from publishers, who may submit up to five books. No short story collections by multiple authors, poetry or picture books.

Brian Way Award
Theatre Centre, Shoreditch Town Hall, London, EC1V 9LT
- 020 7729 3066

☎ 020 7739 9741
✉ admin@theatre-centre.co.uk
🌐 www.theatre-centre.co.uk
Established 2000
Insider Info Formerly the Arts Council Children's Award. The award is named after the late Brian Way, founder of the Theatre Centre, and designed to celebrate the achievements and raise the profile of playwrights who write specifically for young people. The competition takes place annually and offers prize money of £6,000 for a first, second or third production of a play written within the last decade. Writers must either be resident in the UK or Republic of Ireland, or have had a writing association with a UK theatre company or group.
Genres Plays for young people up to the age of 18.
Submission Guidelines Submissions must be received by November 30 each year, and the play itself must be performed between July 1 the previous year and June 30 of the current year. Postal submissions of scripts may come from agents or writers themselves. Also include details of where and when performances have taken place.
Tips Judges look for plays that demonstrate a special quality in the writing, that stimulate the imagination and use innovative languages and forms.

The British Academy Children's Awards (Children's BAFTAs)
195 Piccadilly, London, W1J 9LN
☎ 020 7734 0022
☎ 020 7292 5858
✉ reception@bafta.org
🌐 www.bafta.org
Established 1947
Insider Info Awards sponsored by Electronic Arts and voted for by members of the British Academy of Film and Television Arts (BAFTA). The awards recognise the skills and achievements of those involved in international children's film and television during the previous year.
Tips Main awards are not open for submissions, but a special award for children - Me and My Movie - is an open competition for child film-makers. See separate entry for further details.

CBI Bisto Book of the Year Award
17 North Great Georges Street, Dublin 1, Republic of Ireland
☎ 00353 1 872 7475
☎ 00353 1 872 8486
✉ info@childrensbooksireland.com

🌐 www.childrensbooksireland.com
Competition/Award Director Mary Shine Thompson
Established 1990
Insider Info The awards consist of: the CBI Bisto Book of the Year Award; three CBI Bisto Honour Awards (authors or illustrators); and The Eilís Dillon Award (for a first children's book). The awards are presented annually and the winner of the Book of the Year Award receives €10,000 as well as a perpetual trophy and framed certificate. Honour Awards winners share a prize fund of €6,000 and each receive a framed certificate. The Eilís Dillon winner wins €3,000, a trophy and a framed certificate. Writers and illustrators must be from Ireland, or resident in Ireland at the time of publication.
Genres Children's Books
Submission Guidelines Submissions must be received by December 15 each year. Titles must have been published between January 1 and December 31 each year. Entries must be submitted by publishers. Send 12 hard copies with an entry form.

Chapter One Promotions Children's Short Story Competition
PO Box 43667, London, SE22 9XU
☎ 0845 456 5364
☎ 0845 456 5347
✉ kidskorner@chapteronepromotions.com
🌐 www.chapteronepromotions.com
Insider Info A short story competition for children writing stories of up to 1,000 words. Themes to choose from are published on the website. Individuals may enter, as may groups from particular schools or colleges. Age categories are: 7–9; 10–12; 13–15 and 16–18. In each category, first, second and third place winners will receive £150, £75 and £50 respectively. Open to any writer that either lives within the Commonwealth and is English speaking, or an English national.
Submission Guidelines Submissions must be received by May 31 each year. There is a fee of £5 per story. Schools, colleges and youth clubs can submit group entries of up to 30 stories for £50. Submissions may be made online or by post, and may be typed or handwritten.
Tips Stories must relate to one of the set themes on the website.

The Children's Laureate
Book House, 45 East Hill, London, SW18 2QZ
- ☎ 020 8516 2976
- ☎ 020 8516 2978
- ✉ childrenslaureate@booktrust.org.uk
- 🌐 www.childrenslaureate.org

Established 1998

Insider Info Sponsored by Booktrust, the Children's Laureate is a title awarded to a writer or illustrator for a children's book that has made an outstanding contribution to children's publishing. 2007–2009's Laureate is Michael Rosen. Awarded every two years (odd years), the prize consist of the title, a medal and £10,000.

Tips Nominations are usually accepted from organisations representing librarians, critics, writers and booksellers. Contact Nikki Marsh at the above email address for further details.

Christopher Tower Poetry Prize
Tower Poetry, Christ Church, Oxford, OX1 1DP
- ☎ 01865 286591
- ✉ info@towerpoetry.org.uk
- 🌐 www.towerpoetry.org.uk/prize

Established 1990

Insider Info The Christopher Tower Poetry Prizes aim to encourage the writing of poetry amongst young people in the 16–18 year-old age group, by establishing an annual set of prizes on a given theme. The winning poet receives £3,000, second place gets £1,000 and third gets £500. Commended entries also receive £200 each.

Genres Themed Poetry

Tips The Christopher Tower Prize only accepts submissions from young poets aged 16–18.

CILIP Carnegie Medal
7 Ridgmount Street, London, WC1E 7AE
- ☎ 020 7255 0650
- ☎ 020 7255 0651
- ✉ ckg@cilip.org.uk
- 🌐 www.carnegiegreenaway.org.uk

Established 1936

Insider Info Awarded to an outstanding children's book in any category. The award is presented annually, and the winner receives a golden medal and £500 worth of books to donate to a library of their choice. Books must be in English and have had their first publication in the UK, or have had a co-publication within a three month time lapse.

Genres Children's Fiction or Non-fiction

Submission Guidelines Submissions must be previously published.

Tips Both e-books and short stories are eligible for this award. Nominations for the award are made by members of CILIP.

CILIP Kate Greenaway Medal
7 Ridgmount Street, London, WC1E 7AE
- ☎ 020 7255 0650
- ☎ 020 7255 0651
- ✉ ckg@cilip.org.uk
- 🌐 www.carnegiegreenaway.org.uk

Established 1955

Insider Info Awarded for excellence in children's book illustrating during the previous year. The award is presented annually, and the winner receives a golden medal and £500 worth of books to donate to a library of their choice. Winners are also granted the Colin Mears Award, which is worth £5,000.

Genres Illustrated Children's Books

Submission Guidelines Submissions must be previously published.

Tips Nominations are taken from members of CILIP. Books for both older and younger children are included.

The CLPE Poetry Award
CLPE, Webber Street, London, SE1 8QW
- ☎ 020 7633 0840
- ☎ 020 7928 4624
- ✉ ann@clpe.co.uk
- 🌐 www.clpe.co.uk

Competition/Award Director Ann Lazim

Established 2003

Insider Info Awarded by the Centre for Literacy in Primary Education (CLPE), the CLPE Poetry Award celebrates excellence in poetry for young people. It is awarded annually for a single poet collection or anthology published the preceding year.

Genres Children's Poetry.

Costa Book Awards
Booksellers Association, Minster House, 272 Vauxhall Bridge Road, London, SW1V 1BA
- ☎ 020 7802 0802
- ✉ dionne.parker@whitbread.com
- ✉ naomi.gane@booksellers.org.uk
- 🌐 www.costabookawards.com

Established 1971

Insider Info These awards have been designed to celebrate British contemporary writing and were formerly known as the Whitbread Book Awards.

There are five categories: Novel; First Novel; Biography; Poetry; and Children's Books. The awards are held annually and each of the category winners receives £5,000, and the overall winner receives a further £25,000. Writers must have been resident in the UK or Ireland for at least six months of each of the previous three years, but do not necessarily have to be of UK or Irish nationality.

Genres Fiction and Non-fiction.

Submission Guidelines Submissions must be received by the end of June each year, and must be previously published between 1st November of the previous year and 30th October in the current year.

Tips Short story collections are not accepted at present. Accepts submissions from publishers only. Contact the Booksellers Association for an application form.

Eleanor Farjeon Award

Ⓦ www.childrensbookcircle.org.uk

Established 1965

Insider Info This award is sponsored by the Children's Book Circle and is awarded to a teacher, publisher, bookseller, librarian, writer, artist or other person who has made an outstanding contribution to the world of children's books. The award is presented annually and the winner receives a cash sum of around £750.

Tips Nominations are from members of the Children's Book Circle only.

Foyle Young Poets of the Year Award

The Poetry Society, 22 Betterton Street, London, WC2H 9BX

Ⓞ 020 7420 9894

Ⓕ 020 7240 4818

Ⓔ education@poetrysociety.org.uk

Ⓦ www.poetrysociety.org.uk

Established 1997

Insider Info The Foyle Young Poets of the Year Award is Britain's most prestigious poetry prize for young writers between the ages of 11–17. The award annually looks for 100 of the best young poets in the UK, split into two age groups: 11–14 and 15–17.

Genres Poetry by children.

Tips The Foyle Award is for children and young poets exclusively, and does not accept submissions from adult writers.

George Devine Award

9 Lower Mall, Hammersmith, London, W6 9DJ

Competition/Award Director Christine Smith

Insider Info A prize awarded to a new playwright, in memory of the former artistic director of the Royal Court Theatre. Prize money is usually £10,000.

Genres Scripts

Submission Guidelines Submissions must be received by the end of March each year. Contact Christine Smith in writing for details.

Tips When submitting include two copies of the script, plus SAE for return.

Grace Dieu Writers' Circle

c/o Rockside, 139 London Road, Coalville, Leicestershire, LE67 3JE

Ⓞ 01530 450203

Ⓕ 01530 811495

Ⓔ kshatri@ntlworld.com

Ⓦ http://beehive.thisisleicestershire.co.uk

Competition/Award Director Tony Gutteridge

Established 2004

Insider Info Annual short story and poetry competition to promote and challenge writing, and to provide reward both financially and by way of publication. £1 from each book sold will be donated to Rainbows Children's Hospice in Leicestershire. Short story prizes are £200/£100/£50/£25/£15, poetry prizes are £100/£75/£50/£25/£15. Short story judge will be Simon Whaley (published author), poetry judge will be Dr. Kerry Featherstone. Winners agree to publication in Grace Dieu's anthology and on the website. All entries must be written in English observing usual competition rules, and competition is open to all (2004 winner was resident in New Zealand).

Genres Fiction, Poetry

Submission Guidelines Submissions should be made by February 28th each year. Accepts simultaneous submissions and submissions from previously published authors. Entry fee for short story competition is £5, poetry fee is £3. Reduction for multiple entries (see website for further information). Submitted material must be unpublished.

The Guardian Children's Fiction Award

119 Farringdon Road, London, EC1R 3ER

Ⓞ 020 7239 9694

Ⓕ 020 7239 9933

Ⓔ books@guardian.co.uk

Established 1967

Insider Info Awarded annually to the best children's fiction book for children aged seven plus. Picture books are not eligible. The winner receives £1,500, the award is decided by *The Guardian*'s Children's Book Editor and a selection of authors. Writers must be a resident of Britain or the Commonwealth.

Genres Children's fiction

Submission Guidelines Work should be published in the UK, in the year preceding the award.

Tips Submissions are usually made by publishers.

Hans Christian Andersen Awards
British Section of IBBY, PO Box 20875, London, SE22 9WQ

- 020 8299 1641
- ann@lazim.demon.co.uk
- www.ibby.org

Established 1956

Insider Info This award is sponsored by IBBY (International Board on Books for Young People) and is an award made to a living writer and/or illustrator who is seen to have made a lasting contribution to children's literature. It is the highest international recognition in the field of children's books and her Majesty Queen Margrethe II of Denmark is the Patron. The award is offered every two years (even years). The prize consists of a gold medal and a diploma, presented during the biennial IBBY Congress.

Genres Illustrated Children's books.

Submission Guidelines Submissions must be previously published.

Tips Writer and illustrator prizes may be awarded separately but both must have an entire body of work that has influenced children's literature over a period of time.

Kelpies Prize
15 Harrison Gardens, Edinburgh, EH11 1SH

- 0131 337 2372
- 0131 347 9919
- www.florisbooks.co.uk/kelpiesprize

Insider Info An annual competition, sponsored by Floris Books, for the best unpublished novel for children aged 9–12 set entirely, or mainly, in Scotland. Winners receive a cash prize and their novel will be published in the Kelpies series by Floris Books. Open to any writer, but the book must be set in Scotland. Writers may have been published before, but the winning entry must not have been.

Genres Fiction, Novels, Older Children/Young Teenage Novels

Submission Guidelines Submissions should be made by February of each year. Guidelines are available on the website.

Tips The stories must appeal to both boys and girls within the relevant age group. Novels with animals as main characters, and romantic novels are not generally recommended.

Killie Writing Competition
Killie Writing Competition, Kilmarnock College, KA3 7AT

- 01355 302160
- enquiries@killie.co.uk
- www.killie.co.uk

Established 2000

Insider Info An annual expressive writing competition with four categories: 5 to 7 year olds, 8 to 11 year olds, 12 to 16 year olds, and adults. Submissions are excepted for any style, format or length of writing, whether it is poetry or prose. The winner receives £1,000 and a trophy.

Tips The Killie Writing Competition accepts submissions of any type of writing, but always check the website prior to submission to ensure the competition is running.

Lancashire Country Library Children's Book of the Year Award
Lancashire County Library Headquarters, PO Box 61, County Hall, Preston, PR1 8RJ

- 01772 534751
- 01772 264043
- library@lcl.lancscc.gov.uk
- www.lancashire.gov.uk/libraries

Competition/Award Director Jake Hope

Established 1986

Insider Info An annual award established to offer a forum for young people to draw attention to the sorts of books they rave about and would most like to recommend. Awarded for the best work of fiction for 12–14 year olds, written by a UK author and first published the preceding year. The winner receives £500 and an engraved decanter.

Genres Children's Fiction

Literary Review Grand Poetry Prize
44 Lexington Street, London, W1F 0LW

- 020 7437 9392
- 020 7734 1844
- editorial@literaryreview.co.uk
- www.literaryreview.co.uk

Competition/Award Director Editor, Nancy Sladek

Established 1990

Insider Info The Literary Review magazine run a monthly competition for poems on a given subject, including children's poetry. A grand prize of £5,000 is awarded to the years best submission.

Submission Guidelines Poems must be no longer than 24 lines and must have rhyme, correct scansion and must make sense.

London Writers Competition
Room 224a, The Town Hall, Wandsworth High Street, London, SW18 2PU

- 020 8871 8711
- 020 8871 7630
- arts@wandsworth.gov.uk
- www.wandsworth.gov.uk

Established 1977

Insider Info Sponsored by Wandsworth Council and Roehampton University. An annual competition designed to encourage people who work, live, or study in London to write. The categories include poetry, story, play and fiction for children. There is a total prize fund of £5,000.

Genres Fiction, Poetry, Scripts, Children's Fiction

Submission Guidelines Work should be previously unpublished.

Tips Details of closing dates for future competitions will be published in the arts events section of the Wandsworth Council website.

Macmillan Prize for Children's Picture Book Illustration
Macmillan Children's Books, 20 New Wharf Road, London, N1 9RR

- 020 7014 6124
- 020 7014 6124
- www.panmacmillan.com

Insider Info An annual competition to find the best original illustration for children's books. Entrants are invited to submit a 'mock book' based on their own story or an out of copyright text. Art and illustration students are usually invited to apply. The winner receives £1,000 and the possibility of being published with Macmillan.

Submission Guidelines Work should be previously unpublished.

Tips Details of the scheme are usually advertised through art colleges and the art departments of universities.

Marsh Award for Children's Literature in Translation
National Centre for Research in Children's Literature, Roehampton University, Froebel College, Roehampton Lane, London, SW15 5PJ

- 020 8392 3008
- 020 8392 3819
- g.lathey@roehampton.ac.uk

Competition/Award Director Dr. Gillian Lathey

Established 1995

Insider Info Awarded to the best book translated into English and published by a British publisher. Competition takes place every two years (odd years) and the winner receives £1,000.

Genres Fiction, Non-fiction, and Children's books for ages four and over.

Submission Guidelines Work should be published previously.

Tips Encyclopedias, reference books, audio books and e-books are not eligible.

Mary Vaughan Jones Award
Castell Brychan, Aberystwyth, SY23 2JB

- 01970 624151
- 01970 625385
- wbc.children@wbc.org.uk
- www.wbc.org.uk

Established 1985

Insider Info The award is from the Welsh Books Council, and awarded to a person who has made a significant contribution to children's literature in Wales over a long period of time. Awarded every three years, with the next award in 2009, the winner receives a silver trophy.

Tips Not open to submissions.

Me and My Movie
CBBC, BBC Television Centre, Wood Lane, London, W12 7RJ

- 020 8743 8000
- www.bbc.co.uk/cbbc/meandmymovie

Established 2007

Insider Info An award in partnership with CBBC and BAFTA to recognise child film makers. Winners will be awarded a special prize at the Children's BAFTAs.

Submission Guidelines Children are invited to submit their entire homemade films to CBBC, check the website for submission details.

Tips Visit the website for tips on how to become involved with film making at a young age. There will be *Me and My Movie* touring roadshows throughout the summer of 2007 to promote the award. Further details will appear on the website, or can be obtained from CBBC.

Nasen and TES Special Educational Needs Book Awards

Nasen House, 4–5 Amber Business Village, Amber Close, Amington, Tamworth, B77 4RP
- 01827 311500
- 01827 313005
- welcome@nasen.org.uk
- www.nasen.org.uk

Insider Info Awards to celebrate writers and publishers of books that help and encourage children with special educational needs, as well as teachers. Categories include: Academic Book Award; Books for Teaching and Learning; and Children's Award. Awarded annually, the winners in each category receive £500. Books must have been published in the UK.

Genres Fiction, Non-fiction, Children's Special Educational

Submission Guidelines Deadline for entry is June. Work must be published previously.

Tips The awards usually take place in October, with a shortlist announced in August. Books that portray special educational needs in a positive light are often successful, especially in the children's category.

Nestlé Children's Book Prize

Book House, 45 East Hill, London, SW18 2QZ
- 020 8516 2972
- 020 8516 2978
- query@booktrust.org.uk
- www.booktrusted.co.uk

Established 1985

Insider Info An award designed to stimulate interest and high standards in children's books. The prize is split into three categories by age: 5 years and under; 6–8 years; and 9–11 years. Awarded annually, Gold award winners in each category receive £2,500; Silver Award winners receive £1,500; Bronze award winners receive £500. Books are judged by an adult panel and three are shortlisted in each category. The Gold, Silver and Bronze prizes are decided by children who are selected after the completion of a task at selected schools, who judge the books for their own age category.

Genres Children's Fiction or Poetry.

Submission Guidelines Deadline for entry is July. Work should be previously published.

Tips All work must be submitted by UK publishers.

New Writing North

New Writing North, 2 School Lane, Wickham, Newcastle upon Tyne, NE16 4SL
- 0191 488 8580
- 0191 488 8576
- mail@newwritingnorth.com
- www.nr-foundationwriters.com

Insider Info An annual award of £60,000 split over three years to enable a writer to completely concentrate on writing. Applicants must have lived and worked in Tees Valley, Tyneside, County Durham, Northumberland or Cumbria for at least three years. Open to writers of poetry, prose, children's fiction or biography, who have published at least two novels, collections of poetry, short stories or biography (self-publishing is excluded).

Submission Guidelines Send up to 6,000 words of fiction or up to 40 pages of poems. This work should be taken from your current work in progress. Apply with a sample of up to 6,000 words or 40 poems. This work must be supported by the following items: an outline or synopsis; explanation of the stage the work is at, i.e commissioned, first draft etc. Also include a writing biography. Send five copies to New Writing North. Deadline is 15th December 2007.

Noma Award for Publishing in Africa

PO Box 128, Witney, Oxfordshire, OX8 5XU
- 01993 775235
- 01993 709265
- maryljay@aol.com
- www.nomaaward.org

Competition/Award Director Mary Jay

Established 1979

Insider Info Sponsored by Kodansha Ltd, Japan. Annual US$10,000 award for a book by an African writer and published by an independent/autonomous African publishing house domiciled on the continent. Scholarly works, literature and children's books are eligible. Submission and entry must be made by publisher; three entries are allowed, maximum. The purpose is to encourage African scholars and writers to publish with independent/autonomous African publishers, rather than abroad, with a view to strengthening African publishing. A panel of African and international scholars and book experts, judge the prize, which is chaired by Walter Bgoya, Tanzanian publisher. No entry fee. The writer must be an African national, wherever resident.

Genres Fiction, Non-fiction, Poetry, Essays, Juvenile, Novels, Short stories, Drama

Submission Guidelines Deadline for entry is March each year. Guidelines and entry forms do not need SAE; they can be posted, emailed, or downloaded from the website. Previously published entries must appear in print between January 1 and December 31 the previous year.

Tips If interpretation of guidelines gives rise to questions of eligibility, the Secretariat can advise.

North East Book Award

c/o Eileen Armstrong, Cramlington High School, Cramlington, Northumberland, NE23 6BN

✆ 01670 712311

✆ 01670 730598

✉ earmstrong@cchsonline.co.uk

Insider Info An annual award presented to the best book of children's fiction published the preceding year. The short list is selected by librarians and teachers while the overall winner is voted on by Year 10 pupils.

Tips The North East Book Award is unique in that there is no prize money for the winner, but every student taking part receives a £5 book voucher supplied by Blackwells, to spend in their local bookshop.

Northern Rock Foundation Writer's Award

New Writing North, 2 School Lane, Wickham, Newcastle upon Tyne, NE16 4SL

✆ 0191 488 8580

✆ 0191 488 8576

✉ mail@newwritingnorth.com

🌐 www.nr-foundationwriters.com

About An annual award of £60,000 split over three years to enable a writer to completely concentrate on writing. Applicants must have lived and worked in Tees Valley, Tyneside, County Durham, Northumberland or Cumbria for at least three years. The award is for writers who have already had two or more books published (self-publishing is excluded). It is open to writers of both literary and genre fiction, poetry, biography and children's literature. Apply with a sample of up to 6,000 words or 40 poems. The samples should be taken from your current work in progress. Work must be supported by the following items: an outline or synopsis; explanation of the stage the work is at i.e. commissioned, first draft etc. Also include a writing biography. Send five copies to New Writing North. Deadline is 15th December 2007.

Nottingham Children's Book Awards

Nottingham City Libraries and Information Service, Sneiton Library, Sneiton Boulevard, Nottingham, NG2 4FD

✆ 0115 915 1173

🌐 www.nottinghamchildrensbookaward.co.uk

Competition/Award Director Elaine Dykes; Deborah Sheppard

Established 1999

Insider Info An annual award for best children's fiction books in four categories: Foundation, 5–7 year olds, 8–9 year olds and 10–11 year olds. The award is very popular in the Nottingham area and the short list and eventual winners are voted for by children in participating schools.

Ottakar's Children's Book Prize

Brewery House, 36 Milford Street, Salisbury, Wiltshire, SP1 2AP

✆ 01722 428500

✉ fiona.martin@ottakars.co.uk

Competition/Award Director Fiona Martin

Established 2005

Insider Info An annual award for an unpublished children's book. Nominees must have previously published no more than three children's books. A panel of children and booksellers select the short list and the eventual winner, who receives £1,000.

Genres Children's Fiction.

Tips The award is hosted by Ottakar's bookstore.

Peterloo Poets Open Poetry Competition

The Old Chapel, Sand Lane, Calstock, Cornwall, PL18 9QX

✆ 01822 833473

✉ info@peterloopoets.com

🌐 www.peterloopoets.com

Established 1984

Insider Info An open competition for poems of any style, in English, of up to 40 lines. Awarded annually, the prizes consist of: £1,500 for 1st place; £1,000 for 2nd place; £500 for 3rd place; £100 for 4th place; £50 for ten further runners up, and £100 for ten winners in the 15–19 year age group category. 2007 judges: John Mole, Carole Satyamurti, Peter Sansom, Harry Chambers. Copyright remains with the author, but they must agree to assign first publication rights to Peterloo Poets for inclusion in the Peterloo Competition Booklet.

Genres Poetry

Submission Guidelines Deadline for entry is March each year. Guidelines are available on the website. Entry fee is £5 per poem and £2 for the 15–19 age category. Peterloo Poets members receive one free entry, having submitted two paid-for ones. Work should be previously unpublished.

Tips Each writer may submit a maximum of ten poems. Enclose an entry form, available from the website.

Red House Children's Book Award
The Old Malt House, Aldbourne, Marlborough, Wiltshire, SN8 2DW
- ☎ 01672 540629
- ☎ 01672 541280
- ✉ marianneadey@aol.com
- ⌨ www.redhousechildrensbookaward.co.uk

Competition/Award Director Marianne Adey
Established 1980
Insider Info Sponsored by The Federation of Children's Book Groups. This annual award voted for entirely by children is given in three categories: Books for Younger Children; Books for Young Readers; and Books for Older Children. The top 50 titles are published in Red House's Pick of the Year list. The top ten writers and illustrators receive sets of children's letters and pictures relating to their book. Winners in each category receive an engraved silver bowl and the overall winner receives an oak and silver trophy for a year, and an engraved silver acorn to keep. Nominations are invited from children, writers, illustrators and publishers, and shortlisted books are published on the website. Children may then vote - either individually, or in groups through the website - for the category winners and the overall winner. Books entered must have been published in the UK for the first time in the corresponding year.
Genres Children's Fiction
Submission Guidelines Deadline for entry is December each year. Nomination forms and submissions guidelines are available on the website. Work should be published previously, between January 1 and December 31 the same year.
Tips To submit a book for consideration send 12 copies to the above address. The book must be original, although major re-workings of religious, or folk stories are accepted.

Royal Mail Awards for Scottish Children's Books
Scottish Book Trust, Sandeman's House, Trunk's Close, Edinburgh, EH1 1SR

- ☎ 0131 524 0160
- ☎ 0131 524 0161
- ✉ royalmailawards@braw.org.uk
- ⌨ www.braw.org.uk

Insider Info Awards presented for children's books across three categories; 0–7 years, 8–11 years and 12–16 years. The awards are primarily for Scottish writers and illustrators resident in Scotland. Awarded annually, a shortlist is drawn up from nominated books. The category winners and runners up are then voted on entirely by children, who register through their schools.
Genres Fiction, Non-fiction, Poetry, Children's books
Submission Guidelines Deadline for entry is January each year. Work should be published previously between January 1 and December 31.
Tips Submissions by publishers only. Books may be in English or Scots, but must be available to buy in Scotland, and by authors and illustrators living in Scotland.

Saga Children's Book Competition
c/o Jane Griffiths, HarperCollins Children's Books, 77–85 Fulham Palace Road, London, W6 8JB
- ☎ 020 8307 4080
- ⌨ www.saga.co.uk/magazine

Insider Info An annual competition run by *Saga Magazine* in association with HarperCollins publishers. The competition seeks submissions of books for older children from writers aged 50 or over. The winner will have their book published by HarperCollins.
Genres Children's Fiction
Submission Guidelines Send complete manuscripts of between 20,000 to 60,000 words (including synopsis and official entry form) by post with SAE.
Tips The competition usually begins in the September issue of *Saga Magazine*, with a deadline of the 31st of January. Details will not usually be available on the website until the September issue of *Saga* has been published.

Sheffield Children's Book Award
Schools Library Service, 125 Carter Knowle Road, Sheffield, S7 2EX
- ☎ 0114 250 6840
- ☎ 0114 250 6841
- ✉ schools.library@sheffield.gov.uk
- ⌨ www.sheffieldchildrensbookaward.org.uk

Established 1988

Insider Info The Sheffield Children's Book Award was first started to encourage children and young people to read, and to highlight the very best children's books published each year. It is an annual award, voted for by children and presented in November. The winning author receives a special trophy.

Genres Long and short Children's novels, and Picture books.

Tips The Sheffield Award has grown to the point where it is now recognised as a major children's book award in the literary world.

The Spoken Word Awards
Audiobook Publishing Association, 18 Green Lanes, Hatfield, Hertfordshire, AL10 9JT
- charlotte.mccandlish@ntlworld.com
- www.theapa.net

Competition/Award Director Charlotte McCandlish

Insider Info An annual award for excellence in spoken word publishing, including children's titles. Judges include audiobook reviewers, abridgers, producers and radio broadcasters.

The Tir Na N-Og Award
Castell Brychan, Aberystwyth, SY23 2JB
- 01970 624151
- 01970 625385
- wbc.children@wbc.org.uk
- www.wbc.org.uk

Established 1976

Insider Info The award is sponsored by Cyngor Llyfrau Cymru (Welsh Books Council) and is an award for children's books. The award is split over three categories: English language books; Welsh language books - Primary sector; and Welsh language books - Secondary sector. The award is judged annually. The winner in each category receives £3,000.

Genres Children's books

Submission Guidelines Work should have been previously published.

The UKLA Children's Publishing Awards
4th Floor, Attenborough Building, University of Leicester, Leicester, LE1 7RH
- 01491 836631
- dwright@brookes.ac.uk
- www.ukla.org/conferences_awards

Competition/Award Director Debbie Wright

Insider Info The UKLA Children's Publishing Awards are presented biennially. They are distinguished from other book awards by focusing on literacy, and as such are not given solely on the basis of content, but also on the means of expression. There are different categories of awards: Picture book; Fiction; and Non-fiction.

Submission Guidelines Publishers are invited to submit three copies of each title, to be entered by post to the UKLA Publications Office.

The V&A Illustration Awards
The Word & Image Department, Victoria & Albert Museum, London, SW7 2RL
- 020 7942 2392
- 020 7942 2392
- a.villa@vam.ac.uk
- www.vam.ac.uk/illustrationawards

Competition/Award Director Annemarie Bilclough

Insider Info An annual award given to practising illustrators for work first published the preceding year. There are three award categories: Book cover; Book illustration and Jacket illustration. A first and second prize winner will be chosen from each category. The overall best illustration will receive a prize of £3,500, while the other two first place category winners will receive £1,500. The three second place category winners will each receive £750.

Genres Book and Jacket Illustration.

Tips Also hosts a Student Illustrator of the Year Award, with a first prize of £1,300.

Ver Poets Open Competition
181 Sandridge Road, St. Albans, Hertfordshire, AL1 4AH
- www.verpoets.org.uk

Insider Info An open competition for poetry of up to 30 lines on any theme or subject. The competition is held annually. The overall winner receives £500, second place wins £300 and third place wins £100. The copyright remains with the author.

Genres Poetry

Submission Guidelines Submissions should be received by April of each year. Entry fees are: £3 per poem, £10 for 4 poems, and £2 each for the 11th poem onwards. Work should be unpublished.

Tips Submit two copies of each poem with an application form, downloadable from the website. Please do not submit any translations, or poems that have been entered in any other competition.

Winchester Writers' Conference Competitions

Faculty of Arts, University of Winchester, Winchester, Hampshire, SO22 4NR
- 01962 827238
- barbara.large@winchester.ac.uk
- www.writersconference.co.uk

Competition/Award Director Barbara Large

Insider Info The Winchester Writers' Conference, which takes place at the end of June, features 15 different writing competitions with up to 64 sponsored prizes. Recent categories include: Echo Feature Article, First Three Pages of a Novel, Haiku, The Hyde 900 Scriptwriting Competition, Life Writing, Local History, A Page of Prose, Poetry, Reaching Out, Retirement: The Day I Retired and Now, Short Stories, The Shorter Short Stories, Slim Volume - Small Edition, Writing Can Be Murder, Writing For Children, and Young Writer's Poetry.

Write a Story for Children Competition

PO Box 95, Huntingdon, Cambridgeshire, PE28 5RR
- 01487 832752
- 01487 832752
- enquiries@childrens-writers.co.uk
- www.childrens-writers.co.uk

Competition/Award Director Roger Dewar
Established 1985

Insider Info The competition is sponsored by the Academy of Children's Writers and is for a short story of up to 2,000 words, aimed at children of any age. The author must be over 18 and previously unpublished. The competition is held annually. First Prize is £2,000, Second Prize is £300 and Third Prize is £200. The competition is judged by an independent panel. The competition is open to all.

Genres Fiction, Juvenile and Short Stories
Submission Guidelines Submissions must be received by the end of March each year. Guidelines and entry forms are available with SAE. The entry fee is £2.10, $5, or €5.

Tips Please read the rules and conditions, available on the website.

Writers Inc Writers-of-the-Year Competition

14 Somerset Gardens, London, SE13 7SY
- 020 8305 8844
- 020 8469 2147

Established 1993

Insider Info An open competition for poetry and prose across various categories. The 2007 categories were: Poems; Extended sequences of poems; Short stories (50–2,500 words); and Writing for children (8–12 years, up to 20,000 words). The competition is held annually. The prize money totals £3,000 and winners will be invited to read their work at a Writers Inc event. A portion of the prize fund may be allocated as bursaries, awarded to writers from London to attend a writing weekend at the Abbey in Sutton Courtenay, Oxfordshire. One winner will be submitted to the Forward Poetry Prize and in the category for writing for children, the winning entry will be read by a London literary agency. Judges may change each year. For 2007 the judges were Sue Hubbard, a freelance art critic, novelist and poet and Mario Petrucci, former poet-in-residence at The Imperial War Museum and with BBC Radio 3. Copyright remains with the author, but Writers Inc reserves the right to first publication after the closing date. The competition is open to any writer writing in English.

Genres Fiction, Poetry and Short stories
Submission Guidelines Submissions should be received by April. Guidelines and entry forms are available on the website. Entry fees are: £3 for poems up to 60 lines, £5 for poems over 60 lines, £8 for a poetry sequence of up to 400 lines, £5 for a short story, £12 for three short stories and £4 for a children's story. Work should be previously unpublished.

Tips Competition categories may change from year to year, so please check the website for new competition details.

Young Minds Book Award

48–50 St. John Street, London, EC1M 4DG
- 020 7336 8445
- 020 7336 8446
- bookaward@youngminds.org.uk
- www.youngminds.org.uk/bookaward

Insider Info Awarded to a publication which highlights and explores the ways a child takes in and makes sense of the world, and gives an insight into the minds of children. The competition is held annually. The winner receives £3,000.

Genres Fiction, Non-fiction, Poetry, Novels and Memoirs
Submission Guidelines Work should be previously published.

Tips The award tends be for an adult book that conveys childhood experiences, rather than a children's book, or an academic study.

Young Writers' Programme
Royal Court Theatre, Sloane Square, London, SW1W 8AS

☎ 020 7565 5050

✆ 020 7565 5001

✉ ywp@royalcourttheatre.com

🌐 www.royalcourttheatre.com

Insider Info The Royal Court Young Writers' Programme is open to anyone between the ages of 13 and 25 who wants to submit a play script on any subject. Workshops and projects run all year round, and successful plays may be presented by the Royal Court Theatre.

FOR WRITERS AND ILLUSTRATORS

Aspects Festival
North Down Museum, Bangor, County Down, Northern Ireland
- 028 9127 8032
- 028 9127 1370
- www.northdown.gov.uk

Dates September

About A popular five day festival celebrating the best of Irish writing. Events include readings, workshops and showcases featuring many guest authors. Covering all genres, the festival also includes a children's writing workshop.

Bank of Scotland Children's International Theatre Festival
45a George Street, Edinburgh, EH2 2HT
- 0131 225 8050
- 0131 225 6440
- info@imaginate.org.uk
- www.imaginate.org.uk/festival

Contact Director, Tony Reekie

Dates May/June

About An annual festival of international theatre for children and young people. Also runs a range of outreach programmes, taking live theatre into schools and community groups in the Edinburgh and Lothian area. The festival had over 12,500 visitors in 2007.

Bath Literature Festival
Festival Offices, Abbey Chambers, Kingston Buildings, Bath, BA1 1NT
- 01225 462261
- 01225 445551
- info@bathfestivals.org.uk
- www.bathlitfest.org.uk

Contact Artistic Director, Sarah LeFanu

Dates Late February/early March

About Ten days of literary events covering all forms of writing, including events for children and young people. Presents the best in local, national and international writers to an ever-increasing audience.

Beverley Literature Festival
Wordquake, Council Offices, Skirlaugh, East Riding of Yorkshire, HU11 5HN
- 01482 392745
- john@bevlit.org
- www.beverley-literature-festival.org

Contact Festival Director, John Clarke

Dates October

About Ten days of literature events and readings, including some to live music. The festival covers fiction, poetry and children's books. Many events take place in libraries around the East Riding area. A children's programme runs alongside the main festival in support of Children's Book Week. The festival is funded by the East Riding Library Service and Arts Council England.

Beyond the Border
St. Donats Arts Centre, St. Donats Castle, Vale of Glamorgan, CF61 1WF
- 01446 799100
- 01446 799101
- enquiries@stdonats.com
- www.beyondtheborder.com

Contact Festival Director, David Ambrose

Dates July

About Beyond The Border (BTB) is Wales' leading international storytelling festival. It is dedicated to promoting understanding of the world's pre-literature and oral traditions. The festival takes place over the first weekend of July and features a competition for young storytellers (aged between ten and twenty) to become BTB Young Storyteller of the Year.

Bologna Children's Book Fair
Piazza Costituzione 6, Bologna, 40128, Italy
- 0039 51 282242
- 0039 51 637 4011
- bookfair@bolognafiere.it
- www.bookfair.bolognafiere.it

Dates March/April

About Bologna Book Fair is the world's leading event for children's publishing copyright professionals. It acts as a forum addressing the needs of producers, book publishers, literary agents, television/film companies and licensing developers. An average of 4,000 children's publishing professionals attend the annual fair, from over 70 countries, although entry is restricted to those in the publishing trade.

The fair also serves as a showcase for illustrators who may enter their work into the Bologna Illustrators Exhibition.

Book Now! Literature Festival

The Arts Service, Orleans House Gallery, Riverside, Twickenham, TW1 3DJ
- 020 8831 6000
- 020 8744 0501
- artsinfo@richmond.gov.uk
- www.richmond.gov.uk/literature

Contact Arts Programmer, Sarah Hinsley
Dates November
About A series of high-profile writers and media personalities give lectures on aspects of writing and literature. The festival features events for novelists, poets, storytellers, biographers and historians, as well as exhibitions and storytelling sessions for children and young adults.

Booktide Children's Arts Festival

Ceredigion County Council, Aberystwyth Library, Corporation Street, Aberystwyth, Ceredigion, SW23 2BU
- 01970 633702
- www.aber.ac.uk/artscentre

Contact Elinor Ingham
Dates October
About A festival of readings, workshops and talks for schools throughout the region.

Bournemouth Literary Festival

c/o Lillian Avon, 20A Parkwood Road, Bournemouth, BH5 2BH
- 01202 417535
- info@bournemouthliteraryfestival.co.uk
- www.bournemouthliteraryfestival.co.uk

Contact Director and Founder, Lillian Avon
Dates Summer/Autumn
About Bournemouth's international and multicultural literary festival offers events for both adults and children, including authors' news, views and reviews, competitions, parties, performances

and workshops. Each year has a theme, or set of themes, with events spread across the end of summer and early autumn.

Cambridge Wordfest

ADC Theatre, Park Street, Cambridge, CB5 8AS
- 01223 264404
- cam.wordfest@btinternet.com
- www.cambridgewordfest.co.uk

Contact Festival Director, Cathy Moore
Dates April
About A weekend literature festival with events covering fiction, poetry, biography and politics, as well as workshops and an expanded programme of events for children.

Cheltenham Literature Festival

Town Hall, Imperial Square, Cheltenham, Gloucester, GL50 1QA
- 01242 263494
- 01242 256457
- www.cheltenhamfestivals.com

Contact Artistic Director, Sarah Smyth
Dates October
About An annual festival of literature with talks, lectures, seminars, readings, poetry and workshops. Also runs the *Book It!* festival for children within the main festival.

Chester Literature Festival

Chester Literature Festival Office, Viscount House, River Lane, Saltney, Chester, CH4 8RH
- 01244 674020
- info@chesterlitfest.org.uk
- www.chester-literature-festival.org.uk

Contact Katherine Seddon
Dates Throughout October
About An annual festival covering literature, theatre, politics, journalism, science and sport, alongside events for children and showcases for local writers.

Children's Book Festival

Festival Office, Children's Books Ireland, 17 North Great Georges Street, Dublin 1, Ireland
- 00353 1 872 7475
- 00353 1 872 7476
- info@childrensbooksireland.com
- www.childrensbooksireland.com

Contact Festival Coordinator, James Curtain
Dates October

About The Children's Book Festival is a nationwide celebration of books and reading, with a range of events taking place in libraries around Ireland.

Children's Book Week
Book House, 45 East Hill, London, SW18 2QZ
- 020 8516 2976
- 020 8516 2998
- education@booktrust.org.uk
- www.booktrust.org.uk

Dates October

About The National Children's Book Week celebrates the world of children's book and literature. One of its primary aims is to encourage children to read for pleasure by allowing them to discuss and share their favourite books, and to explore libraries and bookshops around the UK. Events are arranged in participating libraries, schools and bookstores.

Dublin Writers Festival
Dublin City Arts Office, The Lab, Foley Street, Dublin 1, Republic of Ireland
- 00353 1 222 7848
- office@dublinwritersfestival.com
- www.dublinwritersfestival.com

Contact Festival Director, Jack Gilligan; Programme Director, Liam Browne

Dates June

About A writer's festival with readings, workshops and other events, including some events specifically for children.

Edinburgh International Book Festival
5a Charlotte Square, Edinburgh, EH2 4DR
- 0131 718 5666
- 0131 226 5335
- admin@edbookfest.co.uk
- www.edbookfest.co.uk

Contact Festival Director, Catherine Lockerbie

Dates August

About A world-class festival of literature and books, with around 220,000 visitors. Generally features over 500 authors, both new and famous, from over 30 different countries. A large selection of events for toddlers, young readers, teenagers and young adults also runs alongside the main festival.

Essex Poetry Festival
Cramphorn Theatre, Fairfield Road, Chelmsford, Essex, CM1 1JG
- 01245 606505
- derek@essex-poetry-festival.co.uk
- www.essex-poetry-festival.co.uk

Contact Derek Adams

Dates October

About A festival of poetry readings and talks. The festival incorporates the Young Essex Poet of the Year competition and an adult poetry competition. Also hosts a number of fringe poetry events.

Folkestone Literary Festival
Festival Office, The Glassworks, Mill Bayt, Folkestone, CT20 1JG
- 01303 245799
- info@folkestonelitfest.co.uk
- www.folkestonelitfest.com

Contact Festival Programmer, Peter Florence; Festival Director, Ellie Beedham

Dates November

About Literary workshops and events. The festival also runs a short story competition, a poetry competition and a series of children's events.

The Guardian Hay Festival
The Drill Hall, 25 Lion Street, Hay on Wye, HR3 5AD
- 0870 990 1299
- 01497 821066
- admin@hayfestival.com
- www.hayfestival.com

Dates May to June

About Hay on Wye is a paradise for lovers of secondhand books. The Guardian Hay Festival is a major international festival, which includes talks from a number of famous literary personalities, readings, debates and workshops. Also includes many events for children and children's writers. Webcasts and podcasts of events are made available through the festival website.

Guildford Book Festival
c/o Tourist Information Office, 14 Tunsgate, Guildford, GU1 3QT
- 01483 444334
- director@guildfordbookfestival.co.uk
- www.guildfordbookfestival.co.uk

Contact Festival Director, Glenys Pycraft

Dates October

About An annual festival featuring talks, workshops and events, in and around Guildford. Events are available for all age groups, from six months upwards.

Ilkley Literature Festival
Manor House, 2 Castle Hill, Ilkley, West Yorkshire, LS29 9DT
☎ 01943 816714
☎ 01943 817079
✉ admin@ilkleyliteraturefestival.org.uk
🌐 www.ilkleyliteraturefestival.org.uk
Contact Festival Director, Rachel Feldberg
Dates September to October
About A literature festival sponsored by Skipton Building Society. The festival includes a free fringe programme and a children's programme.

Imagine: Children's Literature Festival
Purcell Room, South Bank Centre, London, SE1 8XX
☎ 020 7921 0971
☎ 020 7928 2049
✉ literature&talks@rfh.org.uk
🌐 www.rfh.org.uk/imagine
Dates February
About An annual festival at London's South Bank Centre. Celebrates children's literature with three days of events featuring authors, poets and illustrators.

Jewish Book Week
Jewish Book Council, PO Box 38247, London, NW3 5YQ
☎ 020 8343 4675
☎ 020 8343 4675
✉ jewishbookcouncil@btopenworld.com
🌐 www.jewishbookweek.com
Contact Festival Administrator, Pam Lewis
Dates February–March
About A week celebrating Jewish books and writing, featuring international speakers and events for children and young adults.

Ledbury Poetry Festival
Ledbury Poetry Festival, Church Street, Ledbury, HR8 1DH
☎ 0845 458 1743
🌐 www.poetry-festival.com
Dates July

About Britain's largest poetry festival with a resident poet, and many events for both adults and children. Ten days of poetry events including readings, performances, exhibitions, music, walks and talks and workshops. Also runs a poetry competition.

Lincoln Book Festival
City of Lincoln Council, City Hall, Beaumont Fee, Lincoln, HR8 1DH
☎ 01522 873844/01522 804305
✉ arts@lincoln.gov.uk
🌐 www.lincolnbookfestival.co.uk
Contact Sara Bullimore, Karen Parsons
Dates May
About An annual festival that celebrates books and the art forms they inspire. The programme includes talks, workshops, discussions, exhibitions and performances, as well as events for children.

London Literature Festival
Southbank Centre, Belvedere Road, London, SE1 8XX
☎ 0871 663 2501
✉ webeditor@southbankcentre.co.uk
🌐 www.southbankcentre.co.uk
Dates July
About London Literature Festival is a new festival of literature, ideas, creative writing and performance taking place at the South Bank Centre. The festival lasts two weeks and also has many events for children.

Lowdham Book Festival
The Bookcase, 50 Main Street, Lowdham, NG14 7BE
☎ 0115 966 4143
✉ janestreeter@thebookcase.co.uk
🌐 www.lowdhambookfestival.co.uk
Contact Jane Streeter/Ross Bradshaw
Dates June
About A book festival with many different arts events, including talks, readings and live music. Attracts high profile writers and has a writer in residence for the duration of the festival. Also includes a number of events for children and young writers.

Northern Children's Book Festival
22 Highbury, Newcastle upon Tyne, NE2 3DY
☎ 0191 281 3289
🌐 www.ncbf.co.uk

Contact Chair, Ann Key

Dates November

About Europe's largest free children's book festival. Authors and poets visit schools throughout the North of England, culminating in a gala day of workshops, talks, seminars and activities for children and their families. Events and visits cover two weeks and features guest speakers, workshops and seminars.

Off the Shelf Literature Festival

Central Library, Surrey Street, Sheffield, S1 1XZ

📞 0114 273 4400

📠 0114 273 4716

📧 offtheshelf@sheffield.gov.uk

🌐 www.offtheshelf.org.uk

Contact Maria deSouza, Su Walker, Lesley Webster

Dates October

About An annual festival with events for adults and children, including author visits, creative workshops, storytelling sessions, exhibitions and competitions.

Oundle Festival of Literature

12 Laxton Drive, Oundle, Peterborough, PE8 5TW

📞 01832 274333

📧 enquiries@oundlelitfest.org.uk

🌐 www.oundlelitfest.org.uk

Contact Chair, Nick Turnbull

Dates January–March

About A festival of fiction, theatre, poetry, history, politics, travel and environmental issues, as well as a community events programme. Also has events for children's writers and illustrators. Some events are free, while others are paid for.

Readathon

The Parsonage, St Mary's, Chalford, Stroud, GL6 8QB

📞 0870 240 1124

📧 reading@readathon.org

🌐 www.readathon.org

Dates Throughout the year

About A scheme run in schools throughout the year, especially during Children's Book Week and World Book Day, where children pledge to read books to raise money for children's charities. Readathon organises a range of literary events, mostly at participating schools or libraries.

Redbridge Book and Media Festival

London Borough of Redbridge, Arts and Events Team, 8th Floor, Lynton House, 255–259 High Road, Ilford, IG1 1NY

📞 020 8708 3044

📧 mark.etherington@redbridge.gov.uk

🌐 www.redbridge.gov.uk

Contact Arts Development Officer, Mark Etherington

Dates May

About A festival of the written word in all its forms, including visits from well known writers and performers. The programme includes competitions, workshops, talks and performances, focusing on the written word and words in media. The media element of this festival, alongside the more traditional literature events, makes it unique.

Royal Court Young Writers' Festival

The Royal Court Young Writers' Programme, Sloane Square, London, SW1W 8AS

📞 020 7565 5050

🌐 www.royalcourttheatre.com

Dates January–March

About A biennial festival, the next of which will take place in 2008. Young people aged between 13 and 25 may submit scripts, to win the chance to see them developed and performed at the Royal Court Theatre.

Scottish International Storytelling Festival

43–45 High Street, Edinburgh, EH1 1SR

📞 0131 556 9579

📠 0131 557 5224

📧 reception@scottishhistorytellingcentre.com

🌐 www.scottishhistorytellingcentre.co.uk

Contact Festival Director, Donald Smith

Dates October/November

About An annual festival celebrating Scottish traditional storytelling and folk music. There are events in numerous venues, to coincide with National Tell A Story Day.

StAnza: Scotland's Poetry Festival

Artistic Director, 57 Station Court, Leven, Fife, KY8 4RP

📞 01333 360491

📧 info@stanzapoetry.org

🌐 www.stanzapoetry.org

Contact Artistic Director, Eleanor Livingstone

Dates March

About An annual poetry festival with an international outlook. Programme includes workshops, master classes, readings, performances, discussions, exhibitions and much more. There is also a children's programme. Visiting poets come from all over the world.

Sting in the Tale

Various venues throughout Dorset and Hampshire

☏ 07801 519380

✉ sue@imagine1.co.uk

🌐 www.stinginthetale.org.uk

Contact Festival Co-ordinator, Sue Harmon-Smith

Dates August (18th–27th)

About Sting in the Tale is a festival of traditional oral storytelling, based in Dorset and Hampshire. Events include live stories and workshops at castles, crypts, woodlands and other historical locations, for both children and adults. All events must be booked in advance, including the free ones. See the website for booking information.

Stratford Upon Avon Poetry Festival

The Shakespeare Centre, Henley Street, Stratford upon Avon, CV37 6QW

☏ 01789 204016

✉ info@shakespeare.org.uk

🌐 www.shakespeare.org

Dates July–August

About An annual poetry festival with readings of poetry taking place, mainly on Sunday evenings, in various venues in Stratford. Famous actors read poems of the past, while contemporary poets present their work. There is also a children's event.

The Sunday Times Oxford Literary Festival

Christ Church, Oxford, OX1 1DP

☏ 01865 514149

✉ info@sundaytimes-oxfordliteraryfestival.co.uk

🌐 www.sundaytimes-oxfordliteraryfestival.co.uk

Contact Festival Director, Angela Prysor-Jones

Dates March (Two weeks before Easter)

About An eight day festival featuring workshops, debates and talks on many literary topics, including genre writing and publishing. Also hosts a further two days of events for schools.

Swindon Festival of Literature

Lower Shaw Farm, Shaw, Swindon, Wiltshire, SN5 5PJ

☏ 01793 771080

✉ swindonlitfest@lowershawfarm.co.uk

🌐 www.swindonfestivalofliterature.co.uk

Contact Festival Director, Matt Holland

Dates May

About Workshops, talks and speakers on literature and writing, in and around Swindon. Includes a family and children's weekend.

Warwick Words

The Court House, Jury Street, Warwick, CV34 4EW

☏ 01926 427056

🌐 www.warwickwords.co.uk

Contact Patron, Andrew Davies

Dates October

About A festival of literature and the spoken word. Workshops, talks, performances and children's events are part of the programme.

Winchester Writers' Conference

Faculty of Arts, University of Winchester, West Hill, Winchester, SO22 4NR

☏ 01962 827238

✉ barbara.large@winchester.ac.uk

🌐 www.writersconference.co.uk

Contact Founder/Director, Barbara Large

Dates June–July

About A weekend of workshops, events and talks, covering writing, literature, technique and marketing. Also runs 15 different competitions.

Word

Office of External Affairs, University of Aberdeen, King's College, Aberdeen, AB24 3FX

☏ 01224 274444

☏ 01224 272086

✉ word@abdn.ac.uk

🌐 www.abdn.ac.uk/word

Contact Artistic Director, Alan Spence

Dates May

About A large weekend festival with over 10,000 visitors. Programme includes readings, workshops, music sessions, art exhibitions, children's activities and film screenings. The Word Kid's Programme runs events featuring popular children's writers.

The Word's Out

Perth and Kinross Council, AK Bell Library, York Place, Perth, PH2 8EP

- ☎ 01738 444949
- ✉ cfbeaton@pkc.gov.uk

Contact Community Libraries Manager, Caroline Beaton

Dates October

About A festival that celebrates books and reading, with a particular focus on libraries. Attracts visitors from across the UK, and has dedicated events for children.

World Book Day

c/o The Booksellers Association, 272 Vauxhall Bridge Road, London, SW1V 1BA

- ☎ 01634 729810
- ☎ 01634 290175
- ✉ wbd@education.co.uk
- 🌐 www.worldbookday.com

Dates March

About World Book Day is a partnership of publishers, booksellers and interested parties who work together to promote books and reading for the personal enrichment and enjoyment of all. The main aim of World Book Day is to encourage children to explore the pleasures of books and reading, by providing them with the opportunity to have a book of their own. Children receive a £1 book token that can be exchanged for one of the specially published World Book Day £1 Books, or redeemed against any one of the Recommended Reads list. The Bookseller and National Book Tokens Ltd host and sponsor the day.

Worldplay Literature Festival for Young People

The Dylan Thomas Centre, Somerset Place, Swansea, SA11 1RR

- ☎ 01792 463980
- ☎ 01792 463993
- ✉ dylanthomas.lit@swansea.gov.uk
- 🌐 www.dylanthomas.org

Contact Literature Officer, Derek Cobley

Dates October

About An annual festival with events for young people and their teachers, parents and carers to enjoy. The festival features storytelling, poems, and pictures from writers and illustrators.

Writing on the Wall

60 Duke Street, Liverpool, L1 5AA

- ☎ 0151 707 4313
- ✉ info@writingonthewall.org.uk
- 🌐 www.writingonthewall.org.uk

Contact Festival Administrator, Janette Stowell

Dates May

About A not for profit organisation that runs a series of literature related events. These are designed to encourage young people and the wider community to take part.

Young Readers Birmingham

Children's Office, Central Library, Chamberlain Square, Birmingham, B3 3HQ

- ☎ 0121 303 3368
- ☎ 0121 464 1004
- ✉ gena.gaynor@birmingham.gov.uk
- 🌐 www.birmingham.gov.uk/youngreaders

Contact Gena Gaynor

Dates May–June

About An annual two week festival for children and young people, to encourage them to enjoy books and reading. There are around 150 events across Birmingham during the two week period.